FAULT-TOLERANT COMPUTER SYSTEM DESIGN

B. M. Alhoshin.

FAULT-TOLERANT COMPUTER SYSTEM DESIGN

Dhiraj K. Pradhan

Chair in Computer Science
University of Bristol
Bristol
United Kingdom

For ordering information please contact:

cspress@aol. com

Computer Science Press
Suite 216
14 Clifton Down Road
Clifton Village
Bristol BS8 4BF
United Kingdom

Second print 2003

PRENTICE HALL PTR
Upper Saddle River, New Jersey 07458

Library of Congress Cataloging-in-Publication Data
Pradhan, Dhiraj K.
    Fault-tolerant computer system design / Dhiraj K. Pradhan.
        p.   cm.
    Includes bibliographical references and index.
    ISBN 0–13–057887–8
    1. Fault-tolerant computing.   2. System design.   I. Title.
QA76.9.F38P73   1995
004.2'1—dc20
                                            95–24960
                                               CIP

Acquisitions editor: Mary Franz
Manufacturing buyer: Alexis R. Heydt
Composition/Production services: Pine Tree Composition, Inc.

© 1996 by Prentice Hall PTR
Prentice-Hall, Inc.
A Simon & Schuster Company
Upper Saddle River, New Jersey 07458

The publisher offers discounts on this book when ordered in
bulk quantities.

For more information contact:
    Corporate Sales Department
    Prentice Hall PTR
    One Lake Street
    Upper Saddle River, New Jersey 07458

    Phone: 800–382–3419
    Fax: 201–236–7141
    email: corpsales@prenhall.com

Printed in the United States of America
10 9 8 7 6 5 4 3 2 1

ISBN: 0-13-057887-8

Prentice Hall International (UK) Limited, *London*
Prentice Hall of Australia Pty. Limited, *Sydney*
Prentice Hall Canada, Inc., *Toronto*
Prentice Hall Hispanoamerica, S.A., *Mexico*
Prentice Hall of Japan, Inc., *Tokyo*
Simon & Schuster Asia, Pte. Ltd., *Singapore*
Editora Prentice Hall do Brazil, Ltda., *Rio de Janeiro*

Contents

4.   CASE STUDIES IN FAULT TOLERANT MULTIPROCESSOR AND DISTRIBUTES SYSTEMS   236

Dhiraj K. Pradhan, *University of Bristol*

5.   EXPERIMENTAL ANALYSIS OF COMPUTER SYSTEM DEPENDABILITY

Ravishankar K. Iyer and Dong Tang, *University of Illinois*

6.   RELIABILITY ESTIMATION   393

J.J. Stiffler, *Sequoia Systems*

7.   FAULT TOLERANCE IN SOFTWARE   428

Herbert Hecht and Myron Hecht, *Sohar Inc.*

8. SYSTEM DIAGNOSIS

478

Gerald M. Masson, *Johns Hopkins University*
Douglas M. Blough and Gregory F. Sullivan,
University of California, Irvine

Preface

This book represents an upgrading and enhancement of the earlier work *Fault-Tolerant Computing: Theory and Techniques* [1], published by Prentice Hall in 1986 and widely adopted as a text for graduate students. The field of fault-tolerant system design has broadened in appeal in the intervening decade, particularly with its emerging application in distributed computing, such as the proposed information highway, as well as the advent of multiprocessor computing nodes as the state of the art. This new book, therefore, reflects this quickly and dynamically changing computing environment. In addition to certain of the basic chapters included in its predecessor, this book also incorporates chapters dealing specifically with these newer topics such as fault tolerance in multiprocessor and distributed systems.

Reliability and availability of computing systems remain major concerns, despite frequent misconceptions that a dramatic increase in component reliability has obviated the need for fault tolerance, reflected in Figure 1 [2]. One challenge contained in the newer client-server model of computing guarantees data integrity in the event of failures. In fact, some attribute that persistent interest in mainframes to their perceived robustness. Apart from hardware reliability, robustness of a system is rooted in good design discipline at both the hardware and software levels.

The recent discovery of a design flaw in the Pentium chip reveals the complexity of ensuring reliable operation in advanced microprocessor use. It is widely known that the reliability weaknesses of the Intel Paragon traces, in part, to the persistent design bugs in that microprocessor used in the system. This means that design diversity has, therefore, become another issue of wider acceptance, evidenced in the design of the forthcoming 777 jet aircraft flight-control system. Both the real-time as well as the safety requirements mandate precautionary measures against a wide range of possible failures. The opportunity for fast

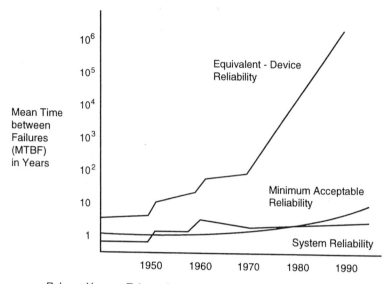

Figure 1: Device reliability and system reliability.

recovery in the event of a fault is greatly aided with the advent of high-speed microprocessors, but new challenges arise regarding reliable synchronization. One other challenge to fault-tolerant design is the increased use of massively parallel systems. Striving to achieve the highest possible performance through innovative architectures, these systems sometimes rely on still unproven technology. It is not surprising, then, that some of these systems suffer from dismal mean-time to failure (MTTF), though achieving spectacular computing speed. The dependability gap only seems to widen over the years, as seen in Figure 2.

One intangible cost of lack of fault tolerance is the loss of computational power in high-performance computing. A small fraction of operational time lost due to faults could easily result in the kind of performance loss approaching that of a mainframe computer. The basic focus, therefore, becomes achieving fault tolerance without significant performance loss. Standard techniques to restart the task may be useless in these computers, one particular task requiring hours of uninterrupted computation on these supercomputers.

One other new, emerging field of computing is mobile computers. These systems require new solutions for their fault tolerance problems because of the mobility consideration as well as low-weight power constraints. Specifically, mobility requires a more dynamic environment for recovery, not encountered in the traditional static environment. Low-power considerations mandate that simple replication techniques, so effective in traditional applications, cannot be used here. For example, those systems powered by batteries do not provide the flexi-

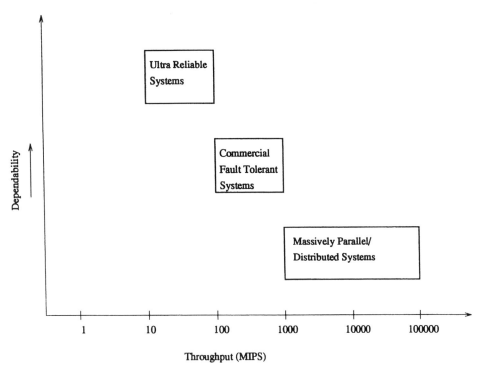

Figure 2: Dependability-Performance trade-off.

bility of replication, seen in Table 1. Assuming, for example, that the nominal capacity of the battery is 10 watt-hours for a typical nickel-cadmiun battery, the MTTF of the widely popular Triple Modular Redundancy (TMR) system often used in many applications is useless in a mobile computing environment because the mean operational time is now limited more by the battery power than the intrinsic reliability. Novel fault-tolerant schemes such as roll-forward techniques as described in Chapter 3 may, therefore, find applications. Consequently, what this book brings into focus are these various issues for both mature and emerging technologies.

An overview of the basic concepts is dealt with in Chapter 1, followed by a discussion of various architectures in Chapter 2. Certain of the newer fault toler-

Table 1: Expected Operational Time for Fault-Tolerant Mobile Computer

	Power/Expected	Operational Time in Minutes
	Simplex	TMR
DEC Alpha	30 W/20 min.	90 W/6 min.
SUN Viking	8W/72 min.	24 W/18 min.

ance issues in the environment of parallel distributed computing are delved into in Chapter 3. In-depth case studies of several major fault-tolerant architectures are offered in Chapter 4. Both experimental and analytical techniques are crucial to accurate prediction of reliability. Too often, the lack of good dependability evaluation tools handicaps fault-tolerant designers and practitioners. Chapters 5 and 6 treat the subject of dependability prediction and measurement techniques. Chapter 7 reviews the ever-important issue of software reliability. Unlike hardware faults, all software faults are design and implementation errors. Because of this, a wide range of issues affects software reliability. This chapter focuses specifically on fault tolerance techniques, rather than the myriad of fault avoidance techniques. Chapter 8 concludes with the theory of system-level diagnosis, a popular subject of academic research receiving recent attention among practicing engineers. A set of problems is included with each chapter, as the book is intended both as text for first-year graduate students and a reference for practitioners.

An undertaking such as this one would not have been possible without the invaluable help and contributions from the leading experts, as well as from my students, Gavin Holland, Nitin Vaidya, and Nick Bowen.

REFERENCES

[1] Pradhan, D. K., *Fault-Tolerant Computing: Theory and Techniques,* Vols. I and II, Prentice Hall, 1986.

[2] Stiffler, J. J., private communication, 1992.

FAULT-TOLERANT
COMPUTER SYSTEM DESIGN

1

An Introduction to the Design and Analysis of Fault-Tolerant Systems*

Barry W. Johnson

1.1 INTRODUCTION

This chapter is devoted to the study of introductory concepts and techniques for designing and analyzing fault-tolerant systems. It is also intended to give the needed background for the remaining chapters which provide in-depth treatment. A *fault-tolerant system* is one that can continue the correct performance of its specified tasks in the presence of hardware and/or software faults. *Fault tolerance* is the attribute that enables a system to achieve fault-tolerant operation. Finally, the term *fault-tolerant computing* is used to describe the process of performing calculations, such as those performed by a computer, in a fault-tolerant manner. This chapter is divided into four primary sections. The remainder of this first section is an introduction to the basic terminology used in the fault tolerance field. The second section is an overview of redundancy techniques employed in the design of fault-tolerant systems. Hardware, software, time, and information redundancy methods are considered. The third section describes evaluation metrics such as reliability, availability, and safety, as well as the modeling techniques used to determine numerical values for these metrics. Finally, the last section provides an overview of the design process and the incorporation of fault avoidance ideas. The material in this chapter is intended to provide an introduction to the various topics important to the fault tolerance field. After completing this chapter the reader should be able to pursue each of the individual topics in more detail in the subsequent chapters.

1.1.1 Fundamental Terminology

Three fundamental terms in fault-tolerant design are fault, error, and failure. There is a cause-effect relationship between faults, errors, and failures. Specifically, faults are the cause of errors, and errors are the cause of failures. Often the term failure is used interchangeably with the term malfunction; however, the term failure is rapidly becoming the more commonly accepted one.

A *fault* is a physical defect, imperfection, or flaw that occurs within some hardware or software component. Essentially, the definition of a fault, as used in the fault tolerance community, agrees with the definition found in the dictionary. A fault is a blemish, weakness, or shortcoming of a particular hardware or software component. An *error* is the manifestation of a fault. Specifically, an error is a deviation from accuracy or correctness. Finally, if the error results in the system performing one of its functions incorrectly then a system *failure* has occurred. Essentially, a failure is the nonperformance of some action that is due or expected. A failure is also the performance of some function in a subnormal quantity or quality.

The concepts of faults, errors, and failures can be presented best by the use of a three-universe model that is an adaptation of the four-universe model originally developed in Avizienis (1982). The first universe is the *physical universe* in which faults occur. The physical universe contains the semiconductor devices, mechanical elements, displays, printers, power supplies, and other physical entities that make up a system. A fault is a physical defect or alteration of some component within the physical universe. The second universe is the *informational universe*. The informational universe is where the error occurs. Errors affect units of information such as data words within a computer or digital voice or image information. An error has occurred when some unit of information becomes incorrect. The final universe is the *external* or *user's universe*. The external universe is where the user of a system ultimately sees the effect of faults and errors. The external universe is where failures occur. The failure is any deviation that occurs from the desired or expected behavior of a system. In summary, faults are physical events that occur in the physical universe. Faults can result in errors in the informational universe, and errors can ultimately lead to failures that are witnessed in the external universe of the system.

The cause-effect relationship implied in the three-universe model leads to the definition of two important parameters: fault latency and error latency. *Fault latency* is the length of time between the occurrence of a fault and the appearance of an error due to that fault. *Error latency* is the length of time between the occurrence of an error and the appearance of the resulting failure. Based on the three-universe model, the total time between the occurrence of a physical fault and the appearance of a failure will be the sum of the fault latency and the error latency.

Faults can be the result of a variety of things that occur within electronic components, external to the components, or during the component or system design process. Problems at any of several points within the design process can result in faults within the system. At the highest level is the possibility of *specification mistakes*, which include incorrect algorithms, architectures, or hardware and software design specifications. The next cause of faults is *implementation mistakes.* Implementation, as defined here, is the process of transforming hardware and software specifications into the physical hardware and the actual software. The implementation can introduce faults because of poor design, poor component selection, poor construction, or software coding mistakes. The next cause of faults is *component defects.* Manufacturing imperfections, random device defects, and component wear-out are typical examples of component defects. Electronic components simply become defective sometimes. The defect can be the result of bonds breaking within the circuit or corrosion of the metal. Component defects are the most commonly considered cause of faults. The final cause of faults is the *external disturbance;* for example, radiation, electromagnetic interference, battle damage, operator mistakes, and environmental extremes.

To describe faults adequately, characteristics other than the cause are required. In addition to the cause, four major attributes are critical to the description of faults: nature, duration, extent, and value Nelson and Carroll (1982). The *nature* of a fault specifies the type of fault; for example, whether it is a hardware fault, a software fault, a fault in the analog circuitry, or a fault in the digital circuitry. Another key attribute of a fault is its *duration.* The duration specifies the length of time that a fault is active. First, there is the *permanent fault* that remains in existence indefinitely if no corrective action is taken. Second, there is the *transient fault* that can appear and disappear within a very short period of time. Third, there is the *intermittent fault* that appears, disappears, and then reappears repeatedly. The next attribute of faults is the *extent.* The extent of a fault specifies whether the fault is localized to a given hardware or software module or globally affects the hardware, the software, or both. The final attribute of faults is the *value.* The value of a fault can be either determinate or indeterminate. A *determinate fault* is one whose status remains unchanged throughout time unless externally acted upon. An *indeterminate fault* is one whose status at some time, T, may be different from its status at some increment of time greater than or less than T.

There are three primary techniques for attempting to improve or maintain a system's normal performance in an environment where faults are of concern: fault avoidance, fault masking, and fault tolerance. *Fault avoidance* is a technique that is used in an attempt to prevent the occurrence of faults. Fault avoidance can include such things as design reviews, component screening, testing, and other quality control methods. *Fault masking* is any process that prevents faults in a system from introducing errors into the informational structure of that system. Finally, *fault tolerance* is the ability of a system to continue to perform its tasks after the occurrence of faults. The ultimate goal of fault tolerance is to prevent system failures from occurring. Since failures are directly caused by errors, the terms *fault tolerance* and *error tolerance* are often used interchangeably.

Fault tolerance can be achieved by many techniques. Fault masking is one approach to tolerating faults. Another approach is to detect and locate the fault and reconfigure the system to remove the faulty component. *Reconfiguration* is the process of eliminating a faulty entity from a system and restoring the system to some operational condition or state. If the reconfiguration technique is used, then the designer must be concerned with fault detection, fault location, fault containment, and fault recovery. *Fault detection* is the process of recognizing that a fault has occurred. Fault detection is often required before any recovery procedure can be implemented. *Fault location* is the process of determining where a fault has occurred so that an appropriate recovery can be implemented. *Fault containment* is the process of isolating a fault and preventing the effects of that fault from propagating throughout a system. Fault containment is required in all fault-tolerant designs. Finally, *fault recovery* is the process of remaining operational or regaining operational status via reconfiguration even in the presence of faults.

Equivalent definitions can be provided in the informational universe. Specifically, *error detection* is the process of recognizing that an error has occurred. *Error location* is the process of determining which specific module produced the error. *Error containment* is the process of preventing the error from propagating throughout a system. Finally, *error recovery* is the process of regaining operational status or restoring the system's integrity after the occurrence of an error.

1.1.2 Objectives of Fault Tolerance

Fault tolerance is an attribute that is designed into a system to achieve some design goal. Just as a design must meet many functional and performance goals, it must also satisfy numerous other requirements, as well. The most prominent of the additional requirements are dependability, reliability, availability, safety, performability, maintainability, and testability; fault tolerance is one system attribute capable of fulfilling such requirements.

Dependability. The term *dependability* is used to encapsulate the concepts of reliability, availability, safety, maintainability, performability, and testability. Dependability is simply the quality of service provided by a particular system (Laprie, 1985). Reliability, availability, safety, maintainability, performability, and testability are examples of measures used to quantify the dependability of a system.

Reliability. The *reliability* of a system is a function of time, $R(t)$, defined as the conditional probability that the system performs correctly throughout the interval of time, $[t_0,t]$, given that the system was performing correctly at time t_0. In other words, the reliability is the probability that the system operates correctly throughout a complete interval of time. The reliability is a conditional probability in that it depends on the system being operational at the beginning of the chosen time interval. The *unreliability* of a system is a function of time, $F(t)$, defined as the conditional probability that a system begins to perform incorrectly during the interval of time, $[t_0,t]$, given that the system was performing correctly at time t_0. The unreliability is often referred to as the probability of failure.

Reliability is most often used to characterize systems in which even momentary periods of incorrect performance are unacceptable, or it is impossible to repair the system. If repair is impossible, such as in many space applications, the time intervals being considered can be extremely long, perhaps as many as ten years. In other applications, such as aircraft flight control, the time intervals of concern may be no more than several hours, but the probability of working correctly throughout that interval may be 0.9999999 or higher. (It is a common convention when reporting reliability numbers to use 0.9_i to represent the fraction that has *i* nines to the right of the decimal point. For example, 0.9999999 is written as 0.9_7.)

Availability.   *Availability* is a function of time, $A(t)$, defined as the probability that a system is operating correctly and is available to perform its functions at the instant of time, t. Availability differs from reliability in that reliability involves an interval of time, while availability is taken at an instant of time. A system can be highly available yet experience frequent periods of inoperability as long as the length of each period is extremely short. In other words, the availability of a system depends not only on how frequently it becomes inoperable but also, how quickly it can be repaired. Examples of high-availability applications include time-shared computing systems and certain transactions processing applications, such as airline reservation systems.

Safety.   *Safety* is the probability, $S(t)$, that a system will either perform its functions correctly or will discontinue its functions in a manner that does not disrupt the operation of other systems or compromise the safety of any people associated with the system. Safety is a measure of the fail-safe capability of a system; if the system does not operate correctly, it is desired to have the system fail in a safe manner. Safety and reliability differ because reliability is the probability that a system will perform its functions correctly, while safety is the probability that a system will either perform its functions correctly or will discontinue the functions in a manner that causes no harm.

Performability.   In many cases, it is possible to design systems that can continue to perform correctly after the occurrence of hardware and software faults, but the level of performance is somehow diminished. The *performability* of a system is a function of time, $P(L,t)$, defined as the probability that the system performance will be at, or above, some level, L, at the instant of time, t (Fortes, 1984). Performability differs from reliability in that reliability is a measure of the likelihood that all of the functions are performed correctly, while performability is a measure of the likelihood that some subset of the functions is performed correctly.

Graceful degradation is an important feature that is closely related to performability. *Graceful degradation* is simply the ability of a system to automatically decrease its level of performance to compensate for hardware and software faults. Fault tolerance can certainly support graceful degradation and performability by providing the ability to eliminate the effects of hardware and software faults from a system, therefore allowing performance at some reduced level.

Maintainability. *Maintainability* is a measure of the ease with which a system can be repaired once it has failed. In more quantitative terms, maintainability is the probability, $M(t)$, that a failed system will be restored to an operational state within a period of time t. The restoration process includes locating the problem, physically repairing the system, and bringing the system back to its operational condition. Many of the techniques that are so vital to the achievement of fault tolerance can be used to detect and locate problems in a system for the purpose of maintenance. Once the problem is located, maintenance can then be performed to implement the necessary repairs. Automatic diagnostics can significantly improve the maintainability of a system because a majority of the time used to repair a system is often devoted to determining the source of the problem.

Testability. *Testability* is simply the ability to test for certain attributes within a system. Measures of testability allow one to assess the ease with which certain tests can be performed. Certain tests can be automated and provided as an integral part of the system to improve the testability. Many of the techniques that are so vital to the achievement of fault tolerance can be used to detect and locate problems in a system for the purpose of improving testability. Testability is clearly related to maintainability because of the importance of minimizing the time required to identify and locate specific problems.

1.1.3 Applications of Fault-Tolerant Computing

Applications of fault-tolerant computing can be categorized into four primary areas: long-life applications, critical computations, maintenance postponement, and high availability. Each application presents differing design requirements and challenges.

Long-life applications. The most common examples of long-life applications are the unmanned space flight and satellites. Typical requirements of a long-life application are to have a 0.95, or greater, probability of being operational at the end of a ten-year period. Unlike other applications, however, long-life systems can often allow extended outages as long as the system can eventually be made operational once again. In addition, long-life applications can frequently allow the system to be reconfigured manually by the operators. The Fault-Tolerant Space-borne Computer (FTSC) (Stiffler, 1976), the Self-Testing And Repairing (STAR) computer (Avizienis, Gillay, Mathur, Rennels, Rohn, and Ruckin, 1971b), and the Fault-Tolerant Building Block Computer (FTBBC) (Rennels, 1980) are classic examples of systems designed for long-life applications.

Critical-computation applications. Perhaps the most widely publicized applications of fault-tolerant computing are those where the computations are critical to human safety, environmental cleanliness, or equipment protection. Examples include aircraft flight control systems, military systems, and certain types of industrial controllers. In critical-computation applications, the incorrect performance of the system will almost certainly yield devastating results. A typical requirement for a critical-computation application is to have a reliability of 0.9_7 at the end of a three-hour time period. Requirements can vary, however, depending on the particular function that the system is performing. One of the most publicly visible critical-computation applications of fault-tolerant computing has been the space shuttle (Sklaroff, 1976). Industrial control systems also perform critical computations. For example, chemical reactions may have to be precisely controlled to prevent explosions or other unwanted effects.

Maintenance postponement applications. Maintenance postponement applications appear most frequently when maintenance operations are extremely costly, inconvenient, or difficult to perform. Remote processing stations and certain space applications are good examples. In space, maintenance can be impossible to perform, while at remote sites the cost of unexpected maintenance can be prohibitive. The main goal is to use fault tolerance to allow maintenance to be postponed to more convenient and cost-effective times. Maintenance personnel can visit a site monthly and perform any necessary repairs. Between maintenance visits, the system uses fault tolerance to continue to perform its tasks. A telephone switching system (Toy, 1978) is an example where maintenance postponement may be required. Many telephone switching systems are located in remote areas where it is necessary to provide telephone service, but it is costly to perform the maintenance and service operations. The primary objective is to design the system such that unscheduled maintenance can be avoided. Therefore, the telephone company can visit the facility periodically and repair the system or perform routine maintenance. Between maintenance visits, the system handles failures and service disruptions autonomously.

High availability applications. Availability is a key parameter in many applications. Banking and other time-shared systems are good examples of high availability applications. Users of these systems want to have a high probability of receiving service when it is requested. The Tandem Nonstop transaction processing system (Katzman, 1977) is a good example of one designed for high availability.

1.2 REDUNDANCY TECHNIQUES

The concept of *redundancy* implies the addition of information, resources, or time beyond what is needed for normal system operation. The redundancy can take one of several forms, including hardware redundancy, software redundancy, information redundancy, and time redundancy. The use of redundancy can provide additional capabilities within a system. In fact, if fault tolerance or fault detection is required, then some form of redundancy is also required. But, it must be understood that redundancy can have a very important impact on a system in the areas of performance, size, weight, power consumption, reliability, and others.

1.2.1 Hardware Redundancy

The physical replication of hardware is perhaps the most common form of redundancy used in systems. As semiconductor components have become smaller and less expensive, the concept of hardware redundancy has become more common and more practical. The costs of replicating hardware within a system are decreasing simply because the costs of hardware are decreasing.

There are three basic forms of hardware redundancy. First, *passive* techniques use the concept of fault masking to hide the occurrence of faults and prevent the faults from resulting in errors. Passive approaches are designed to achieve fault tolerance without requiring any action on the part of the system or an operator. Passive techniques, in their most basic form, do not provide for the detection of faults but simply mask the faults.

The second form of hardware redundancy is the *active* approach, which is sometimes called the *dynamic* method. Active methods achieve fault tolerance by detecting the existence of faults and performing some action to remove the faulty hardware from the system. In other words, active techniques require that the system perform reconfiguration to tolerate faults. Active hardware redundancy uses fault detection, fault location, and fault recovery in an attempt to achieve fault tolerance.

The final form of hardware redundancy is the *hybrid* approach. Hybrid techniques combine the attractive features of both the passive and active approaches. Fault masking is used in hybrid systems to prevent erroneous results from being generated. Fault detection, fault location, and fault recovery are also used in the hybrid approaches to improve fault tolerance by removing faulty hardware and replacing it with spares. Providing spares is one form of providing redundancy in a system. Hybrid methods are most often used in the critical-computation applications where fault masking is required to prevent momentary errors, and high reliability must be achieved. Hybrid hardware redundancy is usually a very expensive form of redundancy to implement.

Passive hardware redundancy.   Passive hardware redundancy relies upon voting mechanisms to mask the occurrence of faults. Most passive approaches are developed around the concept of majority voting. As previously mentioned, the passive approaches achieve fault tolerance without the need for fault detection or system reconfiguration; the passive designs inherently tolerate the faults.

The most common form of passive hardware redundancy is called *triple modular redundancy* (TMR). The basic concept of TMR is to triplicate the hardware and perform a majority vote to determine the output of the system. If one of the modules becomes faulty, the two remaining fault-free modules mask the results of the faulty module when the majority vote is performed. The basic concept of TMR is illustrated in Figure 1.1. In typical applications, the replicated modules are processors, memories, or any hardware entity. A simple example of TMR is shown in Figure 1.2 where data from three independent processors is voted upon before being written to memory. The majority vote provides a mechanism for ensuring that each memory contains the correct data, even if a single faulty processor exists. A similar voting process is provided at the output of the memories, so that a single memory failure will not corrupt the data provided to any one processor. Note that in Figure 1.2, there are three separate voters so that the failure of a single voter cannot corrupt more than one memory or more than one processor.

The primary difficulty with TMR is obviously the voter; if the voter fails, the complete system fails. In other words, the reliability of the simplest form of TMR, as shown in Figure 1.1, can be no better than the reliability of the voter. Any single

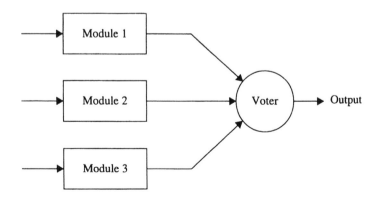

Figure 1.1: Basic concept of triple modular redundancy (TMR). (From Barry W. Johnson, *Design and Analysis of Fault-Tolerant Digital Systems,* Addison-Wesley Publishing Company, Reading, Mass., 1989, p. 52.)

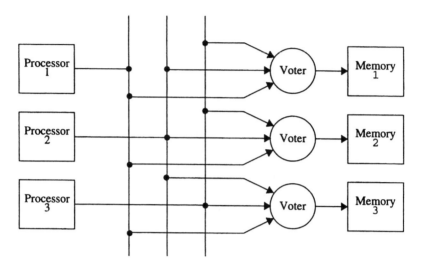

Figure 1.2: The use of triplicated voters in a TMR configuration. (Adapted from Barry W. Johnson, *Design and Analysis of Fault-Tolerant Digital Systems*, Addison-Wesley Publishing Company, Reading, Mass., 1989, p. 327.)

component within a system whose failure will lead to a failure of the system is called a *single-point-of-failure*. Several techniques can be used to overcome the effects of voter failure. One approach is to triplicate the voters and provide three independent outputs, as illustrated in Figure 1.2. In Figure 1.2, each of three memories receives data from a voter which has received its inputs from the three separate processors. If one processor fails, each memory will continue to receive a correct value because its voter will correct the corrupted value. A TMR system with triplicated voters is commonly called a *restoring organ* because the configuration will produce three correct outputs even if one input is faulty. In essence, the TMR with triplicated voters restores the error-free signal. An example of a real world TMR system can be found in Tandem Integrity System, described in Chapter 4.

A generalization of the TMR approach is the N-modular redundancy (NMR) technique. NMR applies the same principle as TMR but uses N of a given module, as opposed to only three. In most cases, N is selected as an odd number so that a majority voting arrangement can be used. The advantage of using N modules rather than three is that more module faults can often be tolerated. For example, a 5MR system contains five replicated modules and a voter. A majority voting arrangement allows the 5MR system to produce correct results in the face of as many as two module faults. In many critical-computation applications, two faults must be tolerated to allow the required reliability and fault tolerance capabilities to be achieved. The primary trade-off in NMR is the fault tolerance achieved versus the hardware required. Clearly, there must be some limit in practical applications on the amount of redundancy that can be employed. Power, weight, cost, and size limitations very often determine the value of N in an NMR system.

Voting within NMR systems can occur at several points. For example, an industrial controller can sample the temperature of a chemical process from three independent sensors, perform a vote to determine which of the three sensor values to use, calculate the amount of heat or cooling to provide to the process (the calculations being performed by three or more separate modules), and then vote on the calculations to determine a result. The voting can be performed on both analog and digital data. The alternative, in this example, might be to sample the temperature from three independent sensors, perform the calculations, and then provide a single vote on the final result. The primary difference between the two approaches is fault containment. If voting is not performed on the temperature values from the sensors, then the effect of a sensor fault is allowed to propagate beyond the sensors and into the primary calculations. Voting at the sensors, however, will mask, and contain, the effects of a sensor fault. Providing several levels of voting, however, does require additional redundancy, and the benefits of fault containment must be compared to the cost of the extra redundancy.

In addition to there being a number of design trade-offs on voting, there are several problems with the voting procedure, as well. The first is deciding whether a hardware voter will be used, or whether the voting process will be implemented in software. A software voter takes advantage of the computational capabilities available in a processor to perform the voting process with a minimum amount of additional hardware. Also, the software voter provides the ability to modify the manner in which the voting is performed by simply modifying the software. The disadvantage of the software voter is that the voting can require more time to perform, simply because the processor cannot execute instructions and process data as rapidly as a dedicated hardware voter. The decision to use hardware or software voting will typically depend upon (1) the availability of a processor to perform the voting, (2) the speed at which voting must be performed, (3) the criticality of space, power, and weight limitations, (4) the number of different voters that must be provided, and (5) the flexibility required of the voter with respect to future changes in the system. The concept of software voting is shown in Figure 1.3. Each processor executes its own version of task A. Upon completion of the tasks, each processor shares its results with processor 2, which then votes on the results before using them as input to task B. If necessary, each processor might also execute its version of the voting routine and receive data from the other processors.

A second major problem with the practical application of voting is that the three results in a TMR system, for example, may not completely agree, even in a fault-free environment. The sensors that are used in many control systems can seldom be manufactured such that their values agree exactly. Also, an analog-to-digital converter can produce quantities that disagree in the least-significant bits, even if the exact signal is passed through the same converter multiple times. When values that disagree slightly are processed, the disagreement can propa-

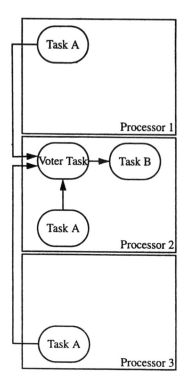

Figure 1.3: Example of software voting.

gate into larger discrepancies. In other words, small differences in inputs can pro-
duce large differences in outputs that can significantly affect the voting process.
Consequently, a majority voter may find that no two results agree exactly in a
TMR system, even though the system may be functioning perfectly.

One approach that alleviates this problem is called the *mid-value select* technique. Basically, the mid-value select approach chooses a value from the three
available in a TMR system by selecting the value that lies between the remaining
two. As an example, consider Figure 1.4. If three signals are available, and two of
those signals are uncorrupted and the third is corrupted, one of the uncorrupted
results should lie between the other uncorrupted result and the corrupted result.
The mid-value select technique can be applied to any system that uses an odd
number of modules, such that one signal must lie in the middle of the others.

The major difficulty with most techniques that use some form of voting is
that a single result must ultimately be produced, thus creating a potential point
where one failure can cause a system failure. Clearly, single-points-of-failure are
to be avoided if a system is to be truly fault-tolerant. The need for a single result
is apparent in many applications. For example, banking systems must display
one balance for each checking account, not three. Even though the banking computers may vote internally on some of the results, one result must ultimately be

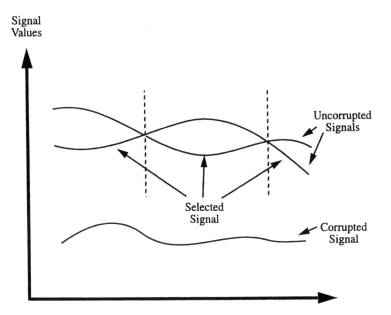

Figure 1.4: Example illustration of the mid-value select technique. (From Barry W. Johnson, *Design and Analysis of Fault-Tolerant Digital Systems,* Addison-Wesley Publishing Company, Reading, Mass., 1989, p. 60.)

created. The same is true in critical-computation applications such as aircraft flight control. Most aircraft, even military aircraft, do not have redundancy of the actuators, or motors, that physically moves the control surfaces. Consequently, a single control signal must be provided. There are several approaches that have been used successfully to create single results from redundant computations. We will consider the *flux-summing* technique.

The fundamental concept of flux-summing is illustrated in Figure 1.5. Here, a TMR system is employed to control the armature current of a small motor. The flux-summing approach uses the inherent properties of closed-loop control systems to compensate for faults. The flux-summer is a transformer that has three primary windings and a single secondary winding. The current produced in the secondary winding is proportional to the sum of the individual currents in the three primary windings. Under fault-free circumstances, each module provides approximately one-third of the total current produced in the secondary winding.

If a module fails, there are several scenarios that can result. First, the faulty module may stop providing current to the transformer. In this case, the motor will lose approximately one-third of the current necessary to maintain the present shaft position, or shaft velocity, depending on what quantity is being controlled. The remaining two modules will sense, via the feedback path, that the motor is

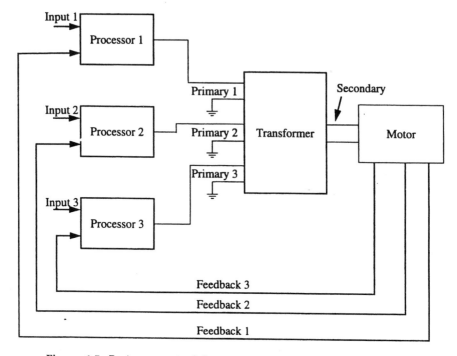

Figure 1.5: Basic concept of flux-summing. (Adapted from Barry W. Johnson, *Design and Analysis of Fault-Tolerant Digital Systems*, Addison-Wesley Publishing Company, Reading, Mass., 1989, p. 61.)

deviating from the desired position or velocity. In other words, the error signal produced by each module, as part of the closed-loop control process, will increase in magnitude. The result will be that the two fault-free modules will change the current they are providing to offset the loss of current from the faulty module.

A second failure scenario that can result is that one module may fail so as to provide a maximum current to the flux-summer, regardless of the input signal values. The inherent feedback of the system will once again compensate for the condition by modifying the currents produced by the remaining fault-free modules. One way to visualize the response of the flux-summer is to consider one of the fault-free modules as providing a current of equal magnitude but opposite polarity of the faulty module so as to cancel the effect of the faulty module. The remaining fault-free module is then capable of controlling the system.

It is important to understand that the flux-summing approach is not a voting process, but it has the same effect of masking faults. The flux-summer can be used in the basic TMR approach or in the more general NMR technique. The primary limitation is the number of coils that can be physically mounted on an iron core. The flux-summers can be designed in a very reliable manner and are extremely insensitive to external disturbances of various types.

Active hardware redundancy.   Active hardware redundancy techniques attempt to achieve fault tolerance by fault detection, fault location, and fault recovery. In many designs, faults can be detected because of the errors they produce, so in many instances error detection, error location, and error recovery are the appropriate terms to use. The property of fault masking, however, is not obtained in the active redundancy approach. In other words, there is no attempt to prevent faults from producing errors within the system. Consequently, active approaches are most common in applications where temporary, erroneous results are acceptable as long as the system reconfigures and regains its operational status in a satisfactory length of time. Satellite systems are good examples of applications of active redundancy. Typically, it is not catastrophic if satellites have infrequent, temporary failures. In fact, it is usually preferable to have temporary failures than to provide the large quantities of redundancy necessary to achieve fault masking.

The basic operation of an active approach to fault tolerance is shown in Figure 1.6. During the normal operation of a system, a fault can obviously occur. It may be noted that the terms fault, error, and failure have been used in various

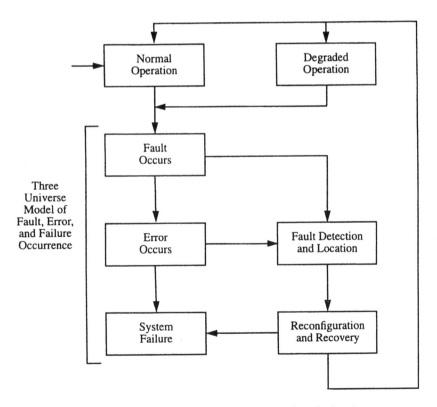

Figure 1.6: Basic operation of an active approach to fault tolerance.

ways in different chapters of this book. However, it is important for the reader to understand the conceptual differences between these three distinct events. After the fault latency period, the fault will produce an error which is either detected or is not detected. If the error remains undetected, the result will be a system failure. The failure will occur after a latency period has expired. If the error is detected, the source of the error must be located, and the faulty component removed from operation. Next, a spare component must be enabled, and the system brought back to an operational state. It is important to note that the new operational state may be identical to the original operational state of the system or it may be a degraded mode of operation. The processes of fault location, fault containment, and fault recovery are normally referred to simply as reconfiguration. It is clear from this description that active approaches to fault tolerance require fault detection and location capabilities.

One example of a fault detection mechanism used in active redundancy is the simple *duplication with comparison* scheme, as seen in the Stratus System, described in Chapter 4. The basic concept of duplication with comparison is to develop two identical pieces of hardware, have them perform the same computations in parallel, and compare the results of those computations. In the event of a disagreement, an error message is generated. In its most basic form, the duplication concept cannot tolerate faults but can only detect them because there is no method for determining which of the two modules is faulty. However, duplication with comparison can be used as the fundamental fault detection technique in an active redundancy approach.

There are several potential problem areas in the duplication with comparison method of active redundancy. First, if the modules both receive the same input, then a failure of the input device, or the lines over which the input signals must be transmitted, will cause both modules to produce the same erroneous results. Second, the comparator may not be able to perform an exact comparison, depending on the application area. While duplicated telephone switching processors may always exactly agree if they are fault-free, the processors in a digital control application may never exactly agree. Finally, faults in the comparator can cause an error indication when no error exists, or, worse yet, the comparator can fail such that eventual faults in the duplicated modules are never detected.

A technique that can be used in a duplicated microprocessor system to overcome some of these problems is illustrated in Figure 1.7. The basic concept is to implement the comparison process in software that executes in each of the microprocessors. Each processor has its own private memory to store programs and data. In addition, there is a shared memory that can be used to transfer results from one processor to the other for comparison purposes. If the shared memory fails, both processors will detect a disagreement between the data stored in their own memories and that contained in the shared memory. If one of the processors fails, the condition can also be detected using this approach.

The comparisons between the two processors can be performed in one of several ways. The first, and most straightforward technique, is to simply compare each digital word bit-by-bit. Bit-by-bit comparisons have the same problems as

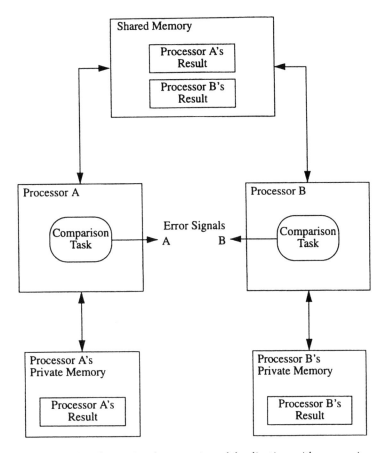

Figure 1.7: A software implementation of duplication with comparison.

voting circuits. Specifically, many applications will require comparing digital words that do not agree exactly, even though the system is fault-free. In such cases, it is common to compare only the most-significant bits of words. For example, in the comparison of two n-bit words, the k least-significant bits might be ignored because their impact on the system is negligible. The feasibility of using such a comparison technique is clearly dependent upon the application. In banking systems, for example, bank balances calculated on duplicate processors must agree exactly. In many real-time control applications, however, minor differences are expected and have little, if any, impact.

A second form of active hardware redundancy is called the *standby replacement* or *standby sparing* technique. In standby sparing, one module is operational while one or more modules serve as standbys, or spares. Various fault detection or error detection schemes are used to determine when a module has become faulty, and fault location is used to determine exactly which module, if any, is faulty. If a fault is detected and located, the faulty module is removed from operation and replaced with one of the spares. The reconfiguration operation in standby sparing can be viewed conceptually as a switch whose output is selected from one, and only one, of the modules providing inputs to the switch. The switch examines error reports from the error detection circuitry associated with each module, to decide which module's output to use. If all modules are providing error-free results, the selection can be made using a fixed priority. Any module that provides erroneous results is eliminated from consideration.

Standby sparing can bring a system back to full operational capability after the occurrence of a fault, but it requires that a momentary disruption in performance occur while the reconfiguration is performed. If the disruption in processing must be minimized, *hot standby sparing* can be used. In the hot standby sparing technique, the spares operate in synchrony with the online modules and are prepared to take over at any time. In contrast to hot standby sparing is *cold standby sparing* where the spares are unpowered until needed to replace a faulty module. The disadvantage of the cold sparing approach is the time required to apply power to a module and perform initialization, prior to bringing the module into active service. The advantage of cold standby sparing is that spares do not consume power until needed to replace a faulty module. A satellite application where power consumption is extremely critical is an example where cold standby sparing may be desirable, or required. A process control system that controls a chemical reaction is an example where the reconfiguration time needs to be minimized, and cold standby sparing is undesirable, or unusable.

One variation on the standby sparing technique is called the *pair-and-a-spare* approach. The technique combines the features present in both standby sparing and duplication with comparison. In essence, the pair-and-a-spare approach uses standby sparing; however, two modules are operated in parallel at all times and their results are compared to provide the error detection capability required in the standby sparing approach. The error signal from the comparison is used to initiate the reconfiguration process that removes faulty modules and replaces them with spares. The reconfiguration process can be viewed conceptually as a switch that accepts the modules' outputs and error reports and provides the comparator with the outputs of two modules, one of which forms the output of the system. As long as the two selected outputs agree, the spares are not used. When a miscompare occurs, however, the switch uses the error reports from the modules to first identify the faulty module and then select a replacement module. In other words, the switch uses the error information from the comparator and the individual modules to maintain two fault-free modules operating in a duplication with comparison arrangement. A prime example of such an architecture is the Stratus System described in Chapters 2 and 4.

A variation on the pair-and-a-spare technique is to always operate modules in pairs. During the design, modules are permanently paired together, and when one module fails, neither module in the pair is used. In other words, modules are always operated and discarded in pairs so that the specific identification of which module is faulty is never required; only the identification of a faulty pair is necessary. Faulty pairs are easily identified based on the outcome of the comparison process.

Hybrid hardware redundancy.   The fundamental concept of hybrid hardware redundancy is to combine the attractive features of both the active and the passive approaches. Fault masking is used to prevent the system from producing erroneous results, and fault detection, fault location, and fault recovery are used to reconfigure the system in the event of a fault. Hybrid redundancy is usually very expensive in terms of the amount of hardware required to implement a system; consequently, hybrid redundancy is most often used in applications that require extremely high integrity of the computations.

There are several approaches to hybrid redundancy. Most, however, are based upon the concept of *N-modular redundancy* (NMR) *with spares*. The idea of NMR with spares is to provide a basic core of N modules arranged in a voting, or a form of voting, configuration. In addition, spares are provided to replace failed units in the NMR core. The benefit of NMR with spares is that a voting configuration can be restored after a fault has occurred. For example, a design that uses TMR with one spare will mask the first module fault that occurs. If the faulty module is then replaced with the spare unit, the second module fault can also be masked, thus providing tolerance of two module faults. For a passive approach to tolerate two module faults, five modules must be configured in a fault-masking arrangement. The hybrid approach can accomplish the same results using only four modules and some fault detection, location, and recovery techniques.

The NMR with spares technique is illustrated in Figure 1.8. The system will remain in the basic NMR configuration until the disagreement detector determines that a faulty unit exists. One approach to fault detection is to compare the output of the voter with the individual outputs of the modules. A module that disagrees with the majority is labeled as faulty and removed from the NMR core. A spare unit is then switched in to replace the faulty module. The reliability of the basic NMR system is maintained as long as the pool of spares is not exhausted. Voting always occurs among the active participants in the NMR core, masking faults and ensuring continuous, error-free computations.

A variation on the basic hybrid redundancy technique is called the *triple-duplex* approach because it combines duplication with comparison and triple modular redundancy. The use of TMR allows faults to be masked and continuous, error-free performance to be provided for up to one faulty module. The use of the duplication with comparison allows faults to be detected and faulty modules removed from the TMR voting process and replaced with spares. The basic structure of the triple-duplex architecture is shown in Figure 1.9. To allow faults to be detected, each module is constructed using the duplication with comparison method. If the comparison process detects a fault, the faulty module is removed from the voting arrangement and replaced with a spare. The removal of faulty modules allows future faults to be tolerated.

The three primary hardware redundancy techniques—passive, active, and hybrid—each have advantages and disadvantages that are important in different applications. The key differences are: (1) Passive techniques rely strictly on fault masking, (2) active techniques do not use fault masking but instead employ de-

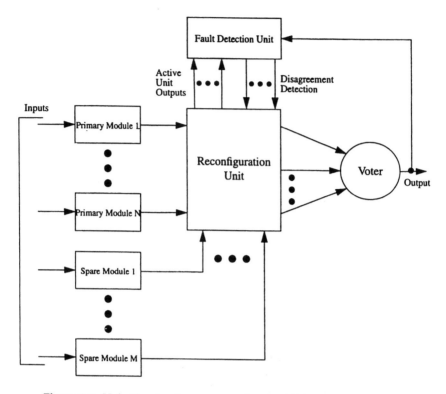

Figure 1.8: Hybrid redundancy approach using NMR with spares. (From Barry W. Johnson, *Design and Analysis of Fault-Tolerant Digital Systems,* Addison-Wesley Publishing Company, Reading, Mass., 1989, p. 70.)

tection, location, and recovery techniques (reconfiguration), and (3) hybrid approaches employ both fault masking and reconfiguration.

The choice of hardware approach depends heavily on the application. Critical-computation applications usually mandate some form of either passive or hybrid redundancy because momentary, erroneous results are not acceptable in such systems. The highest reliability is usually achieved using the hybrid techniques. In long-life and high-availability applications, active approaches are often used because it is typically acceptable to have temporary, erroneous outputs; the important thing is that the system can be restored to an operational state in a short amount of time using reconfiguration techniques.

The cost, in terms of hardware, of the redundancy techniques increases as we go from active to passive and finally to hybrid. Active techniques typically use less hardware but have the disadvantage of potentially producing momentary, erroneous outputs. Passive techniques provide fault masking but use substantial investments in hardware. Finally, hybrid approaches provide the advantage of fault masking but require enough hardware to use voting, and require

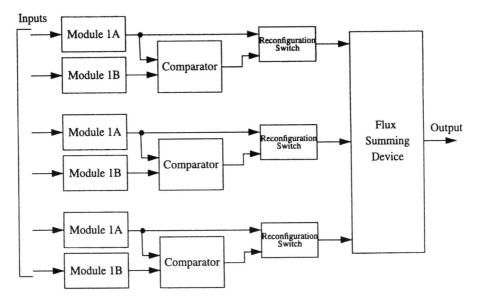

Figure 1.9: The triple-duplex approach to hybrid redundancy. (Adapted from Barry W. Johnson, *Design and Analysis of Fault-Tolerant Digital Systems*, Addison-Wesley Publishing Company, Reading, Mass., 1989, p. 80.)

hardware for spares. Hybrid approaches are typically the most costly in terms of hardware and are used when the highest levels of reliability are required.

Redundancies can take various other forms that can provide various trade-offs between performance and reliability as seen in the rollforward scheme described in Chapter 3.

1.2.2 Information Redundancy

Information redundancy is the addition of redundant information to data to allow fault detection, fault masking, or possibly fault tolerance. Good examples of information redundancy are error-detecting and error-correcting codes, formed by the addition of redundant information to data words, or by the mapping of data words into new representations containing redundant information. Before beginning the discussions of various codes, we will define several basic terms that will appear throughout this section (Tang, 1969).

In general, a *code* is a means of representing information, or data, using a self-defined set of rules. A *codeword* is a collection of symbols, often called digits if the symbols are numbers, used to represent a particular piece of data based upon a specified code. A *binary code* is one in which the symbols forming each codeword consist of only the digits 0 and 1. For example, a binary coded decimal (BCD) code defines a four-bit codeword for each decimal digit. The BCD code, for example, is clearly a binary code. A codeword is said to be *valid* if the codeword adheres to all of the rules that define the code; otherwise, the codeword is said to be *invalid*.

The *encoding operation* is the process of determining the corresponding codeword for a particular data item. In other words, the encoding process takes an original data item and represents it as a codeword using the rules of the code. The *decoding operation* is the process of recovering the original data from the codeword. In other words, the decoding process takes a codeword and determines the data that it represents. Of primary interest here are binary codes. In many binary codewords, a single error in one of the binary digits will cause the resulting codeword to no longer be correct, but, at the same time, the codeword will be valid. Consequently, the user of the information has no means of determining the correctness of the information. It is possible, however, to create a binary code for which the valid codewords are a subset of the total number of possible combinations of 1s and 0s. If the codewords are formed correctly, errors introduced into a codeword will force it to lie in the range of illegal, or invalid codewords, and the error can be detected. This is the basic concept of the *error-detecting codes*. The basic concept of the error-correcting code is that the codeword is structured such that it is possible to determine the correct codeword from the corrupted, or erroneous, codeword. Typically, the code is described by the number of bit errors that can be corrected. For example, a code that can correct single-bit errors is called a *single-error correcting code*. A code that can correct two-bit errors is called a *double-error correcting code*, and so on.

A fundamental concept in the characterization of codes is the *Hamming distance*. The Hamming distance between any two binary words is the number of bit positions in which the two words differ. For example, the binary words 0000 and 0001 differ in only one position, and therefore, have a Hamming distance of 1. The binary words 0000 and 0101, however, differ in two positions; consequently, their Hamming distance is 2. Clearly, if two words have a Hamming distance of 1, it is possible to change one word into the other simply by modifying one bit in one of the words. If, however, two words differ in two bit positions, it is impossible to transform one word into the other by changing one bit in one of the words.

The Hamming distance gives insight into the requirements of error-detecting codes and error-correcting codes. We define the *distance* of a code as the minimum Hamming distance between any two valid codewords. If a binary code has a distance of two, then any single-bit error introduced into a codeword will result in the erroneous word being an invalid codeword because all valid codewords differ in at least two bit positions. If a code has a distance of three, then any single-bit error or any double-bit error will result in the erroneous word being an invalid codeword because all valid codewords differ in at least three positions. However, a code distance of three allows any single-bit error to be corrected, if it is desired to do so, because the erroneous word with a single-bit error will be a Hamming distance of 1 from the correct codeword and at least a Hamming distance of 2 from all others. Consequently, the correct codeword can be identified from the corrupted codeword.

A second fundamental concept of codes is *separability*. A *separable code* is one in which the original information is appended with new information to form the codeword, thus allowing the decoding process to consist of simply removing the additional information and keeping the original data. In other words, the original data is obtained from the codeword by stripping away extra bits, called the code bits or check bits, and retaining only those associated with the original information. A *nonseparable code* does not possess the property of separability, and, consequently, requires more complicated decoding procedures.

Parity codes.   Perhaps the simplest form of a code is the parity code. The basic concept of parity is very straightforward, but there are variations on the fundamental idea. Single-bit parity codes require the addition of an extra bit to a binary word such that the resulting codeword has either an even number of 1s or an odd number of 1s. If the extra bit results in the total number of 1s in the codeword being odd, the code is referred to as *odd parity*. If the resulting number of 1s in the codeword is even, the code is called *even parity*. If a codeword with odd parity experiences a change in one of its bits, the parity will become even. Likewise, if a codeword with even parity encounters a single-bit change, the parity will become odd. Consequently, a single-bit error can be detected by checking the number of 1s in the codeword. The single-bit parity code (either odd or even) has a distance of 2, therefore allowing any single-bit error to be detected but not corrected. It is important to note that the basic parity code is a separable code.

The most common application of parity is in the memories of computer systems. Before being written to memory, a data word is encoded to achieve the correct parity; the encoding consists of appending a bit to force the resulting word to have the appropriate number of 1s. When the data word is subsequently read from memory, the parity is checked to verify that it has not changed as a result of a fault within the memory. If an error is detected, the user of the memory is notified via an error signal that a potential problem exists. The extra information (the extra bit appended to each word) requires additional hardware to handle it. For example, the memory must contain one extra bit per word to store the extra information, and the hardware must be designed to create and check the parity bit. As can be seen, the information redundancy concept often requires hardware redundancy as well.

One of the biggest problems with single-bit parity codes is their inability to guarantee the detection of some very common multiple-bit errors. For example, a memory can be constructed from individual chips that each contains several bits; four bits is a very common number. If a chip in the memory becomes faulty, the simple parity code may be unable to detect the resulting error because multiple bits are affected. The basic parity scheme can be modified to provide additional error detection capability. There are five basic parity approaches including the fundamental odd and even parity; they are bit-per-word, bit-per-byte, bit-per-chip, bit-per-multiple-chips, and interlaced parity.

The *bit-per-word* parity concept has already been discussed. The basic idea is to append one parity bit to each word. The primary disadvantage of the bit-per-word approach is that certain errors can go undetected. For example, if a word, including the parity bit, becomes all 1s because of a complete failure of a bus or a set of data buffers, the odd parity method will detect the condition only if the total number of bits, including the parity bit, is even. Likewise, even parity will detect this problem only if the total number of bits is odd. In a similar manner, the condition of all bits becoming 0 will never be detected by the even bit-per-word parity method because 0 is considered to be an even number of 1s. Odd bit-per-word parity will always detect the condition of all bits being 0.

An alternate approach that uses parity is the *bit-per-byte* technique. Here, two parity bits are used on two separate portions of the original data. The technique is called bit-per-byte, but the parity groups can be any number of bits, not just the eight bits normally associated with the terminology, byte. To gain the full advantages of the approach, however, the number of information bits associated with each parity bit should be even. Also, the parity of one group should be even while the parity of the other group should be odd. The primary advantage of this approach is the ability to detect both the *all 1s* and *all 0s* conditions. If the complete codeword becomes all 1s, the even parity bit will be erroneous. If the complete codeword becomes all 0s, the odd parity bit will be erroneous. In both cases, the erroneous conditions are detected. The bit-per-byte technique also provides additional protection against multiple-bit errors; for example, two-bit errors will always be detected as long as one bit is in the even parity group and the other is in the odd parity group.

The fundamental disadvantage of both the bit-per-word and bit-per-byte parity approaches is the ineffective detection capability for multiple-bit errors. Many memories are organized using memory chips that contain either four bits, eight bits, or more, of memory. Several of these chips are then used in parallel to form the complete number of bits of each word in the memory. If one chip fails (this is called the *whole-chip failure mode*), several bits of each word of memory can be affected. Therefore, the single-bit error assumption is often ineffective.

One approach that is useful to detect the failure of a complete chip is the *bit-per-multiple-chips* method. The basic concept is to have 1 bit from each chip of the memory associated with a single parity bit. Sufficient parity bits are provided to allow each data bit within a chip to be associated with a distinct parity bit. For example, consider a 16-bit word which includes data bits 0 through 15. Suppose parity bit P_0 establishes the parity of a group of bits including bits 0, 4, 8, and 12; parity bit P_1 establishes the parity of a group including bits 1, 5, 9, and 13; parity bit P_2 establishes parity for the group 2, 6, 10, and 14; and P_3 establishes parity for the group 3, 7, 11, and 15. Assume that chip 0 contains all of the parity bits, chip 1 contains bits 0, 1, 2, and 3, chip 2 contains 4, 5, 6, and 7, chip 3 contains 8, 9, 10, and 11, and chip 4 contains 12, 13, 14, and 15. Notice that each parity group includes 1, and only 1, bit from each chip. If one chip fails, all of the parity groups will be affected, but no more than 1 bit in each parity group will be corrupted, so the parity code will detect the error.

One disadvantage of the bit-per-multiple-chips parity approach is that the failure of a complete chip is detected, but it is not located. The failure of any one of the chips will cause all parity groups to be in error, so the cause of the problem cannot be identified. One procedure that overcomes this problem is the *bit-per-chip* parity organization. Here, each parity bit is associated with one chip of the memory. Using the same 16-bit example as before, parity bit P_0 establishes correct parity for the group containing data bits 0, 1, 2, and 3. The other parity groups are defined accordingly. If a single bit becomes erroneous, the existence of the error is detected, and the chip that contains the erroneous bit is identified. This is extremely valuable from a maintenance standpoint; not only does the system have the capability to warn of the occurrence of a problem, but the system can also direct the maintenance personnel to the source of the problem. The primary disadvantage of the bit-per-chip parity method is the susceptibility to the whole-chip failure mode. Because the basic parity code can detect only single errors, the multiple error condition associated with the failure of a complete chip can go undetected.

An alternate organization of the parity code is called *interlaced parity*. Interlaced parity is very similar in form to the bit-per-multiple-chips approach with one key difference. In interlaced parity, the parity groups are formed without regard to the physical organization of the memory. This is in contrast to the bit-per-multiple-chips organization which is intimately tied to the physical structure of the memory. In interlaced parity, the information bits are divided into equal-sized groups, and one parity bit is associated with each group. The bits of each group are then positioned such that no two adjacent bits are from the same parity group. This is accomplished by placing the first bit from group 0 in the least-significant bit position, the first bit from group 1 in the next most-significant position, the first bit from group 2 in the next position, and so on. Once the first bits of each group are placed, the remaining bits are added to the word in a similar manner. The interlaced parity method is most often used when errors in adjacent bits are of major concern. Because no two adjacent bits are in the same parity group, errors in any two adjacent bits will be detected. A good example is a parallel bus; in many buses, two adjacent bits can become shorted together. The interlaced organization of parity will detect errors due to this type of fault.

The final organization of parity that will be considered is *overlapping parity*. In the overlapping parity approach, parity groups are formed with each bit appearing in more than one parity group. This is in contrast to the other approaches we have considered where each bit was contained in one and only one parity group. The primary advantage of overlapping parity is that errors can be located in addition to being detected. Once the erroneous bit is located, it can be corrected by a simple complementation, if desired. Overlapping parity is the basic concept of some of the Hamming error-correcting codes.

Figure 1.10 illustrates the basic idea of overlapping parity when applied to four bits of information. Three parity groups are required to uniquely identify each erroneous bit in the four bits of information. The basic concept of overlapping parity is to place each bit in a unique combination of the parity groups. For example, referring to Figure 1.10, bit 3 appears in each parity group while bits 0, 1, and 2 appear in different combinations of two groups. If any one bit becomes erroneous, the impact is unique, as illustrated in Figure 1.10. For example, if bit 3 is in error, all of the parity groups will be affected, but if bit 1 is erroneous, the parity groups associated with P_0 and P_2 will be affected, while P_1 will be unaffected. As shown in Figure 1.10, each possible single-bit error produces a unique impact on the parity of the three groups.

The overlapping parity approach can be implemented as an error correction scheme by using several comparators and a decoder in conjunction with the parity checking circuits. In addition, the correction process is performed by comple-

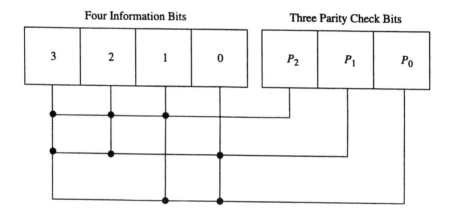

Bit in Error	Parity Group Affected		
3	P_2	P_1	P_0
2	P_2	P_1	
1	P_2		P_0
0		P_1	P_0
P_2	P_2		
P_1		P_1	
P_0			P_0

Figure 1.10: The fundamental concept of overlapped parity. (From Barry W. Johnson, *Design and Analysis of Fault-Tolerant Digital Systems,* Addison-Wesley Publishing Company, Reading, Mass., 1989, p. 91.)

menting the corrupted bit. For example, consider the case of four bits of information and three parity groups. When the four bits of information are written to memory, the three parity bits are generated and stored with the original four bits of information as a single codeword. When the codeword is subsequently read from memory, the parity bits are regenerated using parity generation circuits. The regenerated parity bits are compared to the parity bits that were stored with the information in memory. The results of the comparisons can be used to uniquely identify which bit is corrupted, as is clear from Figure 1.10.

The penalty for using overlapping parity on four bits of information is high; three parity bits are required to detect and locate errors for the four bits of information, a redundancy of 75 percent. As the number of information bits increases, however, the number of parity bits required becomes a smaller percentage of the number of actual information bits. One can determine the required relationship between the number of information bits and the number of parity bits in a fairly simple manner. Let m be the number of information bits to be protected using an overlapping parity approach, and let k be the number of parity bits required to protect those m information bits. Each bit error that can occur must produce a unique result when the parity is checked. With k parity bits, there are 2^k unique outcomes of the parity checking process. With k parity bits and m information bits, there are $m + k$ different, single errors that can occur. So, we know that 2^k must be, at least, as large as $m + k$. Also, we must have a unique result of the parity checks when there is no error, so the total number of unique combinations must be, at least, as large as $m + k + 1$. Therefore, the relationship between k and m must be

$$2^k \geq m + k + 1$$

In Chapter 2 and Chapter 4 we discuss several fault-tolerant architectures that use a variety of parity codes in memory, buses, and I/O units.

m-of-n codes.   The basic concept of the m-of-n *code* is to define codewords that are n bits in length and contain exactly m 1s. As a result, any single-bit error will force the resulting erroneous word to have either $m + 1$ or $m - 1$ 1s, and the error can be detected. The primary advantage of the m-of-n code is the conceptual simplicity; it is very easy to visualize the error detection process. The major disadvantage, however, is that the encoding, decoding, and the detection processes are often extremely difficult to perform, despite their conceptual simplicity.

The easiest way to construct an m-of-n code is to take the original i bits of information and append i bits. The appended bits are chosen such that the resulting $2i$-bit codewords each have exactly i 1s, therefore producing an i-of-$2i$ code. The obvious disadvantage of using the i-of-$2i$ code is that twice as many bits are required to represent the information; consequently, the redundancy of the code is 100 percent. The advantage of creating an i-of-$2i$ code is that both the encoding and the decoding processes are simple because the code is separable. The encoding procedure can be performed by counting the number of 1s in the information to be encoded and looking up in a table the desired bits to append, based on the number of 1s in the original information. The decoding can be performed by simply removing the appended bits from the codeword and retaining the original information.

It is easy to see that *m-of-n* codes have a distance of two. Any single-bit error in an *m-of-n* codeword will change the number of 1s to either $m + 1$ or $m - 1$, depending upon whether the error changed a 0 to a 1 or a 1 to a 0. A second bit error, however, can change the number of 1s back to *m*. For example, if one bit is changed from 0 to 1 and a second bit is changed from 1 to 0, the number of 1s in the codeword remains unchanged. Consequently, the error goes undetected. If the errors are all *unidirectional*, meaning that all errors are either a change of a 1 to a 0 or a change of a 0 to a 1, but not combinations of the two changes, the *m-of-n* code will provide detection of the multiple errors. Consequently, the *m-of-n* code provides detection of all single errors and all multiple, unidirectional errors. The *m-of-n* codes can often be constructed in a more efficient manner, but the separable nature of the code is usually lost.

Duplication codes. *Duplication codes* are based on the concept of completely duplicating the original information to form the codeword. The primary advantage of the duplication code is simplicity. The major disadvantage is clearly the number of extra bits that must be provided to allow the code to be constructed. Duplication codes are found in many applications, including memory systems and some communication systems. The encoding process for the duplication code consists of simply appending the original *i* bits of information to itself to form a codeword of length 2*i* bits. If a single-bit error occurs, the two halves of the codeword will disagree, and the error can be detected. In communication systems, the duplication concept is often applied by transmitting all information twice; if both copies agree, the information is assumed to be correct. The penalty paid in the communications application is a decrease in the information rate of the system because 2*i* bits must be transmitted to obtain *i* bits of information.

A variation on the basic duplication code is to complement the duplicated portion of the codeword. The use of complemented duplication is particularly advantageous when the original information and its duplicate must be processed by the same hardware. The primary advantage of all variations of the duplication codes is the simplicity associated with generating the codewords and the ease of obtaining the original information from the codeword. The advantage is usually offset, however, by the cost of completely duplicating the original information. Also, it is usually very time consuming to implement the duplication codes. In memory applications, each word must be written and read twice. In communication applications, each word must be transmitted twice. In both cases, the time required to perform the operation is doubled. So, the duplication code often requires not only the 100 percent redundancy in information, but typically a 100 percent redundancy in hardware and time, as well.

Checksums.   The checksum is another form of separable code that is most applicable when blocks of data are to be transferred from one point to another. Examples where checksums are used frequently include data transfers between mass storage devices—such as disks—and a computer, and packet-switched networks. The *checksum* is a quantity of information that is added to the block of data to achieve error detection capability. Four primary types of checksums are typically used: single-precision, double-precision, Honeywell, and the residue checksum.

The basic concept of the checksum is illustrated in Figure 1.11. When the original data is created, an additional piece of information, called the checksum, is appended to the block of data. The checksum is then regenerated when the data is received at the destination or, in some applications, when the data is read from memory. The regenerated checksum and the original checksum are compared to determine if an error has occurred in the data, the checksum generation, checksum regeneration, or the checksum comparison.

The checksum is basically the sum of the original data. The difference be-

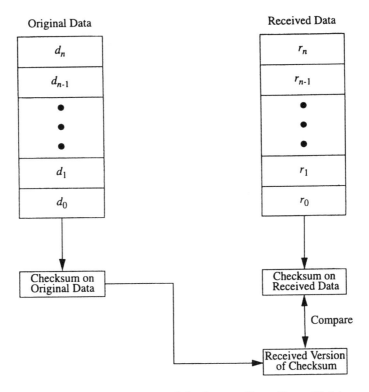

Figure 1.11: The basic concept of checksums. (From Barry W. Johnson, *Design and Analysis of Fault-Tolerant Digital Systems,* Addison-Wesley Publishing Company, Reading, Mass., 1989, p. 98.)

tween the various forms of the checksum is the way in which the summation is generated. The simplest form of the checksum is the *single-precision checksum*. The single-precision checksum is formed by performing the binary addition of the data that is to be protected and ignoring any overflow that occurs. For example, if each data word is n bits, the checksum will be n bits, as well. If the true binary sum of the data exceeds $2^n - 1$, then an overflow will have occurred; in the single-precision checksum, the overflow is ignored. In other words, the single-precision checksum is formed by adding the n-bit data in a modulo-2^n fashion.

The primary difficulty with the single-precision checksum is that information, and, as a result, error detection capability are lost in the ignored overflow. One technique that is often used to overcome the limitations of the single-precision checksum is to compute the checksum in double precision, thus, the name *double-precision checksum*. The basic concept of the double-precision checksum is to compute a $2n$-bit checksum for a block of n-bit words using modulo-2^{2n} arithmetic. Overflow is still a concern, however, but it is now overflow from a $2n$-bit sum, as opposed to an n-bit sum.

A third form of the checksum is called the *Honeywell checksum*. The basic idea of the Honeywell checksum is to concatenate consecutive words to form a collection of double-length words. For example, if there are k n-bit words, a set of $k/2$ 2 n-bit words is formed, and a checksum is calculated over the newly structured data. The primary advantage of the Honeywell checksum is that a bit error that appears in the same bit position of all words will affect at least two bit positions of the checksum. For example, if a complete column of the original data is erroneous, the modified data structure has two erroneous columns.

The final form of the checksum that will be considered is the *residue checksum*. The concept of the residue checksum is the same as the single-precision checksum except that the carry bit out of the most-significant bit position is not ignored but is added back to the checksum in an end-around carry fashion.

One important point concerning checksums is that they are capable of error detection but not error location. If the checksum generated at the receiving point differs from the checksum generated at the transmission point, an error is indicated, but there is not enough information available to determine where the error has occurred. The complete block of data over which the checksum was formed must be corrected.

Cyclic codes.

The fundamental feature of *cyclic codes* is that any end-around shift of a codeword will produce another codeword (Lin, 1983). In other words, the cyclic code is invariant to the end-around shift operation. Cyclic codes are frequently applied to sequential-access devices such as tapes, bubble memories, and disks. In addition, cyclic codes are extremely popular for use in data links. One reason the cyclic codes are attractive is because the encoding operation can be implemented using simple shift registers with feedback connections.

A cyclic code is characterized by its generator polynomial, $G(X)$, which is a polynomial of degree $(n - k)$ or greater, where n is the number of bits contained in the complete codeword produced by $G(X)$, and k is the number of bits in the original information to be encoded. For binary cyclic codes, the coefficients of the generator polynomial are all either 0 or 1. The integers n and k specify the characteristics of the cyclic code. A cyclic code with a generator polynomial of degree $(n - k)$ is called an (n,k) cyclic code. Such codes possess the property of being able to detect all single errors and all multiple, adjacent errors affecting less than $(n - k)$ bits (Lin and Costello, 1983). The error detection property of cyclic codes is particularly important in communications applications where *burst errors* can occur. A burst error is the result of a transient fault and usually introduces a number of adjacent errors into a given data item. For example, a word that is transmitted serially can have several adjacent bits corrupted by a single disturbance; one would hope that the coding scheme could detect such errors. (n,k) cyclic codes will detect adjacent errors as long as the number of adjacent bits affected does not exceed $(n - k)$.

The properties of cyclic codes are generated by representing the codewords as coefficients of a polynomial. For example, suppose we have the codeword, $v = (v_0, v_1, \ldots, v_{n-1})$. This codeword corresponds to the polynomial $V(X)$ where

$$V(X) = v_0 + v_1 X + v_2 X^2 + \ldots + v_{n-1} X^{n-1}$$

Each n-bit codeword is represented by a polynomial of degree $(n - 1)$ or less. The polynomial, $V(X)$, is called the *code polynomial* of the codeword, v.

The code polynomials for a nonseparable cyclic code are generated by multiplying a polynomial, representing the data to be encoded, by another polynomial known as the generator polynomial. The generator polynomial determines the characteristics of the cyclic code. Any additions required during the multiplication of the two polynomials are performed using modulo-2 addition. For example, suppose that we have a generator polynomial, $G(X) = 1 + X + X^3$, and we wish to encode the binary data, (1101). The data (1101) can be represented by the data polynomial, $D(X) = 1 + X + X^3$. The code polynomial is generated by multiplying the data polynomial and the generator polynomial. Specifically, the code polynomial is generated as $V(X) = D(X)G(X) = (1 + X + X^3)(1 + X + X^3) = 1 + X^2 + X^6$. In more exact terms, the code polynomial is given by $V(X) = 1 + (0)X + (1)X^2 + (0)X^3 + (0)X^4 + (1)X^6$, and the codeword, v, consists of the coefficients of that code polynomial. In other words, $v = (1010001)$.

Perhaps the most interesting aspect of the nonseparable cyclic codes is the manner in which they can be generated. Recall that the code polynomial is generated by multiplying the data polynomial by the generator polynomial, and adding the coefficients in a modulo-2 fashion. If we consider the blocks labeled X as multipliers by the factor, X, and the addition elements as modulo-2 adders, the circuit shown in Figure 1.12 performs the multiplication of two polynomials. For example, if $D(X) = 1$, the output, $V(X)$, of the circuit will be $1 + X^2 + X^3$. Likewise, if $D(X) = 1 + X + X^3$, the output will be given by

$$V(X) = 1 + X + X^3 + [X(1 + X + X^3) + (1 + X + X^3)]X^2$$

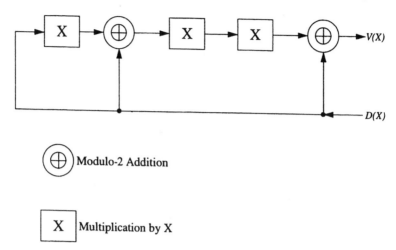

$\bigoplus$ Modulo-2 Addition

$\boxed{X}$ Multiplication by X

Figure 1.12: Example circuit for generating a cyclic code. (From Barry W. Johnson, *Design and Analysis of Fault-Tolerant Digital Systems*, Addison-Wesley Publishing Company, Reading, Mass., 1989, p. 98.)

or

$$V(X) = 1 + X + X^2 + X^3 + X^4 + X^5 + X^6$$

Therefore, if the generator polynomial is $G(X) = 1 + X^2 + X^3$, the circuit shown in Figure 1.12 will generate the code polynomial by multiplying the data polynomial by the generator polynomial. For example, if the data to be encoded is (1101), the data polynomial will be $D(X) = 1 + X + X^3$. The resulting code polynomial yields the codeword (1111111).

The version of the cyclic code that has been presented thus far is not a separable code, so the decoding process involves more than simply picking certain bits from the codeword. The structure of the cyclic code, however, makes the decoding process relatively easy.

Suppose that we have a codeword $(r_0, r_1, r_2, \ldots, r_{n-1})$, and we wish to determine if this codeword is valid. We know that the codeword, $(r_0, r_1, r_2, \ldots, r_{n-1})$, can be represented by the code polynomial, $R(X) = r_0 + r_1 X + r_2 X^2 + \ldots + r_{n-1} X^{n-1}$. We also know that the correct code polynomial was generated by multiplying the original data polynomial by the generator polynomial. In other words, if $R(X)$ is a valid code polynomial, then it was generated as $R(X) = D(X)G(X)$ where $G(X)$ is the generator polynomial and $D(X)$ is the original data polynomial. If we write

$$R(X) = D(X) G(X) + S(X)$$

then the quantity $S(X)$ should be zero if the polynomial $R(X)$ is a valid code polynomial. In other words, $R(X)$ should be an exact multiple of the generator polynomial. One way to determine if $R(X)$ is indeed an exact multiple of the generator polynomial is to divide the polynomial $R(X)$ by the generator polynomial, $G(X)$, and check to see if the remainder of the division is zero. If the remainder is zero, the polynomial is an exact multiple of the generator polynomial and is a valid code polynomial. The quantity $S(X)$ is called the *syndrome polynomial.*

The process of division may, at first, seem complicated and difficult to implement; it turns out to be quite simple, however, when feedback circuits similar to the cyclic code generators are used. The circuit shown in Figure 1.13, for example, is capable of dividing a polynomial by the polynomial $1 + X + X^3$. Once again, the blocks labeled as X perform multiplication by the factor, X. The adders in the circuit of Figure 1.13 are modulo-2 adders. The polynomial that appears on line $B(X)$ of the circuit will be given by

$$B(X) = (X^3 + X) D(X)$$

But the values present on line $D(X)$ are determined by both line $B(X)$ and line $V(X)$. Specifically,

$$V(X) + B(X) = D(X)$$

or

$$V(X) = D(X) - B(X) = D(X) - (X^3 + X)D(X)$$

Because the functions of addition and subtraction are the same in the modulo-2 system, we obtain by replacing $-$ by $+$

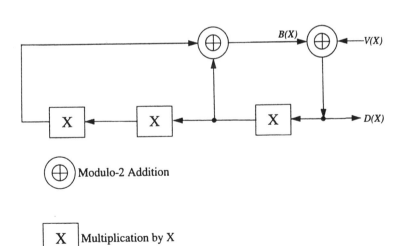

Figure 1.13: An example of division circuit for decoding cyclic codes. (From Barry W. Johnson, *Design and Analysis of Fault-Tolerant Digital Systems*, Addison-Wesley Publishing Company, Reading, Mass., 1989, p. 109.)

$$V(X) = (X^3 + X + 1)\, D(X)$$

or

$$D(X) = \frac{V(X)}{X^3 + X + 1}$$

The circuit of Figure 1.13 will divide the polynomial, $V(X)$, by the polynomial, $X^3 + X + 1$.

The primary disadvantage of the cyclic codes discussed thus far is that they are not separable. It is possible, however, to generate a separable, cyclic code (Nelson and Carroll, 1986). To generate an (n,k) code, the original data polynomial, $D(X)$, is first multiplied by X^{n-k}, and the result is divided by the generator polynomial, $G(X)$, to obtain a remainder, $R(X)$. The code polynomial is then computed as $V(X) = R(X) + X^{n-k}D(X)$, and $V(X)$ is an exact multiple of the generator polynomial, $G(X)$. Notice that the multiplication by X^{n-k} can be performed by simply shifting the coefficients of the data polynomial. Also notice that the addition of the remainder polynomial is equivalent to simply appending the remainder to the polynomial $X^{n-k}D(X)$.

It is relatively straightforward to see the validity of the encoding process described in the previous paragraph. Suppose we have an arbitrary data polynomial, $D(X)$, and a generator polynomial, $G(X)$. The code polynomial, $V(X)$, is given by

$$V(X) = X^{n-k}D(X) + R(X)$$

where $R(X)$ is the remainder obtained when $X^{n-k}D(X)$ is divided by $G(X)$. In other words,

$$\frac{X^{n-k}D(X)}{G(X)} = Q(X) + \frac{R(X)}{G(X)}$$

where $Q(X)$ is the quotient computed in the division process.

Multiplying both sides of the previous equation by $G(X)$ yields

$$X^{n-k}D(X) = G(X)Q(X) + R(X)$$

or

$$X^{n-k}D(X) - R(X) = G(X)Q(X)$$

Recall, however, that all addition and subtraction operations are performed using modulo-2 arithmetic, so addition and subtraction are identical. Consequently,

$$X^{n-k}D(X) - R(X) = X^{n-k}D(X) + R(X) = G(X)Q(X) = V(X)$$

Therefore, the code polynomial, $V(X)$, formed as

$$V(X) = X^{n-k}D(X) + R(X)$$

is an exact multiple of the generator polynomial, $G(X)$.

Arithmetic codes.   *Arithmetic codes* are very useful when it is desired to check arithmetic operations such as addition, multiplication, and division (Avizienis, 1971a). The basic concept is the same as in all other coding techniques. The data presented to the arithmetic operation are encoded before the operations are performed. After completing the arithmetic operations, the resulting codewords are checked to make sure that they are valid codewords. If the resulting codewords are not valid, an error condition is signaled.

An arithmetic code must be an invariant to a set of arithmetic operations. An arithmetic code, A, has the property that $A(b*c) = A(b)*A(c)$, where b and c are operands, $*$ is some arithmetic operation, and $A(b)$ and $A(c)$ are the arithmetic codewords for the operands b and c, respectively. Stated verbally, the performance of the arithmetic operation on two arithmetic codewords will produce the arithmetic codeword of the result of the arithmetic operation. To completely define an arithmetic code, the method of encoding and the arithmetic operations for which the code is invariant must be specified. The most common examples of arithmetic codes are the AN codes, residue codes, and the inverse residue codes.

The simplest arithmetic code is the AN *code* which is formed by multiplying each data word, N, by some constant, A. The AN codes are invariant to addition and subtraction but not multiplication and division. If N_1 and N_2 are two operands to be encoded, the resulting codewords will be AN_1 and AN_2, respectively. If the two codewords are added, the sum is $A(N_1 + N_2)$, which is the codeword of the correct sum. The operations performed under an AN code can be checked by determining if the results are evenly divisible by the constant, A. If the results are not evenly divisible by A, an error condition is signaled.

The magnitude of the constant, A, determines both the number of extra bits required to represent the codewords and the error detection capability provided. The selection of the constant, A, is critical to the effectiveness and the efficiency of the resulting code. First, for binary codes, the constant must not be a power of 2. To see the reason for this limitation, suppose that we encode the binary number $(a_{n-1} a_{n-2} \cdots a_2 a_1 a_0)$ by multiplying by the constant, $A = 2^a$. Multiplication by 2^a is equivalent to a left arithmetic shift of the original binary word, so the resulting codeword will be $(a_{n-1} a_{n-2} \cdots a_2 a_1 a_0 \, 0 \, 0 \ldots 0)$, where a 0s have been appended to the original binary number. The decimal representation of the codeword is given by

$$a_{n-1}2^{a+n-1} + \ldots + a_2 2^{a+2} + a_1 2^{a+1} + a_0 2^a + 0 2^{a-1} + \ldots 0 2^1 + 0 2^0$$

which is clearly, evenly divisible by 2^a. It is also easy to see, however, that changing just one coefficient will still yield a result that is evenly divisible by 2^a. For example, if the coefficient of the 2^a term changes from 0 to 1, the result will remain evenly divisible by 2^a. Thus, an AN code that has $A = 2^a$ is not capable of detecting single-bit errors.

An example of a valid AN code is the $3N$ code where all words are encoded by multiplying by a factor of 3. If the original data words are n bits in length, the codewords for the 3N code will require $n + 2$ bits. The encoding of operands in the 3N code can be performed by a simple addition if we recognize that we can multiply any number by 3 by adding the original number to a value that is twice that number. In other words, we form 3N by adding N and 2N. The quantity, 2N, is easily created by shifting the binary number left by one place. The numbers, N and 2N, can then be added.

The next example class of arithmetic codes is the residue codes. A residue code is a separable arithmetic code created by appending the residue of a number to that number. In other words, the codeword is constructed as $D \backslash R$, where D is the original data and R is the residue of that data. The encoding operation consists of determining the residue and appending it to the original data. The decoding process involves simply removing the residue, thus leaving the original data word.

The residue of a number is simply the remainder generated when the number is divided by an integer. For example, suppose we have an integer, N, and we divide N by another integer, m. N may be written as an integer multiple of m as

$$N = Im + r$$

or

$$\frac{N}{m} = I + \frac{r}{m}$$

where r is the remainder, sometimes called the residue, and I is the quotient. The quantity m is called the check base, or the modulus. For example, if $N = 14$ and $m = 3$, the quotient, I, will be 4 and the residue will be 2. We often write this as

$$14 = 2 modulo\ (3)$$

Separable residue codes, as mentioned previously, are formed by appending the residue of a data word to that data word. The number of extra bits required to represent the codeword depends on the particular modulus selected. The residue will never be larger than the modulus; in fact

$$0 \leq r < m$$

For example, if the original data is n bits and the modulus is 3, the codeword will require $n + 2$ bits.

The primary advantages of the residue codes are that they are invariant to the operation of addition, and the residues can be handled separately from the data during the addition process. The basic structure of an adder that uses the separable residue code for error detection is shown in Figure 1.14. The two data words, D_1 and D_2, are added to form a sum word, S. The residues, r_1 and r_2, of D_1 and D_2, respectively, are also added using a modulo-m adder, where m is the modulus used to encode D_1 and D_2. If the operations are performed correctly, the modulo-m addition of r_1 and r_2 will yield the residue, r_s, of the sum, S. A separate

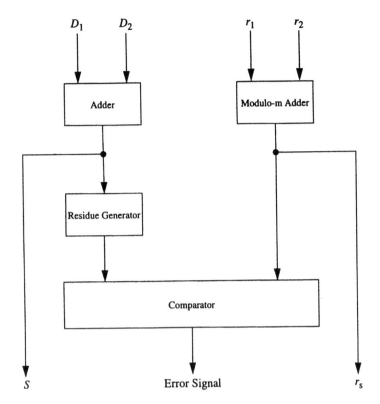

Figure 1.14: An adder using a residue code for error detection. (From Barry W. Johnson, *Design and Analysis of Fault-Tolerant Digital Systems*, Addison-Wesley Publishing Company, Reading, Mass., 1989, p. 118.)

circuit is then used to calculate the residue of S. If the calculated residue, r_c, differs from r_s, an error has occurred in one part of the process. For example, errors can be detected that occur in the generation of S, r_s, or r_c.

If the modulus for the residue code is selected in a special manner, a so-called *low-cost residue code* results. Specifically, low-cost residue codes have a modulus of $m = 2^b - 1$, where b is some integer greater than or equal to 2. The number of extra bits required in a low-cost residue code is equal to b. The main advantage of the low-cost residue code is the ease with which the encoding process can be performed. Recall that we must determine a remainder to encode information using a residue code; therefore, a division is necessary. The low-cost residue codes, however, allow the division to be recast as an addition process. The information bits to be encoded are first divided into groups, each group containing b bits. The groups are then added in a modulo-$(2^b - 1)$ fashion to form the residue of the information bits.

A modification of the separable residue code is the separable *inverse-residue code.* The inverse-residue code is formed in a manner similar to that of the residue code by appending information to the original data. Rather than append the residue, the inverse residue is calculated and appended. The inverse residue, Q, is calculated for a data word, N, as $m - r$, where m is the modulus and r is the residue of N. The codeword for N then becomes $N \backslash Q$.

The inverse-residue codes have been found to have better fault detection capability for so-called repeated-use faults (Avizienis, 1971a). A *repeated-use fault* is one that is encountered multiple times before the code is checked because the hardware is used multiple times before the code is checked. For example, if repeated addition is used to perform multiplication and the adder has a fault of some type, a repeated-use fault will occur. Repeated-use faults are particularly difficult to detect because subsequent effects of the fault can cancel the previous effects of the fault, thus rendering the fault undetectable.

Berger codes. A very simple form of coding is the *Berger code* (Lala, 1985). Berger codes are formed by appending a special set of bits, called the check bits, to each word of information. Therefore, the Berger code is a separable code. The check bits are created based on the number of 1s in the original information. A Berger code of length n will have I information bits and k check bits where

$$k = \lceil \log (I + 1) \rceil$$

and

$$n = I + k$$

A codeword is formed by first creating a binary number that corresponds to the number of 1s in the original I bits of information. The resulting binary number is then complemented and appended to the I information bits to form the $(I + k)$-bit codeword. For example, suppose that the information to be encoded is (0111010), such that $I = 7$. The value of k is then

$$k = \lceil \log (7 + 1) \rceil = 3$$

The number of 1s in this word of information is four, and the three-bit binary representation of 4 is (100). The complement of (100) is (011), so the resulting codeword is (0111010011) which is simply the original information with 011 appended.

If the number of information bits is related to the number of check bits by the relationship

$$I = 2^k - 1,$$

the resulting code is called a *maximal length Berger code*. For example, the code constructed for $I = 7$ and $k = 3$ is a maximal length Berger code. The primary advantages of the Berger codes are that they are separable and they detect all multiple, unidirectional errors. For the error detection capability provided, the Berger codes use the fewest number of check bits of the available separable codes (Lala, 1985).

Hamming error-correcting codes.   Possibly the most common extension of the fundamental parity approach is the Hamming error-correcting code (Hamming, 1950). Many memory designs incorporate error correction for several reasons. First, Hamming error correction is relatively inexpensive; typically, the Hamming codes require anywhere from 10 to 40 percent redundancy. Second, the Hamming codes are efficient in terms of the time required to perform the correction process; the encoding and the decoding processes inject relatively small time delays. Third, the error correction circuit is readily available on inexpensive chips. Finally, the memory can contribute as much as 60 to 70 percent of the faults in a system. In addition, transient faults are becoming much more prevalent as memory chips become denser. The combination of permanent and transient faults in memories makes the use of error correction very attractive.

The Hamming codes are best thought of as overlapping parity. As we saw in the overlapping parity approach, the check bits provide one unique combination for each possible information bit that can be erroneous, one combination for each parity check bit that can be erroneous, and one combination for the error-free case. The Hamming code is formed by partitioning the information bits into parity groups and specifying a parity bit for each group. The ability to locate which bit is faulty is obtained by overlapping the groups of bits. In other words, a given information bit will appear in more than one group in such a way that if the bit is erroneous, the parity bits that are in error will identify the erroneous bit.

The basic process involved in the Hamming codes is no different from that of other codes. First, the original data is encoded by generating a set, call it C_g, of parity check bits. When it is desired to check the information for its correctness, the encoding process is repeated and a set, call it C_c, of parity check bits is regenerated. If C_g and C_c agree, the information is assumed to be correct. If, however, C_g and C_c disagree, the information is incorrect and must be corrected. To aid in the correction, we define the syndrome, S, as the result obtained by forming the EXCLUSIVE-OR of C_g and C_c. The syndrome is a binary word that is 1 in each bit position in which C_g and C_c disagree. A syndrome that is all 0s is indicative of correct information.

The basic structure of a memory that uses the Hamming single-error correcting code is shown in Figure 1.15. When data is written to memory, the check bits are generated and stored in memory along with the original information. Upon reading the information and the check bits from memory, the check bits are regenerated and compared to the stored check bits to generate the syndrome. The syndrome is then decoded to determine if a bit is erroneous, and if so, the erroneous bit is corrected by complementation. The corrected data is then passed to the user of the memory. Memories that use this type of correction are usually designed such that data is corrected without interrupting the normal operation of

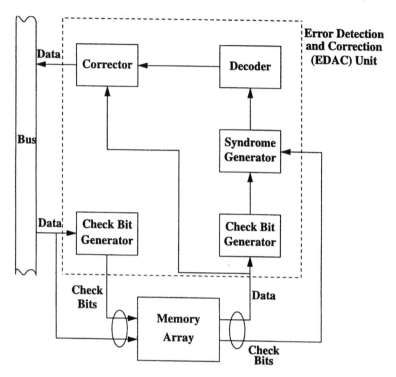

Figure 1.15: Memory organization using an error-correcting code. (From Barry W. Johnson, *Design and Analysis of Fault-Tolerant Digital Systems,* Addison-Wesley Publishing Company, Reading, Mass., 1989, p. 132)

the system. The user of the memory might be informed, however, that a correction has occurred such that maintenance can be performed if corrections are continually required.

The basic Hamming code provides for the correction of single-bit errors. Unfortunately, double-bit errors will be erroneously corrected using the basic Hamming code. To overcome the problem of erroneous correction and provide a code that can correct single-bit errors and identify double-bit errors, the basic Hamming code is modified. The resulting code is called the modified Hamming code. The modification consists of simply adding one additional parity check bit that checks parity over the entire Hamming codeword. If a single bit is in error, the additional parity bit will indicate that the overall parity is incorrect. The syndrome will then point to the bit that is erroneous. If a double-bit error occurs, the additional parity bit will indicate that the overall parity is correct because a single parity check cannot detect a double-bit error. But, the syndrome will be nonzero because the remaining parity checks will indicate an error. Therefore, the double error can be detected, and an erroneous correction prevented. To summarize, if the overall parity is incorrect and the syndrome is not 0, a single-bit error is corrected. If the overall parity is correct and the syndrome is not 0, a double-bit error is identified and no correction occurs. If the overall parity is correct and the syndrome is 0, the data is assumed to be correct.

An in-depth discussion of various memory codes used in computers can be found in Fujiwara and Pradhan (1990).

Self-checking concepts.   The concept of *self-checking logic* has increased in popularity because of the traditional problem of "checking the checker." In many designs that use coding schemes or duplication with comparison, it is necessary to compare the outputs of two modules or to verify that the output is a valid codeword. The basic problem with such techniques, as we have seen, is the reliance of the approaches on the correct operation of comparators or code checkers. If the code checker fails, for example, the system can indicate that an error exists when in fact one does not, or the system can fail to detect a legitimate error that occurs. In many applications, either condition is unacceptable. One possible solution is to design comparators and code checkers that are capable of detecting their own faults. Consequently, the concept of *self-checking logic* has been developed. Before beginning the discussions of self-checking logic, we must first introduce several important terms that are crucial to the understanding of self-checking technology.

In general, a circuit is said to be *self-checking* if it has the ability to automatically detect the existence of a fault without the need for any externally applied stimulus (Lala, 1985). In other words, a self-checking circuit determines if it contains a fault during the normal course of its operations. Self-checking logic is typically designed using coding techniques similar to those discussed already. The basic idea is to design a circuit that when fault-free and presented a valid input codeword, will produce the correct output codeword. If a fault exists, however, the circuit should produce an invalid output codeword so that the existence of the fault can be detected.

To formalize the concept of self-checking logic, we will define the terms *fault secure, self-testing,* and *totally self-checking.* In presenting each definition, it is important to understand that we are considering circuits designed to accept codewords on their input lines and produce codewords on their output lines.

A circuit is said to be *fault secure* if any single fault within the circuit results in that circuit either producing the correct codeword or producing a noncodeword for any valid input codeword (Lala, 1985). In other words, a circuit is fault secure if the fault either has no affect on the output or the output is affected such that it becomes an invalid codeword. A circuit would not be fault secure, for example, if a fault resulted in the output becoming incorrect but still a valid codeword.

A circuit is said to be *self-testing* if there exists at least one valid input codeword that will produce an invalid output codeword when a single fault is present in the circuit (Lala, 1985). In other words, a circuit is self-testing if each single fault is detectable since a fault that resulted in valid output codewords for each possible input codeword would be undetectable.

Finally, a circuit is said to be *totally self-checking* if it is both fault secure and self-testing (Lala, 1985). The fault secure property guarantees that the circuit will either produce the correct codeword output or an invalid codeword output when any single fault occurs. The self-testing property guarantees that there is at least one input codeword that will produce an invalid codeword output from the circuit when a fault is present. In summary, a circuit is totally self-checking if all single faults are detectable by at least one valid codeword input, and when a given input combination does not detect the fault, the output is the correct codeword output.

Another way of looking at these basic concepts is as follows. The primary inputs of the circuit are encoded to produce the set of valid input codewords that is a subset of the total set of inputs. Similarly, the total set of output values is partitioned into valid output codewords and is further partitioned into the correct output codewords. During normal operation, a fault-free circuit will accept a valid input codeword and produce the correct output codeword. A fault secure circuit will accept a valid input codeword, and, when a fault is present, produce either the correct output codeword or a noncode word. A self-testing circuit will produce correct codeword outputs, valid but incorrect codeword outputs, or completely invalid codeword outputs. However, for any single fault that can be present, you are guaranteed that there is, at least, one valid input codeword that will result in the output being an invalid codeword. Finally, a totally self-checking circuit will always produce either the correct codeword at the output or an invalid codeword. Also, there will be at least one valid input codeword that will result in an invalid output codeword when any single fault is present.

The general structure of a totally self-checking (TSC) circuit is shown in Figure 1.16. During normal operation, coded inputs are applied to the functional circuit and coded outputs are produced at the circuit's output. A checker verifies that the outputs are indeed valid codewords and provides an error indication if they are not. To provide a truly TSC design, both the functional circuit and the checker must possess the TSC property. Perhaps the key to the correct operation of the circuit is the TSC checker, so we will consider its operation.

The function of the checker is to determine if the output of the functional circuit is a valid codeword or not. In addition, the checker must indicate if any faults have occurred in the checker itself. To accomplish both tasks, the output of the checker is encoded to produce a coded error signal. Rather than have a single-bit output that provides a "faulty" or "not faulty" indication, the output consists of two bits that are (1) complementary if the input to the checker is a valid codeword *and* the checker is fault-free, or (2) noncomplementary if the input to the checker is not a valid codeword *or* the checker contains a fault. One obvious reason for using two checker outputs is to overcome the problem of the checker output becoming *stuck* at either the logic 0 or the logic 1 value.

The checker must possess the *code disjoint* property (Lala, 1985). Code disjoint implies that when the checker is fault-free, valid codewords on the checker's input lines must be mapped into valid error codes (the checker's outputs are complementary) on the checker's output lines. Likewise, invalid codewords on the checker's input lines must be mapped into invalid error codewords (the checker's outputs are not complementary) on the checker's outputs.

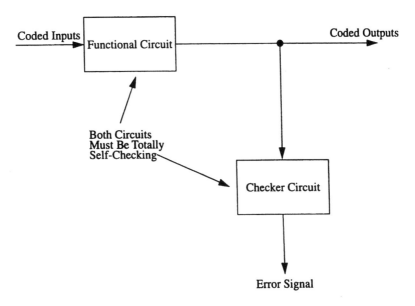

Figure 1.16: Basic structure of a totally self-checking circuit. (From Barry W. Johnson, *Design and Analysis of Fault-Tolerant Digital Systems*, Addison-Wesley Publishing Company, Reading, Mass., 1989, p. 397.)

Data path and storage can easily be checked by parity; however, arithmetic and logical operations are not easily amenable to parity checks. The only known parity check coding scheme which preserves parity under arithmetic and logical operations is the scheme proposed by Pradhan and Reddy (1972a,b). Consider two operands, X and Y, encoded into codewords $C(X)$ and $C(Y)$. Let $Z = C(X) * C(Y)$ where $*$ is a bit by bit logical operation such as AND, OR, NAND, or NOR. The fundamental question is whether there can exist a parity check code for which $Z = C(X * Y)$. In Pradhan and Reddy (1972a,b), it is observed that for Reed-Muller codes, $C(X) * C(Y) = C(X * Y)$. Based on these observations, a scheme was presented for error control in arithmetic and logical operations.

One scheme that was used in some of the early systems is the so-called parity-prediction technique, Pradhan (1986). However, with VSLI, attractiveness of parity prediction has been reduced because simple duplication and comparison can be just as cost effective. Furthermore, duplication can be implemented at any level, independent of functionality.

1.2.3 Time Redundancy

The fundamental problem with the forms of redundancy discussed thus far is the penalty paid in extra hardware for the implementation of the various techniques. Both hardware redundancy and information redundancy can require large amounts of extra hardware for their implementation. In an effort to decrease the hardware required to achieve fault detection or fault tolerance, time redundancy has recently received much attention. Time redundancy methods attempt to reduce the amount of extra hardware at the expense of using additional time. In many applications, the time is of much less importance than the hardware because hardware is a physical entity that impacts weight, size, power consumption, and cost. Time, on the other hand, may be readily available in some applications. It is important to understand that the selection of a particular type of redundancy is very dependent upon the application. For example, some systems can better stand additional hardware than additional time; others can tolerate additional time much easier than additional hardware. The selection in each case must be made by examining the requirements of the application and the available techniques that can meet such requirements.

Transient fault detection.   The basic concept of time redundancy is the repetition of computations in ways that allow faults to be detected. Time redundancy can function in a system in several ways. The fundamental concept is to perform the same computation two or more times and compare the results to determine if a discrepancy exists. If an error is detected, the computations can be performed again to see if the disagreement remains or disappears. Such approaches are often good for detecting errors resulting from transient faults but cannot provide protection against errors resulting from permanent faults.

The main problem with many time redundancy techniques is assuring that the system has the same data to manipulate each time it redundantly performs a computation. If a transient fault has occurred, a system's data may be completely corrupted, making it difficult to repeat a given computation.

Permanent fault detection.   In the past, time redundancy has been used primarily to detect transients in systems. One of the biggest potentials of time redundancy, however, now appears to be the ability to detect permanent faults while using a minimum of extra hardware. The fundamental concept is illustrated in Figure 1.17. During the first computation or transmission, the operands are used as presented and the results are stored in a register. Prior to the second computation or transmission, the operands are encoded in some fashion using an encoding function. After the operations have been performed on the encoded data, the results are then decoded and compared to those obtained during the first operation. The selection of the encoding function is made so as to allow faults in the hardware to be detected. Example encoding functions might include the complementation operator and an arithmetic shift.

The complementation operator has been applied to the transmission of digital data over wire media and the detection of faults in digital circuits. Suppose that we wish to detect errors in data transmitted over a parallel bus using the time redundancy approach. At time t_0, we transmit the original data, and at time $t_0 + \Delta$, we transmit the complement of the data. If a line of the bus is stuck at either a 1 or a 0, the two versions of the information that are received will not be complements of each other. Therefore, the fault can be detected. In general, if a se-

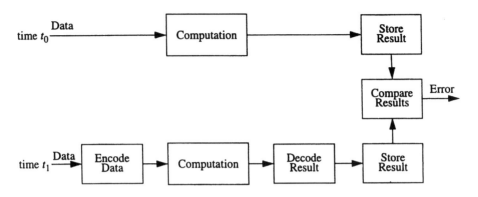

Figure 1.17: Permanent fault detection using time redundancy. (From Barry W. Johnson, *Design and Analysis of Fault-Tolerant Digital Systems*, Addison-Wesley Publishing Company, Reading, Mass., 1989, p. 137.)

quence of information is transmitted using this approach, each bit line should alternate between a logic 1 and a logic 0 provided the transmission is error free; thus, the reason for the name *alternating logic* being applied to this approach.

The concept of alternating logic can be applied to general, combinational logic circuits if the circuit possesses the property of self-duality. A combinational circuit is said to be *self-dual* if and only if $f(X) = \overline{f(\overline{X})}$, where f is the output of the circuit and X is the input vector for the circuit. Stated verbally, a combinational circuit is self-dual if the output for the input vector, X, is the complement of the output when the input vector, $\overline{X}$, is applied. For a self-dual circuit, the application of an input, X, followed by the input, $\overline{X}$, will produce outputs that alternate between 1 and 0. The key to the detection of faults using the alternating logic approach is determining that at least one input combination exists for which the fault will not result in alternating outputs.

A key advantage of the alternating logic approach is that any combinational circuit with n input variables can be transformed into a self-dual circuit with no more than $n + 1$ input variables. To see this, we first define the dual of a function. The dual, f_d, of an n-variable function, f, is given by

$$f_d = \overline{f(\overline{x_1}, \ \overline{x_2}, \ \ldots, \ \overline{x_n})}$$

In other words, the dual of the function f is obtained by first complementing f and then replacing each variable with the complement of the variable. The function f_{sd} given by

$$f_{sd} = x_{n+1}f + \overline{x_{n+1}}f_d$$

is then a self-dual function.

The use of alternating logic will detect a set of faults if for every fault within the set, there is at least one input combination that produces nonalternating outputs. It is important to note, however, that faults may not be immediately detected using alternating logic. Depending upon the application, the time elapsed before the detection of the fault may or may not be significant.

Another form of encoding function is called recomputing with shifted operands (RESO) (Patel, 1982). RESO was developed as a method to provide concurrent error detection in arithmetic logic units (ALUs). RESO uses the basic time redundancy method that was shown in Figure 1.17, and the encoding function is selected as the left shift operation with the decoding function being the right shift operation. In many cases, the shift operations can be either arithmetic or logical shifts. The RESO technique was derived assuming bit-sliced organizations of the hardware.

In logical operations, it is relatively easy to understand the error detection capability of the RESO technique. Suppose that bit slice i of a circuit is faulty and produces an erroneous value for the function's output at that bit slice. During the first computation with the operands not shifted, the ith output of the circuit will be erroneous. When the operands are shifted by one bit, the faulty bit slice will then operate on, and corrupt, the $(i - 1)$th bit. When the result is shifted back to the right, the two results—the first with unshifted operands and the second with shifted operands—will either both be correct or they will disagree in either (or both) the ith or the $(i - 1)$th bits. If only one bit slice is faulty and that faulty slice has no impact on any other bit slices, a single left shift will detect the errors that occur in logical operations.

For a bit-sliced, ripple-carry adder, a two-bit arithmetic shift is required to guarantee the detection of errors that can occur (Patel and Fung, 1982). Once again, suppose that bit slice i is faulty. In a ripple-carry adder, a faulty bit slice can have one of three effects: the carry out of the bit slice can be erroneous, the sum bit out of the bit slice can be erroneous, or both may be in error. If the sum bit is 0 when it should be 1, the resulting sum will be in error by -2^i. In other words, the sum will be 2^i smaller than it should be. If the sum bit is 1 when it should be 0, the sum will be 2^i larger than it should be. If the carry bit out of the bit slice is affected, the sum bit in position $(i + 1)$ will be impacted. If the carry bit is 0 when it should be 1, the sum will be decreased by $2^{i + 1}$. If the carry bit is 1 when it should be 0, the sum will be increased by $2^{i + 1}$. If both the sum bit and the carry bit are affected, the resulting sum can be in error in one of four ways: the sum and carry are both erroneously 1; the sum and carry are both erroneously 0; the sum is erroneously 1 and the carry is erroneously 0; and the sum is erroneously 0 and the carry is erroneously 1. When both the sum and the carry are erroneously 1, the resulting sum will be increased by $2^{i + 1} + 2^i = (3)2^i$. If both the sum and the carry are erroneously 0, the resulting sum will be decreased by $(3)2^i$. If the carry is erroneously 1 and the sum erroneously 0, the resulting sum will be increased by $2^{i + 1}$ because of the carry and decreased by 2^i because of the sum. The overall impact is a decrease of 2^i, as was the case when only the sum bit was erroneously 0. Finally, if the carry is erroneously 0 and the sum is erroneously 1, the resulting sum will be decreased by $2^{i + 1}$ because of the carry-bit error and increased by 2^i because of the sum-bit error. The net effect is a decrease of 2^i. In summary, the result generated for the unshifted operands if bit i is faulty will be incorrect by one of $[0, + -2^i, + -2^{i + 1}, + - (3)2^i]$.

When the operands are shifted to the left by two bits, a similar analysis can show that the result will be incorrect by one of $[0, +-2^{i-2}, +-2^{i-1}, +-(3)2^{i-2}]$. As can be seen, the results of the two computations cannot agree unless both are correct. Therefore, the error will be detected.

Time redundancy techniques form an important class of options for designing fault-tolerant systems. Just like all other redundancy approaches, however, time redundancy cannot be used in all applications because of the additional time that must be employed. If time is available, however, time redundancy techniques do provide an opportunity to minimize the amount of additional hardware required.

Recomputation for error correction.   The time redundancy approach can also provide for error correction if the computations are repeated three or more times. Consider, for example, a logical AND operation. Suppose the operation is performed three times: first, without shifting the operands; second, with a one-bit, logical shift of the operands; and third, with a two-bit, logical shift of the operands. The results generated using the shifted operands are then shifted the appropriate number of bits to the right to properly position the bits of the results. Because each of the three operations used operands that were displaced from each other by at least one bit position, a different bit in each result will be affected by the faulty bit slice. If the bits in each position are then compared, the results due to the faulty bit slice can be corrected by performing a majority vote on the three results obtained for each bit position. Unfortunately, this approach will not work for arithmetic operations because the adjacent bits are not independent. A single, faulty bit slice can affect more than one bit of the result.

1.2.4 Software Redundancy

In applications that use computers, many fault detection and fault tolerance techniques can be implemented in software. The redundant hardware necessary to implement the capabilities can be minimal, while the redundant software can be substantial. Redundant software can occur in many forms; you do not have to replicate complete programs to have redundant software. Software redundancy can appear as several extra lines of code used to check the magnitude of a signal, or as a small routine used to periodically test a memory by writing and reading specific locations. In this section, we will consider the basic concepts of several major software redundancy techniques: consistency checks, capability checks, and software replication methods (Chen and Avizienis, 1978). More detailed discussion of software redundancy techniques can be found in Chapter 7.

Consistency checks.   A consistency check uses a priori knowledge about the characteristics of information to verify the correctness of that information. For example, in some applications, it is known, in advance, that a digital quantity should never exceed a certain magnitude. If the signal exceeds that magnitude, then an error of some sort is present. A consistency check can often be implemented easily in hardware, but is most likely to appear in the software of a system. For example, a processing system can sample and store many sensor readings in a typical control application. Each sensor reading can be checked to verify that it lies within an acceptable range of values. As another example, the amount of cash requested by a patron at a bank's teller machine should never exceed the maximum withdrawal allowed. Likewise, the address generated by a computer should never lie outside the address range of the available memory.

An example of consistency checking that can be performed in hardware is the detection of invalid instruction codes in computers. Many computers use n-bit quantities to represent 2^k possible instruction codes where $2^k < 2^n$. In other words, there are $2^n - 2^k$ instruction codes that are illegal. Each instruction code can be checked to verify that it is not one of the illegal codes. If an illegal code occurs, the processor can be halted to prevent an erroneous operation from occurring. This technique is particularly useful in detecting a *run-away* processor that is erroneously interpreting data as instructions.

Another form of consistency checking that can prove valuable in many control applications is to compare the measured performance of the system with some predicted performance. This technique is particularly useful in control applications where some dynamic system is under control. The dynamic system can be modeled, and the predicted performance obtained, from a software implementation of the model. The actual performance of the system can then be measured and compared with the model-predicted performance. Any significant deviations of the measured performance from the predicted performance can be indicative of a fault. The difficulty with this approach is twofold. First, the model must be accurate if good results are to be obtained. Second, it is difficult to establish the level of deviation that will be allowed before an error is signaled. In some applications, the nonlinearity of a system can result in a linearized model deviating substantially from the actual performance, under certain input conditions.

Capability checks. Capability checks are performed to verify that a system possesses the capability expected. For example, you would like to know whether you have your complete memory available or if all the processors in your multiprocessor system are working properly. As another example, you might want to know if the ALU in your processor is working properly.

Several forms of capability checks exist. The first is a simple memory test. A processor can simply write specific patterns to certain memory locations and read those locations to verify that the data was stored and retrieved properly. In many cases, it is not necessary to write and read a large number of locations to achieve reasonably good fault coverage. The memory test can be a supplement to parity, as protection against faults in the memory.

Another example of a capability check is a set of ALU tests. Periodically, a processor can execute specific instructions on specific data and compare the results to known results stored in a read only memory (ROM). This form of capability check can verify both the ALU and the memory in which the known results are stored. The instructions that are executed can consist of additions, multiplications, logical operations, and data transfers.

Another form of capability check consists of verifying that all processors in a multiple processor system are capable of communicating with each other. This can consist of periodically passing specific information from one processor to another. For example, each processor may be required to set a specific bit in a shared memory to indicate the processor's capability to communicate with that memory, and, as a result, communicate with other processors through that memory.

_N_ Self-checking programming. The software redundancy techniques that we have considered, thus far, have been those that use extra, or redundant, software to detect faults that can occur in hardware. We have not yet considered approaches for detecting, or possibly tolerating, faults that can occur in the software of a system. Software faults are unusual entities. Software does not break as hardware does; instead, software faults are the result of incorrect software designs or coding mistakes. Therefore, any technique that detects faults in software must detect design flaws. A simple duplication and comparison procedure will not detect software faults if the duplicated software modules are identical, because the design mistakes will appear in both modules.

The concept of N self-checking programming is illustrated in Figure 1.18. Essentially, N unique versions of the program are written, and each version includes

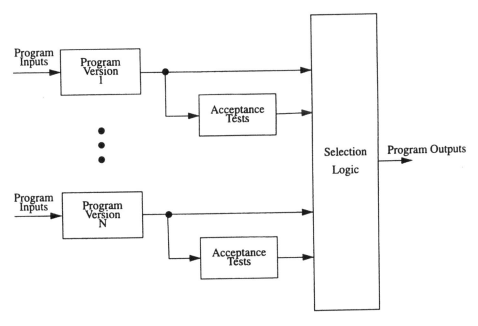

Figure 1.18: The N self-checking programming approach to software fault tolerance.

its set of acceptance tests. The acceptance tests are, essentially, checks performed on the results produced by the program and may be created using consistency checks and capability checks, for example. The selection logic, which may be a program itself, chooses the results from one of the programs that passes the acceptance tests. This approach is analogous to the hardware technique known as hot standby sparing. Since each program is running simultaneously, the reconfiguration process can be very fast. Provided that the software faults in each version of the program are independent of those in any of the other versions, and the faults are detected as they occur by the acceptance tests, this approach can then tolerate $N-1$ faults. It is important to note that the assumptions of fault independence and perfect fault coverage are very big assumptions to make in almost all applications.

N-version programming.   The concept of N-version programming was developed to allow certain design flaws in software modules to be tolerated (Chen and Avizienis, 1978). The basic concept of N-version programming is to design and code the software module N times, and to vote on the N results produced by these modules, as illustrated in Figure 1.19. Each of the N modules is designed and coded by a separate group of programmers. Each group designs the software from the same set of specifications such that each of the N modules performs the same function. However, it is hoped that by performing the N designs independently, the same mistakes will not be made by the different groups. Therefore, when a fault occurs, the fault will either not occur in all modules or it will occur differently in each module, so that the results generated by the modules will differ. Assuming that the faults are independent, the approach can tolerate $(N-1)/2$ faults.

Certainly, the importance of software fault tolerance is easy to see. If we design a microprocessor-based system to be fault-tolerant using a TMR configuration, the hardware redundancy will be of little use if a single software fault can disable each of the redundant processors. The N-version programming technique

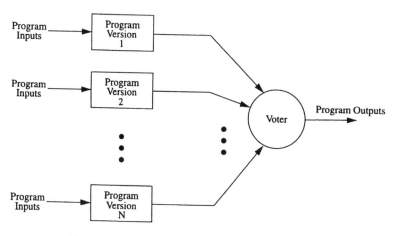

Figure 1.19: The N-version programming concept.

states that each of the three processors' software should be designed and coded independently, such that a common fault is less likely to occur.

The primary difficulties with the N-version approach are twofold. First, software designers and coders can tend to make similar mistakes. Therefore, we are not guaranteed that two completely independent versions of a program will not have identical faults. Second, the N versions of a program are still developed from a common specification, so the N-version approach will not allow the tolerance of specification mistakes.

To overcome many of the problems associated with N-version programming, software designers employ rigid design rules and methods to attempt to prevent faults from occurring. This approach we know as fault avoidance, and it is very important in the design of reliable software. If the software is designed correctly in the first place, fault tolerance techniques for the software will not be necessary.

Recovery blocks.   The recovery block approach to software fault tolerance is analogous to the active approaches to hardware fault tolerance; specifically, the cold standby sparing approach. N versions of a program are provided, and a single set of acceptance tests is used. One version of the program is designated as the primary version, and the remaining $N-1$ versions are designated as spares, or secondary versions. The primary version of the software is always used unless it fails to pass the acceptance tests. If the acceptance tests are failed by the primary version, then the first secondary version is tried. This process continues until one version passes the acceptance tests, or the system fails because none of the versions can pass the tests. The concept of the recovery block approach is illustrated in Figure 1.20. Assuming perfect coverage and independent faults, the approach can tolerant up to $N-1$ faults.

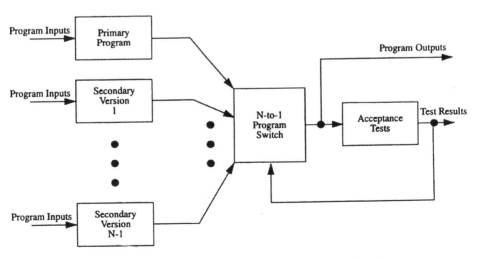

Figure **1.20**: The recovery block approach to software fault tolerance.

1.2.5 Redundancy Example

As an example of active redundancy, consider the memory system which is illustrated in Figure 1.21 (Clark and Johnson, 1992). The system was designed for satellite applications and uses two levels of active redundancy. The memory is organized into M modules, each of which is designed to store 256 megabits (Mb) of data, in this particular example. A total of S_M spare memory modules is provided in the system, and each spare module can substitute for any of the M primary memory modules. Consequently, the memory system can tolerate up to S_M complete memory module failures before the memory becomes inoperable. Each module also has internal redundancy, as will be discussed later, so the total number of memory integrated circuit (IC) faults that can be tolerated is greater than S_M. It is important to note, however, that if we performed a reliability analysis of the system, we would need to incorporate the concept of coverage at both levels of redundancy.

The organization of the memory control unit is shown in Figure 1.22. The memory control unit is responsible for performing the reconfiguration of the memory modules, if one of the modules is diagnosed as being failed. In other words, the memory control unit selects M of the $M + S_M$ modules for use in the memory. The memory control unit performs the top level of reconfiguration ac-

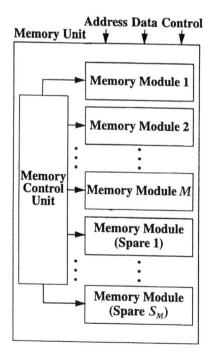

Figure 1.21: Example of a memory using two-level active redundancy.

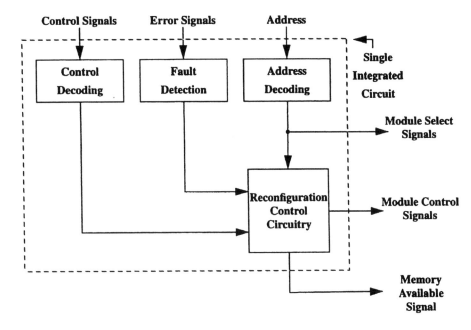

Figure 1.22: Organization of the memory control unit.

tions. The memory control unit is also responsible for the normal operations of the memory. Specifically, the memory control unit must partially decode addresses to determine which module should be enabled to respond to a particular memory address.

A more detailed organization of each module is shown in Figure 1.23. Each module uses column sparing as the means of providing spare columns of memory integrated circuits (ICs). If a memory IC fails, then the column containing that IC is eliminated from the system and replaced with a spare column. If the memory module runs out of spare columns, then the entire module is replaced with a spare module. This type of redundancy is often referred to as a two-level redundancy: the first level is the spare columns and the second level is the spare memory modules. Both forms of reconfiguration are active techniques, and they require that the fault be detected, located, and successfully removed from the system. One of the primary fault detection mechanisms in this memory is the use of an error detecting and correcting code, as illustrated in Figure 1.23.

Figure 1.24 shows the organization of each column in the memory. The column control circuitry can be used to eliminate any specific column from the memory, and replace that column with one of the spare columns. In other words, the column control circuitry directs the data to the active columns and prevents data from being directed to an inactive column.

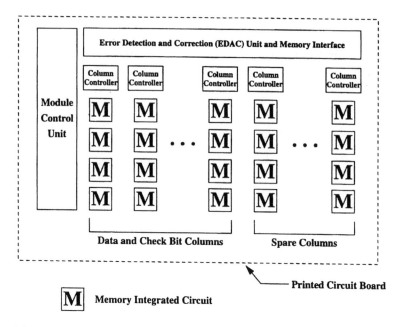

Figure 1.23: Specific organization of a memory module using column sparing.

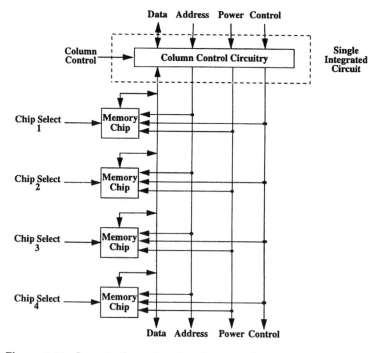

Figure 1.24: Organization of each column within a memory module which uses column sparing.

1.3 DEPENDABILITY EVALUATION TECHNIQUES

In this section, we introduce several approaches to quantitative evaluation, including the failure rate, mean time between failures (MTBF), mean time to failure (MTTF), fault coverage, reliability analysis, availability analysis, maintainability analysis, and safety analysis. Several techniques for generating the reliability, safety, and availability of a system will be presented.

1.3.1 Basic Definitions

This section examines several basic definitions which are fundamental to quantitative evaluation techniques. Once the basic definitions are in place, the various modeling approaches will be considered in more detail.

Failure rate and the reliability function.   Intuitively, the *failure rate* is the expected number of failures of a type of device or system per a given time period (Shooman, 1968). The failure rate is typically denoted as λ when it is assumed to have a constant value. The failure rate is one measure that can be used to compare systems or components.

To more clearly understand the mathematical basis for the concept of a failure rate, first recall the definition of the reliability function. The reliability, $R(t)$, of a component, or a system, is the conditional probability that the component operates correctly throughout the interval (t_0, t), given that it was operating correctly at the time t_0. Suppose that we run a test on N identical components by placing all N components in operation at time t_0 and recording the number of failed and working components at time t. Let $N_f(t)$ be the number of components that have failed at time t, and $N_o(t)$ be the number of components that are operating correctly at time t. It is assumed that once a component fails, it remains failed indefinitely. The reliability of the components at time t is given by

$$R(t) = \frac{N_o(t)}{N} = \frac{N_o(t)}{N_o(t) + N_f(t)}$$

which is simply the probability that a component has survived the interval $[t_0, t]$. The probability that a component has not survived the time interval is called the unreliability and is given by

$$Q(t) = \frac{N_f(t)}{N} = \frac{N_f(t)}{N_o(t) + N_f(t)}$$

Notice that at any time t, $R(t) = 1.0 - Q(t)$ because

$$R(t) + Q(t) = \frac{N_o(t) + N_f(t)}{N_o(t) + N_f(t)} = 1.0$$

If we write the reliability function as a differentiation of $R(t)$ with respect to time, we obtain

$$R(t) = 1.0 - \frac{N_f(t)}{N}$$

$$\frac{dR(t)}{dt} = \left(-\frac{1}{N}\right)\frac{dN_f(t)}{dt}$$

which can be written as

$$\frac{dN_f(t)}{dt} = (-N)\frac{dR(t)}{dt}$$

The derivative of $N_f(t)$, $dN_f(t)/dt$ is simply the instantaneous rate at which components are failing. At time t, there are still $N_0(t)$ components operational. Dividing $dN_f(t)/dt$ by $N_0(t)$, we obtain

$$z(t) = \frac{1}{N_0(t)}\frac{dN_f(t)}{dt}$$

$z(t)$ is called the *hazard function, hazard rate,* or *failure rate function.* The units for the failure rate function are failures per unit of time.

There are a number of different ways in which the failure rate function can be expressed. For example, $z(t)$ can be written strictly in terms of the reliability function, $R(t)$, as

$$z(t) = \frac{1}{N_0(t)}\frac{dN_f(t)}{dt} = \frac{1}{N_0(t)}(-N\frac{dR(t)}{dt}) = \frac{\frac{dR(t)}{dt}}{R(t)}$$

Similarly, $z(t)$ can be written in terms of the unreliability, $Q(t)$, as

$$z(t) = \frac{\frac{dR(t)}{dt}}{R(t)} = \frac{\frac{dQ(t)}{dt}}{1 - Q(t)}$$

The derivative of the unreliability, $dQ(t)/dt$, is called the *failure density function.*

The failure rate function is clearly dependent upon time; however, experience has shown that the failure rate function for electronic components does have a period where the value of $z(t)$ is approximately constant. The commonly accepted relationship between the failure rate function and time for electronic components is called the bathtub curve and is illustrated in Figure 1.25. The bathtub curve assumes that during the early life of systems, failures occur frequently due to substandard or weak components. The decreasing part of the bathtub curve is

Failure Rate Function

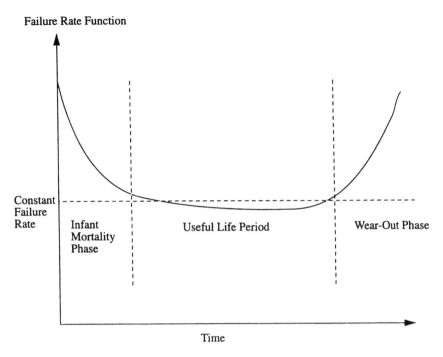

Figure 1.25: Illustration of the bathtub curve relationship. (From Barry W. Johnson, *Design and Analysis of Fault-Tolerant Digital Systems,* Addison-Wesley Publishing Company, Reading, Mass., 1989, p. 173.)

called the early-life or infant mortality region. At the opposite end of the curve is the wear-out region where systems have been functional for a long period of time and are beginning to experience failures due to the physical wearing of electronic or mechanical components. The increasing part of the bathtub curve is called the wear-out phase. During the intermediate region, the failure rate function is assumed to be a constant. The constant portion of the bathtub curve is called the useful life phase of the system, and the failure rate function is assumed to have a value of λ during that period. λ is referred to as the failure rate and is normally expressed in units of failures per hour.

The period of a constant failure rate is, typically, the most useful portion of a system's life. During the useful life phase, the system is providing its most predictable service to its users. We usually attempt to get a system beyond the infant mortality stage by using the concept of burn-in to remove weak components. Burn-in implies operating a system, often at an accelerated pace, prior to placing the system into service to get the system to the beginning of the useful life period. In addition, the system is normally replaced before it enters the wear-out phase of its life. Thus, the primary interest is the performance of the system during the useful life phase.

As noted previously, the failure rate function can be related to the reliability function as

$$z(t) = \frac{1}{N_o(t)} \frac{dN_f(t)}{dt} = -\frac{N}{N_o(t)} \frac{dR(t)}{dt} = -\frac{\frac{dR(t)}{dt}}{R(t)}$$

The result is a differential equation of the form

$$\frac{dR(t)}{dt} = -z(t)\, R(t)$$

The general solution of this differential equation is given by

$$R(t) = e^{-\int z(t)dt}$$

If we assume that the system is in the useful life stage where the failure rate function has a constant value of λ, the solution to the differential equation is an exponential function of the parameter λ given by

$$R(t) = e^{-\lambda t}$$

where λ is the constant failure rate. The exponential relationship between the reliability and time is known as the *exponential failure law* which states that for a constant failure rate function, the reliability varies exponentially as a function of time.

The exponential failure law is extremely valuable for the analysis of electronic components, and is by far the most commonly used relationship between reliability and time. Many cases, however, cannot assume that the failure rate function is constant, so the exponential failure law cannot be used; other modeling schemes and representations must be employed. An example of a time-varying failure rate function is found in the analysis of software. Software failures are the result of design faults, and as a software package is used, design faults will be discovered and corrected. Consequently, the reliability of software should improve as a function of time, and the failure rate function should decrease.

A common modeling technique used to represent time-varying failure rate functions is the Weibull distribution (Siewiorek and Swarz, 1982). The failure rate function associated with the Weibull distribution is given by

$$z(t) = \alpha\lambda\, (\lambda t)^{\alpha - 1}$$

where α and λ are constants that control the variation of the failure rate function with time. The failure rate function given by the Weibull distribution is intuitively appealing. For example, if the value of α is 1, $z(t)$ is simply the constant λ. If α is greater than 1, $z(t)$ will increase as time increases, and if α is less than 1, $z(t)$ will decrease as time increases.

The reliability function that results from the Weibull distribution is the solution to the differential equation

$$\frac{dR(t)}{dt} = -z(t)\,R(t) = -\alpha\lambda(\lambda t)^{\alpha-1}R(t)$$

and is given by

$$R\,(t) = e^{-(\lambda t)^{\alpha}}$$

The expression for $R(t)$ can be verified by calculating the derivative of $R(t)$. Specifically,

$$\frac{dR(t)}{dt} = -e^{-(\lambda t)^{\alpha}}\alpha\lambda(\lambda t)^{\alpha-1} = -\alpha\lambda(\lambda t)^{\alpha-1}e^{-(\lambda t)^{\alpha}} = -z(t)\,R(t)$$

As stated earlier, certain values of α result in a reliability function that increases as time increases. For example, if $\alpha = -1$, the reliability is given by

$$R(t) = e^{-\frac{1}{\lambda t}}$$

which approaches 1 as t approaches infinity and is 0 when t is 0. Also note that for $\alpha = 1$, the reliability function is identical to the exponential failure law.

Mean time to failure.   In addition to the failure rate, the mean time to failure (MTTF) is a useful parameter to specify the quality of a system. The MTTF is the expected time that a system will operate before the first failure occurs. For example, if we have N identical systems placed into operation at time $t = 0$, and we measure the time that each system operates before failing, the average time is the $MTTF$. If each system, i, operates for a time, t_i, before encountering the first failure, the $MTTF$ is given by

$$MTTF = \sum_{i=1}^{N} \frac{t_i}{N}$$

The $MTTF$ can be calculated by finding the expected value of the time of failure. From probability theory, we know that the expected value of a random variable, X, is

$$E[X] = \int_{-\infty}^{\infty} xf(x)dx$$

where $f(x)$ is the probability density function. In reliability analysis we are interested in the expected value of the time of failure (MTTF), so

$$MTTF = \int_{-\infty}^{\infty} tf(t)dt$$

where $f(t)$ is the failure density function, and the integral runs from 0 to ∞ because the failure density function is undefined for times less than 0. We know, however, that the failure density function is

$$f(t) = \frac{dQ(t)}{dt}$$

so, the MTTF can be written as

$$MTTF = \int_0^\infty t\frac{dQ(t)}{dt}\,dt$$

Using integration by parts and the fact that $\dfrac{dQ(t)}{dt} = -\dfrac{dR(t)}{dt}$, we can show that

$$MTTF = \int_0^\infty t\frac{dQ(t)}{dt}\,dt = -\int_0^\infty t\frac{dR(t)}{dt}\,dt = \left[-tR(t) + \int R(t)dt\right]_0^\infty = \int_0^\infty R(t)dt$$

The term $-tR(t)$ clearly disappears when $t = 0$; but, it also disappears when $t = \infty$ because $R(\infty) = 0$. Consequently, the MTTF is defined in terms of the reliability function as

$$MTTF = \int_0^\infty R(t)dt$$

which is valid for any reliability function that satisfies $R(\infty) = 0$.

Mean time to repair.   The mean time to repair (MTTR) is simply the average time required to repair a system. The MTTR is extremely difficult to estimate and is often determined experimentally by injecting a set of faults, one at a time, into a system and measuring the time required to repair the system in each case. The measured repair times are averaged to determine an average time to repair. In other words, if the ith of N faults requires a time t_i to repair, the MTTR will be estimated as

$$MTTR = \frac{\sum_{i=1}^N t_i}{N}$$

The MTTR is normally specified in terms of a repair rate, μ, which is the average number of repairs that occur per time period. The units of the repair rate are normally number of repairs per hour. The MTTR and the repair rate, μ, are related by

$$MTTR = \frac{1}{\mu}$$

Mean time between failure.   It is very important to understand the difference between the MTTF and the mean time between failure (MTBF). Unfortunately, these two terms are often used interchangeably. While the numerical difference is small in many cases, the conceptual difference is very important. The MTTF is the average time until the first failure of a system, while the MTBF is the average time between failures of a system. As noted in the previous section, we can estimate the $MTTF$ for a system by placing each of a population of N identical systems into operation at time $t = 0$, measuring the time required for each system to encounter its first failure and averaging these times over the N systems. The $MTBF$, however, is calculated by averaging the time between failures, including any time required to repair the system and place it back into an operational status. In other words, each of the N systems is operated for some time T, and the number of failures encountered by the ith system is recorded as n_i. The average number of failures is computed as

$$n_{avg} = \sum_{i=1}^{N} \frac{n_i}{N}$$

Finally, the $MTBF$ is

$$MTBF = \frac{T}{n_{avg}}$$

In other words, the $MTBF$ is the total operation time, T, divided by the average number of failures experienced during the time T.

If we assume that all repairs to a system make the system perfect once again, just as it was when it was new, the relationship between the MTTF and the MTBF can be determined easily. Once successfully placed into operation, a system will operate, on the average, a time corresponding to the MTTF before encountering the first failure. The system will then require some time, MTTR, to repair the system and place it back into operation once again. The system will then be perfect once again and will operate for a time corresponding to the MTTF before encountering its next failure. The time between the two failures is the sum of the MTTF and the MTTR, and is the MTBF. Thus, the difference between the MTTF and the MTBF is the MTTR. Specifically, the $MTBF$ is given by

$$MTBF = MTTF + MTTR$$

In most practical applications, the MTTR is a small fraction of the MTTF, so the approximation that the MTBF and MTTF are equal is often quite good. Conceptually, however, it is crucial to understand the difference between the MTBF and the MTTF.

Fault coverage.   An extremely important parameter in the design and analysis of fault-tolerant systems is fault coverage. The fault coverage available in a system can have a tremendous impact on the reliability, safety, and other attributes of the system. There are several types of fault coverage, depending upon whether the designer is concerned with fault detection, fault location, fault containment, or fault recovery. In addition, there are two primary definitions of fault coverage: one that is intuitive, and another that is more mathematical.

The intuitive definition is that coverage is a measure of a system's ability to perform fault detection, fault location, fault containment, and/or fault recovery. The four primary types of fault coverage are fault detection coverage, fault location coverage, fault containment coverage, and fault recovery coverage. Fault detection coverage is a measure of a system's ability to detect faults. For example, a system requirement may be that a certain fraction of all faults be detected; the fault detection coverage is a measure of a system's capability to meet such a requirement. Fault location coverage is a measure of a system's ability to locate faults. Once again, it is very common to require a system to locate faults within easily replaceable modules, and the fault location coverage is a measure of the success with which fault location is performed. Fault containment coverage is a measure of a system's ability to contain faults. Finally, fault recovery coverage is a measure of a system's ability to recover from faults and maintain an operational status. Clearly, a high fault recovery coverage will require high fault detection, location, and containment coverages.

In the evaluation of fault-tolerant systems, the fault recovery coverage is the most commonly considered, and the general term fault coverage is often used to mean fault recovery coverage. In other words, the term fault coverage is interpreted as a measure of a system's ability to successfully recover after the occurrence of a fault, therefore tolerating the fault. When using the term fault coverage, however, it is important to understand whether the coverage applies to detection, location, containment, or recovery. In the remainder of this chapter, we will use the term fault coverage to imply fault recovery coverage since fault recovery is the most common form of coverage encountered. In all cases, however, it will be made clear whether detection, location, containment, or recovery coverage is being considered.

Fault coverage is mathematically defined as the conditional probability that, given the existence of a fault, the system recovers (Bouricius, Carter, and Schneider, 1969). Recall that fault recovery is the process of maintaining or regaining operational status after a fault occurs. The fundamental problem with fault coverage is that it is extremely difficult to calculate. Probably the most common approach to estimating fault coverage is to develop a list of all of the faults that can occur in a system and to form, from that list, a list of faults that can be detected, a list of faults that can be located, a list of faults that can be contained, and a list of faults from which the system can recover. The fault detection coverage factor, for example, is then computed as simply the fraction of faults that can be detected; that is, the number of faults detected divided by the total number of faults. The remaining fault coverage factors are calculated in a similar manner.

Several important points should be made about the estimation of coverage. First, the estimation of fault coverage requires the definition of the types of faults that can occur. Stating that the fault detection coverage is 0.9, for example, is meaningless unless the types of faults considered are identified. A second important point about the fault coverage is that it is typically assumed to be a constant. It is easy to envision applications in which the probability of detecting a fault, for example, increases as a function of time, after the occurrence of the fault. However, to simplify the analysis, the various fault coverages are normally assumed to be constants.

1.3.2 Reliability Modeling

Reliability is perhaps one of the most important attributes of systems. Almost all specifications for systems mandate that certain values for reliability be achieved and, in some way, demonstrated. The most popular reliability analysis techniques are the analytical approaches. Of the analytical techniques, combinatorial modeling and Markov modeling are the two most commonly used approaches. Here, we consider both the combinatorial and the Markov models.

Combinatorial models.   Combinatorial models use probabilistic techniques that enumerate the different ways in which a system can remain operational. The probabilities of the events that lead to a system being operational are calculated to form an estimate of the system's reliability. The reliability of a system is generally derived in terms of the reliabilities of the individual components of the system. The two models of systems that are most common in practice are the series and the parallel. In a series system, each element of the system is required to operate correctly for the system to operate correctly. In a parallel system, on the other hand, only one of several elements must be operational for the system to perform its functions correctly.

The series system is best thought of as a system that contains no redundancy; that is, each element of the system is needed to make the system function correctly. In general, a system may contain N elements, and in a series system, each of the N elements is required for the system to function correctly. The reliability of the series system can be calculated as the probability that none of the elements will fail. Another way to look at this is that the reliability of the series system is the probability that all of the elements are working properly.

Suppose we let $C_{iw}(t)$ represent the event that component C_i is working properly at time t, $R_i(t)$ be the reliability of component C_i at time t, and $R_{series}(t)$ be the reliability of the series system. Further suppose that the series system contains N series components. The reliability at any time, t, is the probability that all N components are working properly. In mathematical terms,

$$R_{series}(t) = P\ \{C_{1w}(t) \cap C_{2w}(t) \cap \ldots \cap C_{Nw}\}$$

Assuming that the events, $C_{iw}(t)$, are independent, we have

$$R_{series}(t) = R_1(t)R_2(t) \ldots R_N(t)$$

or

$$R_{series}(t) = \prod_{i=1}^{N} R_i(t)$$

An interesting relationship exists in a series system if each individual component satisfies the exponential failure law. Suppose that we have a series system made up of N components, and each component, i, has a constant failure rate of λ_i. Also assume that each component satisfies the exponential failure law. The reliability of the series system is given by

$$R_{series}(t) = e^{-\lambda_1 t} e^{-\lambda_2 t} \ldots e^{-\lambda_N t}$$

or

$$R_{series}(t) = e^{\sum_{i=1}^{N} \lambda_i t}$$

The distinguishing feature of the basic parallel system is that only one of N identical elements is required for the system to function. The unreliability of the parallel system can be computed as the probability that all of the N elements fail. Suppose that we let $C_{if}(t)$ represent the event that element i in the parallel system has failed at time t, $Q_{parallel}(t)$ be the unreliability of the parallel system, and $Q_i(t)$ be the unreliability of the ith element. $Q_{parallel}(t)$ can be computed as

$$Q_{parallel}(t) = P\{ C_{1f}(t) \cap C_{2f}(t) \cap \ldots \cap C_{Nf}(t) \}$$

or

$$Q_{parallel}(t) = Q_1(t)Q_2(t) \ldots Q_N(t) = \prod_{i=1}^{N} Q_i(t)$$

The reliability of the parallel system can now be computed because we know that the reliability and the unreliability must add to 1.0. Mathematically, we must have $R(t) + Q(t) = 1.0$ for any system. Consequently, we can write

$$R_{parallel}(t) = 1.0 - Q_{parallel}(t) = 1.0 - \prod_{i=1}^{N} Q_i(t) = 1.0 - \prod_{i=1}^{N} (1.0 - R_i(t))$$

It should be noted that the equations for the parallel system assume that the failures of the individual elements that make up the parallel system are independent. For random hardware failures, the independence of failures is a good assumption; however, for failures that are the result of items such as external disturbances, the independence assumption is not very good. Therefore, the combinatorial modeling techniques are most often applied to the analysis of random failures in the hardware of a system.

M-of-N systems are a generalization of the ideal parallel system. In the ideal parallel system, only one of N modules is required to work for the system to work. In the M-of-N system, however, M of the total of N identical modules are required to function for the system to function. A good example is the TMR configuration where two of the three modules must work for the majority voting mechanism to function properly. Therefore, the TMR system is a two-of-three system.

In general, if there are N identical modules and M of those are required for the system to function properly, then the system can tolerate $N - M$ module failures. The expression for the reliability of a M-of-N system can be written as

$$R_{M-of-N}(t) = \sum_{i=0}^{N-M} \binom{N}{i} R^{N-i}(t)(1.0 - R(t))^i$$

where

$$\binom{N}{i} = \frac{N!}{(N-i)!i!}$$

Markov models.   The primary difficulty with the combinatorial models is that many complex systems cannot be modeled easily in a combinatorial fashion. The reliability expressions are often very complex. In addition, the fault coverage that we have seen to be extremely important in the reliability of a system is sometimes difficult to incorporate into the reliability expression in a combination model. Finally, the process of repair that occurs in many systems is very difficult to model in a combinatorial fashion. For these reasons, we often use Markov models, which are sometimes referred to as Markov chains.

The purpose of the presentation in this chapter is not to delve into the mathematical details of Markov models but to understand how to use Markov models. For the reader interested in more explicit mathematical details, please refer to Chapter 6 of this text. The discussions here will provide sufficient mathematical background to apply the Markov model, but will not pursue various techniques for solving the models.

The two main concepts in the Markov model are the state and the state transition. The state of a system represents all that must be known to describe the system at any given instant of time. For reliability models, each state of the Markov model represents a distinct combination of faulty and fault-free modules. The state transitions govern the changes of state that occur within a system. As time passes and failures and reconfigurations occur, the system will go from one state to another. The state transitions are characterized by probabilities, such as the probability of failure, fault coverage, and the probability of repair.

As an example of the state transitions that can occur, consider the TMR system. The state diagram that results for the TMR system is shown in Figure 1.26. As can be seen, the system begins in state (111), and, upon the first module fail-

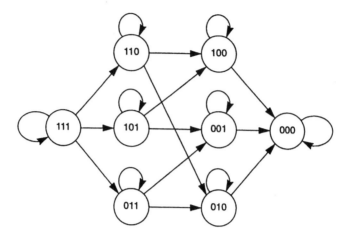

Figure 1.26: Markov model of a TMR system. (From Barry W. Johnson, *Design and Analysis of Fault-Tolerant Digital Systems,* Addison-Wesley Publishing Company, Reading, Mass., 1989, p. 201.)

ure, will transition to either state (110), (101), or (011), depending upon whether module 1, 2, or 3 is the module that fails. Notice that the transition exists for the model to remain in a state if a module failure does not occur. The states in the diagram shown in Figure 1.26 can be partitioned into three major categories: the perfect state (111), in which all modules function correctly; the one-failed states (110), (101), and (011), in which a single module has failed; and the system-failed states (100), (001), (010), and (000), in which enough modules have failed to cause the system to fail. State partitioning will be useful later on when we attempt to reduce the Markov model.

Each state transition has associated with it a transition probability. If we assume that each module in the TMR system obeys the exponential failure law with a constant failure rate of λ, the probability of a module being failed at some time, $t + \Delta t$, given that the module was operational at time t, is given by

$$1 - \frac{R(t + \Delta t)}{R(t)} = 1 - \frac{e^{-\lambda(t + t\Delta)}}{e^{-\lambda t}}$$

$$= 1 - e^{-\lambda \Delta t}$$

If we expand the exponential, we obtain

$$1 - e^{-\lambda \Delta t} = 1 - \left[1 + (-\lambda \Delta t) + \frac{(-\lambda \Delta t)^2}{2!} + \dots \right] = (-\lambda \Delta t) - \left(\frac{(-\lambda \Delta t)^2}{2!} \right) - \dots$$

For values of Δt such that $\lambda \Delta t < 1$, the expression reduces to

$$1 - e^{-\lambda \Delta t} \approx \lambda \Delta t$$

Thus, using the exponential failure law allows us to state that the probability that a component will fail within the time period Δt, given that the component was operational at time t, is approximately $\lambda \Delta t$. When states are "collapsed," the transition probability to the resulting state is the sum of all the transitions from an arbitrary state to the individual categorized states. This is illustrated in Figure 1.27 and is usually referred to as a reduced or collapsed Markov chain. The advantage of state reduction is the lower cost in computation; instead of evaluating an eight-state Markov chain, through state reduction, we now have to evaluate only a three-state Markov chain.

Examining the TMR system further, we can now specify the transition probabilities as shown in Figure 1.27. Note that the state space shown can be partitioned into three categories: a perfect state, a one-module failed state, and a system failed state. In other words, by revising the state transition probabilities appropriately, we have collapsed the enumerated TMR state space to these three states.

With the revised Markov chain of a TMR system, let state 3 correspond to the perfect state (111), state 2 correspond to the grouping of one-failed states (110), (101), (011), and state F correspond to the group of states with two modules failed and the completely failed state. The transition probabilities are derived to account for one of several failures occurring. Consequently, the transition from state 3 to state 2 is the sum of all transitions from the perfect state to the one failed state, $3\lambda \Delta t$. In other words, $3\lambda \Delta t$ is the probability that one out of three of the components will fail. The transition from state 2 to state F is the sum of the transitions from a one-module failed state to a two-module failed state, $2\lambda \Delta t$.

Once the transitions for a Markov chain have been determined, extracting a state transition matrix from the chain is straightforward. Given the Markov property, we can state that the probability of being in any given state, s, at some time, t, $+ \Delta t$, depends both on the probability that the system was in a state from which it could transition to state s as well as the probability of that transition occurring. For example, the probability that the TMR system will be in state 3 at time $t + \Delta t$ depends on the probability that the system was in state 3 at time t *and* the probability of the system transitioning from state 3 back into state 3. In other words,

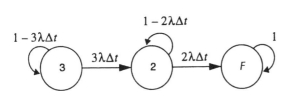

Figure 1.27: Reduced Markov model of a TMR system. (From Barry W. Johnson, *Design and Analysis of Fault-Tolerant Digital Systems*, Addison-Wesley Publishing Company, Reading, Mass., 1989, p. 203.)

$$p_3\,(t + \Delta t) = (1 - 3\lambda \Delta t)\, p_3\,(t)$$

where $p_3(t)$ is the probability of being in state 3 at time t and $p_3(t + \Delta t)$ is the probability of being in state 3 at time $t + \Delta t$. Similarly, the remaining equations for states 2 and F are

$$p_2(t + \Delta t) = 3\lambda \Delta t p_3\,(t) + (1 - 2\lambda \Delta t)p_2(t)$$
$$p_F(t + \Delta t) = 2\lambda \Delta t p_2(t) + p_F(t)$$

Likewise, definitions for the $p_2(t + \Delta t)$, $p_2(t)$, and $p_F(t + \Delta t)$, $p_F(t)$ exist.

The three equations, $p_3(t + \Delta t)$, $p_2(t + \Delta t)$, $p_F(t + \Delta t)$, can be written in matrix form as

$$\begin{bmatrix} p_3(t + \Delta t) \\ p_2(t + \Delta t) \\ p_F(t + \Delta t) \end{bmatrix} = \begin{bmatrix} 1 - 3\lambda \Delta t & 0 & 0 \\ 3\lambda \Delta t & 1 - 2\lambda \Delta t & 0 \\ 0 & 2\lambda \Delta t & 1 \end{bmatrix} \begin{bmatrix} p_3(t) \\ p_2(t) \\ p_F(t) \end{bmatrix}$$

In a more compact manner, this is written as

$$\mathbf{P}\,(t + \Delta t) = \mathbf{A}\mathbf{P}\,(t)$$

where

$$\mathbf{P}(t + \Delta t) = \begin{bmatrix} p_3(t + \Delta t) \\ p_2(t + \Delta t) \\ p_F(t + \Delta t) \end{bmatrix} \quad \mathbf{A} = \begin{bmatrix} 1 - 3\lambda \Delta t & 0 & 0 \\ 3\lambda \Delta t & 1 - 2\lambda \Delta t & 0 \\ 0 & 2\lambda \Delta t & 1 \end{bmatrix} \quad \mathbf{P}(t) = \begin{bmatrix} p_3(t) \\ p_2(t) \\ p_F(t) \end{bmatrix}$$

and $\mathbf{P}(t)$ is the probability state vector at time t, $\mathbf{P}(t + \Delta t)$ is the probability state vector at time $t + \Delta t$, and $\mathbf{A}$ is the transition matrix. Note that the above equation can be viewed as a difference equation. If we set $t = 0$, we then have $\mathbf{P}(\Delta t) = \mathbf{A}\mathbf{P}(0)$. Similarly, for time $2\Delta t$, $\mathbf{P}(2\Delta t) = \mathbf{A}\mathbf{P}(\Delta t) = \mathbf{A}^2 \mathbf{P}(0)$. Extending this result to $n\Delta t$ yields

$$\mathbf{P}(n\Delta t) = \mathbf{A}^n \mathbf{P}(0)$$

It is also possible to obtain closed-form solutions to the Markov models. The above set of equations can be manipulated algebraically to form

$$\frac{p_3(t + \Delta t) - p_3(t)}{\Delta t} = 3\lambda p_3(t)$$

$$\frac{p_2(t + \Delta t) - p_2(t)}{\Delta t} = 3\lambda p_3(t) - 2\lambda p_2(t)$$

$$\frac{p_F(t + \Delta t) - p_F(t)}{\Delta t} = 2\lambda p_2(t)$$

Taking the limit as Δt approaches zero results in a set of differential equations given by

$$\frac{dp_3(t)}{dt} = 3\lambda p_3(t)$$

$$\frac{dp_2(t)}{dt} = 3\lambda p_3(t) - 2\lambda p_2(t)$$

$$\frac{dp_F(t)}{dt} = 2\lambda p_2(t)$$

The solution to this set of differential equations is

$$p_3(t) = e^{-3\lambda t}$$

$$p_2(t) = 3e^{-2\lambda t} - 3e^{-3\lambda t}$$

$$p_F(t) = 1 - 3e^{-2\lambda t} + 2e^{-3\lambda t}$$

Note that the reliability is the sum of the probabilities of being in states 3 and 2, or conversely, the reliability is 1.0 minus the probability of being in the failed state.

1.3.3 Safety Modeling

As mentioned before, the prime benefit of using Markov chains in dependability modeling is the ability to handle coverage in a systematic fashion. Coverage is the probability that a fault will be handled correctly, given that the fault has occurred; it is usually denoted as C. The incorporation of coverage in a Markov chain analysis of a system allows us to model the safety of a system because it accounts for the effectiveness of a fault coverage strategy. Previously, we considered only systems that had perfect coverage, where $C = 1.0$. Now, we will look at the case where $0 \leq C < 1.0$.

The implication of incorporating coverage in a Markov chain is that now, every unfailed state in the state space has two transition paths to two different states, one of which is covered, and the other, uncovered. This implies that given n states in a fully covered system, for an identical system that is not fully covered, there can be a maximum of $2^n - 1$ states in the system's state space. Figure 1.28 illustrates this case for a simplex (one-component) system. For a simplex system, there are three states: a fully operational state, O; a failed-safe state FS, and a failed-unsafe state FU. Converting this graph to a transition matrix, we get

$$\begin{bmatrix} p_O(t+\Delta t) \\ p_{FS}(t+\Delta t) \\ p_{FU}(t+\Delta t) \end{bmatrix} = \begin{bmatrix} 1-\lambda\Delta t & 0 & 0 \\ \lambda\Delta t C & 1 & 0 \\ \lambda\Delta t(1-C) & 0 & 1 \end{bmatrix} \begin{bmatrix} p_O(t) \\ p_{FS}(t) \\ p_{FU}(t) \end{bmatrix}$$

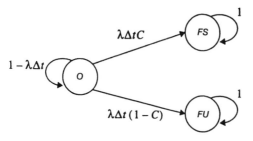

Figure 1.28: Markov model of a simplex system with coverage. (From Barry W. Johnson, *Design and Analysis of Fault-Tolerant Digital Systems,* Addison-Wesley Publishing Company, Reading, Mass., 1989, p. 214.)

The safety of the system described by the Markov model of Figure 1.28 can be written as

$$S(t) = p_O(t) = p_{FS}(t)$$

where $S(t)$ is the safety, $p_O(t)$ is the probability of being in the operational state at time t, and $p_{FS}(t)$ is the probability of being in the failed-safe state at time t. The time domain solutions to this set of equations can be written as

$$p_{FS}(t) = C - Ce^{-\lambda t}$$

$$p_{FU}(t) = (1 - C) - (1 - C) e^{-\lambda t}$$

$$p_O(t) = e^{-\lambda t}$$

The safety of the system can now be written as

$$S(t) = p_O(t) + p_{FS}(t) = C + (1 - C) e^{-\lambda t}$$

At time zero, the safety of the system is 1.0, as expected. As time approaches infinity, however, the safety will approach a steady-state value known as the steady-state safety of the system. Specifically, we find that

$$S(\infty) = C$$

In other words, the steady-state safety depends directly on the fault coverage provided by the system. There are also other tradeoffs between safety and reliability as seen in Chapter 3.

1.3.4 Availability Modeling

Now consider a system that incorporates repair. For all of the Markov chains previously described, each chain had the property of being acyclic. Introducing the notion of repair implies being able to return from a less operational or failed state to a state that is more operational or fully operational. As such, all that needs to be done to incorporate repair in a Markov chain is to specify a return transition probability. Assume that the system has a constant repair rate μ. Given that the repair rate is analogous to the failure rate in that it represents the number of repairs expected to occur within a certain time period, the probability of repair occuring within a certain time period, Δt, given that the system was failed or less operational at time t, would be $\mu \Delta t$. To illustrate repair, consider the example of a fully covered simplex system with repair. Figure 1.29 shows the enumerated state space of such a system. The Markov equations for this system are

$$\begin{bmatrix} p_O(t + \Delta t) \\ p_F(t + \Delta t) \end{bmatrix} = \begin{bmatrix} 1 - \lambda \Delta t & \mu \Delta t \\ \lambda \Delta t & 1 - \mu \Delta t \end{bmatrix} \begin{bmatrix} p_O(t) \\ p_F(t) \end{bmatrix}$$

Extraction of an availability calculation is identical in method to the reliability calculation, with one difference: for a reliability model, there can be no repair from a nonoperational state. Availability permits the model to have a cyclic Markov chain, thus allowing one to examine the effect of repair on system performance. For this simplex example, the availability $A(t) = p_O(t)$.

The differential equations describing the model of Figure 1.29 are

$$\frac{dp_F(t)}{dt} = \lambda p_O(t) - \mu p_F(t)$$

$$\frac{dp_O(t)}{dt} = \lambda p_O(t) + \mu p_F(t)$$

Assuming that the model initially starts in state O, the solutions to the above equations are

$$p_O(t) = \frac{\mu}{\lambda + \mu} + \frac{\lambda}{\lambda + \mu} e^{-(\lambda + \mu)t}$$

$$p_F(t) = \frac{\mu}{\lambda + \mu} + \frac{\lambda}{\lambda + \mu} e^{-(\lambda + \mu)t}$$

Several interesting features are apparent in the above solutions. For example, as time approaches infinity, the probability of being in the operational state approaches a steady-state value given by

$$p_O(\infty) = \frac{\mu}{\lambda + \mu} + \frac{1}{\dfrac{\lambda}{\mu} + 1}$$

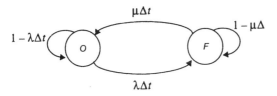

Figure 1.29: Markov model illustrating the concept of repair. (From Barry W. Johnson, *Design and Analysis of Fault-Tolerant Digital Systems*, Addison-Wesley Publishing Company, Reading, Mass., 1989, p. 222.)

Subsequently, we will see that this constant is known as the steady-state availability.

Recall that the availability, $A(t)$, of a system is defined as the probability that a system will be available to perform its tasks at the instant of time, t. Intuitively, we can see that the availability can be approximated as the total time that a system has been operational divided by the total time elapsed since the system was initially placed into operation. In other words, the availability is the percentage of time that the system is available to perform its expected tasks. Suppose that we place a system into operation at time $t = 0$. As time moves along, the system will perform its functions, perhaps fail, and hopefully be repaired. At some time, $t = t_{current}$, suppose that the system has operated correctly for a total of t_{op} hours and has been in the process of repair, or waiting for repair to begin, for a total of t_{repair} hours. The time, $t_{current}$, is then the sum of t_{op} and t_{repair}. The availability can be determined as

$$A(t_{current}) = \frac{t_{op}}{t_{op} + t_{repair}}$$

where $A(t_{current})$ is the availability at time $t_{current}$.

The above expression lends itself well to the experimental evaluation of the availability of a system; we can simply place the system into operation and measure the appropriate times required to calculate the availability of the system at a number of points in time. Unfortunately, the experimental evaluation of the availability is often not possible because of the time and expense involved. Also, we would like to have some means of estimating the availability before we actually build the system, so that availability considerations can be factored into the design process. One approach is based on the single parameter measures such as MTTF and MTTR, and yields what is typically called the steady-state availability, A_{ss}.

We have seen that availability is, basically, the percentage of time that a system is operational. Using knowledge of the statistical interpretation of the MTTF and the MTTR, we expect that, on the average, a system will operate for MTTF hours and then encounter its first failure. Once the failure has occurred, the system will then, again on average, require MTTR hours to be repaired and placed into operation once again. The system will then operate for another MTTF hours before encountering its second failure.

If the average system experiences N failures during its lifetime, the total time that the system will be operational is $N(MTTF)$ hours. Likewise, the total time that the system is down for repairs is $N(MTTR)$ hours. In other words, the operational time, t_{op}, is $N(MTTF)$ hours and the downtime, t_{repair}, is $N(MTTR)$ hours. The average, or steady-state, availability is

$$A_{ss} = \frac{N(MTTF)}{N(MTTF) + N(MTTR)}$$

We know, however, that the MTTF and the MTTR are related to the failure rate and the repair rate, respectively, for simplex systems, as

$$MTTF = \frac{1}{\lambda}$$

$$MTTR = \frac{1}{\mu}$$

Therefore, the steady-state availability is given by

$$A_{ss} = \frac{\dfrac{1}{\lambda}}{\dfrac{1}{\lambda} + \dfrac{1}{\mu}} = \frac{1}{1 + \dfrac{\lambda}{\mu}}$$

Recall that the repair rate is expressed in repairs per hour, while the failure rate is in failures per hour. One would expect that if the failure rate goes to zero, implying that the system never fails, or the repair rate goes to infinity, implying that no time is required to repair the system, the availability will go to 1. Looking at the expression for the steady-state availability, we can see that this is true.

1.3.5 Maintainability Modeling

As defined previously, the maintainability is the probability that a failed system will be restored to working order within a specified time. We will use the notation that $M(t)$ is the maintainability for time, t. In other words, $M(t)$ is the probability that a system will be repaired in a time less than or equal to t.

An important parameter in maintainability modeling is the repair rate, μ. The repair rate is the average number of repairs that can be performed, per time unit. The inverse of the repair rate is the $MTTR$, which is the average time required to perform a single repair. Mathematically, the relationship between the repair rate and the $MTTR$ is given by

$$MTTR = \frac{1}{\mu}$$

An expression for the maintainability of a system can be derived in a manner similar to that used to develop the exponential failure law for the reliability function. Suppose that we have N systems. We inject one unique fault into each of the systems, and we allow one maintenance person to repair each system. We begin this experiment by injecting the faults into the systems at time $t = 0$. Later, at some time t, we determine that $N_r(t)$ of the systems have been repaired and $N_{nr}(t)$ have not been repaired. Since the maintainability of a system at time t is the probability that the system can be repaired by time t, an estimate of the maintainability can be computed as

$$M(t) = \frac{N_r(t)}{N} = \frac{N_r(t)}{N_r(t) + N_{nr}(t)}$$

If we differentiate $M(t)$ with respect to time, we obtain

$$\frac{dM(t)}{dt} = \frac{1}{N}\frac{dN_r(t)}{dt}$$

which can also be written as

$$\frac{dN_r(t)}{dt} = N\frac{dM(t)}{dt}$$

The derivative of $N_r(t)$ is simply the rate at which components are repaired at the instant of time t.

At time t, we have $N_{nr}(t)$ systems that have not been repaired. If we divide $dN_r(t)/dt$ by $N_{nr}(t)$, we obtain

$$\frac{1}{N_{nr}(t)}\frac{dN_r(t)}{dt}$$

which is called the repair rate function and is assumed to have a constant value of μ, the repair rate.

Using the expression for the repair rate and the expression for the derivative of $N_r(t)$, we can write

$$\mu = \frac{1}{N_{nr}(t)}\frac{dN_r(t)}{dt} = \frac{N}{N_{nr}(t)}\frac{dM(t)}{dt}$$

which yields a differential equation of the form

$$\frac{dM(t)}{dt} = \mu\frac{N_{nr}(t)}{N}$$

We know, however, that $N_{nr}(t)/N$ is $1 - M(t)$, so we can write

$$\frac{dM(t)}{dt} = \mu(1 - M(t))$$

The solution to the differential equation is well known and is given by

$$M(t) = 1 - e^{-\mu t}$$

The relationship developed for $M(t)$ has the desired characteristics. First, if the repair rate is zero, the maintainability will also be zero since the system cannot be repaired in any length of time. Second, if the repair rate is infinite, the maintainability will be 1.0 since repair can be performed in zero time.

The repair rate is typically specified for several levels of repair. The most common partitioning is to provide three levels of repair. The first is called the organizational level and consists of all repairs that can be performed at the site where the system is located. Organizational repairs typically include all faults that can be located to specific circuit cards such that the cards can simply be replaced and the system made operational once again. For example, if an aircraft can be repaired without bringing it off the runway, it is considered an organizational level repair. The key to organizational repairs is the ability to locate the fault. It is seldom feasible to bring sophisticated fault detection and location equipment to the site of the system. Repairs at the organizational level must often depend on the built-in test provided by the system to locate the specific problem.

The second level of repair is called the intermediate level. Intermediate level repairs cannot be performed at the organizational level but can be performed in the immediate vicinity of the system. For example, a computer firm can have a local repair facility to which the faulty pieces of equipment are taken for repair. Intermediate level repair is not as good as being able to perform the repair on-site, but it is better than having to return a piece of equipment to the factory. In the case of an airplane, for example, an intermediate level repair might be made in the hanger as opposed to on the runway.

The final level of repair is called the depot level or the factory level. In depot level repairs, the equipment must be returned to a major facility for the repair process. For example, if a calculator cannot be repaired at home (organizational level), then it is taken to the store from which it was purchased (intermediate level). If the store is unable to perform the repair, they will send it to a site designated by the manufacturer as a major repair facility (depot level). The length of time required to perform the repair depends upon the level at which it is performed. It may take less than an hour to repair a device at the organizational level, several hours or perhaps days at the intermediate level, and as long as several weeks or months at the depot level.

In general, the analytical modeling techniques can be quite useful in validating the fault-tolerant designs as discussed in Chapter 6. However, the emerging experimental techniques as seen in Chapter 5 can also prove to be useful.

1.4 DESIGN METHODOLOGY

The design process consists of many phases, each of which may be performed numerous times before an acceptable solution is obtained (Johnson, 1987). The fact that the design process is iterative is extremely important. The process of performing trade-offs will naturally result in modifications during the design process. For example, the derivation of the requirements can cause us to revisit the definition of the problem, and perhaps eliminate certain aspects of the design to make the requirements more reasonable.

1.4.1 The Design Process

The five primary phases of the design process are the requirements phase, the conceptual phase, the specifications phase, the design phase, and the test phase. The five phases are necessary to develop one or more prototypes of a design; we will not consider in this development the phases necessary to arrive at a manufacturable system. Embedded within the five phases are the primary steps of the design process, including problem definition, requirements determination, partitioning, candidate designs, high-level analysis, hardware and software specifications, hardware and software design, detailed analysis, testing, system integration, and system testing. Each step of the design process is briefly described in the paragraphs that follow.

Problem definition. All designs clearly begin with the existence of a problem. For example, the problem may be to develop a flight-control system for a helicopter, an attitude-control system for a satellite, a network of computers to handle the transactions processing of a large bank, or a system to accurately control a nuclear reaction in a power generation plant. The first step in any design process is to develop a description of the problem. In many cases, the ability to write on paper a clear and concise statement of the problem is a major step toward the problem's solution.

System requirements. The second step in the design process is to extract, or create, a set of requirements from the problem description. The system requirements will typically consist of requirements on reliability, cost, weight, power consumption, physical size, performance (for example, speed), maintainability, and other system attributes. Many of the requirements, such as reliability, will be quantitative in nature, while others, such as compatibility with existing designs, will be more qualitative features. The derivation of the requirements may cause us to revisit the problem description as we learn more about the problem and its specific attributes. Also, the definition of the problem can make certain requirements impossible to attain.

System partitioning. Once the system requirements are well defined and understood, the design process requires partitioning the problem into manageable subproblems, called subsystems, that can each be handled easily by individual teams of design engineers. For small projects, each team may be a single engineer, or one designer may handle several portions of the total design. In more complicated systems, each design team may consist of tens or hundreds of engineers. The objective of the partitioning process is to divide the complete problem into manageable pieces. The partitioning can be in terms of hardware and software or perhaps a specific division of hardware subsystems. One form of partitioning can be performed, based on the system requirements.

A portion of the partitioning process involves categorizing various parts of the system, based on the reliability (or availability, maintainability, or some other attribute) requirements. For illustrative purposes, we will consider the reliability. One way to partition a system based on reliability requirements is into categories of varying degrees of criticality (Johnson and Julich, 1985). For example, the aerospace industry classifies functions as either flight-critical, mission-critical, or convenience functions. Flight-critical functions are those functions that, if discontinued or performed incorrectly, could result in the loss of the aircraft or the crew. In simple terms, a flight-critical function is one that is required to keep the aircraft flying. For example, the flight-control system in a fly-by-wire airplane is a flight-critical function. Flight-critical functions are the most important functions and, as a result, usually require the highest reliability.

Mission-critical functions are those functions that are required for the aircraft and its crew to complete its intended mission. For example, an airplane could certainly fly if the radio were to fail, but it is highly unlikely that the crew could complete its intended job. The mission-critical functions usually follow immediately the flight-critical functions in the level of reliability required.

Convenience functions are those functions that are relevant but have little impact, if discontinued. Compared to the flight-critical and mission-critical functions, the convenience functions, if discontinued, will produce relatively minor impacts. The electronic maintenance log in a military aircraft is an example of a convenience function. While the maintenance log is convenient and significantly improves the maintenance process, neither the crew, the mission, nor the aircraft will be endangered during flight if the maintenance log becomes inoperative.

Concept development.   One of the most important steps in the design of a fault-tolerant system is the creation of several candidate designs. Certainly, the initial candidates will be significantly deficient in the detail required of a complete design, but they will illustrate a basic approach that can be taken. For example, you may consider triple modular redundancy (TMR) as a candidate approach. You may not have yet defined the mechanism to be used to perform the voting, the manner in which synchronization will be achieved, or even the degree of synchronization required, but the basic features of TMR can be analyzed, in depth, to determine if they are appropriate for the particular application. TMR can be contrasted with standby sparing or the triple-duplex approach to determine, at least initially, which approach, if any, is best for the application at hand. One key reason for developing several candidate designs is that the process of determining the advantages of one approach will very likely uncover the disadvantages of another approach, and vice versa. The analysis of the candidate designs is a key step in the overall design process.

High-level analysis.   Once candidate systems are defined, the next step in the design process is to perform a preliminary analysis of each candidate architecture. A preliminary analysis can consist of a reliability estimate, cost estimates, weight estimates, and so on. At this stage of the design, many candidates that are obviously not suitable for the particular application can be eliminated quickly from consideration and further detailed development. A good high-level analysis can easily save the designers much expense by significantly decreasing the number of candidates. For example, you might initially consider TMR to be a viable alternative for an industrial control system, but you may eliminate TMR from consideration when a high-level analysis indicates that TMR significantly exceeds the reliability requirements and the weight limitations.

The importance of some type of high-level analysis cannot be overemphasized. Analysis, in general, must be an integral part of any successful design process. The earlier that deficiencies in a candidate design are identified, the more cost-effective the design process will be. You do not want a candidate to remain in consideration if significant problems exist in the approach. You also do not want to spend large amounts of time further developing a candidate that clearly cannot meet the requirements.

The difficulty with performing a high-level analysis is that many of the analysis techniques require a substantial amount of information on the specific design before an analysis can be performed. For example, we need some idea of the failure rate of the system's modules before we can determine the system's reliability (Johnson and Julich, 1984). Likewise, if we want to simulate the system as a means of functional evaluation, many of today's simulation tools require that significant detail be available before the simulation can be constructed (Breuer and Friedman, 1976). In many instances, we overcome these problems by analyzing the system for a range of parameters. For example, we can calculate the reliability as a function of the failure rate, and determine the reliability for a range of failure rates.

Hardware and software specifications.   The term specification is often used interchangeably with the term requirement. In this chapter, however, a requirement is considered to be some attribute, or quality, that is demanded of a system. A specification, on the other hand, is a detailed plan for a design that is capable of meeting certain requirements. For example, the requirement might be to achieve a reliability of 0.995 for a simple digital filter. The specification would be the outline of the design that could meet the requirement.

Once a high-level solution to the problem has been developed, analyzed, and refined, the specifications for the hardware and software to implement the design must be developed. At this point in the design process, it is crucial that much interaction occur between the systems engineers who created the high-level design and the hardware and software design engineers who will actually create the implementation designs. The specifications must achieve a delicate balance necessary to meet the system requirements and, at the same time, produce a practical, implementable, and manageable design.

Hardware and software design and analysis.   The result of the high-level analysis should be the selection of a final set of candidate solutions to the original problem. The set of possible solutions can contain only one candidate if all others have been eliminated for one reason or another. On the other hand, the set can contain two or more solutions that will each be carried through the complete design process to allow more detailed comparisons to be conducted. Each candidate that remains after the high-level analysis will be carried through a complete hardware and software design and construction process resulting in both hardware and software prototypes. In most instances, the hardware and software design can be performed in parallel with close interaction between the two groups to assure that hardware decisions do not negatively impact the software, and vice versa.

It is very important to continue the analysis of the designs in parallel with the actual design and construction, to assure that the system requirements (reliability, availability, maintainability, cost, and so on) are not compromised by design decisions that are made. Many times the analysis portion of the design process is overlooked until the design has been completed. At that point, it is often too late to make substantial changes to remedy any design problems. As the hardware is developed, more specific data can be provided to the analysis; for example, the failure rate information and the fault coverage data. Therefore, the analysis can be refined as the design is refined. Once the design is complete, the analysis should also be complete.

Testing.   An extremely important part of the design process is the development of a plan for testing the resulting designs and the actual testing, itself. During the design process, it is mandatory that testing be considered such that a testable design is conceived. Testing involves searching for faults of all types, including faults resulting from design mistakes, implementation mistakes, and component defects. The overall purpose of the test phase of the design process is to assure the correct operation of the system.

System integration and test.   Once the hardware and software prototypes have been tested adequately, they must be combined to form a complete, operational system. The process of combining the hardware and the software is usually called system integration. The fundamental purpose of system integration is to get all of the subsystems working together to perform the desired functions of the system. Each of the subsystems can work perfectly when tested independently of the remainder of the system; however, when all of the subsystems are required to coordinate, interfacing problems can arise. Once the system integration is complete, the system must be tested. Software faults, for example, that never create errors in the emulators used to develop the software can suddenly produce erroneous results because of hardware idiosyncracies. Likewise, hardware faults can emerge because the software is exercising the hardware in a manner slightly different than expected.

1.4.2 Fault Avoidance in the Design Process

The basic goal of fault avoidance is to prevent the occurrence of items that cause faults. For example, fault avoidance can be used to prevent design mistakes or implementation mistakes. The underlying theme of fault avoidance is that you do not achieve fault tolerance, high reliability, high availability, or any other key system attribute unless the design process ensures that the desired attributes are being designed into the system. In other words, simply testing for quality at the end of the design process is insufficient. We must incorporate procedures at all phases of the design to guarantee the achievement of a system's requirements. There are several fault avoidance techniques that can be applied at different points during the design process. Examples include various types of design reviews, adherence to design rules, shielding against external disturbances, and quality control checks.

Requirements design review. The purpose of the requirements design review is to have an independent team of design engineers review and concur with the requirements that have been derived as part of the problem definition and partitioning. It is important at this point to ensure that the requirements are reasonable and will be verifiable during the analysis and testing process. It is also important to ensure that all necessary requirements have been identified. The requirements design review helps eliminate specification mistakes as a cause of faults.

Conceptual design review. The conceptual design review occurs immediately after a high-level candidate design has been developed. The purpose of the conceptual design review is to assure that the basic concept of the candidate design is correct and meets the requirements that have been developed. During the conceptual design review, the design engineers will normally present the results of their initial analysis, to justify their belief that the candidate design is capable of fulfilling all of the system requirements. In addition, the conceptual design review will examine candidates that were eliminated from consideration, to verify that the reason for elimination is sufficient. The conceptual design review attempts to eliminate specification mistakes as a cause of faults by assuring that the concept that is ultimately specified is correct. The review should be performed by a team of independent designers to guarantee that the reviewers are not biased prematurely, in any way, toward, or against, the proposed candidate solution.

Specifications design review.   The result of the specifications phase of the design process is a detailed hardware and software specification, and a plan for testing the resulting hardware and software. The specifications design review attempts to verify the specifications to ensure their validity. Before the hardware and software designs are begun, it is important to make sure that the specifications are both correct and understood completely. Otherwise, faults due to specification mistakes will inevitably occur in the design. Also, it is extremely important to guarantee that the designs will be testable. As in the other design reviews, the specifications review should be conducted by an independent team of designers capable of completely understanding and critiquing the material. After the completion of the review and any resulting modifications, the specifications for the hardware and software should be ready to pass along to the designers, and the detailed design process begun.

Detailed design review.   Detailed design reviews must be performed on both the hardware and software designs before beginning the actual implementations. The purpose of the review is to ensure that the specific designs meet the specifications and are capable of fulfilling the system requirements. A detailed design review is one of the most important and difficult reviews that must be performed because the specific details of the design must be reviewed and verified. The detailed design review must encompass both the detailed design and the detailed analysis. For example, once the detailed design is performed, specific failure rates should be known such that the accuracy of the reliability analysis can be refined.

Final review.   The final review is intended to be a last checkpoint in the design process. At the time of the final review, a working prototype is often available. The basic purpose of the final review is to examine the performance of the prototype and the results of the final analysis, to ensure that specifications have been adhered to and the system requirements have been met. If the design has been performed correctly and the design reviews have been successful throughout the design process, the final review should not uncover any major problems.

Parts selection.   The selection of parts for a system can be critical to the achievement of reliability, availability, or some other system attribute. There are many levels of quality in the components that are available for use in designs; in many cases, there is a factor difference of hundreds in the failure rate of a high-quality part, and that same part of a lower quality. As might be expected, however, there is also a tremendous difference in the cost of parts of different qualities. Therefore, it is extremely important to guarantee that the components are selected appropriately. The primary trade-offs in the parts selection are (1) the cost of the part versus the failure rate of the part, (2) availability of the part versus the failure rate, and (3) the cost (both financial and otherwise) of a failure of the part.

Design rules.   Design rules often play an extremely important role in the design of a system; the strict adherence to design rules can substantially improve the system. Design rules can address items such as packaging, testing, shielding, or circuit layout. For example, a design rule may require that the system be partitioned into subsystems that are no larger than some predefined value. The size of the subsystem can be controlled in terms of the number of logic gates, the physical size of the subsystem, the total number of cards required, or some other metric. By partitioning based upon size, each subsystem becomes more manageable, and the probability of design mistakes is significantly decreased.

Documentation.   Documentation is another example of an extremely important aspect of fault avoidance. Design projects often require that different phases of the design be handled by different teams of designers. For example, a system's architecture can be developed by a team of so-called systems engineers. Next, a team of design engineers will take the specifications developed by the systems engineers and design the hardware and software. If the top-level architecture is incorrectly documented by the systems engineers, the final hardware and software designs can be incorrect. The design reviews described in the preceding sections are mechanisms that can be used to detect the existence of documentation errors. It is critical to the success of a project that each stage of the design be described correctly and clearly in the documentation. In this chapter we have presented various concepts in fault-tolerant designs. How these concepts are used in real world systems are discussed next.

REFERENCES

[Avizienis71a] Avizienis, A., "Arithmetic Error Codes: Cost and Effectiveness Studies for Application in Digital System Design," *IEEE Transactions on Computers,* vol. C-20, no. 11 (November 1971), pp. 1322–1331.

[Avizienis71b] Avizienis, A., G. C. Gilley, F. P. Mathur, D. A. Rennels, J. A. Rohn, and D. K. Rubin, "The STAR (Self-Testing and Repairing) Computer: An Investigation of the Theory and Practice of Fault-Tolerant Computer Design," *IEEE Transactions on Computers,* vol. C-20, no. 11 (November 1971), pp. 1312–1321.

[Avizienis82] Avizienis, A., "The Four-Universe Information System Model for the Study of Fault Tolerance," *Proceedings of the 12th Annual International Symposium on Fault-Tolerant Computing,* Santa Monica, Calif., June 22–24, 1982, pp. 6–13.

[Bouricius69] Bouricius, W. G., W. C. Carter, and P. R. Schneider, "Reliability Modeling Techniques for Self-Repairing Computer Systems," *Proceedings of the 24th ACM Annual Conference,* 1969, pp. 295–309.

[Breuer76] Breuer, M.A., and A. D. Friedman, *Diagnosis and Reliable Design of Digital Systems,* Computer Science Press, Inc., Potomac, Md., 1976.

[Chen78] Chen, L., and A. Avizienis, "N-Version Programming: A Fault Tolerant Approach to Reliability of Software Operation," *Proceedings of the International Symposium of Fault Tolerant Computing,* Toulouse, France, June 21–24, 1978, pp. 3–9.

[Choi92] Choi, C. Y., "WPc: A Software Package for the Dependability Analysis of Powered Wheelchair Systems," Master of Science Thesis, University of Virginia, Department of Electrical Engineering, Charlottesville, Va., May 1992.

[Clark92] Clark, K. A., and Johnson, B. W., "A Fault-Tolerant Solid-State Memory for Spaceborne Applications," *Proceedings of the Government Microelectronics Applications Conference (GOMAC)*, Las Vegas, Nev., November 9–12, pp. 441–444.

[Fortes84] Fortes, J. A. B., and C. S. Raghavendra, "Dynamically Reconfigurable Fault-Tolerant Processing Arrays," *Proceedings of the 14th Annual International Symposium on Fault-Tolerant Computing*, Kissimmee, Fl., June 20–22, 1984, pp. 386–392.

[Fujiwara90] Fujiwara, E., and D. K. Pradhan, "Error-Correcting Codes in Fault-Tolerant Computers," *IEEE Computer Special Issue on Fault-Tolerant Computing*, April, 1990.

[Hamming50] Hamming, R. W., "Error Detecting and Error Correcting Codes," *Bell System Technical Journal*, vol. 26, no. 2 (April 1950), pp. 147–160.

[Hayes85] Hayes, J. P., "Fault Modeling," *IEEE Design and Test*, vol. 2, no. 2 (April 1985), pp. 88–95.

[Herbert83] Herbert, E., "Computers: Minis and Mainframes," *IEEE Spectrum*, vol. 20, no. 1 (January 1983), pp. 28–33.

[Hopkins78] Hopkins, A. L., Jr., T. B. Smith III, and J. H. Lala, "FTMP—A Highly Reliable Fault-Tolerant Multiprocessor for Aircraft," *Proceedings of the IEEE*, vol. 66, no. 10 (October 1978), pp. 1221–1239.

[Johnson84] Johnson, B. W., and P. M. Julich, "Reliability Analysis of the A129 Integrated Multiplex System," *Proceedings of the National Aerospace and Electronics Conference (NAECON)*, Dayton, Ohio, May 1984, pp. 1229–1236.

[Johnson85] Johnson, B. W., and P. M. Julich, "Fault Tolerant Computer System for the A129 Helicopter," *IEEE Transactions on Aerospace and Electronic Systems*, vol. AES-21, no. 2 (March 1985), pp. 220–229.

[Johnson87] Johnson, B. W., "A Course on the Design of Reliable Digital Systems," *IEEE Transactions on Education*, vol. E-30, no. 1 (February 1987), pp. 27–36.

[Johnson89] Johnson, B. W., *Design and Analysis of Fault-Tolerant Digital Systems*, Addison-Wesley Publishing Company, Reading, Mass., 1989.

[Katzman77] Katzman, J. A., "System Architecture for NonStop Computing," *Proceedings of the 14th Computer Society International Conference (Compcon)*, San Francisco, February 1977, pp. 77–80.

[Kohavi78] Kohavi, Z., *Switching and Finite Automata Theory*, McGraw-Hill, New York, 1978.

[Lala85] Lala, P. K., *Fault Tolerant and Fault Testable Hardware Design*, Prentice Hall, Englewood Cliffs, N. J., 1985.

[Laprie85] Laprie, J-C., "Dependable Computing and Fault Tolerance: Concepts and Terminology," *Proceedings of the 15th Annual International Symposium on Fault-Tolerant Computing*, Ann Arbor, Mich., June 19–21, 1985, pp. 2–11.

[Lin83] Lin, S., and D. J. Costello, Jr., *Error Control Coding: Fundamentals and Applications*, Prentice Hall, Inc., Englewood Cliffs, N. J., 1983.

[Nelson82] Nelson, V. P., and B. D. Carroll, "Fault-Tolerant Computing (A Tutorial)," presented at the AIAA Fault Tolerant Computing Workshop, Fort Worth, Tex., November 8–10, 1982.

[Nelson86] Nelson, V. P., and B. D. Carroll, *Tutorial: Fault-Tolerant Computing*, IEEE Computer Society Press, Washington, D. C., 1986.

[Patel82] Patel, J. H., and L. Y. Fung, "Concurrent Error Detection in ALUs by Recomputing with Shifted Operands," *IEEE Transactions on Computers*, vol. C-31, no. 7 (July 1982), pp. 589–595.

[Pradhan72a] Pradhan, D. K., and S. M. Reddy, "Error Correcting Techniques for Logic Processors," *IEEE Transactions on Computers*, vol. C-21, (December 1972), pp. 1331–1335.

[Pradhan72b] Pradhan, D. K., and S. M. Reddy, "A Design Technique for Synthesis of Fault-Tolerant Adders," *Digest of Papers of 1972 International Symposium on Fault-Tolerant Computing*, IEEE Computer Society Publications, (June 1972), pp. 20–25.

[Pradhan86] Pradhan, D. K., "Fault-tolerant Computing: Theory and Techniques," Vol. I, Chapter 5, 1986.

[Rennels80] Rennels, D. A., "Distributed Fault-Tolerant Computer Systems," *IEEE Computer*, vol. 13, no. 3 (March 1980), pp. 55–64.

[Shooman68] Shooman, M. L., *Probabilistic Reliability: An Engineering Approach*, McGraw-Hill, New York, New York, 1968.

[Siewiorek82] Siewiorek, D. P., and R. S. Swarz, *The Theory and Practice of Reliable System Design*, Digital Press, Bedford, Mass., 1982.

[Sklaroff76] Sklaroff, J. R., "Redundancy Management Technique for the Space Shuttle Computers," *IBM Journal of Research and Development*, vol. 20, no. 1 (January 1976), pp. 20–28.

[Stiffler76] Stiffler, J. J., "Architectural Design for Near-100% Fault Coverage," *Proceedings of the International Symposium on Fault Tolerant Computing*, Pittsburgh, Pa., June 21–23, 1976, pp. 134–137.

[Tang69] Tang, D. T., and R. T. Chien, "Coding for Error Control," *IBM Systems Journal*, vol. 8, no. 1 (January 1969), pp. 48–86.

[Toy78] Toy, W. N., "Fault-Tolerant Design of Local ESS Processor," *Proceedings of the IEEE*, vol. 66, no. 10 (October 1978), pp. 1126–1145.

[Trivedi82] Trivedi, K. S., *Probability and Statistics with Reliability, Queuing, and Computer Science Applications*, Prentice Hall, Englewood Cliffs, N. J., 1982.

[Wadsack78] Wadsack, R. L., "Fault Modeling and Logic Simulation of CMOS and MOS Integrated Circuits," *The Bell System Technical Journal*, vol. 57, no. 5 (May–June 1978), pp. 1449–1475.

[Wensley78] Wensley, J. H., et al., "SIFT: Design and Analysis of a Fault-Tolerant Computer for Aircraft Control," *Proceedings of the IEEE*, vol. 66, no. 10 (October 1978), pp. 1240–1255.

PROBLEMS

1.1. Explain the differences between faults, errors, and failures, and explain how each term relates to the three-universe model. Illustrate your explanation with an ex-ample.

1.2. Some systems are designed for high reliability while others are designed for high safety. Explain the difference between reliability and safety and give an example of an application requiring high reliability and another example which requires high safety. How would you expect the four causes of faults to complicate the designs of high reliability applications as compared to high safety applications?

1.3. Faults can be characterized by five major attributes. Give examples of faults that illustrate each of these attributes.

1.4. Fault masking is an attractive technique for use in systems that cannot allow even momentary erroneous results to be generated. However, fault masking does have several serious limitations. What are the disadvantages of using a fault masking approach?

1.5. An industrial controller is needed to maintain the temperature of a process during a chemical reaction. The nonredundant controller is fairly simple and consists of an analog-to-digital (A/D) converter, processor, and a digital-to-analog (D/A) converter. Develop two alternatives for making the controller tolerant of any two component failures. The term component here means an A/D, processor, or D/A. Show block diagrams of your approaches and compare them. Which approach would you recommend and why?

1.6. Show the organization of an eight-bit memory with Hamming single-error correction and double-error detection. Be explicit in your descriptions and show the parity groups that result. Associate the syndromes with the particular bit that they identify as erroneous.

1.7. Show the separable and nonseparable cyclic codewords that result for four-bit information words when the generator polynomial is $G(X) = 1 + X + X^2 + X^5$. Also, develop a circuit that is capable of encoding the original information and a second circuit that is capable of decoding the codewords.

1.8. Calculate the MTTF of a TMR system that contains three identical modules, each with a failure rate of λ failures per hour. You may assume that the modules obey the exponential failure law. Compare the MTTF of the TMR system with the MTTF of a single module having the same failure rate. Show a plot of each MTTF versus λ.

1.9. Construct the Markov model of a TMR system with a single spare. Incorporate a coverage factor associated with the process of identifying the failed module and switching in the spare. Assume that the spare is always powered and is just as likely to fail as the primary modules. If the failure rate of each module is 0.001 failures per hour, what is the reliability of the TMR system with the single spare at the end of a ten-hour time period, as a function of the fault coverage factor? If the coverage is perfect, how does the reliability of the TMR system with the single spare compare with the reliability of a TMR system without a spare (again, at the end of a ten-hour time period)?

1.10. The architecture of a flight control system is simply a TMR system that uses flux-summing as the voting mechanism. Each of the three processors in the system performs self-diagnostics to allow faults to be detected. If a fault is detected, the affected processor will remove itself from the flux-summing arrangement. Because of concerns about the safety of the system, it has been decided to perform a safety analysis of the proposed architecture. Construct a Markov model of the system and develop a safety analysis. Compare the reliability and safety of the system as functions of the fault coverage factor associated with the self-diagnostics.

1.11. A satellite memory uses a technique known as column sparing to improve the reliability. Specifically, each k-bit memory word is expanded by s spare memory cells so each of the n memory rows contains $k + s$ memory cells. Assume that you have n by 1 (n rows with each row having one memory cell) memory chips that have a failure rate of λ. Also, assume that each memory chip obeys the exponential failure law. Write an expression for the reliability of the complete memory system which uses column sparing. The expression must account for fault coverage. Suppose that $k = 16$, fault coverage is 0.95, and $\lambda = 9.15 \times 10^{-6}$ failures per hour. Determine the number of spares, s, which will maximize the reliability of the memory at the end of a ten-year space mission. What is the reliability of the memory at the end of ten years (for both zero spares and the optimal number of spares)?

1.12. A possible alternative to the traditional hybrid TMR system with a spare (three operational units and one spare to replace any one of the three) is to use TMR and provide a spare for one, and only one, of the modules. In other words, the spare can only replace module 3, for example. Using combinatorial modeling techniques, develop an expression for the reliability of such a system. Assume that the voter circuitry and the reconfiguration circuitry, including coverage, are perfect. Also assume that each module has a failure rate of λ and obeys the exponential failure law. Using a failure rate of 0.001 failures per hour, compare the reliability of this hybrid system to traditional TMR with no spares (compare the reliabilities at three or four time points).

1.13. In many digital systems, transient failures are much more prevalent than permanent ones, particularly when the operating environment for the system is extremely harsh. Consequently, it is very important to be able to analyze the effect of transients. Assume that you have an electronic device (say, a microprocessor) that has a permanent failure rate of λ_p and a transient failure rate of λ_t. Further assume that the device has built-in detection capabilities that provide a coverage factor of C_p for permanent failures and C_t for transients. Finally, assume that the repair rate for transient failures is μ_t and the repair rate for permanent failures is μ_p. Develop a discrete-time, discrete-state Markov model that accounts for both permanent and transient failures and allows the availability of the device to be calculated. Show the state diagram of the model, and write the state equations (in matrix form) that describe the model. You do not have to solve the model.

1.14. A satellite memory system uses an error detecting and correcting (EDAC) code as a means of overcoming bit errors due to alpha particles. Essentially, alpha particles can occur at random times and cause random bits to change state in the memory. The memory cells are not permanently damaged by the alpha particles, but the state of the cell is changed. The memory uses a Hamming code which can correct all single errors and detect all double errors. The memory contains n words with each word having k data bits and c Hamming check bits. Assume that the memory cells have a "hit rate" of h bit errors per day-cell. The hit rate is the rate at which alpha particles are expected to corrupt the memory cells, assuming that the hits occur according to a Poisson process. You may assume that all bit errors are independent. Determine an expression for the probability that the memory with the EDAC will produce an uncorrectable bit error in any one of its n words. Also, write the expression for the memory without the EDAC coding. Suppose that $n = 134,217,728$ (128 megawords), $k = 16$, $c = 6$, and $h = 0.0000027$ bit errors per day-cell. What is the probability of an uncorrectable bit error occurring after ten years of operation in space for both the memory with the EDAC and the memory without the EDAC. Remember that if the EDAC is not used, each memory word will have exactly k cells.

1.15. One of the most difficult problems with duplication with comparison is the inability to detect faults that occur in the comparator. Using your knowledge of the four types of redundancy (and using any type redundancy you want), develop a gate-level design for a two-bit comparator (it compares two two-bit binary numbers) with two outputs. The combination of the two outputs should identify whether the two input numbers agree and whether the comparator has a fault. For example, you might use one output to report on the comparison and the other to report the health of the comparator. Or, you might choose to encode the outputs in such a way that 00 (just as an example) implies that the two numbers agree and the comparator is fault-free. Any stuck-at-1 or stuck-at-0 fault should be detected if it, in any way, affects the output of the comparator. Use your "self-checking comparator" to design a full adder that uses duplication with comparison.

1.16. Suppose that a bus between a microprocessor and a memory is 32-bits wide and is protected by four interlaced parity bits. Parity bits 1 and 3 are odd parity, and parity bits 3 and 4 are even parity. Show the organization of the parity groups and the design of the parity generation circuits. Show specifically which bits are in which parity groups. Describe the types of errors that are detected by this particular scheme and give an example of each type. For example, does the approach detect all single-bit errors? What types, if any, of double-bit errors does the approach detect? Does the approach detect the all-ones and all-zeros cases?

1.17. Standby sparing is a very popular form of redundancy used in many fault-tolerant designs. Consider a simple system containing two processors that operate in a standby sparing arrangement. One processor is designated as the online processor and performs all of the system's computations, as long as it remains fault-free. The second processor serves as a backup that is only used in the event of a fault in the online processor. Both the online and the spare processors execute self-test routines which attempt to detect faults that occur. If, and only if, a fault is detected in the online processor, the spare processor is brought online to assume the functions of the system. If faults are detected in both processors, the system shuts down. The purpose of this problem is to compare the effectiveness of the standby sparing approach with a nonredundant (simplex) system. For the simplex system, you may assume that it also has self-diagnostics, but it does not possess the attribute of fault tolerance (since there is no redundant processor). If a fault is detected in the simplex system, it will simply shut down. How does the reliability of these two approaches vary as a function of fault coverage (this question is best answered by developing a combinatorial model of each system and sketching the reliability function versus coverage)? Suppose that we define safety as the probability that the system is either functioning correctly or has performed a successful shutdown. What value does the safety approach as time approaches infinity for each of the two architectures? You may assume that the coverage provided by the self-diagnostics, in both the simplex and the standby sparing cases, is some arbitrary number, C. Also, you may assume that the processors have a constant failure rate (λ) and obey the exponential failure law.

1.18. Suppose that a simplex (no redundancy) computer system has a failure rate of λ and a fault detection coverage of C. The fault detection capability is the result of self-diagnostics that are run continuously. If the self-diagnostics detect a fault, the time required to repair the computer system is 24 hours because the faulty board is identified, obtained overnight, and easily replaced. If, however, the self-diagnostics do not detect the fault, the time required to repair the system is 72 hours, because a repair person must visit the site, determine the problem, and perform the repair. The disadvantage of including the self-diagnostics, however, is that the failure rate of the computer system becomes $\alpha\lambda$. In other words, the failure rate is increased by a factor of α because of the addition of the self-diagnostics. Using analytical techniques and a Markov model, determine the value of α, for a coverage factor of 0.95, at which including the self-diagnostics begins to degrade the steady-state availability of the system.

2

Architecture of Fault-Tolerant Computers

D. Siewiorek

2.1 INTRODUCTION

This chapter provides a basic overview of ten different architectures. Some of these architectures, as well as others, are also detailed in Chapter 4. Historically, reliable computers have been limited to military, industrial, aerospace, and communications applications in which the consequence of computer failure was significant economic impact and/or loss of life. Reliability is of critical importance in situations where a computer malfunction could have catastrophic results. Examples include the space shuttle, aircraft flight control systems, hospital patient monitors, and power system control.

Reliability techniques have become of increasing interest for general applications of computers because of several recent trends. A few of these trends are:

Harsher environments: With the advent of microprocessors, computer systems have left the clean environments of computer rooms for industrial environments. The cooling air contains more particulate matter. Temperature and humidity vary widely and are frequently subject to spontaneous changes. The primary power supply may fluctuate, and there may be more electromagnetic interference.

Novice users: As computers proliferate, the typical user is less sophisticated about the operation of the system. Consequently, the system has to be more robust, including toleration of inadvertent user abuse.

Increasing repair costs: As hardware costs continue to decline and labor costs escalate, a user cannot afford to have frequent calls to field service. Figure 2.1 depicts the relationship between hardware purchase price and the addition of reliability, maintainability, and availability features. Note that as hardware cost increases, service costs decrease, due to less frequent and shorter field service calls.

Larger systems: As systems become larger, there are more components that can fail. Since the overall failure rate is directly related to the failure rates of the individual components, fault-tolerant designs may be required to keep the overall system failure rate at an acceptable level.

The ultimate use of the system affects not only the design philosophy but also the trade-offs between design alternatives. The cost of fault tolerance must be weighed against the cost of error. Error costs include the cost of downtime as well as the cost of incorrect computation. Some questions about system usage that directly affect design philosophy include: Is the system to be highly reliable or highly available? Do all outputs have to be correct, or only data committed to

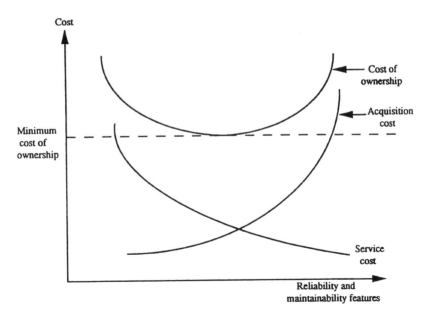

Figure 2.1: Cost of ownership as a function of reliability and maintainability features.

Table 2.1: Ten Computer Systems Grouped According to the Application Taxonomy[a]

General-Purpose Commercial Systems	High Availability	Long Life	Critical Computations
VAX 8600 IBM 3090	AT&T Tandem Stratus VAXft 310	Voyager Galileo	SIFT Space Shuttle

[a]Note that a system is not necessarily uniquely defined by one application area.

long-term storage? How familiar must the user be with the architecture and software redundancy? Is the system dedicated so that attributes of the application can be used to simplify fault-tolerant techniques? Is the system constrained to use existing components? Even if the design is new, what is the cost and/or performance penalty to the user who does not require fault tolerance? Is the design stand-alone or are there other processors that can be called upon to assist in times of failure?

Rather than enumerate a long list of design goals addressed by an architecture, it is more insightful to group fault-tolerant architectures by their intended applications (Table 2.1). Architectures designed for the same application area not only have similar design goals but also have similar features designed to respond to these goals. Despite these similarities, the detailed designs can differ significantly. Case studies for architectures in this chapter are organized into four application areas in Table 2.1 (Rennels, 1980): general-purpose computing, high availability, long life, and critical computations. These features will provide more insight for readers as they compare and contrast systems with similar design goals.

2.2 TAXONOMY OF APPLICATIONS

This section provides a perspective of various applications of fault-tolerant computing which differ from those discussed in the previous chapter.

2.2.1 General-Purpose Computing

General-purpose computing is the most familiar application to the computer user, referred to as highly available applications, in the previous chapter. Programs from a wide variety of disciplines—ranging from engineering analysis to business and from computational science to databases—can simultaneously coexist in a general-purpose computer. Since no single computational model exists and the interactions between applications are unknown, attributes of the applications cannot be used to detect or recover from errors. Thus, general-purpose computers represent both the biggest challenge and the largest opportunity because of their pervasive use throughout business and science. General-purpose computers define the minimum that can be expected from a fault-tolerant computer. Their users are more forgiving of failure. Occasional errors that disrupt processing for several seconds are tolerable as long as automatic restart follows.

Section 2.3 provides case studies of high-end general-purpose computers designed by the two largest computer companies. The Digital Equipment Corporation's VAX 8600 is summarized. International Business Machine's 3090 mainframes are the subject of the other major case study. The case studies emphasize design trade-offs, hardware manufacturing, operating system software, diagnosis, maintenance, and repair. These activities are common to all computer systems regardless of their degree of fault tolerance. Features built into commercial systems represent the minimal attributes to which all fault-tolerant systems should aspire.

2.2.2 High-Availability Systems

High-availability systems share resources when the occasional loss of a single user is acceptable, but a systemwide outage or common database destruction is unacceptable. Not only must the source of errors be rapidly detected, but also, corrective action must be swiftly implemented to minimize downtime. Indeed, downtime required to install new software releases is often unacceptable, thus necessitating a well-conceived approach to incrementally updating running software.

Section 2.4 compares and contrasts the evolution of four high-availability computer families that employ multiple copies of processors, memory, and input/output to detect and/or tolerate errors. The AT&T Switching Systems pioneered duplication and matching techniques in the domain of real-time switching of telephone calls. A model of the process for establishing and maintaining a telephone call provides the basis for several application-specific fault-tolerant techniques that could be used to detect and recover from errors. The other two case studies—the Tandem family and the Stratus family—focus on the transaction processing computational model that has been successfully applied to such diverse applications as electronic funds transfer, inventory management, and airline reservation systems. The similarities in end-user applications provide a unique opportunity to compare and contrast a software-intensive approach (Tandem) to a hardware-intensive solution (Stratus). The DEC VAXft 310 applies the duplication approach to general-purpose computing.

2.2.3 Long-Life Systems

There are many mobile systems (such as airplanes, ships, and mass transit systems) that depart from a central facility for a period of time and return. Stocking spares and maintenance expertise are most cost-effective if maintenance can be postponed until the mobile unit returns to the central facility. Since on-site repair may be difficult, the use of redundancy is more cost-effective than unscheduled maintenance. For some systems like spacecraft, maintenance could be postponed for the entire system life.

Section 2.5 focuses on long-life unmanned spacecraft systems which cannot be manually maintained over the operating life—frequently five or more years. Often, as in spacecraft monitoring of planets, the peak computational requirement comes at the end of system life. These systems are highly redundant and are equipped with enough spares to survive the mission with the required computational power. Error detection, diagnosis, and reconfiguration may be performed automatically (on the spacecraft) or remotely (from ground stations). While a substantial period of downtime might occur, serious operational mistakes or exhaustion of resources cannot be tolerated and must be removed through careful design. The Galileo spacecraft, which will orbit Jupiter and inject a probe into Jupiter's atmosphere, exemplifies the design of long-life redundant systems. The Galileo architecture is contrasted with the earlier generation Voyager Jupiter probe which had a less complex fly-by mission.

2.2.4 Critical Computations

The most stringent requirement for fault tolerance is in real-time control systems in which faulty computations can jeopardize human life or have high economic impact. Not only must computations be correct, but also recovery time from faults must be minimized. Specially designed hardware and software operate with concurrent error detection so that incorrect data never leave the faulty module.

Section 2.6 illustrates critical computations in two diverse domains. SIFT (Software-Implemented Fault Tolerance) is an avionic computer designed to control dynamically unstable aircraft. The design goal is a failure of probability of less than 10^{-9} for a ten-hour mission. The space shuttle computer also controls flight operations.

In conclusion, we feel these four categories cover the spectrum of contemporary applications for fault-tolerant computing systems. These categories have been refined into more numerous subcategories in the literature, and in the future, one can expect the introduction of new categories as computing systems are applied to even more innovative applications.

2.3 GENERAL-PURPOSE COMPUTING

2.3.1 Introduction

Most users had some interaction with general-purpose computing, such as direct access to a mainframe timesharing system, workstation, or personal computer. General-purpose computing indirectly touches our everyday lives in many ways, ranging from the preparation of our utility bills to the use of cash registers at our favorite restaurants. Thus, the concept of general-purpose computing needs no introduction. However, people may not realize the degree to which fault tolerance is used in these systems.

While occasional errors that disrupt processing for several seconds are tolerable as long as automatic recovery follows, the frequency of severe outages, such as system crashes, must be reduced. In addition, user programs are becoming more sophisticated and require more instructions to be executed to complete a task. Table 2.2 depicts the two attributes of most interest to users: mean time to crash (MTTC) and mean number of instructions executed (MNIE) between crashes. Both numbers have been steadily increasing. Note that the MNIE between crashes must increase at a faster rate than the MNIE per user task in order for useful work to be done. One way to increase MNIE is through the use of fault tolerance. Table 2.2 illustrates that a substantial gap exists between the capabilities of a general-purpose computer and a high-availability system such as Tandem. Nevertheless, improvements continue to be made in general-purpose computing, as illustrated by the 26 percent per year compounded improvement in mean time to hard failures per MIPS (million instructions per second) per year for IBM mainframes (Siewiorek and Swarz, 1992).

Since general-purpose computers must execute a wide range of applications, one cannot depend upon particular attributes of the application (such as transactions processing) to improve fault tolerance. Thus, the redundancy technique employed in general-purpose computers can be utilized in any fault-tolerant machine.

Therefore, general-purpose computing is an appropriate place to start our in-depth case studies of fault-tolerant computers. First generic general-purpose computers leading vendors—DEC and IBM—are considered in preparation for the case studies that follow.

Table 2.2: Number of Instructions Executed Between System Crashes for Several Systems

System	Mean Time to Crash MTTC (hours)	Mean Number of Instructions Executed MNIE ($\times 10^{10}$)
B5500 (Yourdan, 1972)	15	3
PDP-10 (Castillo, 1982)	10	4
Chi/05 (Univac 1108) (Lynch, Wagner, & Schwartz, 1975)	17	7
Dual 370/165 (Reynolds & Kinsberger, 1975)	9	28
SLAC	20	23
Cray-1 (Keller, 1976)	4	190
Sun II (Lin & Siewiorek, 1990)	1,000	720
Tandem (Gray, 1987)	16,000	5,760

2.3.2 Generic Computer

From its inception, the computer has been divided into three main sections: processor, main memory, and input/output. Most contemporary computers have augmented this structure by adding a fast memory (called a cache) between the processor and main memory. Since each section has unique attributes, they typically employ slightly different fault-tolerant strategies. Error detection mechanisms in a typical system include the following:

- *Memory:* Double-error detecting code on memory data and parity on address and control information.
- *Cache:* Parity on data, address, and control information.
- *Input/Output:* Parity on data and control information.
- *Processor:* Parity on data paths, parity on control store, and duplication and comparison of control logic.

As can be seen, the dominant error detection mechanisms are parity on multibit logic and duplication of random logic. Based on the assumption that most errors are transient, recovery consists primarily of retry by the error detection mechanisms:

- *Memory:* Single-error correction code (ECC) on data and retry on address or control information parity error.
- *Cache:* Retry on address or control information parity error and disable portions of cache on data parity errors.
- *Input/Output:* Retry on data or control parity errors
- *Processor:* Retry on control store parity error, invert and retry control store, and macro instruction retry.

Instead of attempting a number of retries immediately after an error is detected, systems typically pause so that the source of a transient error (such as power supply instability) can die out. The pause usually ranges from 5 milliseconds to 5 seconds. The pause value can be set to cope with site-dependent conditions. Hard failures are typically tolerated in main memory through ECC; in the cache, through performance degradation; and in the control store, by inverting the bits in the microinstruction, if required for a bit to match a stuck-at value.

With the advent of low-cost microprocessors, it became cost-effective to concentrate in a console processor the functionality traditionally provided by front console switches and maintenance panels. Once the basic functionality was provided for system control, expansion to include functionality for reliability followed naturally. A console processor typically consists of a 50K- to 100K-instructions-per-second processor, a small amount of nonvolatile ROM (such as 4K words), RAM (up to 256K words), secondary storage (floppy disk), remote access port, and interfaces to buses and control signals internal to the CPU. Some of the functionality associated with console processors (Kunshier, 1980) includes:

- System console
- System boot
- System quick tests of boot path
- Error logger
- Diagnostic tool: microdiagnostics, scan/set/computer internal state, fault injection, and remote diagnosis
- Error recovery: writeable control store reload, transplant state

The maintenance strategy for general-purpose computers has evolved over time as more error detection and correction techniques have been added. Table 2.3 for example, sketches the evolution of IBM's maintenance strategy. Techniques are listed for a representative machine from each major era. These techniques can be loosely grouped in three major categories: internal hardware, error detection circuits, diagnostics (including software and microcode), and display (such as lights, error logs, and tracing). The IBM strategy has evolved from "failure recreation" to "failure capture," to "failure recovery." Prior to the S/370, IBM field service engineers attempted to recreate the failure by running diagnostics, sometimes in conjunction with varying voltage, and clock frequency, until the failure reoccurred. The system was placed in a tightly programmed loop to produce a continuous failure condition for analysis. In failure recovery, the information captured by the detection circuits is utilized by recovery techniques, in hardware, microcode, and software, to allow the application or job to complete. The information is also logged at a remote support facility to assist engineering design activity.

2.3.3 VAX 8600

The reliability, availability, and maintainability program (RAMP)[1] of the VAX family is representative of contemporary general-purpose computing design. Some RAMP features are defined in the system architecture and must appear in every implementation. Other features are implementation-specific.

The VAX architecture defines three types of exceptions: aborts, faults, and traps. *Aborts* are the most severe form of exception. When an instruction is aborted, the machine registers and memory may be left in an indeterminate state. Because the system state is destroyed, the instruction cannot be correctly restarted, completed, simulated, or undone.

Faults, on the other hand, leave the machine registers and memory in a con-

---

[1]IBM uses the acronym RAS for reliability, availability, and serviceability.

Table 2.3: Evolution by IBM's Maintenance Strategy

Machines	Era	Techniques
650	Late 1950s	Six internal checkers Stand-alone diagnostics on punched cards Light and switch panel
1401	Early 1960s	20 internal checkers Stand-alone diagnostics Light and switch panel
S/360-50	Mid-1960s	75 internal checkers OLTEP (On-line Test Executive Program) Microdiagnostics Log fault data to main memory, EREP (Error Recording and Edit Program) for computing logged data
370/168 Mod	Early 1970s	Error detection circuits OLTEP Microdiagnostics for fault isolation Service processor, including trace unit—trace up to 199 fixed and 8 movable logic points over 32 machine cycles for intermittent or environmental faults
303 X	Mid-1970s	Error detection circuits OLFT (On-Line Functional Tests) Console and processor microdiagnostics EREP Scope loops Support processor, including trace and remote (telephone) access to log data and trace information
4341	Late 1970s	Error detection circuits 25,000 shadow latches Support processor—error logging and environmental monitoring
3090	Mid-1980s	Error detection circuit Error correction circuits Recovery techniques Processor controller, duplicate for availability Fault isolation circuits Fault threshold and isolation analysis Autocall and remote access to service information EREP Online tests Reconfiguration capability Internal machine environment monitoring
ES/9000	Early 1990s	Total concurrent error detection: ECC on data paths, memory arrays, control buses; parity prediction on state machines. Checkers on input/output of replaceable units. Identify error in same machine cycle. Memory: ECC on data paths and memory arrays, array reconfiguration, sparing, scrubbing, complement/recomplement to recover from dual errors. Input/Output channels: redundant paths, dynamic reconfiguration, on-line replacement. Processor retry: instruction retry, thresholds, transplant program to another processor. NH power supplies. Processor Controller: duplex, service interface recovery.

sistent state. Once the fault is eliminated, the instruction may be restarted and the correct results obtained. Faults restore only enough state to allow restarting. The state of the process may not be the same as before the fault occurred.

Finally, a *trap* occurs at the end of the instruction causing the exception. The machine registers and memory are consistent and the address of the next instruction to execute is stored on the machine stack. The process can be restarted with the identical state as before the trap occurred.

Exceptions are defined for overflow/underflow and other violations of arithmetic operations (trap), reserved instruction/operand/addressing mode usage, memory management violations (fault), memory errors (e.g., correctable data, nonexisting memory), backplane bus parity and protocol violations, and machine check (abort). The machine check is the most damaging exception. It is triggered when internal CPU error-checking circuitry detects an exceptional condition. The processor may be restartable if the exception is related to redundant logic whose sole purpose is to improve machine performance (e.g., instruction cache, instruction look-ahead buffer).

A generic VAX implementation is composed of a processor connected to memory and I/O devices by a backplane bus. Bus adapters convert I/O bus protocols to the backplane bus protocol. A set of internal system registers is associated with each subunit (cache, memory, translation buffer, backplane, etc.). Most subunits are associated with up to four types of registers: configuration/control, status, data, and diagnostic/maintenance. The configuration/control register contains information on the state of the element (checking enabled, reporting enabled, and so forth). The status register contains flags summarizing the state of the element, including error reports. Data registers capture relevant information about the system state when an error is detected (for example, the address used on cache lookup when a cache parity error is detected). Finally, the diagnostic/ maintenance register contains control and status information generated by the error detection and correction logic.

The console subsystem of a VAX provides control (halt, restart, initialize, etc.) over the processor as well as access to internal system registers. It has a mass storage device containing the main system bootstrap code, and some diagnostics. The console subsystem also has access to the visibility bus, which makes several hundred internal logic signal values visible to the microdiagnostics.

The main memory in VAX systems is protected by error-correcting code (ECC). An optional backup battery preserves the contents of memory over short-term power failures.

VAX systems also have a port for remote diagnosis, an integral part of the VAX maintenance philosophy. A typical VAX maintenance scenario is as follows. Disk-resident user mode diagnostics periodically execute under the VMS operating system. The goal of user mode diagnostics is to exercise and detect functional errors in memory, bus adapters, device controllers, and disk drives. Errors reported by user mode diagnostics or hardware check circuits prompt a customer call to the diagnostic center (DC). The customer replaces the removable disk media with diagnostic and scratch disks, turns a key on the front of the console to *Remote*, and calls the DC (unauthorized access is not possible). The DC engineer calls the customer's processor, logs into the system, and begins to execute a script of diagnostics. Micro- and macrodiagnostics can be loaded from the diagnostic disk and executed. The error log can be examined, memory locations deposited or examined, and so on. If the diagnostic disk is not operable, the diagnostics can be loaded from the console subsystem mass storage device or downline-loaded over the phone. The DC will attempt to isolate the failure to a subsystem. If the processor is faulty, the diagnostics on the console subsystem mass storage device are executed to verify the processor status.

The DC notifies the local field service office of the failing subsystem. Upon arrival at the customer's site, a field service engineer replaces the faulty board and reverifies the system. If the failing subsystem is the processor, microdiagnostics are loaded into the writable control store.

Remote diagnosis has at least three major advantages: (1) faster mean time to repair, especially when the problem is trivial and can be resolved over the remote link; (2) faster resolution of difficult problems because the person at the DC is an expert in VAX system fault determination; and (3) greater certainty that the field service engineer is sent to the site with the correct part in hand.

The VAX 8600 consists of four parts: I box (instruction fetch), E box (instruction execute), M box (memory interface), and F box (floating point). Since the system is heavily pipelined, the box structure provides unique opportunities and challenges. For example, four copies of the general-purpose registers are available for high-speed performance. Thus, if one general register set detects a parity error, the error can easily be corrected by updating from one of the other register sets. On the other hand, since several partially executed instructions can be in the pipeline at any given time, a detected error must be mapped to the appropriate instruction, and that instruction must be backed up and retried without disturbing the other partial results.

Many design decisions were applied uniformly across the boxes. The following is an overview of their common features:

- All memories and buses are checked by parity. Furthermore, parity continuity is carried through all the major data paths. Parity is kept not only for data but also for physical addresses and microcode. The console processor corrects bad data in a writable memory, such as a control store or table lookup constants, from the files it uses during machine initialization.
- Address parity and a bad data flag are "folded" into the ECC for main memory and cache. Thus, not only incorrectly accessed words but also data that was stored corrupted can be identified.
- Instruction retry is used to recover from transient and intermittent errors.
- Errors are dynamically logged and analyzed by the Standard Package for

Error Analysis and Reporting (SPEAR). By analyzing trends, SPEAR more accurately isolates failures to field-replaceable units.

- A diagnostic bus gives the console access to hundreds of internal logic signals.
- The environmental monitoring module (EMM) determines that all boards are in the proper place through electronic keying. It also detects the ambient temperature gradient across the card cage. An overheated regulator, a failed blower, inadequate airflow, inadequate output voltage, or a dangerously high-temperature gradient will cause the EMM to shut the system down.

Table 2.4 lists the RAMP features common to different VAX implementations. The benefit of each feature is listed as well as an indication of whether the feature improves mean time to failure (MTTF) and/or MTTR. Table 2.5 continues

Table 2.4: Common VAX RAMP Features

Feature	Example	Benefit	Aid MTTF	Aid MTTR
Processor consistency checking	Arithmetic traps, memory address protection, limit checking, reserved opcodes	Limits damage due to hardware or software errors	Yes	Yes
Interval timer	1 µsecond resolution	Used by diagnostics to test time-dependent functions	No	Yes
Disk error-correcting codes	Detect multiple bit errors and correct single burst errors	Tolerates transient and media-related faults	Yes	Yes
Peripheral write-verify checking hardware	Read after write followed by comparison	Error detection	No	Yes
Track offset retry hardware	Upon error, disk retries read. If retry fails, disk head is offset for retry	Tolerates gradual changes in hardware	Yes	Yes
Bad block handling	VMS removes bad disk blocks from use	Tolerates media defects	Yes	Yes
Online error logging	Records exceptional conditions in an error log including time and system state	Aids permanent and intermittent fault isolation	No	Yes

Table 2.5: VAX 8600 RAMP Features

Feature	Example	Benefit	Aid MTTF	Aid MTTC	Aid MTTR
Fault Avoidance					
Aid Flow	Blowers	Lowers chip junction temperature	Yes	No	No
VLSI	Motorola Cell Arrays, Memory chips	Fewer chips result in fewer boards, more reliable per function, lower power consumption, hence cooler junction temperatures	Yes	No	Yes
Heat Sinks		Conducts heat away from chips resulting in cooler junction temperatures	Yes	No	No
CPU Complexity	12 boards	Lower complexity implies lower overall failure rate, isolation to field replaceable unit	Yes	No	Yes
Sensors and Indicators	Environmental Monitoring Module observes power loss, temperature, air flow	Protects system from damage resulting from emergency conditions	Yes	No	Yes
Modular Power Supply		Easy replacement	No	No	Yes
Fault Tolerance					
Main Memory	7-bit ECC over 32-bit data word, address parity, and bad data bit.	Tolerates transient and permanent failures, logging of error information allows quick fault isolation	Yes	Yes	Yes
	5 bits even parity, 2 bits odd parity.	Detects all zero, all one errors due to timing or selection error	No	No	Yes

Component	Mechanism	Description		
Control Stores	Parity on control store in each of E, M, I, F boxes. E, M Box also check microaddress and microstack parity.	Provides detection of transient errors as well as partial isolation to failing chip	No	No	Yes
	Console corrects errors detected in E Box microstore. Retry on I, F Box.	Provides tolerance of transient errors	No	Yes	Yes
Translation Buffer	Direct mapped. Parity on tag, data, and valid bit fields	Provides faulty chip isolation. Tolerates transients by recalculating TB contents. Tolerates permanent failures by disabling portion of TB	Yes	Yes	Yes
Cache	Parity over tag and written bit; byte parity for error detection, ECC for error correction	Provides faulty chip isolation. Tolerates transients by error correction code. Detect all zero, all one errors due to timing or selection error	Yes	Yes	Yes
Backplane Bus	Parity on address, data, timeout	Detects errors and isolates to faulty bus port Transients tolerated by retry.	No	Yes	Yes
	Silo captures last 256 bus cycles	Isolates faulty chips	No	No	Yes
Input/Output Bus	Parity on address, data, control	Provides faulty chip isolation. Transients tolerated by retry	No	Yes	Yes
Data Paths	Parity on decode RAM, general register file, instruction buffer, ALU input with source indicated	Provides faulty chip isolation	No	No	Yes
	Redundant copies of general-purpose registers	Content of one general register set can be restored from a redundant copy without loss of user data	No	Yes	No

the list of RAMP-related model-specific features for the VAX 8600. More details can be found in Siewiorek and Swarz (1992) and Bruckert and Josephson (1985).

2.3.4 IBM 3090

Table 2.6 lists the feature in the IBM 3090 series. The hardware error detection, error correction, and monitoring circuits described in Table 2.6 are used in the following maintenance scenario. The processor controller analyzes the error detection data and develops a field replacement unit (FRU) call or a maintenance action plan. Automatically, at the customer's option, the processor controller establishes a data link for service. A customer engineer reviews the FRU information and responds to the site with the appropriate part or parts needed to effect the repair. For additional information, the customer engineer can communicate via data link with a central database (called RETAIN) for the latest service tips. A Field Technical Support Center specialist can use the data link to monitor remotely and/or control diagnostics on the IBM 3090. The reliability, availability, and serviceability (RAS) features of the IBM 308X and 3090 processor complexes can be found in Siewiorek and Swarz (1992). The goal of both hardware and software is high availability with minimized impact of failures. Four stages of corrective action are identified, each with successively larger impact on users: transparent recovery, one user affected, multiple users affected, and down. The successively higher severity stage recovery structure is common in systems with high-availability goals, or in real-time data processing environments in which temporary loss of data is tolerable. The IBM strategy of "first failure capture" is evident in the design of both hardware and software.

Error detection and recovery in general-purpose computers have evolved a long way from the first electronic computer design. The evolution is continuing into techniques for high-availability systems.

2.4 HIGH-AVAILABILITY SYSTEMS

The following presents an overview of some of the systems. Further discussion can be found in Chapter 4.

2.4.1 AT&T

The AT&T Switching Systems pioneered fault-tolerant computing in the telephone switching application. They have an aggressive availability goal: two hours downtime in 40 years (i.e., three minutes per year) with less than 0.01 percent of the calls handled incorrectly.

The Bell System has collected data on the historic trends of causes of system downtime (Toy, 1978). Twenty percent is attributed to hardware. Good diagnostics and trouble-location programs can help minimize hardware-induced downtime. Fifteen percent is attributed to software. Software deficiencies included im-

Table 2.6: IBM 3090 Series RAS (Reliability, Availability, Serviceability)

Reliability
- Low intrinsic failure rate technology
- Extensive component burn-in during manufacture
- Dual processor controller that incorporates switchover
- Multiple consoles for monitoring processor activity and for backup
- LSI packaging reduces number of circuit connections
- Internal machine power and temperature monitoring
- Chip sparing in memory replaces defective chips automatically

Availability
- Two, four, or six central processors
- Automatic error detection and correction in central and expanded storage
  - Single-bit error correction and double-bit error detection in central storage
  - Double-bit error correction and triple-bit error detection in expanded storage
- Storage deallocation in 4K-byte increments under system program control
- Ability to vary channels offline in one channel increment
- Error detection and fault isolation circuits provide improved recovery and serviceability
- Multipath I/O controllers and units

Data Integrity
- Key controlled storage protection (store and fetch)
- Critical address storage protection
- Storage error checking and correction
- Processor cache error handling
- Parity and other internal error checking
- Segment protection (S/370 mode)
- Page protection (S/370 mode)
- Clear, reset of registers and main storage
- Automatic remote support authorization
- Block multiplexer channel command retry
- Extensive I/O recovery by hardware and control programs

Serviceability
- Automatic fault isolation (analysis routines) concurrent with operation
- Automatic support capability—auto call to IBM is authorized by customer
- Trace facilities
- Error logout recording
- Microcode update distribution via remote support facilities
- Remote service console capability
- Automatic validation tests after repair
- Customer problem analysis facilities

proper translation of algorithms into code or improper specifications. Thirty-five percent of downtime is attributed to recovery deficiencies. These deficiencies can be caused by undetected faults or incorrect fault isolation. The remaining 30 percent is attributed to human procedural error.

Since that time, other studies of system downtime have been published. Table 2.7 depicts the relative frequency of outage attributed to five major sources across a variety of systems ranging from general-purpose commercial to dedi-

Table 2.7: Probability of Operational Outage Due to Various Sources[a]

	AT&T Switching Systems[b] (Toy, 1978)	Bellcore[b] (Ali, 1986)	Japanese Commercial Users	Tandem (Gray, 1985)	Tandem (Gray, 1987)	Northern Telecom	Mainframe Users
Hardware	0.20	0.26[d]	*[g]	0.18	0.19	.19	.45
Software	0.15	0.30[e]	0.75[g]	0.26	0.43	.19	.20
Maintenance	—	—	*[g]	0.25	0.13	—	.05
Operations	0.65[c]	0.44[f]	0.11	0.17	0.13	.33	.15
Environment	—	—	0.13	0.14	0.12	.28[h]	.15

[a]Dashes indicate that no separate value was reported for that category in the cited study.

[b]Fraction of downtime attributed to each source. Downtime is defined as any service disruption that exceeds 30 seconds duration. The Bellcore data represented a 3.5-minute downtime per year per system.

[c]Split between procedural errors (0.3) and recovery deficiencies (0.35).

[d]47% of the hardware failures occurred due to the second unit failing before the first unit could be replaced.

[e]Recovery software.

[f]Split between procedural errors (0.42) and operational software (0.02).

[g]Study only reported probability of vendor-related outage (i.e., 0.75 is split between vendor hardware, software, and maintenance).

[h](.15) attributed to power.

cated fault-tolerant applications. As we see from the table, there is no single dominant source of outage. Equal attention must be given to the various sources if more than a factor of two improvements is sought in system reliability.

There is some natural redundancy in the telephone switching network and in the data (i.e., a telephone user will redial if he or she gets a wrong number or is disconnected). However, there is a user aggravation level that must be avoided: users will redial as long as it does not happen too frequently. Note, however, that the thresholds are different for failure to establish a call (moderately high) and disconnection of an established call (very low). Thus, a staged failure recovery process is followed, as depicted in Table 2.8.

A substantial portion of the complexity of a switching system is in the peripheral hardware. Since the telephone switching application leads to a substantially different organization from general-purpose computers, a brief description of a typical system will be given. More details can be found in Kulzer (1977).

Figure 2.2 depicts a typical long-distance switching office. Various types of analog and digital telephone trunks enter the office. A transmission interface converts the different types of signals into eight-bit pulse-code-modulated (PCM) signals that are used in the time-space-time (TST) switch. The information received over one line is retransmitted over another line after routing by interchanging time slots (time portion of TST) and switching buses (space portion of TST), and again interchanging time slots. The information is changed back to analog or digital signals by the transmission interface.

Table 2.8: Levels of Recovery in a Switching System

Phase	Recovery Action	Effect
1	Initialize transient memory	Affects temporary storage, no calls lost
2	Reconfigure peripheral hardware; initialize all transient memory	Lose calls in process of being established, calls in progress not lost
3	Verify memory operation, establish a workable processor configuration, verify program, configure peripheral hardware, initialize all transient memory	Lose calls in process of being established, calls in progress not affected
4	Establish a workable processor configuration; configure peripheral hardware, initialize all memory	All calls lost

Signal processors scan the telephone trunks for any change in status, thus relieving the central control (CC) of this simple but time-consuming task. An interoffice signaling channel provides an independent channel (in addition to the telephone trunks) over which switching offices communicate.

Finally, the central control provides overall system control, administration,

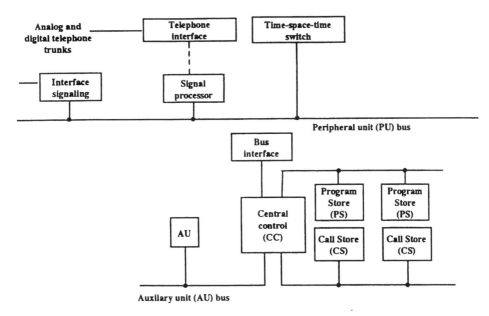

Figure 2.2: Typical switching system diagram.

call processing, and system maintenance. System maintenance includes automatic isolation of faulty units, defensive software strategies, and support for rapid repair. The CC instructions reside in the program store (PS) while transient information (e.g., telephone calls, routing, equipment configuration) is held in the call store (CS). The auxiliary unit (AU) bus interfaces to disk and magnetic tape mass storage.

The primary redundancy technique employed in the switching processors for tolerating failures has been duplication. Figure 2.3 illustrates a system with duplicate CC, CS, PS, and their associated buses. Assuming that only one of each component is required for a functional system, there are 64 possible system configurations.

Duplication can be used, not only for toleration of hard failures, but also for error detection, provided that both units are executing in synchronization and there is a mechanism for matching their results. A historical summary of the switching systems is given in Table 2.9, together with the processors used in each system. Table 2.10 traces the variations of duplication and matching devised for the switching systems to detect failures and to automatically resume computations. The primary form of detection is hardware lock-step duplication and comparison, requiring about two and one-half times the hardware cost of a nonredundant system. Even though all the processors are based upon full duplication, it is interesting to observe the evolution from tightly lock-stepped matching every machine cycle in the early processors to a higher dependence on self-checking and matching only, on writes to memory. Furthermore, as the processors evolved from dedicated, real-time controllers to multiple-purpose processors, the operating system and software not only became more sophisticated, but also became a dominant portion of the system design and maintenance effort (Toy, 1992). Following is a brief description of the switching system family evolution.

Table 2.9: Summary of Installed AT&T Telephone Switching Systems

System	Number of Connected Telephone Lines	Year Introduced	Number Installed	Processor Used in System	Comments
1 ESS	5,000–65,000	1965	1,000	No. 1	First processor with separate control and data memories
2 ESS	1,000–10,000	1969	500	No. 2	
1A ESS	100,000	1976	2,000	No. 1A	Four to eight times faster than No. 1
2B ESS	1,000–20,000	1975	>500	No. 3A	Combined control and data store. Microcoded, emulates No. 2
3 ESS	500–5,000	1976	>500	No. 3A	
5 ESS	1,000–85,000	1982	>1,000	No. 3B2	Multipurpose processor

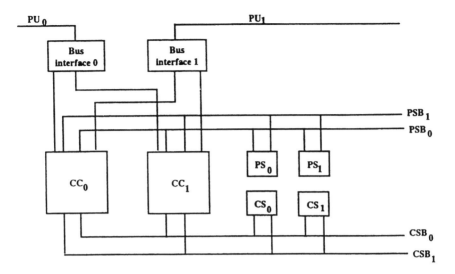

Figure 2.3: Duplex configuration for a switching computer.

Processor 1 was the initial proving ground for the duplicate-and-match philosophy. It can be shown that the mean time to failure (MTTF) of a duplex computer, where only one computer has to work for the system to be working and where the switchover upon failure to a simplex computer is assumed perfect, is

$$MTTF = \frac{\mu}{2\lambda^2}$$

where λ is the failure rate of a computer and μ is the repair rate. Processor 1 was specified to handle up to 65,000 telephone lines in a large metropolitan telephone office. This requirement led to a relatively large, 12,000-gate processor built from diode transistor logic. The failure rate of processor 1 was too large to meet the MTTF goal. Thus the system was divided into six subsystems, as depicted in Figure 2.3, peripheral unit (PU), central control (CC), call store (CS), program store (PS), call store bus (CSB), and program store bus (PSB). If the failure rate for subsystems is identical, the mean time to failure is approximated by

$$MTTF = \frac{6\,\mu}{2\lambda^2}$$

where λ is the failure rate of the entire computer and μ is the repair rate. For a constant λ and μ, the division into subsystems has improved MTTF by a factor of 6. The major form of fault detection and location in the central computer is duplication and matching. Both CCs operate in synchronism. Two matched circuits compare 24 bits of internal state during each 5.5-μs machine cycle. There are six

Table 2.10: Summary of AT&T Telephone Switching

Processor	Year Introduced	Complexity (gates)	Unit of Switching	Matching	Other Error Detection/Correction
No.1	1965	12,000	Program Store (PS) Control Store (CS) Central Controller (CC)	Six internal nodes, 24 bits per node; one node matched each machine cycle, node selected to be matched dependent on instruction being executed	Hamming codes on PS Parity on CS Automatic retry on CS, PS Watchdog timer Sanity program to determine if reorganization led to a valid configuration
No.2	1969	5,000	Entire computer	Single match point on call store input	Diagnostic programs Parity on PS Detection of multiword accesses in CS Watchdog timer
No. 1A	1976	50,000	PS, CS, CC, buses	16 internal nodes, 24 bits per node, four nodes matched each machine cycle	Two parity bits on PS Roving spares (i.e., contents of PS not completely duplicated, can be loaded from disk upon error detection) Two parity bits on CS Roving spares sufficient for complete duplication of transient data Processor configuration circuit to search automatically for a valid configuration

No. 3A	1975	Entire computer	None	Online processor writes into both stores m-of-$2m$ code on microstore plus parity Self-checking decoders Two parity bits on registers Duplication of ALU Watchdog timer Maintenance channel for observability and controllability of the other processor 25% of logic devoted to self-checking logic and 14% to maintenance access
3B20D	1981	Entire computer	None	Online processor writes into both stores Byte parity on data paths Parity checking where parity preserved, duplication otherwise Modified Hamming code on main memory Maintenance channel for observability and controllability of the other processor 30% of control logic devoted to self-checking Error correction codes on disks Software audits, sanity timer, integrity monitor

different sets of internal nodes that can be monitored, depending on the instruction being executed. A mismatch generates an interrupt which calls fault recognition programs to determine which half of the system is faulty. Information can be sampled by the matchers and retained for later examination by diagnostic programs. The program store employs a Hamming code on the 37 data bits. There is also parity over address plus data. The call store has one parity bit on address and data and another parity bit just on address. Both the program store and call store automatically retry operations upon error detection.

After a fault has been detected, the system configuration logic attempts to establish various combinations of subunits. First a configuration is established and a sanity timer started. A sanity program is then executed. The sanity program is similar to a maze that the hardware must transverse before the sanity timer times out. If a timeout occurs, the reconfiguration logic generates a new configuration to be tried.

Processor 2 was specified to handle 1,000 to 10,000 telephone lines. Due to its smaller size, cost was more of an issue than in the ESS-1 systems design. Thus, there was only one subsystem composed of the central computer, program store, call store, and appropriate buses. The design required 5,000 gates of resistor-transistor logic. Only one point, the input to the call store, was matched. Thus, it might take 10 to 100 ms for an internal error to manifest itself as a mismatch. Upon mismatch, the online processor runs error detection programs in an attempt to locate a hard failure. If the failure is detected, control passes to the standby processor. The program store is 22 bits wide and is protected by parity. Program words have odd parity, while data words have even parity. Thus, any attempt to execute data as program would be detected. In addition, logic circuits detected multiword accesses. The control store was 16 bits wide and employed no error detection codes. A watchdog timer was also employed for error detection. The watchdog timer would be set at various places in the program flow. If an error occurred, the chances are that the program would not be able to reset the watchdog timer before it zeroed.

Processor 1A was meant to be the replacement for the processor 1 ESS in large offices. It was used in the 1A ESS and 4 ESS systems. Constructed from bipolar, small-scale integration, it was from four to eight times faster than processor 1. The program store was now in read-write memory with a disk for backup. There were two matched circuits which compared 24 bits each 700 ns machine cycle. There were 16 internal nodes, 4 of which were matched every machine cycle. The 24-bit-wide program store was protected by two parity bits. Program store was not fully duplicated. Instead, two 64,000-word blocks of memory were used as roving spares. Backup disk storage made it possible to regenerate information in the failed unit. The two parity bits were interlaced so that double adjacent errors were detected. The call store contained transient data which would be difficult to regenerate. Thus the call store was duplicated and protected by two parity bits. There was separate processor configuration hardware in each central computer. Upon a timeout of a timer, the system would be reset, initialized, and reconfigured.

Processor 3A was designed to handle 500 to 5,000 telephone lines in low-cost applications. The central control was microprogrammed and 3A could emulate the processor 2. The call store and program store were combined in one main memory with an access time of 1 µs (this is to be compared to the 6-µs access time in processor 1). The entire system was duplicated. However, there was no matching operation. Instead, self-checking circuits were used to detect and isolate failures. This led to improved diagnostics over previous switching system designs. The standby processor would be halted, but its memory would be updated on writes. Parity errors on reads would automatically switch to the other main memory. An internally detected error would cause switching to the standby processor. Approximately 25 percent of the 16,500 gates in processor 3A were devoted to self-checking circuits.

The 3B20D processor is a UNIX-based system designed to handle from 1,000 to 85,000 telephone lines. The 3B20D is a general-purpose processor that uses duplication at the computer level to tolerate failures. The online processor uses internal self-checks to detect errors. It also modifies memories in both computers upon writing data so that the second computer has an up-to-date set of data.

2.4.2 Tandem

Tandem Computers was founded in 1976 to build high-availability computer systems for commercial transaction processing. The Tandem NonStop 1 was the first commercially available modularly expandable system designed specifically for high availability. Design objectives for Tandem systems include:

- Nonstop operation: Failures are detected, components are reconfigured out of service, and repaired components are configured back into the system without stopping the other system components.
- Data integrity: No single hardware failure can compromise the data integrity of the system.
- Modular system expansion: Processing power, memory, and peripherals are added without impacting applications software.

Tandem systems eliminate single points of failure by means of dual paths to all system elements (including disks and I/O controllers), processor replication, redundant power supplies, mirrored disks (two identical copies of files on two independent disk drives), and a message-based operating system.

Systems are composed of up to 16 computers interconnected by two message-oriented buses (Dynabus), as depicted in Figure 2.4. System designers chose a loosely coupled, shared-memory architecture because they believed it allows more complete fault containment. Upon this hardware structure, the software builds a process-oriented system with all communications handled as messages. This abstraction allows the blurring of the physical boundaries between processors and peripherals. Any I/O device or resource in the system can be accessed by a process, no matter where the resource and process reside.

The hardware and software modules are designed to be "fast-fail"—that is,

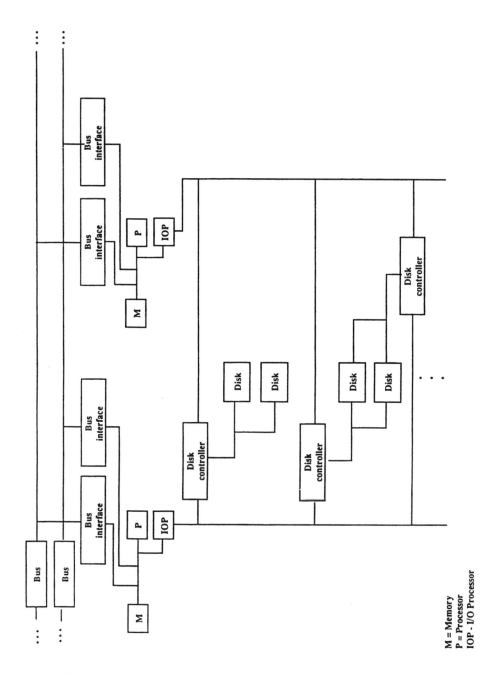

Figure 2.4: Tandem's system organization.

M = Memory
P = Processor
IOP - I/O Processor

112

to terminate processing immediately after detection of errors. Techniques employed in hardware modules include checksums on bus messages, parity on data paths, error-correcting-code memory, and watchdog timers. Software modules employ consistency checks and defensive programming techniques.

Tandem systems use retry extensively to access I/O devices. First, hardware and/or firmware retry the access, assuming a temporary fault. Next, software retries, followed by alternative path retry and finally alternative device retry. Data integrity is maintained through the mechanism of I/O process pairs: one I/O process is designated as primary, the other as backup. All modification messages are delivered to the primary I/O process. The primary sends a message with checkpoint information to the backup so that it can take over if the primary's processor or access path to the I/O device fails. Files can also be duplicated on physically distinct devices controlled by an I/O process pair on physically distinct processors. Thus, in the event of physical failure or isolation of the primary, the backup file is up-to-date and available.

Consider an example given in Bartlett (1981) of I/O process pairs as depicted in Figure 2.5. Initially, all sequence numbers (SeqNo) are set to zero. The requester sends a request to the server. If the sequence number is less than the server's local copy, a failure has occurred and the status of the completed operation is returned. Note that the requested operation is done only once. Next, the operation is performed and a checkpoint of the request is sent to the server

Step	Requester SeqNo = 0	Requester Backup SeqNo = 0	Server SeqNo = 0	Server Backup SeqNo = 0
1	Issue request to write record ——————→			
2			If SeqNo > MySeqNo, then return saved status	
3			Otherwise, read disk, perform —→ operation, check‑ point request	Saves request
4			Write to disk SeqNo = 1 ——→ Checkpoint result	Saves result SeqNo = 1
5	←———————		Return results	
6	Checkpoint results ——→	SeqNo = 1		

Figure 2.5: Sample process pair transactions.

backup. The disk is written, the sequence number incremented to one, and the results checkpointed to the server backup, which also increments its sequence number. The results are returned from the server to the requester. Finally, the results are checkpointed to the requester backup, which also increments its sequence number. Now, consider failures. If either backup fails, the operation completes successfully. If the requester fails after the request has been made, the server will complete the operation but be unable to return the result. When the requester backup becomes active, it will repeat the request. Since its sequence number is zero, the server test at step 2 will return the result without performing the operation again. Finally, if the server fails, the server backup either does nothing or completes the operation using checkpointed information. When the requester resends the request, the new server (i.e., the old server backup) either performs the operation or returns the saved results.

User applications can also use the process pair mechanism. Consider "non-stop" application program A in Figure 2.6. Program A starts up a backup process, Ab, in another processor. There are also duplicate file images, one designated primary and the other backup. Program A periodically (at user specified points) sends checkpoint information to Ab. Ab is the same program as A, but it knows that it is a backup program. Ab reads checkpoint messages to update its data

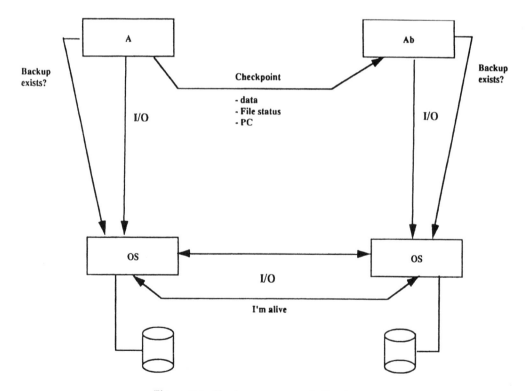

Figure 2.6: Shadow processor in Tandem.

area, file status, and program counter. Ab loads and executes if the system reports that A's processor is down (i.e., error message sent from A's operating system image of A's processor fails to respond to a periodic "I'm alive" message). All file activity by A is performed on both the primary and the backup file copies. When Ab starts to execute from the last checkpoint, it may attempt to repeat I/O operations successfully completed by A. The system file handler will recognize this situation and send Ab a successfully completed I/O message. Ab periodically asks the operating system if a backup process exists. Since one no longer does, it can request the creation and initialization of a copy of both the process and file structure. (More information on the operating system and the programming of nonstop applications can be found in Bartlett (1978).) Maintenance is the key to restoring redundant operation. The longer a repair action takes, the more likely that a second failure will bring the system down. To minimize maintenance time, Tandem averages one field support person for each customer. A remote diagnostics system provides more expert backup for the customer.

Tandem's Network Systems Management Program provides a set of operators that help reduce the number of administrative errors typically encountered in complex systems. The maintenance and diagnostic system analyzes the event log to call out failed field-replaceable units successfully 90 percent of the time. Available networking software allows interconnection of up to 255 geographically dispersed Tandem systems. Tandem applications include order entry, hospital records, bank transactions, and library transactions. The overall Tandem architecture has remained largely invariant through the seven processor upgrades and one Dynabus performance upgrade shown in Table 2.11. Chapter 4 in this text provides further details on the Tandem Architectures including the recent multiprocessor versions.

2.4.3 Stratus

Stratus Computers, founded in 1980, uses an alternative to the Tandem approach for online transaction processing, by employing single-chip microprocessors. The following provides a brief overview, and a detailed discussion can be found in Chapter 4 of this text. The design goal is continuous processing, which Stratus defines as uninterrupted operations without data loss, performance degradation, or special programming. Stratus systems are continuous checking between duplexed components for detection of errors at the actual points of failure. The Stratus self-checking, duplicate-and-match architecture is shown in Figure 2.7. A module (or computer) is composed of replicated power and backplane buses (StrataBus) into which a variety of boards can be inserted. Up to 32 modules can be interconnected to form a system via a message-passing Stratus Intermodule Bus (SIB). Access to the SIB takes place via dual 14-Mbyte-per-second links. Systems, in turn, are tied together by an X.25 packet-switched network.

Now, consider how the system in Figure 2.7 handles failure. The two processor boards (each containing a pair of microprocessors) are self-checking modules used in a pair-and-spare configuration. Each board operates indepen-

Table 2.11: Evolution of Tandem Systems

System Year	NonStop I 1976	NonStop II 1981	TXP 1983	VLX 1986	CLX 600 1987	CLX 700 1989	Cyclone 1989	CLX 800 1991
Processor								
MIPS/IPU	0.7	0.8	2.0	3.0	1.0	1.3	10.0	2.2
Instructions	173	285	285	285	306	306	306	306
Technology	MSI	MSI STTL	MSI Fast PAL	ECL Gate array	Custom 2μ CMOS	Custom 1.5μ CMOS	ECL Gate array	Custom 1μ CMOS
Cycle Time	100 ns	100 ns	83 ns	83 ns	133 ns	91 ns	45 ns	61 ns
Microstore	—	8k × 4B	Two-level: 8k × 5B 4k × 10B	10k × 15B dual	14k × 7B	14k × 7B	8k × 20B std + 8k × 20B pairs	14k × 8B
Cache (data and instructions)	—	—	64 KB direct map	64 KB direct map	64 KB direct map	128 KB direct map	2 × 64 KB direct map	192 KB direct map
Gates (approx.)	20K	30K	58K	86K	81K	81K	275K	81K
Proc. boards	2	3	4	2	1	1	3	1
Procs./system	2–16	2–16	2–16	2–16	1–6	2–8	2–16	2–16
Memory								
Virtual	512 KB	1 GB	1 GB	1 GB	1 GB	1 GB	2 GB	1 GB
Physical	2 MB	16 MB	16 MB	256 MB	32 MB	32 MB	2 GB	32 MB
Per board	64 KB	512 KB	2 MB	8 MB	4 MB (on processor board)	8 MB (on processor board)	32 MB	32 MB
Max. boards	2	2	4	2	1	1	2	0
Cycle time	500 ns/2B	400 ns/2B	666 ns/8B	416 ns/8B	933 ns/8B	637 ns/8B	495 ns/16B	4/4 nsec/8B
Input/Output								
Interprocessor bus speed	2 × 13 MB/s	2 × 13 MB/s	2 × 13 MB/s	2 × 20 MB/s	2 × 20 MB/s	2 × 20 MB/s	2 × 20 MB/s	2 × 20 MB/s
Channel speed	4 MB/s	5 MB/s	5 MB/s	5 MB/s	3 MB/s	4.4 MB/s	2 × 5 MB/s	4.4 MB/s

B   = Byte
IPU = Instruction processing unit
PAL = Processor array logic
ECL = Emitter-couple logic
MSI = Medium-scale integration

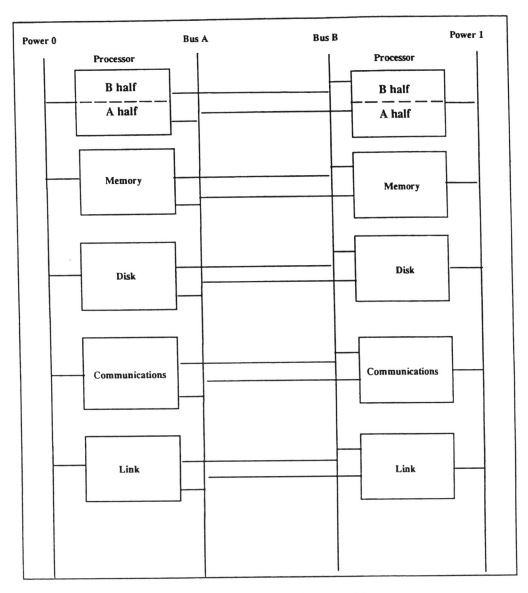

Figure 2.7: The Stratus pair-and-spare architecture.

dently. Each half of each board (for example, the A half) receives inputs from its own bus (bus A) and drives its own bus (bus A). Each bus is the wired-OR of one-half of each board (bus A is the wired-OR of all A board halves). The boards constantly compare their two halves; upon disagreement, a board removes itself from service, a maintenance interrupt is generated, and a red light is turned on.

The spare pair on the other processor board continues processing and is now the sole driver of both buses. The operating system executes a diagnostic on the failed board to determine whether the error was due to a transient or permanent fault. In the case of a transient fault, the board is returned to service. Permanent faults are reported by phone to a customer assistance center. The CAC reconfirms the problem, selects a replacement board of the same revision, prints installation instructions, and ships the board by overnight courier.

The user, learning of the problem only when the board is delivered, removes the old board and inserts the new board without disrupting the system (this replacement is known as a hot swap). The new board interrupts the system, and the processor that has been running brings the replacement into synchronization, making the full configuration available again. Detection and recovery are transparent to the application software.

Detection and recovery procedures for other system components are similar, although full implementation of the pair-and-spare strategy is restricted to the processor and memory. The disk controllers contain duplicate read/write circuitry. The communications controllers are also self-checking. The memory controllers, in addition, monitor the bus for parity errors. These controllers can declare a bus broken and instruct all boards to stop using it. Other boards monitor the bus for data directed to them. If the board detects an inconsistency, but the memory controllers have not declared the bus broken, the board assumes that its bus receivers have failed and declares itself failed.

The Stratus hardware approach is attractive in that it does not require on-line recovery from faults. The spare component continues processing until its faulty counterpart can be replaced. No data errors are injected into the system, so no software recovery mechanisms are required for the pair-and-spare components. Complexities due to checkpointing, restart programming, and other software fault tolerance considerations are eliminated. In addition to being easy to program, the Stratus approach to maintenance reduces yearly service cost to 6 percent of life-cycle cost, compared to an industrial average of 9 percent.

As in all other fault-tolerant systems, certain combinations of rare events can cause the system to fail. For example, multiple failures affecting the two independent halves of a board could cause the module to hang as it alternates between buses seeking a fault-free path. Furthermore, Stratus uses a single system clock.

Like the Tandem architecture, the Stratus architecture has remained essentially constant through the evolution of its systems, listed in Table 2.12. Chapter 4 provides further details about Stratus Systems.

2.4.4 VAXft 310

The VAXft 310 was introduced in 1990 to serve as a fault-tolerant stand-alone processor, as a processor in a cluster, or as a front end to high-availability VAX cluster systems. Data-capture front ends must correctly record real-time data

Table 2.12: Evolution of Stratus Systems

Year	System	Significant Features
1981	FT200	2 CPU. 68000-based (2 logical CPUs/board) Up to 16 Mbytes of memory User and executive CPUs (not symmetric) 20 slots in main chassis
1984	XA400	4 CPU. 68010-based (4 logical CPUs/board) Symmetric multiprocessing
1984	XA600	6 CPU. 68010-based (6 logical CPUs/board) Symmetric multiprocessing 8-Kbytes cache per CPU Floating-point assist in hardware 40 slots in main chassis
1987	XA2000 Model Nos. (110–160)	1 to 6 CPU. 68020-based (1 logical CPU/board) Up to 96 Mbytes of memory 64-Kbytes cache per CPU Floating-point coprocessor Dynamic processor upgrades Power failure ride-through
1988	XA2000 Model Nos. (50–70)	4 CPU. 68020-based (4 logical CPUs/board) Generalized I/O controller 10-slot chassis Fault-tolerant I/O communications bus
1989	XA2000 Model 30	1 to 6 CPU. 68030-based (1 logical CPU/board) 6-slot chassis Increased integration to eliminate cables and simplify service
1990	XA2000 Models (210–260)	1 to 6 CPU. 68030-based (1 logical CPU/board) Up to 256 MB memory Bus watching for cache consistency

(such as data generated by transaction processing and by manufacturing or laboratory monitoring) and recover in microseconds if a fault occurs. Once the data has been captured, it can be handed to high-availability clusters. A VAXft 310 front end combined with a traditional VAX cluster back end can be more cost-effective than a large-scale system that uses hardware fault tolerance uniformly throughout.

The design objectives for the VAXft 310 were similar to those of the Tandem and Stratus systems: no single point of failure, online repair, self-checking checkers, and tolerance of power interruptions. An additional goal was to minimize the possibility of an error during repair.

Figure 2.8 presents an overview of the VAXft 310. The system is composed

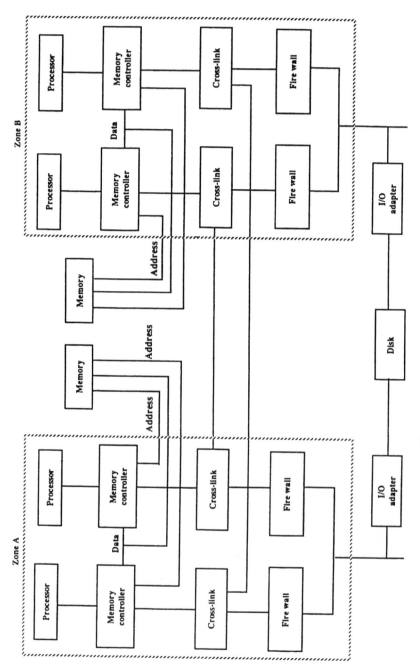

Figure 2.8: The VAXft 310 architecture.

of two complete computers, identified as zone A and zone B, each with its own processor, memory, backplane, cabinet, and uninterruptible power supply. If a physical failure occurs in one zone, that zone can be powered down, repaired, and resynchronized without physically disturbing the online zone. A duplicated cross-link carries data and timing signals to ensure that the two zones operate synchronously. The cross-links provide the communication path between the processor and I/O devices. Their basic function is to make I/O devices in both zones see a single processor and to make the processors believe that all I/O devices reside in a single zone.

The main error-checking method in each zone is duplication and matching. The processor (CVAX), memory controller, cross-link, and fire wall are all duplicated. Error detection and correction codes are used on nonduplicated elements such as the memory and the I/O adapter. Master/slave checking is performed by the memory controller (the gateway to the processors and memory) and the fire wall (the gateway to the I/O devices).

The memory controllers compare the data from both processors and forward a single copy to the memory. Both copies of the address bits, the ECC bits, and the control signals are also forwarded to the memory. The memory module generates the ECC bits from the data and compares them with the ECC bits received. In addition, the address and control signals for both copies must match for all transitions during the memory operation.

Input/output is performed via message packets exchanged between the processor and various I/O devices. Packets include the error detection code (EDC) normally associated with the I/O device (X.25, Ethernet, and others). Packets are formulated in a replicated region of the system and their data and EDC contents are compared by the fire walls before release to the nonreplicated I/O section. The I/O devices store the EDC with the data so that when it is retrieved, the replicated fire walls independently calculate the EDC bits from the data and compare them not only with each other but also with the stored EDC bits. Thus, the protection given by the replicated operation and by the EDC overlaps so that the data is never left unprotected. As the packets progress through the replicated portions of the system, their values are recorded in trace memories. When the fire walls detect a mismatch, the origin of the error is quickly isolated by comparing the contents of the two trace memories and noting the first point of disagreement.

Upon detecting an error, the system retries the operation, using alternate paths to I/O, if necessary. If the error persists or exceeds the set error rate threshold, the system reports the failure by phone to field service. After the repair, the contents of the running system are copied into the newly repaired system as a background activity of the operating system. All intervening write operations are transmitted via the cross-links to update locations that have changed since the copying occurred. After the copying is completed, the operating system places its state information into main memory, forcing a current state into the newly resynchronized memory. A hardware reset is issued and both zones restore state and resume lockstep operation.

2.5 LONG-LIFE SYSTEMS

2.5.1 Spacecraft Systems

Spacecraft are the primary example of systems requiring long periods of unattended operation. Unlike most other applications, spacecraft must directly control their environment, including electrical power, temperature, and even stability. Thus one must treat all aspects of a spacecraft (e.g., structural, propulsion, power, analog, and digital) when designing for reliability. Spacecraft missions cover a range from simple (e.g., weather satellites in low earth orbit) to sophisticated (e.g., deep-space planetary probes passing through uncharted environments). Some points in the range are low-earth-orbit sensing, low-earth-orbit communications or navigation, low-earth-orbit scientific observation, synchronous-orbit communication, and deep-space scientific observation. For nondemanding missions, system reliability goals are met by reducing complexity and simplicity of design. Before examining the reliability techniques used for more demanding missions, let us first explore an archetypal spacecraft. A typical spacecraft can be divided into five subsystems.

Propulsion. This system provides the means for controlling the stability and orientation (e.g., attitude) of the spacecraft. Multiple, often redundant, chemical or pressurized gas thrusters are used most frequently. Occasionally, spacecraft employ a spin for stability instead of the active control implied by thrusters.

Power. The generation and storage of electrical energy must be closely monitored and controlled since all other spacecraft systems rely on electricity to operate. Most often, spacecraft electrical systems are composed of solar cells and battery storage. The batteries are used to ride through loss of sun or loss of orientation periods. Control of solar cell orientation, battery charging, power transients, and temperature is the most frequent, time-consuming task for the spacecraft computers.

Data communications. Communications is divided into three, often physically distinct, channels. The first is commands from the ground to the spacecraft over the uplink. (It is even possible to reprogram a spacecraft computer over the uplink.) The other two channels are from the spacecraft to the ground (e.g., downlinks). One downlink carries data from the satellite payload and the second carries telemetry data about the spacecraft subsystems (e.g., temperature, power supply state, thruster events).

Attitude control.   A dedicated computer is often used to sense and control the orientation and stability of the spacecraft.

Command, control, payload.   All aspects of spacecraft control are usually centered in a single command/control computer. This computer is also the focus for recovery from error events. Recovery may be automatic or under control from the ground via uplink commands.

Typically, each of these five subsystems is composed of a string of elements. Table 2.13 depicts seven stages in a representative power subsystem. Solar panels are physically oriented by tracking motors. Power is delivered to the spacecraft via slip rings (such as those used on the armature of motors). A charge controller automatically keeps the batteries at full potential. A power regulator smoothes out voltage fluctuations while a power distributor controls the load connected to the power subsystem. At each stage in the string, redundancy is used to tolerate anticipated fault modes. To save complexity, the output of a string is usually all that is reported via telemetry.

A typical maintenance procedure would be as follows. When a failure has been detected, the spacecraft automatically enters a "safe" or "hold" mode. All nonessential loads on the power subsystem are shed. Normal mission sequencing and solar array tracking are stopped. The spacecraft is oriented to obtain maximum solar power. Meanwhile, the ground personnel must infer what possible failures could cause the output behavior of each of the strings. A possible failure scenario is selected as most likely and a reconfiguration (e.g., "work around") of the spacecraft subsystems devised. A command sequence implementing the "work around" is sent to the satellite. Depending on the severity of the failure, this entire procedure may take days, or even weeks to complete. Spacecraft fault responses vary from automatic in hardware for critical faults (e.g., power, clocks, and computer), to on-board software for serious faults (e.g., attitude, and command subsystems), to ground intervention for noncritical faults. Faults can be detected by one of several means:

Self-tests: Subsystem fails self-test, such as checksums on computer memories.

Cross-checking between units: Either physical or functional redundancy may be used. When a unit is physically duplicated, one is declared online and the other as monitor. The monitor checks all the outputs of the online unit. Alternatively, there may be disjoint units capable of performing the same function. For example, there is usually a set of sensors and actuators for precision attitude control. Attitude may also be less precisely sensed by instruments with other primary functions. The less precise calculation can be used as a sanity check on the more precise units.

Ground-initiated special tests: These are used to diagnose and isolate failures.

Ground trend analysis: Routine processing and analysis of telemetry detects long-term trends in units that degrade or wear out.

Typical redundancy techniques used in contemporary spacecraft are:

Propulsion: Redundant thrusters; multiple valves for propellant flow control; automatic switchover-based, excessive attitude change rates. Multiple commands required to initiate any firing sequence.

Power: Redundant solar cell strings, batteries, power buses; automatic load shedding.

Data Communications: Redundant transponders; digital error detection and correction technique; switch from directional to omni antennas for backup.

Attitude Control: Redundant sensors, gyros, and momentum wheels; automatic star reacquisition modes.

Command and Control: Hardware testing of parity, illegal instructions, memory addresses; sanity checks; memory checksums; task completion timed; watchdog timers; memory write protection; reassemble and reload memory to map around memory failures.

We will now consider two planetary probes that were launched to Jupiter: Voyager and Galileo. Since the missions were a decade apart in time, it is interesting to compare the architectural changes that technology made possible and mission requirements dictated. The Voyager missions were lower-cost substitutes for a "Grand Tour" mission. The Grand Tour was to take advantage of the alignment of the five outer planets of the solar system. In support of the Grand Tour mission, the Jet Propulsion Laboratory (JPL) designed and breadboarded a self-test and repair (STAR) computer (Avizienis, et. al., 1971).

2.5.2 Voyager

Table 2.14 depicts the major features of each spacecraft subsystem for JPL's Voyager. Voyager is a deep-space probe used in the Jupiter and Saturn planetary fly-bys (Jones, 1979).

Figure 2.9 displays the interconnection of subsystems on the Voyager spacecraft. Standby redundancy is used in all but the sensor payload. The standby spares are "cross-strapped" so that either unit can be switched in to communicate with other units. This form of standby redundancy is called "block" redundancy in that redundancy is provided at subsystem level rather than internal to each subsystem. The attitude control subsystem (ACS) is composed of redundant computers; one is an unpowered standby spare. The command and control subsystem (CCS) is also a redundant computer, but the standby is powered and monitors the online unit. Cross-strapping and switching allow reconfiguration around failed components. The CCS executes self-testing routines prior to issuing commands to other subsystems. Tables 2.15 and 2.16 list the error detection mechanisms in the Voyager attitude control and command control subsystems. Memory

Table 2.13: Typical Power Subsystem

Element	Tracking Solar Array	Solar Array Drive	Slip-Ring Assembly	Charge Controller	Batteries	Power Regulation	Power Distribution
Redundancy	Extra capacity series/parallel connections of individual solar cells allows for graceful degradation	Redundant drive elements and motors	Parallel rings for power transfer	Automatic monitoring and control of battery charge state	Series/parallel connections; diode protection	Redundant spares	Automatic load shedding

Table 2.14: Attributes of the Voyager Spacecraft

Systems Characteristics	Propulsion	Power	Data Communications	Attitude Control	Command and Payload
Planetary probe Three-axis stabilized Mission life: 7 years	Hydrazine thrusters	Three radioactive thermal generators; 430 W at Jupiter	Downlink, 2; uplink, 1; two antennas (high gain and low gain)	Redundant sun sensors and Canopus (star) trackers	Command rate:16 bps Redundant computers, 4K words each; data storage on board

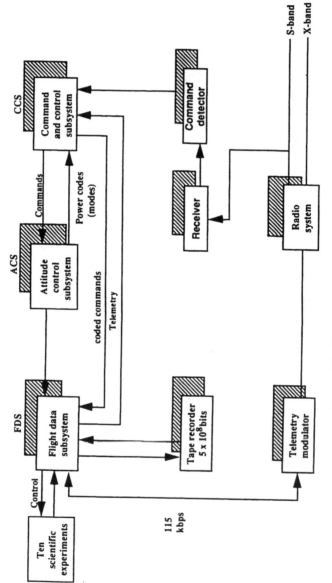

Figure 2.9: Voyager system block diagram.

Table 2.15: Error Detection in Voyager Attitude Control Subsystem

CCS fails to receive "I'm healthy" report every 2 seconds
Loss of celestial (sun and Canopus) reference
Power supply failure
Fail to rewrite memory every 10 hours
Spacecraft takes longer to turn than expected (thruster failure)
Gyro failure
Parity error on commands from CCS
Command sequence incorrect
Failure to respond to command from CCS

is only 4K words. The tape recorders are used for storage of scientific data only. New programs for memory have to be loaded from the ground.

2.5.3 Galileo

A follow-on to the Voyager Jupiter fly-by mission is the Galileo Jupiter orbiting and probe insertion mission. Figure 2.10 depicts a block diagram of the major subsystems in the Galileo orbiter. As can be seen, the Galileo architecture borrows heavily from the experiences gained with the Voyager system. Block redundancy is used throughout the subsystems comprising the orbiter. All but the command and data subsystem (CDS) operate as an active/standby pair. The CDS operates as active redundancy wherein each block can issue independent commands, or they can operate in parallel on the same critical activity. The major departure from the Voyager architecture is the extensive use of microprocessors in the Galileo orbiter. A total of 19 microprocessors with 320 Kbytes of ROM form a distributed system communicating over 806 kilohertz data bus. Scientific instruments add 8 further microprocessors to the total system. The bus is used to pass network-like messages between sources and destinations. Due to the volatile na-

Table 2.16: Error Detection in Voyager Command and Control Subsystem

Hardware
Low voltage
Primary command received before preceding one processed
Attempt to write into protected memory without override
Processor sequencer reached an illegal state

Software
Primary output unit unavailable for more than 14 seconds
Self-test routine not successfully completed
Output buffer overflow

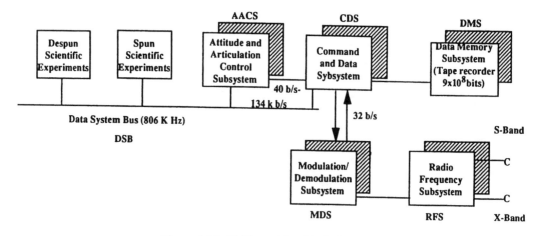

Figure 2.10: Galileo orbiter block diagram.

ture of the random access memory, a further requirement for the Galileo orbiter was memory keep-alive inverters to maintain power to the command and data subsystem (CDS) and attitude and articulation control subsystem (AACS) memories, in case of power faults. The orbiter accommodates a total of nine scientific instruments (five fields and particles and four remote sensing science). Due to the nature of the phenomena to be measured, fields and particles instruments demand a spinning platform to make total spherical observations while the remote science instruments require very accurate and very stable pointing. These requirements produced a dual-spin structure wherein a portion of the spacecraft is spun at three to ten revolutions per minute, while the other portion is held in a stable fixed configuration. Power is transmitted across the spun/despun interface via slip rings, while rotary transformers are used for data signals. The downlink data rates vary as a function of the experiment. Nonimaging science experiments require a high quality bit-error rate (less than $5 * 10^{-5}$) and are encoded in a Golay (24, 12) error-correcting code. Imaging experiments can use a lower quality bit-error rate (less than $5 * 10^{-3}$). The orbiter has been designed to operate reliably and autonomously in the harsh Jovian radiation and electrostatic discharge environments during the critical phase of relaying probe data and orbit insertion. The Galileo spacecraft has few hardware error detection mechanisms.

Faults are detected by monitoring the performance of various spacecraft subsystems. A partial list of error detection mechanisms (Kocsis, 1992) includes the following:

- test of event durations including transfers between subsystems; transition between all spin and spun/despun modes; parity or checksum errors on messages
- unexpected command codes

- loss of "heartbeat" between the AACS and the CDS
- spin rates above or below set values
- loss of sun or star identification detected by no valid pulse from acquisition sensor for a given period of time
- error between control variable setting and measured response is too great

The on-board fault protection software is designed to alleviate the effects and symptoms of faults, rather than to pinpoint the exact faults, themselves. Fault identification and isolation are performed by ground intervention. The Galileo mission was scheduled to fly from the space shuttle in May 1986. However, the Challenger explosion postponed the launch until 1989.

2.6 CRITICAL COMPUTATIONS

2.6.1 Sift

SIFT (Software-Implemented Fault Tolerance), designed by SRI International (Wensley, 1972), was intended for real-time control of aircraft. Due to concerns over fuel efficiency and performance, the aircraft of the future will be dynamically unstable. The loss of computer control for even a few milliseconds could lead to disaster. Thus, these experimental systems are designed for a failure probability of 10^{-9} during a 10-hour mission. An interesting problem arises from this reliability goal: How does one verify that the systems meet their design specification? 10^{-10} failures per hour translates into 1.14 million operating years before failure. Reliability verification requires both experimental and analytical techniques, as outlined in Chapters 5 and 6 respectively. The approach taken in SIFT is to mathematically prove the correctness of the system software. As the name implies, Software-Implemented Fault Tolerance relies primarily on software mechanisms to achieve reliability. The hardware consists of independent computers communicating with other computers over unidirectional serial links. Thus, for N computers, there are $N(N-1)$ links.

The SIFT software is divided into a set of tasks. The input to a task is produced by the output of a collection of tasks. Reliability is achieved by having tasks done independently by a number of computers. Typically, the correct output is chosen by a majority vote. If all copies of the output are not identical, an error has been detected. Such errors are recorded for use by the executive for determining faulty units and system reconfiguration. Voting is performed only on the input data to tasks rather than on every partial result. Thus, the tasks need to be only loosely synchronized (e.g., to within 50 μs). Figure 2.11 depicts the distribution for tasks among three processors. Application task A receives its input from task B. Task A receives the majority voted input from three copies of task B provided by the executive. When Task A finishes, it places its output into a buffer

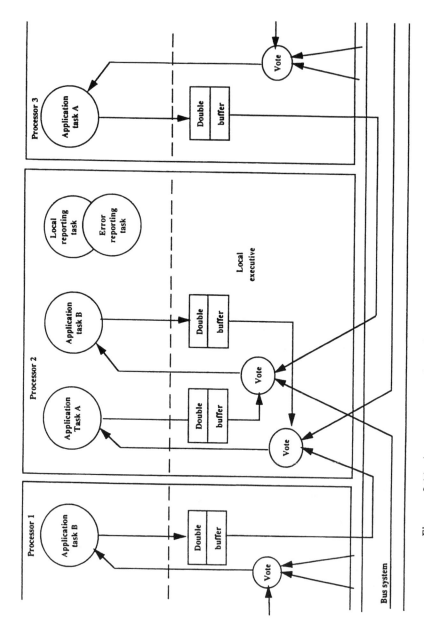

Figure 2.11: Arrangement of application tasks within SIFT configuration. (Adapted from Wensley 1978).

130

so that the executive can provide the majority voted data as input to the next task. The number of processors executing a task can vary with the task, and even with the execution instance of the task. The SIFT project had to solve a number of challenging problems, including distributed clock synchronization, reaching consensus on system health in the presence of faults, and mathematical proof of software correctness (Wensley, 1978).

2.6.2 Space Shuttle Computer

In an approach somewhat similar to SIFT, the space shuttle computer (Cooper, 1976); (Sklaroff, 1976; AWST, 1981) employs software voting in a five-computer complex. The computer complex is responsible for guidance, navigation, and pre-flight checkouts. Four of the five computers are used as a redundant set during critical mission phases. The fifth computer performs noncritical tasks and acts as a backup to the primary system. The control outputs of the four primary computers are voted on at the control actuators. In addition, each computer listens to the outputs of the three other computers and compares those signals with its own, via software. If a computer detects a disagreement, it signals the disagreeing computer. The received disagreement detection signals are voted on in the redundancy management circuitry of each computer. If the vote is positive, the redundancy management unit removes its computer from service. Up to two computer failures can be tolerated in voting mode operation. After the second failure, the system converts to a duplex system that can survive an additional computer failure by using comparison and self-tests to isolate the failure. The fifth computer contains a backup flight software package written by Rockwell International (the primary software package was written by IBM). These separate software packages minimize the probability of a common software error.

2.7 SUMMARY

In this chapter, the architecture of ten fault-tolerant computers has been briefly sketched. As indicated in the introduction, there will be a growing demand for fault-tolerant systems, as our society becomes increasingly dependent on computers for day-to-day operation. Indeed, one airline has estimated that it loses up to $20,000 per minute of downtime in its computer reservation system. As the cost of downtime and errors increases, we will see more and more effort devoted to toleration of failures. As in any other engineering discipline, there are design trade-offs between the cost of implementation and the cost of failure. The challenge is, then, to couple the potential of new technology with fault-tolerant techniques, to produce increasingly better systems. The next chapter discusses various concepts that underly the designs discussed here, as well as systems which are distributed.

REFERENCES

[Ali86] Ali, Private communication.

[Avizienis71] Avizienis, A., G. C. Gilley, F. P. Mathur, D. A. Rennels, J. A. Rohr, and D. K. Rubin, "The STAR (Self-Testing and Repairing) Computer: An Investigation on the Theory and Practice of Fault-Tolerant Computer Design," *IEEE Trans. Comput.*, vol. C-20, no. 11, (November 1971), pp. 1312–1321.

[AWST81] "Velocity, Altitude Regimes to Push Computer Limits," *Aviation Week Sp. Technol.*, April 6, 1982, pp. 49–51.

[Bartlett78] Bartlett, J. F., "A 'NonStop' Operating System," *Hawaii Int. Conf. Syst. Sci.*, 1978.

[Bartlett81] Bartlett, J. F., "A 'NonStop' Operating System," *ACM 8th Symp. Operat. Syst. Principles*, Pacific Grove, Calif. (December 1981), vol. 15, no. 5, pp. 22–29.

[Bartlett92] Bartlett, J., W. Bartlett, R. Carr, D. Garcia, J. Gray, R. Horst, R. Jardine, D. Jewett, D. Lenoski, and D. McGuire, "The Tandem Case: Fault Tolerance in Tandem Computer Systems," in *Reliable Computer Systems: Design and Evaluation*, Siewiorek and Swarz, Digital Press, Bedford Mass., 1992.

[Bruckert85] Bruckert, W. F., and R. W. Josephson, "Designing Reliability into the VAX 8600 System," *Digital Technical J.*, vol. 1 (August 1985), pp. 71–77.

[Castillo82] Castillo, X., S. R. McConnel, and D. P. Siewiorek, "Derivation and Collaboration of a Transient Error Reliability Model," *IEEE Trans. Comput.*, vol. C-31, no. 9, (July 1982), pp. 658–671.

[Cooper76] Cooper, A. E., and W. T. Chow, "Development of On-Board Space Computer Systems," *IBM J. Res Dev.* vol. 20, no. 1 (January 1976), pp. 5–19.

[Droulette71] Droulette, D. L. "Recovery Through Programming System/360—System/ 370". In *SJCC AFIPS Conf. Proc.* Vol. 38, Montvale, NJ.; AFIPS Press, 1971, pp. 467–476.

[Gray85] Gray, J. "Why Do Computers Stop and What Can Be Done About It?" Tandem TR85.7, June 1985, Tandem Computers, Cupertino, CA.

[Gray90] Gray, J. "A Consensus of Tandem System Availability Between 1985 and 1990." *IEEE Trans. on Rel., Special Issue on Experimental Evaluation of Computer Systems Reliability*, vol. 39, no. 4 (October 1990), pp. 409–418.

[Hopkins78] Hopkins, A. L., Jr., T. B. Smith III, and J. H. Lala, "FTMP—A Highly Reliable Fault-Tolerant Multiprocessor for Aircraft," *Proc. IEEE*, vol. 66, no. 10 (October 1978), pp. 1221–1239.

[Hsaio81] Hsaio, M. R., W. C. Carter, J. W. Thomas, and W. R. Stringfellow, "Reliability, Availability, and Serviceability of IBM Computer Systems: A Quarter Century of Progress," *IBM J. Res. Dev.*, vol. 25, no. 5 (September 1981), pp. 453–465.

[Jones79] Jones, C. P., "Automatic Fault Protection in the Voyager Spacecraft," Jet Propulsion Laboratory, California Institute of Technology AIAA Paper 79-1919, Pasadena, Calif.

[Katzman77] Katzman, J. A., "A Fault-Tolerant Computing System," Tandem Computers, Inc., Cupertino, Calif., 1977.

[Keller76] Keller, T. W., "CRAY-1 Evaluation Final Report," Los Alamos Scientific Laboratory, December 1976.

[Kocsis92] Kocsis, J. W., "Galileo Orbiter Fault Protection System," in *Reliable Computer Systems: Design and Evaluation*, Bedford, MA, Digital Press, 1992.

[Kulzer77] Kulzer, J. J., "Systems Reliability—A Case Study of No. 4 ESS," in *System Security and Reliability*, Infotech State of the Art Report, 1977, pp. 186–188.

[Kunshier80] Kunshier, D. J., and D. R. Mueller, "Support Processor Based System Fault Recovery," in *Dig., 10th Int. Symp. Fault Tolerant Comput.*, Kyoto, Japan, (October 1–3, 1980), 197–301.

[Lin90] Lin, Ting-Ting Y., and Daniel P. Siewiorek, "Error Log Analysis: Statistical Modeling and Heuristic Trend Analysis". *IEEE Transactions on Reliability*, vol. 39, no. 4, (October 1990), pp. 419–432.

[Lunde77] Lunde, A., "Empirical Evaluation of Some Features of Instruction Set Processor Architectures," *Commun. ACM*, vol. 20, no. 3, (March 1977), pp. 143–153.

[Lynch75] Lynch, W. C., W. Wagner, and M. S. Schwartz, "Reliability Experience with Chi/OS," *IEEE Trans. Soft. Eng.*, vol. SE-1, no. 2, (June 1975), pp. 253–257.

[Reynolds75] Reynolds, C. H., and J. E. Kinsbergen, "Tracking Reliability and Availability." *Datamation 21*, no. 11 (November 1975), pp. 106–116.

[Rennels80] Rennels, D. A., "Distributed Fault-Tolerant Computer Systems," *Computer* (March 1980), pp. 55–65.

[Siewiorek92] Siewiorek, D. P., and R. Swarz, *Reliable Computer Systems: Design and Evaluation*, Digital Press, Bedford, Mass., 1992.

[Sklaroff76] Sklaroff, J. R., "Redundancy Management Technique for Space Shuttle Computers," *IBM J. Res. Dev.*, vol. 20, no. 1 (January 1976), pp. 20–28.

[Toy78] Toy, W. N., "Fault-Tolerant Design of Local ESS Processors," *Proceedings of IEEE 66* (October 1978), pp. 1126–1145.

[Toy92] Toy, W., and L. Toy, "Fault-Tolerant Design of Electronic Switching Systems," in *Reliable Computer Systems: Design and Evaluation*, Siewiorek and Swarz, Digital Press, Bedford, Mass., 1992.

[Webber92] Webber, S., "The Stratus Architecture," in *Reliable Computer Systems: Design and Evaluation*, Siewiorek and Swarz, Digital Press, Bedford, Mass., 1992.

[Wensley72] Wensley, J. H., "SIFT Software Implemented Fault Tolerance," in *FJCC, AIPS Conf. Proc.*, Montvale, NJ.: AFIPS Press, vol. 41, (1972), pp. 243–253.

[Wensley78] Wensley, J. H., L. Lamport, J. Goldberg, M. W. Green, K. N. Levitt, P. M. Melliar-Smith, R. E. Shostak, and C. B. Weinstock, "SIFT: Design and Analysis of a Fault-Tolerant Computer for Aircraft Control," *Proc. IEEE*, vol. 66, no. 10 (October 1978), pp. 1240–1255.

[Yourdan72] Yourdan, E., *Design of On-Line Computing Systems*, Prentice Hall, Englewood Cliffs, N.J., 1972.

PROBLEMS

2.1. Compare and contrast the dual processor approaches to redundancy, as exemplified by Tandem, AT&T ESS No. 1, and Stratus functional redundancy checking. Specifically comment on cost, performance, fault detection ability, and fault latency (i.e., time between fault occurrence and detection).

2.2. Create a Markov model for dual redundancy. Assume that the system fails only when both computing elements have failed. Include the effects of fault detection and repair. (Note that a successful repair activity restores the system to a nonfailed state. Thus, the model has a transition from the one failed processor state to the nonfailed processor state.) Explain how the model differs for the Tandem, AT&T ESS No. 1, Stratus, and VAXft 310 architectures. Calculate the availability (i.e., the probability of being in nonfailed state) for the Tandem architecture, assuming a computing element failure rate, 1, of $1,000/10^6$ per hour and a repair rate, μ, of one-fourth per hour.

2.3. Estimate the cost and fault detection coverage (i.e., percent of logic protected) for reliability, availability, and maintainability features for the VAX 8600 and IBM 3090 general-purpose commercial computers.

2.4. Discuss the impact of technology evolution (e.g., small-scale integration to medium-scale integration to large-scale integration) on fault-tolerant architectures. In particular, contrast the Tandem (circa 1976) with the Stratus (circa 1980).

2.5. Pick one of the ten architectures described in this chapter and discuss how you would improve its design. Contrast the cost, performance, fault detection ability, and fault latency of your design with the original design. How have you taken advantage of the technology evolution? Create a Markov model for both architectures. Plot a graph using values of failure rate, 1, and repair rate, m, that indicate the region in which your design is superior to the original design.

3

Fault-Tolerant Multiprocessor and Distributed Systems: Principles

Dhiraj K. Pradhan and Prith Banerjee

3.1 INTRODUCTION

The last two chapters offered the fundamentals of fault-tolerant system design as well as review of several architectures. This chapter and the next extend this discussion to multiprocessors and distributed systems. Here we review the basics of incorporating fault-tolerance in multiprocessor and distributed systems. Then, in Chapter 4 gives case studies of real fault-tolerant multiprocessor and distributed systems.

Over the past decade, the motivation for higher throughput from existing technology has forced multiprocessor and parallel computing systems into the mainstream. A recent trend is massively parallel processors (MPP), where hundreds of computing nodes are interconnected to form an integrated system. From a recent article in the *IEEE Spectrum* (Zorpette, 1990), Table 3.1 portrays that more than 1,000 such parallel machines sold for more than $200 million. Despite such popularity, these new systems remain largely unsuitable for applications which, because of high failure rates, demand high reliability or prolonged availability.

Parallel systems suffer from high failure rates, despite the common perception of their inherent reliability. The following, from a recent publication by Harper and Lala (1991), points this out:

Table 3.1: Sales of Parallel Computers

Company	Number Sold to Date	1991 Sales in $(millions)
Intel	>325	$90
Meiko Scientific	>425	25
nCUBE	>300	18
Parsytec Gmbh	100	8
Thinking Machines	90	85
TOTAL	>1,240	$226

The assertion is often made that parallel processors are intrinsically reliable, fault tolerant, and reconfigurable due to their multiplicity of processing resources. In fact, the only intrinsic attribute guaranteed by multiple processors is *a higher total failure rate.*

Multiprocessor systems, in fact, are in real need of fault-tolerant features if dependable service is to be expected akin to their uniprocessor ancestors, as can be seen in Table 3.2. The Mean Time To Failure (MTTF) of the Intel Paragon system, for example, is thought to be as low as just several hours, clearly unacceptable for most applications. As parallel systems increase in scale, reliability needs increase as well.

Because massively parallel processors currently are solely driven by performance requirements, availability and reliability have not been investigated much. Table 3.2 illustrates how availability of these systems has already become a serious problem. Scaling up these systems drastically reduces the Mean Time Between Failures (MTBF).

Fault tolerance in complex multiprocessor systems, it is generally agreed, should incorporate both hardware and software techniques. Typically designed in a hierarchical fashion, dependability issues need to be addressed:

1. Circuit and technology levels concerning the exact technology required to implement various functions (e.g., radiation-hardened memory, gallium ar-

Table 3.2: MTBFs for Different Manufacturers

Manufacturer	1 Node Workstation	1,000 Node MPP
DEC	35,872 hours[a]	35 hours
HP	58,700 hours[a]	58 hours
SUN	40,601 hours[a]	40 hours
NASA/IBM AP101S	20,000 hours[b]	20 hours

[a]*IEEE Spectrum,* April 1992.
[b]EDN 1992.

senide chips for CPUs) along with circuit design techniques to improve testability and reliability of individual modules;

2. Node-level architecture concerning design of the VLSI chips which implement a processing node (e.g., which functions need to be checked using which mechanism?);

3. Internode architecture relating to how these nodes are connected together and how the system will be reconfigured in the presence of faulty processors and interconnection switches and links;

4. Operating system level dealing with checkpointing and rollback after certain portions of a system have been identified as faulty, the work load of a faulty processor being distributed to other processors (software errors may be present at this level);

5. Applications level where the user puts in some reasonableness checks on the results of computations (programming errors may be present at this level).

Fault tolerance typically is directed at each level in the design. Faults not detected (recovered from) at lower levels need to be handled at higher levels. This chapter reviews the basic issues and techniques of fault tolerance; the next chapter provides detailed reviews of some of the existing systems.

Before the detailed discussion of various fault tolerance techniques proposed in the literature, a brief review of the various classification of multiprocessors available is provided, along with some examples.

3.2 REVIEW OF MULTIPROCESSORS AND FAULT TOLERANCE

This section will first briefly enumerate the different classifications of multiprocessors that exist, and discuss their organizations. The next chapter provides an overview of some of the systems mentioned here. A large variety of multiprocessors needs to be characterized by different parameters.

3.2.1 Shared Memory versus Distributed Memory

General-purpose multiprocessors also can be classified as shared-memory multiprocessors and distributed-memory multiprocessors. In a shared-memory multiprocessor, all processors can access all memory locations. In a distributed-memory multiprocessor (more accurately, termed multicomputer), each processor has its own local memory which it can access (illustrated in Figure 3.1). The Sequent Symmetry, the Encore Multimax, the Sequoia and the Stratus machines are shared-memory multiprocessors. The Intel iPSC hypercube, the Intel Paragon, the Connection Machine CM-5, the IBM SP-1, and the Tandem Nonstop systems are distributed-memory multicomputers.

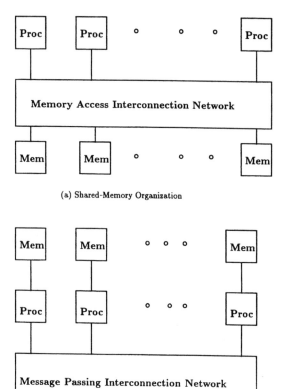

(a) Shared-Memory Organization

(b) Distributed-Memory Organization

Figure 3.1: Shared- and distributed-memory multiprocessors.

3.2.2 Fine Grain versus Coarse Grain

The term grain size refers to the number of instructions executed in a processor before synchronizing or communicating some data with another processor. *Fine-grain* parallel processing involves synchronizing the processors after every few instructions. *Coarse-grain* parallel processing involves synchronizing the processors after tens of thousands of instructions. More recently, the term *medium-grain* parallel processing has characterized a grain size somewhere in the middle, for example, several hundred instructions between synchronizations. The Connection Machine CM-2 synchronizes all the processors after every clock cycle and is considered a fine-grained parallel processor. The Intel iPSC hypercube and the Sequent Symmetry synchronize after several hundred to thousand clock cycles, and are medium-grained parallel processors. A distributed network of workstations synchronizes after several hundreds of thousands of clock cycles and can be classified as coarse-grained.

3.2.3 Moderate Parallel versus Massively Parallel

Whereas parallel processing has been present for quite some time, the terms massively parallel and moderate parallel have been used in a somewhat ad hoc manner. An accepted definition for *massively parallel* processing refers to an architecture using hundreds of processors. An architecture using 10 to 100 processors is termed *moderately parallel*. A Connection Machine CM-2, the CM-5, and the Kendall Squares KSR machines are massively parallel, while the Sequent Symmetry and the Intel iPSC hypercubes are moderately parallel machines. The fault-tolerant multiprocessors from Tandem Nonstop 16, Sequoia, and Stratus are moderately parallel machines. The Tandem Cyclone and Himalaya fault-tolerant systems can connect up to 4,096 processors and can be considered as massively parallel systems in this configuration.

3.2.4 SIMD versus MIMD

General-purpose multiprocessors are broadly classified as single instruction multiple data (SIMD) or multiple instruction multiple data (MIMD) multiprocessors. In a SIMD multiprocessor, a central controller broadcasts the same instruction to different processors, each processor then executing the instruction on its data. Some processors can be masked from the instruction by appropriately setting some mask registers at each processor. In a MIMD multiprocessor, the processors execute different instructions on different data. That is, there are multiple instruction streams, as opposed to a single instruction stream (in the case of SIMD multiprocessors). The Connection machine CM-2, and the Masspar MP-1 machines are SIMD machines, while the Intel iPSC, the Connection Machine CM-5, and the BBN Butterfly machines are MIMD machines. All the commercial fault-tolerant multiprocessors (for example, the Tandem, the Sequoia, and the Stratus multiprocessors) are MIMD machines.

3.2.5 Topology of Interconnect

In the case of both shared-memory multiprocessors and distributed-memory multicomputers, the different processors are connected through an interconnection network. Typical interconnection networks include the bus, the crossbar, multistage networks, rings, meshes, trees, and hypercubes. The Sequent Symmetry, the Encore Multimax, the Sequoia, the Stratus, and the Tandem Nonstop machines use buses as the interconnection. The Alliant FX multiprocessors use a crossbar. The BBN Butterfly multiprocessors use a multistage interconnection network. The Intel iPSC uses a hypercube connection. The Intel Paragon and the Masspar MP-1 use a two-dimensional mesh topology. The Connection Machine CM-5 uses a FAT-tree topology. The Kendall Squares KSR machine uses a hierarchical ring of rings topology.

3.2.6 Programming Model

Shared-memory MIMD multiprocessors are programmed assuming that all the necessary variables are shared by all processors, and that they may read and write any shared variable. Distributed memory MIMD multiprocessors are programmed assuming that each processor can read and write only its own local memory. Any synchronization has to be done using explicit message passing between processors. The Sequent Symmetry, the Encore Multimax, the Sequoia and the Stratus machines provide a shared-memory programming model. The Intel iPSC hypercube, the Intel Paragon, the Connection Machine CM-5, the IBM SP-1, and the Tandem Nonstop systems provide a message passing distributed-memory programming model.

3.3 IMPLICATIONS ON FAULT TOLERANCE

To distinguish the difference between shared-memory and distributed-memory multiprocessors, some issues relevant to fault tolerance are now discussed. A shared-memory multiprocessor consists of a number of processors connected to a global memory, accessible by all processors. In the extreme case, all instructions and data reside in a common memory available to any processor, so that processors are *anonymous*. Given a suitable initial program state (e.g., program counter and data on internal registers), any processor can execute any procedure from any starting point. The main motivation for multiprocessors comes from increasing the productivity (that is, throughput of applications) but they also are a means to increase the availability. The parallelism in various applications running on a multiprocessor allows execution of concurrent procedures on various processors. Also, when some processors fail, the remaining active processors can continue the work, though at a lesser throughput, ensuring high availability.

Shared-memory multiprocessors always have local cache memories private to each processor, so that frequently used data and codes reside in the local caches, not having to be accessed from global memory. This reduces memory conflicts for the same memory modules by multiple processors. Clearly, as the size of the cache memory increases, after a point, the total cache capacity becomes adequate to contain everything in common memory, the usefulness of global shared memory becoming reduced to the buffering of interprocess data. Here, the system begins behaving like a distributed-memory message passing multiprocessor. The cache memory, though, reduces the anonymity of the processor, depending on the amount of the contents of the cache memory unique to the one processor. However, the important requirement is that different copies of the same data residing in different processors must always be consistent. This poses some special considerations for fault tolerance. During failures, the cache coherence between multiple caches of different processors becomes affected; this is discussed in greater detail later in the section on recovery in shared-memory multiprocessors.

A problem exists with fault effect propagation in shared-memory multiprocessors. A faulty processor can potentially write into any global memory location, thereby completely corrupting the contents of memory, unless a check is performed before every write to main memory.

Distributed-memory multiprocessors are organized as a set of processor memory units that communicate among themselves via messages. A processor cannot write into another processor's memory but only into its own, even under failures. One need only check for correctness of the data during message passing which happens less frequently than normal instruction executions. So, from the point of view of error containment, distributed-memory multiprocessors can provide better containment. Recovery and process redistribution after a failure is, though, more difficult to perform in distributed-memory multiprocessors.

With this background, some specific approaches to fault tolerance in multiprocessors will now be discussed. Two basic approaches exist to achieve fault tolerance in multiprocessors. In *static or masking redundancy*, N copies of each processor are used and the minimum degree of replication is triplication. The replicated results are voted on. In *dynamic or standby redundancy*, first, the presence of a faulty processor is detected; then it is replaced with a spare. The following sections discuss in detail the various techniques available for each step.

3.4 FAULT TOLERANCE THROUGH STATIC REDUNDANCY

There are three distinct applications of static redundancy in multiprocessor environment: (i) redundancy for reliability and availability, (ii) redundancy for safety, and (iii) redundancy to tolerate non-classical faults.

3.4.1 Redundancy for Reliability and Availability

As already seen in Chapters 1 and 2, the first approach to fault tolerance in multiprocessors is a pure system-level approach, involving the use of static redundancy where N copies of a module perform the computation simultaneously to be voted. The scheme can be combined with the use of a disagreement detector and a switching unit that produces a hybrid redundant system. Clearly, one can apply this in a multiprocessor at several levels. Each processor can be replicated and the result of each processor's computation voted on, or the entire multiprocessor can be replicated and the combined result voted on. A third option divides the P processors of the multiprocessor into P/N groups of N processors, each group voting on its results before communicating to other groups.

Also, to provide robust communications, all critical transactions between groups may be replicated and voted upon. Replication and voting in varying degrees have been used in many early designs as discussed in Chapter 2, such as FTMP (Hopkins, Smith, and Lala 1978), the C.VMP (Siewiorek, Kini, Mashburn, McConnel, and Hsao 1978), and the SIFT multiprocessor (Wensley, Lamport,

Goldberg et al, 1978). The FTMP and C.VMP performed the voting in hardware, while the SIFT performed the voting in software. Various static redundancy scheme classifications are presented in Section 3.10.1.

The SIFT multiprocessor was specifically targeted toward computations in aircraft control involving voting on iterative tasks. This notion of performing triplicated computations and voting on the computations in software has been proposed for general-purpose distributed-memory multiprocessors by Kiskis and Shin (1988). This use of replication in general-purpose systems raises certain interesting concepts in scheduling of tasks. In a life-critical and ultrareliable system, in addition to reliability, safety is also a major concern. Safety and reliability are not necessarily the same. When a system is operating in a reliable mode, it is also safe but the reverse is not necessarily true. For example, when a nuclear plant is shut down, it is in a safe state although not in a reliable state.

3.4.2 Redundancy for Safety

Present-day fault-tolerant systems are increasingly used in critical applications such as nuclear reactor control and fly-by-wire aircraft. Dependability considerations mandate that besides reliability, the system must have a high level of safety. Operation which is both reliable under adverse conditions, as well as safe under severely adverse conditions, must be ensured.

Reliability refers to the probability that the system produces correct output. Safety is defined as the probability that the system output is either correct, or that the error in the output is detectable, Johnson (1989). High safety is ensured by making negligible the probability of an undetected error in the output. When an uncorrectable error in the output is detected, a recovery or safe shutdown can be carried out. A fault tolerance scheme must be, in practice, chosen which meets the reliability-safety requirement. As mentioned above, it may be noted that when a system is reliable, it is also safe although a safe system does not have to be reliable. A system can be highly safe with only a small Mean Time To Failure. Therefore in general, a system's safety is at least equal to reliability. Thus, high reliability implies high safety whereas the reverse is not always true.

Recent work, Vaidya and Pradhan (1993), establishes certain fundamental redundancy trade-offs between reliability and safety. To illustrate the reliability-safety trade-off, consider a simple five-modular redundant (5MR) system with each module producing a single bit output. When the modules produce a single bit output, two faulty modules produce the same erroneous output value. A k-out-of-n voter produces output v only if at least k modules agree on the output v; otherwise, the voter asserts an unsafe flag, indicating that no k modules can agree and the voter output should be discarded. For 5MR with binary module outputs, k may be 3, 4, or 5, where the 3-out-of-5 voter is the traditional majority voter. If p_{good} is the likelihood that a module is fault-free, then reliability R and safety S of a k-out-of-5 strategy are given by

Table 3.3: Example of the Reliability-Safety Trade-off
$$p_{good} = 0.9$$

Voter	Reliability	Safety
3-out-of-5	0.99144	0.99144
4-out-of-5	0.91854	0.99954
5-out-of-5	0.59049	0.99999

$$R = \sum_{i=k}^{5} \binom{5}{i} p_{good}^i (1 - p_{good})^{5-i} \quad \text{and} \quad S = 1 - \sum_{i=k}^{5} \binom{5}{i} p_{good}^{5-i} (1 - p_{good})^i$$

Table 3.3 lists reliability and safety for these three strategies. Observe that the traditional 3-out-of-5 voter achieves the highest reliability but the lowest safety. The three strategies achieve different combinations of reliability and safety. Observe in Table 3.3 that reliability can be traded with safety. Indeed, as shown later, this is true in general. In applications with moderate reliability and high safety requirements, the 4-out-of-5 scheme may be preferable to the traditional 3-out-of-5 majority voter. The 5-out-of-5 scheme, though, guarantees the best possible safety with reduced reliability.

Design strategies can achieve both high reliability and safety using the generic model illustrated in Figure 3.2. The system is formed using multiple identical modules, all performing the same function. The outputs of all the modules are input to an arbiter. The output of the arbiter constitutes the system output which consists of two components: (i) data output and (ii) unsafe flag. The unsafe flag indicates that the data output is erroneous. Thus, when the unsafe flag is asserted, the data output may not be accepted and an alternate recovery mechanism is invoked. These systems are termed *safe modular redundant* (or SMR) systems. An SMR system consisting of n modules will be called an nSMR system.

An arbitration strategy is the function implemented by the arbiter to decide what the correct output is and when the errors in the module outputs exceed the correction capability, so that the correct output cannot be provided. When the correct output cannot be provided, the unsafe flag can be asserted by the arbiter

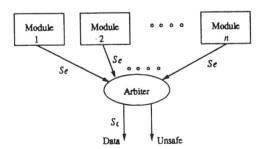

Figure 3.2: A safe modular redundant (SMR) system.

and the output can thus be discarded. So, reliability and safety of an nSMR system depend both on the individual module reliability and on the particular arbitration strategy used.

The usual expectation is that reliability and safety should improve with added redundancy. However, Vaidya and Pradhan (1993), establish that increased redundancy may not necessarily contribute to an increase in *both* reliability and safety. Specifically, for the symmetric error model, which models errors in VLSI circuits, Pradhan and Gupta (1991), the following holds: in systems with irredundant modules (e.g., modules with noncoded outputs), there exists an nSMR system compared to which *no* $(n + 1)$SMR system can achieve both higher reliability as well as safety (addition of one module need *not* improve both reliability and safety simultaneously). However, given any nSMR system system, there always *exists* an $(n + 2)$SMR system with higher reliability (safety) and at least the same level of safety (reliability). Thus, the addition of a minimum of *two* modules can *always* be effective in improving both reliability and safety. Also, it is shown that if individual modules, themselves, have any built-in redundancy whatsoever, there always exists an $(n + 1)$SMR system with higher reliability and safety compared to any given nSMR. Thus, if modules have *built-in* detection ability, addition of a single module may be sufficient. Consequently, a fundamental observation may be made that built-in detection ability within each module provides a certain intrinsic ability to improve safety with added redundancy. If the modules have no built-in detection ability, then added redundancy is not always guaranteed to improve safety. This may be contrasted with the general observation that added redundancy can always be used to improve reliability with or without built-in detection. It may be noted that this is true, independent of the degree of redundancy or the error detection capability (any nonzero error detectability is sufficient). Thus, the addition of one module can enhance both reliability and safety, provided the modules have some built-in error detection capability. However, all these above observations were made with the assumption of the symmetric error model, which assumes all error patterns are equally likely. Further investigations are warranted to explore other redundancy-reliability-safety tradeoffs. In safety-critical systems, one of the concerns is the accuracy of the fault model. Therefore, besides the usual permanent, transient and intermittent fault models, a very general model called the Byzantine model has been the focus of much investigation and is discussed next.

3.4.3 Redundancy for Tolerating Non-Classical Faults

While the simplest approach to masking redundancy involves triplicated computations, where voting on the results takes place to tolerate a single permanent or intermittent failure, voting becomes more complicated in the presence of arbitrary non-classical failures.

In environments requiring extremely high reliability, voting methods must be provided which can give tolerance against arbitrary failures. Even malicious failures, where two or more faulty nodes may cooperate and attempt to foil the operation, must be tolerated. The Byzantine failure model was proposed for precisely such an environment in Pease, Shostak, and Lamport (1980). The problem receiving significant attention is the so-called Byzantine Agreement problem introduced by Lamport, Shostak, and Pease (1982).

The Byzantine failure model allows arbitrary behavior for the faulty module. A faulty module may not only produce incorrect values but also send different values to different destinations instead of identical values, as expected. Under this model, two or more faulty modules can inadvertently or deliberately cooperate in a way to have the most detrimental effect on system operation, even malicious failures being permitted.

Byzantine resilience owes its name to the *Byzantine General's problem*, Lamport, Shostak, and Pease (1982). The Byzantine General's problem is an analogy traditionally used for relating the difficulties encountered in reaching an agreement between good processors in the presence of faulty processors, even if the faulty processors exhibit behavior that can be interpreted as intentional and malicious. Among the reasons why the designers chose such a professedly extreme level of fault tolerance, even when the actual faults may be more realistic, is its suitability for reliability validation, simplicity, and abstraction of fault tolerance techniques. In safety critical systems, some advocate the Byzantine fault model to overcome the effect of timing-related complex failures that are more easily covered by this model.

Traditional methods for the validation of a system's probability of failure are tedious and costly. For instance, failure mode and effects analysis is a common approach to reliable system development that involves researching the likely failure modes of the system, predicting their extent and effects, and then developing appropriate fault-tolerant techniques. This approach is time-consuming and its effectiveness is subject to the ability of the designers to *predict* the likely failure modes of the system. Thus, validating the system's predicted reliability hinges on the designers' ability to prove that all failure modes not accounted for have a sufficiently small probability of occurring. However, a Byzantine resilient system does not require foreknowledge of component misbehavior and can tolerate faulty components with even the most malevolent behavior, thus avoiding the need for the costly task of proving the validity of assumptions regarding faulty component behavior.

With respect to the level of reliability required, designing a Byzantine resilient system is, however, surprisingly *simple*. Such a system need contain only a prespecified minimum number of processors and interconnections, provide for their synchronization, and utilize certain simple information exchange protocols, since most existing fault-tolerant systems already employ synchronized redundant processors and redundant interprocessor communication channels. Meeting the first two requirements involves relatively little modification; meeting the third requirement requires the simple implementation of existing exchange protocols. Such protocols, though, are restricted. For a protocol to tolerate f faults, dubbed an f-*Byzantine resilient system*, the following requirements must be met:

At least $(3f + 1)$ members must participate.

At least $(2f + 1)$ disjoint communications paths must exist between members.

At least $(f + 1)$ rounds of communication must take place.

All members must be synchronized within a known skew of each other.

Thus, a protocol for a 1-Byzantine resilient system must execute two rounds of communication between at least four synchronized members connected by at least three disjoint communications paths.

Several real-life situations may be approximated as Byzantine failures. For example, consider a modular redundant system which receives its input from a sensor that monitors the environment. The output of the sensor varies continuously with time. In a typical control system, the system receives input from a sensor and then produces an output for the actuators. In a redundant system with multiple modules, the outputs of the modules in the system are voted on to determine the correct output. The sensor, when faulty, or problems in synchronization can result in different modules reading different values from the same sensor. This type of failure behavior can easily be modeled using the Byzantine failure model. If the fault-free modules do not receive the same value from the sensor, they will not produce the same output, and the vote may not result in the correct output. Therefore, it must be ensured that all the modules use the same reading from the sensor. A Byzantine agreement protocol can be used to ensure that all modules agree on the same value for sensor output, before using it in their computations.

To specify the requirements to be satisfied by a Byzantine agreement protocol, let us consider an abstract problem using the example of an army consisting of a general and his subordinates. In a computing environment, the general and subordinates can be viewed as communicating nodes. The general needs to send a command—ATTACK or RETREAT—to all his subordinates. The general and the subordinates use a Byzantine agreement protocol to agree on the command issued by the general. Let the agreement protocol require the general and the subordinates to exchange oral messages to arrive at a final decision. A faulty subordinate, though, may send incorrect messages. The requirements that must be satisfied by a Byzantine agreement algorithm may be summarized as follows:

C1: All fault-free subordinates agree on the same command.

C2: If the general is fault-free, all the fault-free subordinates agree on the command issued by the general.

For example, consider four nodes A, B, C, and D. Assume that D wants to convey a message to A, B, and C. Byzantine agreement requires that all the fault-free nodes in the set $\{A, B, C, D\}$ agree on the same message. Let D be a general and A, B, and C be his subordinates. D may send a message to either ATTACK or

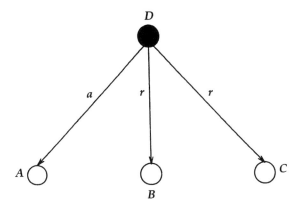

a = ATTACK   **r = RETREAT**   **Figure 3.3:** Byzantine agreement.

RETREAT (see Figure 3.3). The fault-free subordinates must agree on the command that D sent if D is fault-free. However, if D is faulty, then the fault-free subordinates are required to agree on an identical command, regardless of the actual command received from D. Consider the following scenario: D is faulty and A, B, and C are fault-free. D sends the command ATTACK to A and RETREAT to B and C. To detect such a case, the subordinates must exchange the message received from D. After the exchange has been completed, each of the subordinates has three copies of the message. The subordinate accepts the majority of these copies as the agreed value. Thus, each of the subordinates obtains RETREAT as the agreed value (see Figure 3.4). It is easy to verify that the above procedure works even when D is fault-free but one of the subordinates is faulty.

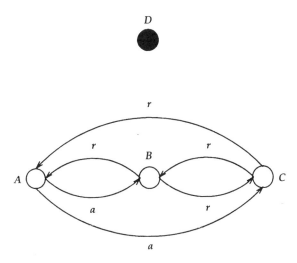

Figure 3.4: Byzantine agreement achieved.

Now, consider a scenario where two of the subordinates, A and B, are faulty and the general is fault-free. The general sends the command ATTACK to all three subordinates. However, A and B behave maliciously and send the command RETREAT to C (see Figure 3.5). Therefore, C will obtain the command RETREAT as the majority of the three copies of the command it received. Thus, two faulty subordinates can foil this Byzantine agreement algorithm. It can, in fact be shown that any system that can tolerate t Byzantine failures must contain at least $3t + 1$ nodes. This implies that to tolerate the two faulty subordinates, our example system must have one general and six subordinates in all. This can be interpreted to imply that m Byzantine fault resilence in a computing environment requires at least $(3m + 1)$ communicating nodes. We now present a Byzantine algorithm OM(m) that tolerates m Byzantine failures. The algorithm specification is recursive (Lamport, 1982). The total number of people (general and subordinates) involved is $n \geq 3m + 1$. The following algorithm is defined recursively: OM(0) followed by OM(1), OM(2), . . . ,OM(m). In a computing environment, the general can be interpreted as the transmitting node and the subordinates as receiving nodes. The terms ATTACK and RETREAT can be interpreted as binary messages. However, for general messages, the majority operation below refers to the usual majority operation.

Algorithm 3.1. OM(0).

1. The value from the general is sent to every subordinate.
2. Each subordinate uses the value received from the general or uses the value RETREAT if none received.

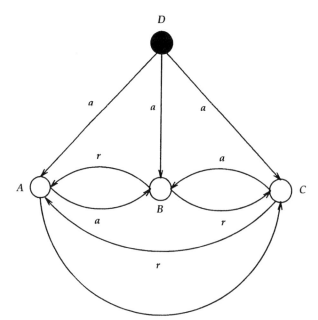

Figure 3.5: Byzantine agreement not possible.

Algorithm 3.2. OM($t > 0$).

1. The value from the general is sent to every subordinate.
2. For each i, let v_i be the value that subordinate i received from the general, or else be RETREAT if none is received. Subordinate i acts as the general in Algorithm OM($t - 1$) to send the value v_i to each of the other $(n - 2)$ subordinates.
3. For each i and each $j \neq i$, let v_j be the value subordinate i received from subordinate j in step 2 (using Algorithm OM($t - 1$), or else RETREAT if none is received. Subordinate i uses the value *majority* $(v_1, v_2, \ldots, v_{n-1})$.

Observe that the algorithm used for the example with one general and three subordinates was OM(1).

In Vaidya and Pradhan (1995) a different form of Byzantine agreement protocol termed as "Degradable Agreement Protocol" is proposed. Degradable agreement is defined using two parameters, m and u, where $u \geq m$. m is the largest number of faults up to which Lamport's Byzantine agreement can be achieved, and u is the largest number of faults up to which degraded agreement can be achieved. Degradable agreement defined by parameters m and u is hereafter called m/u-degradable agreement. m/u-degradable agreement is now formally defined.

m/u-**Degradable Agreement:** Let f be the number of faulty nodes.

- if $f \leq m$, then conditions D.1 and D.2 stated below must be satisfied.
- if $m < f \leq u$, then conditions D.3 and D.4 stated below must be satisfied.

(D.1) If the sender is fault-free, then all fault-free receivers must agree on the sender's value.

(D.2) If the sender is faulty, then all fault-free receivers must agree on an identical value.

(D.3) If the sender is fault-free, then the fault-free receivers may be partitioned into at most two classes. The fault-free receivers in one class must agree on the sender's value, and the fault-free receivers in the other class must agree on the default value.

(D.4) If the sender is faulty, then the fault-free receivers may be partitioned into at most two classes. The fault-free receivers in one class must agree on the default value, and the fault-free receivers in the other class must agree on an identical value.

Conditions D.1 and D.2 are identical to those satisfied by Lamport's Byzantine agreement. Conditions D.3 and D.4 define degraded agreement and are applied in fault situations with more than m but at most u faults. Thus, when $m = u$, degradable agreement is equivalent to Lamport's Byzantine agreement.

Let N be the number of nodes in the system. Observe that, if $N > 2m + u$ then m/u-degradable agreement defined above ensures that at least $m + 1$ fault-free nodes (possibly including the sender) agree on an identical value, even when the number of faults is more than m (but at most u). Thus, graceful degradation can be achieved. Note that graceful degradation is possible up to u faults even when $u \geq N/3$ only if we insist on achieving Lamport's Byzantine agreement only up to m faults for some $m < [N-1)/3]$. In other words, the ability to achieve Byzantine agreement can be traded with the ability to achieve degraded agreement up to a larger number of faults.

Specifically, to achieve m/u-degradable agreement, the system must consist of at least $2m + u + 1$ nodes (including the sender), and $2m + u + 1$ nodes are also sufficient. Therefore, given a system consisting of 7 nodes, one may achieve any one of the following: (i) 2/2-degradable agreement, or (ii) 1/4-degradable agreement, or (iii) 0/6-degradable agreement. This illustrates the trade-off between Byzantine agreement and degraded agreement.

Many algorithms for Byzantine agreement have been proposed under various assumptions about the system under consideration. Byzantine agreement has also been used in real fault-tolerant implementations. For example, FTPP (fault-tolerant parallel processor) uses a Byzantine Agreement protocol introduced by Harper, Lala, and Deyst (1988). Byzantine Agreement is also used in distributed systems to synchronize the clocks at different nodes in the system, set forth by Ramanathan, Shin, and Butler (1990). An interesting practical problem encountered in the real world is a mixture of so-called benign as well as Byzantine faults. This problem was first addressed by Meyer and Pradhan (1987) and extended later in Kieckhafer, Walter, Finn, and Thambidurai (1988) and Lincoln and Rushby (1993). The MAFT architecture is an example of a system designed to tolerate mixed mode faults, as seen in the next chapter.

3.5 FAULT TOLERANCE THROUGH DYNAMIC OR STANDBY REDUNDANCY

A lower-cost fault-tolerance technique in multiprocessors uses dynamic redundancy. In this, built-in capability is provided to detect faults in a faulty processor. When a fault is detected, the system is usually reconfigured by activating a spare processor or spare processing capability. This approach provides a mechanism to produce an indication of occurrence of error during the system operation. This is achievable using either hardware or time redundancy. Once the presence of a faulty processor is detected, a fault location or diagnosis procedure is used. The faulty processor is now replaced by a spare processor through reconfiguration techniques. Finally, error recovery is performed, whereby the spare processor, using typically checkpointed information, takes over the computations of the faulty processor from where it left off. This approach is quite cost-effective and is the workhorse of many general-purpose commercial multiprocessors, as seen in the next chapter.

The following sections discuss the various approaches proposed for the three steps of dynamic fault tolerance: (1) fault detection and location, (2) error recovery, and (3) reconfiguration of the system around the faulty processor. If the fault is transient, the module is not discarded and recovery is effected without reconfiguration. However, if the fault is permanent, then system reconfiguration becomes essential.

3.6 FAULT DETECTION IN MULTIPROCESSORS

Several approaches perform fault detection in multiprocessors: (1) scheduled off-line testing for permanent faults, or standard circuit level or module level coding and self-checking techniques on components of a multiprocessor, (2) duplication and comparison using space and time redundancy, and (3) diagnostics and coding techniques. Other fault detection techniques such as algorithm-based methods and system diagnosis methods are discussed in the Appendix.

3.6.1 Fault Detection through Duplication and Comparison

Besides lower-level duplication and comparison techniques for fault detection, some higher subsystem-level techniques have been employed extensively for fault detection. Low-cost multiprocessors find such techniques in common use in systems such as Stratus, Sequoia, and Intel 432. To provide online fault detection, all critical transactions performed in a multiprocessor can be duplicated and compared. The duplication and comparison operations can be performed using space or time redundancy, and can be achieved in several ways. Each processor of the multiprocessor can be duplicated, and the results compared before communicating to the processor pairs. This is precisely what is implemented in the Stratus multiprocessor (Serlin, 1984), and in the Intel 432 multiprocessor building blocks described in Johnson (1984).

An equivalent way of viewing this option is dividing the P processors of a multiprocessor into $P/2$ pairs. The global common memory which consists of M memory modules can again be divided into $M/2$ pairs. However, duplication of memory modules is not usually cost-effective because coding can provide much more effective detection and correction techniques for memories, as seen in the next section. Comparators can be kept inside each processor and memory module, and results of both computations must match for an operation to be executed. The comparison of results of computations can be performed in hardware at each machine cycle during each memory operation. If an error is detected by a processor pair, both processors of the pair are powered off, and the computations are able to proceed on the $P-2$ remaining processors, configured as $(P-2)/2$ pairs of processors.

In another approach, duplication and comparison are used with time redundancy. Such a technique is needed when one cannot afford the redundancy of duplication for cost, weight, power, and space constraints such as space applications. Specifically, the P processors duplicate the same parallel computation in time on a different set of processors, such that each processor affects only one copy of the result. This can readily be achieved by dividing the P processors into $P/2$ groups of two processors (pairs), each of which compares the results of the pair before communicating with other processors.

Figure 3.6 shows an example task graph that is duplicated and compared for detection of faults. Case (a) shows the original task graph that is mapped onto eight processors. Case (b) shows that the task graph is duplicated, and each copy is mapped onto a disjoint set of four processors. The results of the two copies are compared twice, each time by a processor from each subgroup. In the worst case, the above approach may require 100 percent time overhead. It may, though, actually result in less time overhead than that incurred from idleness in processors in the original task mapping. Clearly, if there were no task dependencies in the original task graph, tasks can efficiently be mapped onto all processors of a multiprocessor, and all processors kept busy all the time. Hence, it is not possible to get a perfect speedup of P on P processors on that task graph. In the presence of task dependencies, though, one often finds processors that are idle, since there are no ready tasks. Such situations give rise to speedups that are less than P. In such situations, one can map the original task graph on $P/2$ processors (as shown in case (b)), get better processor utilization, and use the remaining $P/2$ processors to perform the duplicate computation of the task

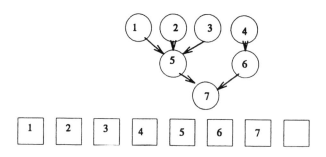

(a) Original task graph mapping

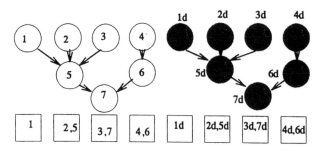

(b) Duplicated task graph mapping

Figure 3.6: Example of mapping duplicated task graphs on disjoint sets of processors.

graph. Hence, in real task graphs, one can observe less than 100 percent time overhead.

The comparison operation also can be performed in software, except that now the granularity of computation before a comparison can be performed has to be larger than a machine cycle, since software comparison takes longer than hardware comparisons. The duplication of tasks and their allocation on different processors of a multiprocessor can be performed, such that the duplicated tasks and their comparison tasks get executed on different processors. The comparison operation can be performed efficiently through checkpoint comparison, as seen in Section 3.10.2. Furthermore, detection through duplication does not necessarily imply time overhead for recovery, as seen later in Section 3.10.

3.6.2 Fault Detection Using Diagnostics and Coding Techniques

As discussed in Chapter 2, diagnosis using a diagnostic program running in the background can be used to detect hard failures in the processors, memories, and interconnection network elements. For example, microdiagnostic checks are run in most conventional computers. This method detects permanent faults but cannot be used for transients and intermittents as the faults usually cannot be recreated during diagnosis. To detect transient and intermittent faults, concurrent fault detection techniques are required using duplication coding and self-checking methods described in Pradhan (1986). Coding techniques can provide low-cost fault detection for buses, memories, and registers. Single parity checks in internal buses and registers are an example of an effective use of coding. Typically, a parity violation results in an exception. The recovery is handled through instruction retry or some analogous procedure. Most modern architectures provide instruction retry capability for most, if not all, instructions. Another effective use of parity checks is in implicating the faulty field replaceable units. A real-world example can be found in mainframe IBM systems where extensive parity checks are provided internally, to allow speedy diagnosis.

In general, coding for computers is a distinct discipline that, unlike coding for communications, must satisfy very restrictive speed, power, and area constraints. For the codes to be useful, any increase in computing speed demands a corresponding increase in the encoding speed. Therefore, high-speed VLSI implementation of encoders and decoders is a major engineering concern. But speed is not the only concern; reliability is equally important. Since encoders and decoders use the same VLSI technology as the unit the code protects, they cannot be assumed to be more reliable than the memory or processing circuits they are supposed to protect. Therefore, unlike in communication world the error detection circuit has to be designed in such a way that one can detect faults in the detection circuit itself. Consequently, fault-tolerant implementation of encoders and decoders is also a topic of importance.

In computer coding, we can sometimes rely on apriori information about error location. For example, single-parity codes are not useful in communications but can be quite useful in computers. In a RAM, fault location can be determined by running diagnosis. Once the location of the error is known, the bit can be treated as an erasure and corrected by a single-parity code. Thus, coding for computers does not always require new, sophisticated codes; a clever use of simple, existing codes may do the job as well.

Error control in high-speed memories.   Because high-speed caches and main memories are prone to soft errors, error-correcting codes are used in their design, and more recently, in the design of on-chip memories. For a code to be useful for high-speed memories, its structure must permit rapid, parallel encoding and decoding. The complexity of the parity check circuit used in the encoder and decoder can be a major factor in determining speed. By examining the structure of the parity check matrix, known as the **H** matrix, we can estimate the complexity of the parity check circuit.

For example, consider a length-6 code, $n = 6$, with three information bits, $k = 3$, and three check bits, $r = 3$. The two **H** matrices below provide the same error-correcting capability, d_0, d_1, and d_2 bits represent data and c_0, c_1 and c_2 represent parity check. The parity check c_i is parity check on d_j if the i-th row of **H** contains a 1 in the d_j column. Since all columns of the **H** matrix are distinct, the code can correct all single errors, but the parity check circuit for $\mathbf{H_1}$ is less complex than that for $\mathbf{H_2}$. Consider the equations for parity checks c_0, c_1, and c_2 as shown below for $\mathbf{H_1}$ and $\mathbf{H_2}$. $\mathbf{H_1}$ requires only three 2-input XOR gates to compute the parity checks, whereas $\mathbf{H_2}$ needs two 2-input XORs to compute c_0 and c_1 and one 3-input XOR to compute c_2. Because of the 3-input XOR gate, the encoder and decoder using $\mathbf{H_2}$ will be slower as well as more complex.

$$
\begin{array}{cccccc}
d_0 & d_1 & d_2 & c_0 & c_1 & c_2
\end{array}
$$
$$
\mathbf{H_1} = \begin{bmatrix} 1 & 0 & 1 & 1 & 0 & 0 \\ 0 & 1 & 1 & 0 & 1 & 0 \\ 1 & 1 & 0 & 0 & 0 & 1 \end{bmatrix}
$$

$$
\begin{aligned}
c_0 &= d_0 \oplus d_2 \\
c_1 &= d_1 \oplus d_2 \\
c_2 &= d_0 \oplus d_1
\end{aligned}
$$

$$
\begin{array}{cccccc}
d_0 & d_1 & d_2 & c_0 & c_1 & c_2
\end{array}
$$
$$
\mathbf{H_2} = \begin{bmatrix} 1 & 0 & 1 & 1 & 0 & 0 \\ 1 & 1 & 0 & 0 & 1 & 0 \\ 1 & 1 & 1 & 0 & 0 & 1 \end{bmatrix}
$$

$$
\begin{aligned}
c_0 &= d_0 \oplus d_2 \\
c_1 &= d_0 \oplus d_1 \\
c_2 &= d_0 \oplus d_1 \oplus d_2
\end{aligned}
$$

Basically, the number of 1's in the **H** matrix determines the overall complexity of the paritycheck circuit. The fewer the number of 1's, the less complex the circuit. Also, the slowest parity check circuit corresponds to the row with the maximum number of 1's overall and the number of 1's in any row to a minimum.

Bit error-correcting error-detecting codes.   In high-speed memories, single-bit error-correcting and double-bit error-detecting codes (SEC-DED codes) are the most commonly used. This is because many semiconductor RAM chips are organized for one bit of data output at a time; therefore, any failure in one chip manifests itself as one bit error.

The codes presented in Hsiao (1970) have been widely used in computer memories and will be reviewed below:

Let's consider the two odd-weight r-tuples. Here, weight refers to the number of 1's. Note that the sum of two odd-weight r-tuples is an even-weight r-tuple. Because of this property, an SEC-DED code with r check bits can be constructed as follows: Here, the **H** matrix consists of odd-weight column vectors. Thus, the double-bit error syndrome is an even-weight r-tuple and is distinguished from the single-bit error syndrome, which is an odd-weight r-tuple. This code is different from the original *Hamming SEC-DED code*, whose **H** matrix has an all-1 row vector in addition to the SEC code **H** matrix.

The Hsiao class of codes is optimal because it has minimum number of 1's in the **H** matrix, which makes the encoding/decoding circuit simple. To obtain a high-speed encoding/decoding circuit, the number of 1's in each row is equal or as close as possible to the average number. The maximum code length is equal to the maximum number of r-tuples of odd weight and thus $n = 2^{r-1}$. An example of this class of code is shown below.

$$
\begin{array}{cccccccc}
\textit{Information bits} & & & & \textit{Check bits} & & & \\
d_0 & d_1 & d_2 & d_3 & c_0 & c_1 & c_2 & c_4
\end{array}
$$

$$
\mathbf{H} = \left[\begin{array}{cccc|cccc}
1 & 1 & 1 & 0 & 1 & 0 & 0 & 0 \\
1 & 1 & 0 & 1 & 0 & 1 & 0 & 0 \\
1 & 0 & 1 & 1 & 0 & 0 & 1 & 0 \\
0 & 1 & 1 & 1 & 0 & 0 & 0 & 1
\end{array}\right]
$$

Syndrome: $S = D \cdot \mathbf{H}^T [s_0, s_1, s_2, s_3]$

$$s_0 = d_0 \oplus d_1 \oplus d_2 \oplus c_0$$
$$s_1 = d_0 \oplus d_1 \oplus d_3 \oplus c_1$$
$$s_2 = d_0 \oplus d_2 \oplus d_3 \oplus c_2$$
$$s_3 = d_1 \oplus d_2 \oplus d_3 \oplus c_3$$

For any SEC-DED code, the probability of miscorrection when triple or more errors occur must be minimal. A miscorrection here refers to an erroneous decoding that results in an erroneous corrected code.

Consider the (72,64) SEC-DED Hsiao code. Simulation gives a 43.72 percent probability of detecting triple errors and a 99.19 percent probability of detecting quadruple errors. On the other hand, a non-odd-weight-column code having the same code parameters has a 24.0 ~ 43.5 percent probability of detecting triple errors and a 98.90 ~ 99.18 percent probability of detecting quadruple errors. Thus, the probability of miscorrection for Hsiao codes when triple or quadruple errors is lower than the standard SEC-DED Hamming codes. Since transient correlated memory failures can manifest as multiple errors this lower probability can be an important practical concern.

In summary, the odd-weight-column SEC-DED codes have two practical advantages: encoder/decoder simplicity and lower probability of erroneous decoding. These codes are therefore widely used, for example, in IBM, Cray, and Tandem systems. Commercially available parallel error-detection-and-correction ICs are based on these codes.

Error Control for Multiple-Bit Errors. High-density memory chips create new reliability problems. One example is the alpha particle problem in high-density semiconductor RAM chips. These soft errors may line up with existing hard errors, giving rise to multiple errors that are not correctable with SEC-DED codes.

The direct method for correcting multiple errors is to use multiple-error-correcting codes. Therefore, random *double-bit error-correcting (DEC) codes* are becoming increasingly important. The well-known *BCH code,* constructed using finite-field theory, and the *majority-logic decodable code* are viable candidates for double error correction in memory. But these codes require twice as many check bits as the SEC-DED codes, and the decoding is ensuingly more complex.

To solve the above problems, low-cost technique using extensions of SEC-DED codes have been proposed in Fujiwara and Pradhan (1990). These techniques use *erasure correction* for errors whose location is already known as a priori. This location information enables a distance-4 code (SEC-DED code) to correct up to three erasures. In a different method based on *address skewing,* multiple errors on the same address are dispersed as single errors in different addresses. These single errors can then be corrected. Another technique for multiple error correction is the *read-retry technique.* In this technique, repeated read cycles are used to eliminate the soft errors. *Sparing* replaces a defective component with a spare one. This *masking* of hard faults requires some additional memory read and write operations for detection and correction.

Byte error-correcting/detecting codes. Certain high-density semiconductor memory chips are organized b bits wide. If a failure occurs, resulting word read-out is likely to have a b-bit block (byte) in error. In this kind of application, it is desirable to have an error-correcting code capable of correcting/detecting byte errors as well as bit errors.

Byte Error-Correcting Codes. The **H** matrix for a single-byte error-correcting code is constructed as follows: Choose as columns of the **H** matrix all the nonzero r-tuples of elements from a finite field F, in particular, from Galois field $GF(2^b)$, such that no column of H is a multiple of another column. Thus, every pair of columns is linearly independent, and there is a minimum Hamming distance-3 for the code. The code, known as *SbEC code*, is capable of correcting all single b-bit byte errors.

Implementing this type of code requires transforming the H matrix over $GF(2^b)$ to a binary form. By using a binary primitive polynomial, $g(x)$ of degree b, we can define a nonsingular matrix T, expressed as a $(b \times b)$ binary matrix. The set of these matrices is a field that is isomorphic to $GF(2^b)$. Therefore, the elements of $GF(2^b)$ can be expressed as $\{0, T, T_2, T_3, \ldots, T^{2b-2}, T^{2b-1} = I\}$, where I is the $(b \times b)$ zero matrix.

The symbols n and k denote the code length and the information length, respectively, of this type of code over $GF(2^b)$. The derived *SbEC* code is an (N,K) code in binary form, where $N = n \cdot b$ and $k = k \cdot b$. Similarly, the number of check bits is $R = r \cdot b = (n - k)$. The maximum length (in bits) of this Hamming-type code is given by $N_H = b \cdot n = b \cdot ((2^{br} - 1)/(2^b - 1))$.

Because *SbEC* codes do not guarantee detection of random double-bit, spanning over double-byte, errors, these codes are not used in computer systems. Instead, computers use single b-bit byte error-correcting and double b-bit byte error-detecting codes, called *SbEC-DbED* codes. Reed-Solomon codes are a general class of codes of any distance-d over $GF(q)$, from which, as a special case, we can derive *SbEC-DbED* codes of distance-4 over $GF(2^b)$. A commonly used extension appends three columns to the H matrix of the distance-4 R-S codes. The H matrix given below shows this extended code, where $\{0, T, T_2, T_3, \ldots, T^{2b-2}, T^{2b-1} = I\} \in GF(2^b)$. The bit length of the code is equal to $b(2^b + 2)$. Therefore, such codes do not exist for information lengths of $k = 64$ and 128 with byte lengths of $b = 2, 3$, and 4.

$$H = \begin{bmatrix} I & I & I & I & I & \\ I & T & \cdots & T^i & \cdots & T^{2^b-2} & & I & \\ I & T^2 & & T^{2i} & & T^{2(2^b-2)} & & & I \end{bmatrix}$$

Both Hamming and Reed-Solomon like codes are widely used in error control in RAMs and disks. Various real world examples can be found in Fujiwara and Pradhan (1990).

Processor error control.   Error correcting codes can be used in memory easily. However, since parity is not preserved under arithmetic or logic operations the use of parity check codes for processing poses formidable challenges. In Pradhan and Reddy (1972), it was shown that effective error control in processing can be achieved if one is allowed to use redundancy of the order of duplication. Consider the parity check matrix H_3 shown below:

$$
\begin{array}{ccccccc}
d_0 & d_1 & d_2 & c_0 & c_1 & c_2 & c_3
\end{array}
$$

$$
\mathbf{H}_3 = \begin{bmatrix}
0 & 1 & 1 & 1 & 0 & 0 & 0 \\
1 & 0 & 1 & 0 & 1 & 0 & 0 \\
1 & 1 & 0 & 0 & 0 & 1 & 0 \\
1 & 1 & 1 & 0 & 0 & 0 & 1
\end{bmatrix}
$$

These 3 data bits d_0, d_1, and d_2, and 4 parity check bits c_0, c_1, c_2, and c_3. The parity check equations are:

$$
\begin{aligned}
c_0 &= d_1 \oplus d_2 \\
c_1 &= d_0 \oplus d_2 \\
c_2 &= d_0 \oplus d_1 \\
c_3 &= d_0 \oplus d_1 \oplus d_2
\end{aligned}
$$

Following are the 8 codewords in this code:

$$
\begin{aligned}
X_0 &= 0000000 \\
X_1 &= 1000111 \\
X_2 &= 0101011 \\
X_3 &= 0011101 \\
X_4 &= 1101100 \\
X_5 &= 1011010 \\
X_6 &= 0110110 \\
X_7 &= 1110001
\end{aligned}
$$

Consider bit by bit AND or OR operation between any two codewords $Z = X * Y$ where $*$ is bit by bit AND or OR operation. The resulting vector Z will always form a single parity check codeword. For example, let $Z = X_1 + X_3$, the bit by bit OR operation between X_1 and X_3. Thus $Z = 1101111$ a codeword in the even parity code. Consequently we can detect all single and odd number of bit errors in the computation because it will result in parity violation. Similar observation can be made for bit by bit AND computation. This theoretical prediction (that coding can provide real fault-tolerance using redundancy of the order duplication, Pradhan and Reddy (1972)) has now been realized in some sense of the (4,2) concept described in the next chapter in detail. This is already seeing use as a commercial product, the Philips S2500 switching system.

Briefly the S2500 uses four processor-memory pairs. Each processor is 16 bits wide, but the memory is only 8 bits wide. Therefore, their is fourfold redundancy in the processor but only twofold redundancy in the memory. The 16-bit output of each processor is encoded into a (4,2) version of $GF(2^8)$ R-S code, yielding a 32-bit code. This code can correct any single 8-bit byte. The output of each processor is encoded by separate encoders. Each encoder produces only 8 bits of the 32-bit code word. The memory associated with the *i*th processor stores the *i*th byte. In other words, the first processor's memory stores the first byte, the second processor's the second byte, and so on.

On the read operation, all four bytes are fetched from the memory and decoded by the decoder, which can correct any single byte in error or any double-bit error in two different bytes. It may be noted that a single processor or memory failure affects only a single byte in the code word; thus, the system can tolerate failure of any single processor-memory pair. In addition, the code can correct single-byte-erasure and single-bit errors. Thus, one can remove a processor-memory pair for repair and continue to operate the system using error-erasure decoding. Any subsequent single-bit-error will get corrected.

This above type of coding in processor control is quite attractive. The only real drawback is that, since the address lines to the memory are not encoded, no error correction takes place on the write operation. In general, we believe that, using non-traditional approaches, such as the one described above, parity check codes can provide effective processor error control. Their use will eliminate the need for code conversion and its associated delay in memory-to-processor transfer, thus providing uniform error control.

3.7 RECOVERY STRATEGIES FOR MULTIPROCESSOR SYSTEMS

We have reviewed various fault detection techniques above. One of the key issues is what specific action must be taken to overcome the effect of the error produced due to the fault. Since most faults are transient or intermittent, a simple recovery procedure may be merely to reexecute the computation. However, there are performance penalties associated with any retry and therefore, these have to be minimized. In high-performance computing, a small sacrifice in speed for retry may be acceptable. Also, the recovery issues are more complex, especially in communicating processes. One has to ensure that the correct execution of one process is not affected by the faulty execution of a communicating process.

Specifically, once a fault in a multiprocessor system has been detected and located and the system has been reconfigured around the faulty processor(s), the last step in any fault-tolerant system is recovering the system and continuing operation. The recovery techniques are different for distributed- and shared-memory multiprocessors.

In the event of a fault occurring in one or more processors in a multiprocessor system during the course of executing a program, one way by which the system may accomplish recovery and error-free execution of its program is by terminating program execution and reexecuting the entire program on all processors from the beginning (global restart). Obviously, this has serious performance disadvantages. If possible, we would like to be able to either continue to execute the program right from where the error was detected and use alternative mechanisms to ensure correctness (forward recovery), or if rolling back the program to a previous incorrect state is inevitable, it is preferable not to have to roll back the program all the way to the beginning (rollback recovery). While this problem exists in uniprocessors as well, the problem is more acute in multiprocessors since multiple processes can access memory and have different or erroneous copies of the same variables, creating an inconsistent state when the error is detected. Therefore, some scheme must be devised that will be able to store enough error-free processor state information at a reliable place from where it can be retrieved and used to restart the program (rollback recovery) from a consistent state, in the event of a transient failure in one or more processors during program execution.

The most popular scheme for this is called *checkpointing*, which involves storing as much information about the processor state as necessary, at discrete points (called *checkpoints* or *rollback points*) in the program to ensure that the program can be rolled back to those points in the event of a node failure, and restarted from there as though no fault had occurred. What exactly constitutes the processor state varies from one system to another, but generally, it involves the register set of the processor, the program counter, the state of cache, and even memory as well, or at least those parts of it that have been altered by the processor since the last checkpoint. These checkpoints are normally stored in reliable storage, that is, memory that is assumed will not fail. Such memory could be a disk or memory protected by using error-correcting codes, or duplicated memory and/or registers.

Checkpoint-based rollback recovery schemes are widely used in many systems. The following section reviews various implementation schemes of this concept.

3.8 ROLLBACK RECOVERY USING CHECKPOINTS

Rollback recovery using checkpoints is a cost-effective method of providing fault tolerance against transient and intermittent faults. Various implementation and overhead issues are illustrated below by considering four specific examples. The first three require specific hardware support for implementation.

3.8.1 Processor Cache-Based Checkpoints

Checkpoint data is defined as the state at the most recent checkpoint, and the *active data* is that which is accessed after the checkpoint. The key requirement is the ability to locate the *active data*. The memory hierarchy provides a natural solution for this problem. The *active data* can be placed in the processor registers and cache, while the *checkpoint data* can be placed in the main memory system. Thus, the basic operation is for the checkpoint state to remain in main memory, and the processor advances past the checkpoint by updating only the processor cache and registers. A checkpoint is initiated by a cache miss that forces a modified cache line to the main memory. Here the main memory is assumed to be stable using ECC, duplexing and battery back-up. A *checkpoint* is performed by copying all modified registers and cache lines to the main memory. In some systems the modified registers are copied into cache. A *rollback* is performed by discarding all modified registers and cache lines and restoring to the previous state using checkpoint data. This scheme is made feasible by using a "copy-back" cache policy. Thus, stores are made to the cache and not to the main memory. The main memory is updated when a cache miss occurs, resulting in the replacement of a dirty line. A line or page is considered *dirty* if it has been modified by its owner since its last checkpoint, and *clean* otherwise. A cache miss thus forces a checkpoint. A write-through policy is generally not used because rollback would require undoing all the updates in memory since the last checkpoint. This can be quite complex, especially in multi-processors (see Section 3.9.1).

Figure 3.7 shows the separation of the active state and the checkpoint state. The basic scheme is now reviewed in detail. Assume some microcode controller controls the checkpoint and rollback processes. It must have the ability to

1. Save the processor registers in the memory (or cache).
2. Flush the modified cache lines to the main memory.
3. Load the CPU registers from the memory (or cache).
4. Invalidate all modified lines in the cache.

Assume that the machine is in a stopped state with the main memory containing a valid checkpoint, and the CPU registers for that state in the main memory save area. The registers and cache are initially empty. The controller then loads the registers from the save area, and the machine begins execution. Data begins to be loaded on demand into the cache. The cache employs a copy-back policy, so writes into memory do not go past the cache (i.e., they are made in the cache). Any changes in state since the last checkpoint exist only in the cache and the registers. These two sets of locations store the active state.

Assume that some transient error is detected (e.g., a parity error on an internal bus). The machine must be rolled back to the prior checkpoint. Since this is contained entirely in the main memory system, the CPU registers and cache memory must be restored to their state at the start of the interval. The cache distinguishes between clean and modified lines, so it is actually only the modified cache lines which represent the active state. Therefore, the modified cache lines must be selectively invalidated. Alternatively, the entire cache could be purged. The next step is to reload the CPU registers from the saved state in memory. Now the machine has been rolled back to the prior checkpoint and execution can resume.

Suppose it is desired to take a checkpoint after the machine has advanced past

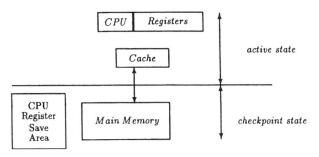

Figure 3.7: Processor-based checkpoint and rollback recovery.

a prior checkpoint. By definition, the goal is to make the active state (i.e., modified cache lines and CPU registers) the checkpoint state. The required actions are to flush all modified cache lines back to the main memory and store the CPU registers into the main memory save area (or in the cache). The trigger for a checkpoint could be a parameter in the hardware. However, the event of a modified line being forced from the cache because of a set full condition must trigger a checkpoint. This is because the main memory, which contains the *prior* checkpoint, cannot be mixed with changes that represent processing after that checkpoint.

The Sequoia is a commercial fault-tolerant multiprocessor that implements the basic scheme described above (Bernstein, 1988). There are many additional fault-tolerant techniques used in this system, which include duplexed microprocessors that run in lockstep mode and duplexed main memory modules. For the purposes of this chapter, we focus on a single aspect of their design which is the mechanics of flushing the cache at a checkpoint. It should be clear that the active and checkpoint states are two distinct sets of memory locations. Having two distinct set of memory locations provides ability to recover from faults that may occur during flushing. In describing the basic scheme, we stated that the checkpoint is accomplished by copying the modified active state to the main memory. However, if a failure occurs during this copy, then the checkpoint state has been partially updated and neither the old checkpoint nor the new checkpoint is valid. The checkpoint process on Sequoia exploits the dual memory banks to provide an atomic checkpoint process that either completes works or retains the prior checkpoint.

In any checkpointing scheme, it is essential to be able to handle failures during checkpointing. The following describes how one such scheme effectively addresses this problem in the Sequoia multiprocessor system described in next chapter. Figure 3.8 shows six steps for flushing the cache to the main memory. The technique can tolerate a single failure at any point. The cache is written sequentially to the two memory banks. A time stamp is written to the memory bank before the flush (T_{A1} or T_{B1}) and after the flush (T_{A2} or T_{B2}). Since the four time stamps are sequentially written, a failure can be described by the time stamps that are different. Using these four time stamps, a failure during any portion of the checkpoint process can be corrected. Table 3.4 describes the various time stamp conditions found after a failure. Although logically there are four distinct time stamps in practice only three distinct time stamps are necessary since $T_{A2} = T_{B1}$. Consequently the recovery steps outlined in lines 3 and 4 in Table 3.4 are the same. Obviously, if they are equal, then the checkpoint processing was completed successfully. If T_{A1} is the only time stamp written, then the failure occurred during the flush to Bank-A. The new checkpoint (Bank-A) is incomplete and the prior checkpoint (Bank-B) must be used. Thus, the

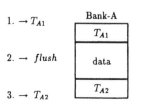

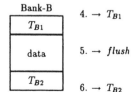

Figure 3.8: Fault-tolerant techniques to flush cache.

Table 3.4: Failure Conditions

Condition	Failure	Action
$T_{A1} = T_{A2} = T_{B1} = T_{B2}$	None.	None.
$T_{A1} > T_{A2} = T_{B1} = T_{B2}$	Flush A	Copy Bank-B to A
$T_{A1} = T_{A2} > T_{B1} = T_{B2}$	Between	Copy Bank-A to B
$T_{A1} = T_{A2} = T_{B1} > T_{B2}$	Flush B	Copy Bank-A to B

recovery procedure would roll back to the prior checkpoint by copying Bank-B to Bank-A. If both T_{A1} and T_{A2} are written ($T_{A1} = T_{A2}$), then the new checkpoint was successfully written. This results in two distinct failure cases both requiring the same action. First, if T_{B1} was not written, then the failure occurred between the two flushes. However, only if T_{B2} was not written; it occurred during the flush to B. In either case, the new checkpoint in Bank-A is copied to Bank-B.

The memory performance overhead of processor cache checkpoint schemes is a significant practical concern, Bowen and Pradhan (1993). One part of the overhead involved in effectively implementing a processor cache checkpoint is the need for using large caches. The size of the cache directly affects the checkpoint frequency.

The larger the size of cache, the less the need to force a checkpoint because of a cache full condition. On the other hand, checkpoint frequency has to relate to failure rate and the ability to recover. Some ingenious solutions to the overhead problem have been proposed in Hunt and Marinos (1987), and Wu, Fuchs, and Patel (1990). Cache-Aided Rollback Error Recovery (CARER) can recover from soft processor transient faults on a uniprocessor by using the basic design described in Hunt and Marinos (1987). One major difference here, compared to what was discussed above is that the CPU contains an internal set of backup registers which decreases the overhead of taking a checkpoint. A major delay of the basic algorithm is the time required to flush all the modified cache lines back to the main memory. This basic scheme is improved by introducing the concept of *unchangeable* cache lines. This allows a dirty line that is part of a checkpoint to remain in the cache without being written back to the main memory. This means that the checkpointed state consists of the backup internal registers, main memory, plus all unchangeable lines in the cache. The unchangeable bit associated with each line can be thought of as a lock bit. Before an unchangeable line can be modified, it must be written back to memory before the change can occur. The Least Recently Used (LRU) replacement algorithm has been modified to select clean lines before unchangeable lines, which further defers having to take a checkpoint.

3.8.2 Virtual Checkpoints

One drawback of the processor cache-based checkpoint techniques is that the checkpoint frequency which depends on the size of the cache can be very high resulting in large performance overheads. One study by Janssens and Fuchs (1991) showed that 50 percent of the checkpoint intervals can be as low as 100 references. However in practice in some systems like Sequoi the checkpoint interval can be several hundred thousand references. However when the checkpoint frequency is high an alternative would be to push the checkpoint and rollback recovery away from the processor cache and into the virtual memory. Many commercial systems therefore include the state of the memory in the checkpoint and use the disk to store the checkpoint. Here the checkpoint size will be larger than that in the processor-cache checkpoints. Thus it can incur a considerable performance overhead in taking checkpoints. Various approaches such as incremental checkpointing have been proposed to reduce this overhead. We now describe an idea called *virtual checkpoints* set out by Bowen and Pradhan (1992) which strives to reduce the performance penalty of checkpointing by using the translation mechanism and additional memory. It combines concepts from two database recovery techniques: shadow paging, described by Lorie (1977) and twin paging, seen in Reuter (1980). The terminology *checkpoint data* refers to the state at the most recent checkpoint and *active data* refers to that which is accessed after the checkpoint. The concept of supporting the active data is implemented by dynamically allowing a second copy of the virtual page. The active pages can be identified by the use of a checkpoint counter associated with each page. In addition to detecting active pages in a rollback situation, the counters also allow the checkpoint processing to be deferred past the exact instance of the checkpoint (assuming a fault-tolerant memory).

A fundamental aspect of the technique is to support two classes of data within the virtual memory system (i.e., active and checkpoint). Each class still supports the traditional two-level store of virtual memory (i.e., real memory and paging disk). There are two important requirements to support the technique. The first is the ability to detect all active pages. This is because a rollback to the prior checkpoint is achieved by purging all the active pages. The second is the ability to make all active pages permanent at the checkpoint time. These requirements are achieved by having a global checkpoint counter (V) covering all the data and local checkpoint counters (v) for individual pages. Essentially, the global checkpoint counter is copied to the local counter on every reference. (*Note:* This is the logical description and does not actually occur on every reference.) Thus, the

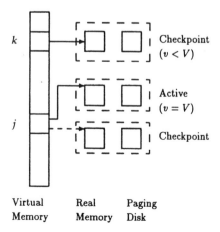

Figure 3.9: Basic concept.

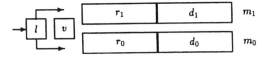

Figure 3.10: Overview of single page mapping.

first requirement is achieved since all active data has the local counter v equal to the global counter V. The global counter V is incremented when a checkpoint is taken. Thus, the second requirement is achieved since all active pages become checkpoint versions when the global counter V is incremented. Figure 3.9 illustrates the basic concepts. Virtual page k has not been referenced since the prior checkpoint. Page j has been accessed in the current interval and has both an active and checkpoint version. Note that in all cases, the mapping refers to both a real storage frame and a disk slot.

To implement this scheme, there are several additional fields which must be added to the virtual translation mechanism. It must have information to distinguish between a checkpoint and active version of each page. To avoid cumbersome notations, the following describes the translation of a single virtual page. This means the notation shall exclude any reference to the virtual page number. For each virtual page, the mappings are replicated and are referred to as m_0 and m_1. A mapping m_l contains mappings in the real frame (r_l) and the disk copy (d_l) as shown in Figure 3.10. Each virtual page has a one bit field, l, which can be thought of as a switch which points to the most recently used mapping (i.e., m_0 or m_1). Thus, the notation m_l refers to the mapping that was used last. In addition, each page has a k-bit local checkpoint number (v) which contains a copy of the global checkpoint number (V) during the most recent reference. The checkpoint number, V, is a global value which is incremented on every checkpoint. Each real frame, designated by r_l, contains a change bit (c_l) which indicates if the data at the real frame has been changed and is different from the disk copy at d_l.

A key feature of this scheme is that the actions of taking a checkpoint are not concentrated at the actual time of the checkpoint but rather are distributed over the time following the checkpoint. This is because, under the assumption of fault-tolerant memory, the only action required to perform a checkpoint is to increment the global checkpoint counter V. The processing for the individual pages is deferred until the first reference to the page after the checkpoint. To determine whether the deferred processing must occur, the values V and v must be compared on every reference. Thus, when a page is referenced, it is either the case where the checkpoint processing must occur ($v \neq V$) or a normal access to the ac-

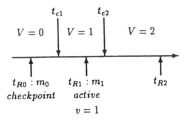

Figure 3.11: Case 1: First reference after checkpoint.

tive page ($v = V$) does. Figure 3.11 shows a situation where checkpoints were taken at times t_{c1} and t_{c2}. Consider the events at time t_{R2}. The active page addressed by m_1 ($l = 1$) was last referenced at time t_{R1} (thus, $v = 1$). The reference at time t_{R2} is the first reference after the checkpoint (because $v \neq V$) and the contents of page m_1 must be preserved as the checkpoint page. Furthermore, the *contents* of page m_1 must be used while the *resources* of the old checkpoint page m_0 (whose contents are no longer required) are used. Once the valid data has been copied to m_0, the l-bit is inverted (to $l = 0$) so that m_0 becomes the active page and m_1 becomes the checkpoint. Finally, the global checkpoint number V is copied to the local checkpoint number for this page so that on the next access in the checkpoint interval, a normal translation occurs. Figure 3.12 shows the situation at the next reference in this checkpoint interval. A reference at time t_{R3} proceeds normally to the active data at m_0 because V matches v.

A rollback is functionally performed by discarding any data that has been modified since the prior checkpoint. If the page has not yet been referenced since the prior checkpoint, then the page is essentially in a rolled-back state and nothing needs to be done (e.g., Case 1 in Figure 3.11). If the page has been referenced since the prior checkpoint, then there is an active page that must be discarded. For example, if a failure occurs at time t_{R3} in Figure 3.12, one wants to discard m_0 and restore m_1. So, for all pages with $V = v$, the v value is decremented and the l bit is inverted. This forces the state to be like Figure 3.11 where m_1 contains the checkpoint and m_0 is no more useful.

The scope of the checkpoint number can take on various ranges. For example, it could be the entire system, in which case there would be a single V for the system. The scope could be a collection of address spaces which would imply that V would have to be part of the process state managed by the operating system. For database applications, it may be desired to have a checkpoint scope of only a portion of an address space. This way, multiple databases could be mapped into a single address space. One possible implementation would be to have a V value for each segment in the address space and maintain the V values in the page tables.

An important concern is the overhead for the test for $V = v$ which must be done on every translation of the virtual address. Two techniques are suggested to minimize the overhead for the test of the $V = v$ equal condition:

1. Add a v field in the Translation Lookaside Buffs (TLB) entry and check in parallel with the TLB access.
2. Purge the TLB at the checkpoint time and only check v on TLB misses.

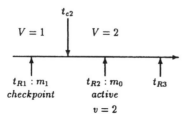

Figure 3.12: Case 2: Page previously referenced.

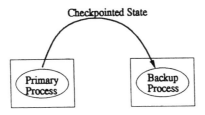

Figure 3.13: Primary process checkpoints the state with the backup process.

The above is discussed in the context of the uniprocessor. However, the scheme can be extended to multiprocessors in a manner similar to how multiprocessor checkpointing is implemented for processor cache-based checkpoints in the next section. Various pertinent issues in the context of communicating multiprocessors are discussed later.

All these schemes require certain specific hardware and/or memory supports for implementation Bowen and Pradhan (1993). The following is an example of software-assisted rollback recovery.

The so-called *process pair* mechanism (Dimmer, 1985) used in Tandem exemplifies this approach. A process pair consists of two replicas of a process scheduled on two processors. One of the replicas is the primary and the other replica is the backup. The primary process executes actively, while the other replica is inactive. The backup process is kept up-to-date by periodically sending the state of the primary process to the backup (Figure 3.13). This state is then copied into the process image of the backup process. This is analogous to the traditional rollback scheme; however, instead of checkpointing the state to a stable storage, the state is saved with the backup process.

The processors executing the processes are assumed to be fail-stop, meaning that whenever a failure occurs, the only visible effect of the failure is that the processor stops functioning. Thus, a fail-stop processor does not perform incorrect computation in the event of a failure. While the fail-stop assumption is difficult to achieve in practice, the implementations use self-checking logic to approximate fail-stop behavior.

Periodically, each processor broadcasts an "I am alive" message (Dimmer, 1985) (Figure 3.14). All processors in the system monitor this message. If this message does not arrive from a particular processor for a predefined period of time, the nontransmitting processor is assumed to be faulty. When failure of a processor is detected, the backup replicas of all the primary processes on the failed

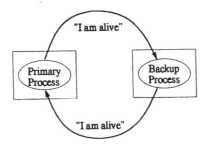

Figure 3.14: "I am alive" messages are used for fault detection.

processor are made active. Beyond this point, these backup replicas become the new primary processes. The computation is performed again by the primary process from the point it last sent its state to the backup process, up to the point where the fault was last detected. The backup process essentially rolls backs to the state last saved by the primary.

3.9 ROLLBACK RECOVERY ISSUES
IN COMMUNICATING MULTIPROCESSORS

Rollback recovery can be a complex issue in communicating multiprocessors because any rollback must take into account all communications and their effect since the last checkpoint. The following elaborates on these issues for both shared- and distributed-memory multiprocessors.

3.9.1 Shared-Memory Multiprocessors

Multiprocessing systems in this category are, generally, tightly coupled and each individual processor has a link to a common fast bus connected to a single main memory. Thus, all processors have equal access to the main memory. To reduce the traffic between processors and memory, each processor is normally equipped with its own cache and can thus access frequently accessed memory locations at CPU speed.

In general, caches used in multiprocessors (as described earlier for uniprocessors) employ a write-back strategy, rather than write-through, to reduce the memory traffic. This, however, implies that it is possible for multiple copies of the same data to be in different caches. This requires that certain cache coherence protocols be used while modifying a particular copy. For example, any processor wishing to modify a copy may broadcast a message so that all other processors with a copy may first invalidate their copy. Also, the copy in the memory must also be updated at the earliest possible time after the processor modifies the copy. In a write-through cache, this modification is done instantly, at the same time when the cache copy is modified. In a write-back policy, this update is done when the cache is copied back because of a cache miss. Most schemes utilize this property of write-back cached processors to make recovery quick, since main memory will not need to be undone in the event of a processor failure. A write-through cache does not offer this optimization, since all cache updates also translate to memory updates, which all have to be undone in the event of processor failure and rollback recovery. Further, the checkpointing frequency will be extremely large since every write to the cache will result in a checkpoint of the cache. Thus, most multiprocessor recovery schemes for shared-memory systems assume a write-back cache protocol.

The presence of caches implies that more than one processor can have copies of the same piece of data, which on subsequent modification, can result in multiple processors having different copies of the same piece of data, resulting in cache and memory incoherence. Thus, many schemes to tag the data in the caches have been proposed to maintain coherence. Both single-bus-based schemes and directory-based schemes to maintain cache coherence have been proposed. Most bus-based schemes proposed fall into two broad categories, namely, the write-invalidate and the write-update schemes. The essence of the write-invalidate scheme is that whenever a memory location is to be written into, a signal is sent out to invalidate all preexisting copies of the same piece of data in other caches before updating the local copy in the cache. Different schemes have been proposed to handle the cases when misses and hits occur.

The second category of bus-based schemes, write-update, is better if writes are less frequent, since they involve delivering write data to all caches simultaneously whenever a write-access to a shared cache block is generated. Directory-based schemes normally use a table (directory) to keep tabs on the state of each memory block. The various schemes differ in the way the table is stored and updated.

The processor cache checkpoint technique described in the previous section is very powerful for building a machine that can tolerate transient faults. In fact, using this structure as a basis, one could focus more effort on the detection of errors rather than a mix of detection and correction capabilities. However, the issue of multiprocessors now creates several problems with the basic scheme. The major problem arises because there may be multiple processes running on different processors and there may be data dependencies among them. This introduces the problem of *rollback propagation* because the rollback of a process could require the rollback of another process, and so on. One technique to avoid this is to remove the data dependencies by maintaining a global checkpoint. This may be addressed by various methods, as the following schemes illustrate.

Consider a multi-processor system, each processor having a private cache, with a shared memory all attached to a single bus. The scheme described by Ahmed et al. (1990) requires three additional lines to support the consistency protocols, as described in Table 3.5. A simple technique to maintain global consistency is to have each processor raise the "establish rollback point" line whenever it must take a checkpoint (i.e., under the conditions for CARER). When this line is raised, all other processors observe the bus line and establish checkpoints. A rollback is implemented by having one processor set the *rollback line,* which causes all other processors to rollback. This has the problem of a very high rate of establishing rollback points as the number of processors increases. However, the number

Table 3.5: Bus Lines

Bus Line	Set by Processor to Indicate . . .
Shared	Sharing of a block on the bus.
Establish Rollback Point	that a rollback point is being established.
Rollback	that it is backing up to the prior rollback point.

of rollback points can be reduced by tracking the interaction among the processors. The interactions consist of a read miss on a modified block, a write hit on a shared block, or a write miss on a shared block. A flag bit vector is used to track the interactions, and allows processors to ignore the *establish rollback point line* if there have been no interactions. The flag bits are also used to selectively determine which processor must roll back when the *rollback line* is set.

Another approach has been proposed for multiprocessors with private caches where shared memory is attached to the processors with an interconnection network (Wu, Fuchs and Patel 1990). This does not have the advantage of a common bus to broadcast intentions. As in the prior scheme, a checkpoint is taken whenever a dirty cache line must be written back to main memory. However, this scheme does not require this event to cause other processors to also checkpoint. To prevent rollback propagation, a checkpoint is also initiated whenever another processor reads a cache line modified since the last checkpoint. The number of modified cache blocks that must be checkpointed is reduced by using *checkpoint identifiers* to identify with which checkpoint a particular modified line is associated. This is a k-bit counter that is a generalization of the one-bit flag in CARER that marked the lines as *unchangeable*. This scheme uses the term *unwritable*. The counter is associated with every block in the cache and there is a global counter which contains the current checkpoint number. A *recovery stack* is used as a destination for the *unwritable* lines which are forced into the checkpoint. This is to further reduce the main memory traffic. A checkpoint is taken by simply incrementing the global checkpoint number similar to that done in the virtual checkpointing scheme described earlier. This number is compared against the block number on all write hits and if the block number is less than the checkpoint number, then the block is *unwritable* and must be pushed onto the recovery stack. The block counter is set equal to the global counter whenever a write is completed. They also allow a pseudocheckpoint to exist for a period of M cycles. This requires two backup register sets and an extra pointer in the recovery stack.

In multiprocessor cache recovery, the frequency of checkpointing must be minimized; otherwise, the performance may be degraded. The following provides an alternative solution to reduce the checkpoint frequency in both uni- and multiprocessors.

One significant advantage of a tightly coupled shared-memory multiprocessor is that moving a failed process from a faulty processor to a good processor can be effected easily. When a processor fails, it can be removed from operation and the work can continue using the remaining processors. If the processor failure is due to a transient fault, then it may roll back to the previous checkpoint or to the beginning. The interesting question is whether to reexecute on the same processor or a different processor. Typically, the failed process may be reexecuted on the same processor and a repeated failure may indicate a hard failure and the need to shift the task to a different processor. In a shared-memory system, this would require activating the checkpoint state of the failed processor in a different processor. This can be achieved fairly easily because in a shared-memory multiprocessor, all that needs to be done is to load the checkpoint state of the failed process into the appropriate processor. On the other hand, in a distributed-memory multiprocessor where there is no global shared memory for communication, the rollback can be complex, as seen below.

3.9.2 Distributed-Memory Multiprocessors

Distributed-memory multiprocessors consist of an interconnected set of processors with local memories which communicate among each other via message passing. There is no global shared memory in these multiprocessors. It is assumed that when a processor fails, the information is communicated to all other processors in the system in a finite amount of time after the failure.

Many different schemes have been proposed for checkpointing programs executing on a distributed-memory multiprocessor. All prevent what is called the *domino* effect described in Randell (1975) as their main aim. The domino effect is a phenomenon where, to obtain a consistent set of checkpoints across the entire set of processors in the event of an error, multiple processors might have to roll back all the way to the beginning of the program. This can happen even in programs that use checkpointing to preserve the processor state as a result of frequent interprocessor communication (when one processor needs to access and possibly alter a memory location that currently resides in the local space of another processor). Thus, if one processor fails and has to be rolled back to its previous checkpoint, some other processors that interacted with the failing processor might also have to roll back to their previous checkpoints, which could set off an entire chain of such rollbacks, ultimately resulting in the program having to roll back all the way to the beginning in order to accomplish rollback recovery. Figure 3.15 shows an example of two processes running on two processors which checkpoint at some intervals and send messages among themselves. When process P2 aborts, both the processes P1 and P2 have to rollback all the way to the beginning.

A recovery line is a set of checkpoints across all the processors in a system to which the programs that execute on various processors can be rolled back, in the event of a failure, to ensure the consistent error-free state of the system. It may be seen that the only consistent recovery line in Figure 3.15, when P2 fails, is the starting point of the process.

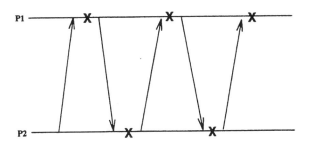

Legend: **X**   **: Checkpoint**

⟶   **: Communication**

Figure 3.15: Domino effect in recovery of multiprocesses.

The schemes that have been proposed to tackle this problem vary depending upon the memory configuration of the system. Some schemes are sufficiently general that they will apply to more than one memory configuration. Others are targeted toward a specific memory configuration or a specific application of the multiprocessor system.

Checkpoint-based recovery in communicating processes. Most networks of this kind use checkpoint-based schemes for recovery. The techniques are of two kinds—*pessimistic* techniques and *optimistic* techniques. The former involve checkpointing by the processors at each communication, which, though correct in the sense that recovery is made possible, is expensive in both the memory used for checkpoint storage as well as the time expended in stopping the processor to initiate checkpoints. The latter techniques tend to be oriented more toward allowing individual processors to initiate checkpoints asynchronously (whenever they *want* to, as opposed to being *compelled* to), but they also simultaneously track message dependencies in such a way that it is possible for a failed processor to recover with a complete record of what needs to be done to achieve consistency. Such techniques to track interprocessor dependencies and record messages received/sent by/to other processors are called logging techniques. Examples of both kinds of techniques will be described.

Pessimistic Checkpointing. Inconsistencies can arise in distributed-memory systems whenever messages are sent between processors in the system, and one or more of them fails in such a way when it is rolled back and reexecuted. There are either messages that one processor has a record of sending to the failed (and rolled-back) processor, which now has no record of having received it, or a processor which failed and rolled back has no record of a message that it sent to another processor which does have a record of having received the message. Koo and Toueg (1987) propose a method of synchronously storing and generating checkpoints for such systems so that at any given time, no more than two checkpoints need to be stored per process in stable storage.

Checkpoints are of two kinds—permanent and tentative. Permanent checkpoints are those which reflect a state of events that cannot be undone. Tentative checkpoints can either be made permanent checkpoints, or can be undone. It can be proven that a system which stores, at most, two such checkpoints at any given time in reliable memory will have a recovery line guaranteed to be in a consistent state when one or more processors fail. A recovery line is said to be consistent here if there are no messages that originate (temporally speaking) after the line and terminate before it. Simply speaking, a recovery line is inconsistent if there is a message that crosses the recovery line from right to left. Such crossing will result in an orphan message when a rollback occurs. Figure 3.16 illustrates examples of consistent and inconsistent recovery lines. The checkpoint algorithm is as follows:

A single process invokes synchronous checkpointing in two phases. In the

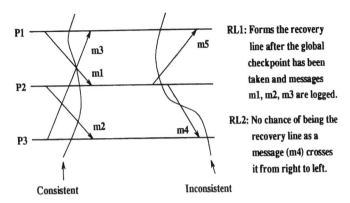

Figure 3.16: Consistent and inconsistent recovery lines.

first phase, the initiator (process p_j) requests all other processes to take tentative checkpoints. Once they have, p_j either could decide to make all checkpoints permanent or could decide to discard them. In the second phase, this decision is propagated to all other processes and carried out. To minimize the number of processes involved in checkpointing, a process p_j will send checkpoint-initiate commands only to all those processes that have sent it messages after their last permanent checkpoints that p_j has a record of receiving.

This is achieved by appending the label of the last message that p_j received from p_i (where p_i is a process that has sent a message to p_j since p_j's last checkpoint) in the checkpoint-initiate command that p_j broadcasts. The processes receiving the initiate command compare the label with the label of the first message that they received from p_j after p_j's last checkpoint (this value is stored in the last permanent checkpoint of p_i). If the last message that p_j received from p_i is temporally after the first message that p_j sent it, then p_i should also checkpoint now since this means that p_i has sent messages to p_j that have not been recorded in p_i's last checkpoint.

All processes, p_i, that meet this condition, then, also initiate tentative checkpoints, as well as indicate their willingness to checkpoint to the initiator, and send checkpoint-initiate commands to all processes that are dependent on it as p_i is dependent on p_j, and so on. Thus, transitive interprocess(or) dependencies are also accommodated. The willing-to-checkpoint indicator is an independent signal assumed to exist in all processes which indicates whether or not the given process can initiate a checkpoint at this time, if so requested.

If for any reason whatsoever p_i, or any of its subsidiary processes, cannot take a checkpoint, the signal indicating willingness to checkpoint (willing-to-checkpoint) is turned off and communicated to p_j, which then decides in the second phase to discard the tentative checkpoints. If all process that are subsidiaries of p_j and their subsidiaries agree to checkpoint, the checkpoints are made permanent, and any previous permanent checkpoints in these processes are discarded.

The system and its processes are set up so that no process that is currently check-pointing is allowed to send messages while checkpointing; that is, checkpointing processes are blocked from any communication until checkpointing is complete.

Rollback is similar, with a single process initiating the rollback signal and propagating it to all the others. The process that is rolling back signals all processes to which it sent messages after its last checkpoint to also roll back with it. The processes receiving the request compare the label of the last message that p_j sent them with the last message that they received from p_j (as recorded in their last checkpoints). If the latter label is larger, it means that they received a message from p_j after their last checkpoints and, hence, have to roll back with it. The roll-back message is similarly propagated to all those processes that are dependent on p_j, and so on. Again, as in checkpointing, this is a two-phase scheme, and unless all processes that meet this criterion and are so signaled agree to rollback, no roll-back actually takes place in the second phase. All rollbacks, when they occur, are to the last permanent checkpoints that the rollback processes have set up in stable storage.

Optimistic Recovery Using Logging.   Under such a scheme, the multiple processor system is assumed to be divided into a number of units called recovery units which may be as large as a whole processing unit (but no larger), and which have the ability to process information as well as to keep track of dependency in-formation between processes, concurrently, while logging input messages to a disk, at the same time. The technique used by most systems that adopt optimistic recovery, Strom and Yemini (1985), is to checkpoint asynchronously while storing input messages (or as much information as is necessary to reconstruct the input messages) in reliable storage for recovery. Checkpoints are not treated as commit-ted checkpoints until all the messages since the last checkpoint to this checkpoint have been logged to the disk. To keep track of interunit dependencies, each unit records its assumptions regarding the events that the current event depends on in a dependency vector. As long as a message which a process received has not been logged to a disk, that message title and the process that sent it are carried in the dependency vector. The vector is updated by gossip between units; that is, when-ever one unit communicates with another, it piggybacks its dependency vector on the message, which the receiver uses to update its own dependency vector. Once a recovery unit has logged a message to a disk, it broadcasts that result to all units, which delete any dependency on that specific message from their vec-tors. When a recovery unit fails, the recovery manager in the operating system examines the reliable log-storage (on disk) to determine which was the last mes-sage that got stored by the failing unit. Then, the recovery manager notifies all units that higher-number messages have been lost, whereupon any processes that received those messages will roll back to their last committed checkpoints.

Optimistic recovery reduces the overhead of checkpointing at each inter-processor interaction while not sacrificing recovery latency, provided failures are rare. Since logging is done in parallel with computation, no CPU time is lost in logging. Nevertheless, the number of messages that have to be logged to disk can consume a lot of disk space. Further, messages that have to be sent to output terminals/ports, and so on (user-visible areas) have to be stalled until all their causal antecedents have been logged, increasing the output latency.

However, it may be noted that Sistla and Welch (1989) show that for the Strom and Yemini (1985) algorithm, in the worst-case, any processor has to roll-back at most $O(2^n)$ times in the presence of a single failure in a n-fault-tolerant system.

With a view to reducing the amount of stable storage needed for logging input messages, Johnson and Zwaenepoel (1987) suggested that for systems that only need to be single fault-tolerant, it is enough that a unit sending a message log it by storing it only in its own volatile storage. Then, when a receiver fails, it can recover and obtain the message again from the sender's log; and if the sender fails, since the receiver will then not fail, it does not need the log anyway. The disadvantage of this is that the single-fault assumption is not always valid, since some kinds of failures (like a power failure) affect multiple processors. Further, since we are dealing with recovery units which could, potentially, be smaller than a processor, when a processor (rather than the network) fails, all the recovery units in it also fail.

Strom, Bacon, and Yemini (1988) describe a technique for optimistic recovery in distributed systems which is application-independent and which allows both asynchronous checkpointing and logging, while avoiding the domino effect. They suggest two optimizations to the sender-based technique of Johnson and Zwaenepoel (1988) to reduce the amount of disk storage needed, as well as to get multiple fault tolerance. Their algorithm takes advantage of the fact that a sender can always reconstruct its messages after a failure by replaying the events of the unit from its last checkpoint to its current checkpoint. A receiver, on the other hand, needs both the data component of the message, as well as the correct receive order sequence, both of which must be logged somewhere for retrieval by a failing receiver. So, if the receive order is stored in the disk, with the data being stored in the sender's volatile storage, there is enough information for recovery for a receiver.

A problem here is that when a sender is recovering, it needs to be able to replay from the checkpoint before the last one, or even before that, to reconstruct the messages that were sent to a receiver process that has not checkpointed since it received them. Potentially, this could cause many such checkpoints to remain stored on the disk, defeating the purpose of the algorithm. One way to avoid this is to make the recovery unit periodically copy some of its input messages from volatile storage to stable storage, so that the older checkpoints can be discarded, and a failed receiver process can still recover some of its input messages. This technique of *spooling* some of the input messages to the disk does not, unlike logging, signal completion of spooling by broadcast, nor does it hold up output messages to the exterior. To know exactly which checkpoints can be discarded, the algorithm can be modified so that each unit dynamically estimates which of the messages needs to be spooled after a new checkpoint and spools only those, allowing old checkpoints to be discarded, while not utilizing too much space in checkpoint retention or naively spooling all messages to the disk. The second optimization reduces disk storage for storing the receive order of the messages. A simple predictor function is used, which on the basis of the state prior to reception of the message, guesses the likely order of arrival of messages into a receiver which requested them. If the guess is right, no logging of the receive sequence takes place; otherwise, the sequence number is logged and the predictor function is run again to guess the next message in the sequence. When recovery takes place by the receiver, the predictor function is used to determine the order of arrival of the messages by loading it with the state immediately prior to reception of the message, and running the function as many times as the count on the next logged message.

3.9.3 Recovery in Distributed Shared-Memory Systems

Typically, distributed shared-memory (DSM) systems are loosely coupled, geographically distributed systems of processors, each processor with its own memory. The fact that loosely coupled multiprocessors tend to be geographically distributed precludes designing them with a physical shared memory. So, the only way to implement a shared-memory system on such systems is by the use of virtual memory, that is, where the programmer sees a single shared memory, which in reality is made up of individual memories residing in different processors.

The first distributed system that was proposed with virtual shared memory was the virtual shared-memory system (Ivy) developed by Li (1990). In this, pages are used as the basic blocks of memory transfer. Each node keeps in its own local memory a subset of the total number of pages from the shared virtual memory. A page fault is generated whenever a node tries to access a nonresident page. A page request is then generated and sent to a distinguished owner node that has a copy of the page needed. Upon reception of the page request, the owner node *migrates* (transfers) the new page to the requester, which then becomes the new owner. The system also allows read-only copies of pages on multiple nodes. All read-only copies are invalidated (to maintain coherence) whenever a write-access to a page is generated. An owner-node keeps a page-table with information on the nodes which have read-only copies of pages that are owned by the owner-node.

Another similar virtual shared-memory system with a similar hardware architecture base was proposed by Fleisch and Popek (1989). The algorithms described below are equally applicable to that and all other virtual shared-memory systems which use a similar algorithm.

A local checkpoint for the above system consists of

1. The contents of locally owned pages that have been modified since the last checkpoint on the local node.

2. The page-table entries for locally owned pages that have been changed since the last checkpoint.

This is in addition to the state information of the local processor, which is also stored with each checkpoint in reliable storage. How the reliable storage is implemented depends upon the resources available, as well as on the level of reliability desired from the system. Read-only pages do not have to be checkpointed since they can be obtained from their owner nodes. Similarly, pages or page-table entries not modified since their last checkpoints do not have to be stored with the checkpoint, either, since they can be retrieved from past checkpoints. A process on a recovering processor is expected to retrieve any clean pages that it might need from previous checkpoints stored on disk, in addition to any dirty pages that were stored in the last checkpoint before failure. The page protocol is set up so that a processor requesting a page from a failed processor, which is in the process of recovering from its failure, is blocked until recovery of the owner is complete.

As discussed earlier, it can be seen that page migrations that cross a recovery line are called *incomplete migrations;* they are the only causes of inconsistencies in the system, since they are the only processes involving internode communication across a recovery line.

Ng (1991) describes and compares various checkpointing schemes for distributed shared memory, which try to prevent the above situations. The first, *global checkpointing,* allows each processor to checkpoint itself independently, but all processors are required to checkpoint *simultaneously.* The independence is to prevent the system from stopping completely to checkpoint; to guarantee that the *i*th local checkpoints across the various processors do form a consistent global recovery line, and that page migrations are not allowed to cross the boundary of a global checkpoint. The sender or the receiver of a page has to initiate a local checkpoint, if necessary, to catch up before processing a migration. Recovery is relatively simple with global checkpointing. If a node fails after its *i*th checkpoint, all nodes are rolled back to their *i*th checkpoints. If a node has not completed its *i*th checkpoint yet, no rollback of that node is necessary. Obviously, the state of the system after the rollback is consistent because there are no incomplete page migrations after the rollback.

Global checkpointing disallows incomplete page migrations, thus guaranteeing consistency. It is the most conservative of the recovery schemes proposed. Another scheme, called synchronous checkpointing, allows such migrations, subject to two conditions: namely, that the sender of a page did not update the migrated page p between the recovery line and the migration if the recovery line is before the migration, and that updates on the page table in the sender can be redone or undone in the event that page-table entries occur after the checkpoint (A *redo* operation is an operation that is redone by a process that is rolled back *not* because it failed, but because it had a dependency on a failed process whose rolling back caused some operations to become invalid on this process. An *undo* is an operation to remove the effects of a failed process on the failed process, itself.)

Synchronous checkpointing guarantees that the last completed checkpoint state of any node is consistent with the current state of other nodes, so that the only nodes that have to be rolled back are the ones that have failed, thus losing less than one checkpoint interval's worth of work and helping to achieve a much lower bound on recovery cost, implemented as follows.

Just before a dirty page p is to be migrated, the processor migrating it initiates a checkpoint, making it a clean page (since the process of checkpointing performs updates and stores a copy of the page). Hence, no dirty migrations occur that have to be redone after failure and during recovery.

Both global and synchronous checkpointing requires some coordination between processes during checkpointing, and checkpointing may be needed when it is least convenient for some of the processors involved. *Asynchronous checkpointing* allows processes to checkpoint locally at their own pace, thus allowing a processor to take advantage of idle machine cycles for checkpointing. Recovery lines are determined iteratively after failure, starting with the last completed checkpoints of the failed nodes, and the current states of nodes that have not failed. After identifying any dirty migrations with respect to the current recovery line, the line which consists of the last completed checkpoints of the failed processors as well as the checkpoints of the still-running nodes, is extended backward until the dirty migrations do not cross the recovery line anymore, at which point it becomes a consistent line and can be used as the point from which recovery begins for the system; that is, program reexecution in rollback recovery begins there anew.

A variation of this, *volatile checkpointing,* not only checkpoints at its own pace, but also initiates checkpoints whenever it is likely that a migration will become a migration of a dirty page. This checkpoint will be initiated by the receiver of the page, with the checkpoint being stored in local (volatile) memory, rather than stable storage (probably a disk). So, whenever a migrated page is subsequently accessed in a manner which potentially could cause rollback if a fault occurred, its contents are copied to the local memory. To avoid copying every single received page as part of a checkpoint, these pages are copied to the checkpoint only in the event of a write-access to it. Then, when a regular checkpoint is taken, all such pages are stored in reliable storage. Such checkpointing is not useful when the node which initiated the volatile checkpoints, itself, fails, since the local memory is then unreliable and unusable for recovery. If, though, the node has to be rolled back because other nodes have failed, potentially it can be rolled back to a volatile checkpoint, rather than further down the line to a regular checkpoint. Each node keeps identifiers of the checkpoints of other processes. These identifiers are updated through *gossip,* and are not always up-to-date; that is, whenever a node sends out a message, it *piggybacks* its last set of checkpoint identifiers for all other nodes (or some selected nodes) on it, and any node that receives the message updates its identifier for a node if the ID sent is later than the ID that it has. This information is also used to determine the recovery line upon failure of a node whose identifier was received by the other nodes.

3.9.4 Recovery in Database Systems

Database systems employ atomic actions known as transactions to maintain consistency and integrity in the presence of concurrent activities. Since transactions are atomic activities, in the event a transaction is aborted, its actions have to be undone to restore consistency to the system. The problem here is the speed at which recovery happens, which is normally very slow because of slow disk I/Os being required to undo actions done to the memory.

Because of the "all-or-nothing" property of atomic actions, an important amount of work might be abandoned needlessly when an internal error is encountered. Svobodova (1984) proposed the notion of nested atomic actions in the domain of structured distributed computations with the use of stable checkpoints. Nested atomic actions form a tree structure. When an internal atomic action terminates, its results are not made permanent until the outermost action commits, but they survive local node failures. Each subtree of atomic actions is recoverable individually. A checkpoint is established in stable storage as part of a remote request, so that results of such a request can be reclaimed if the requesting node fails in the meantime.

Shadowing and logging are two typical implementations of recovery-oriented mechanisms on database systems. The former involves using a new disk page to write the modified version of a database page. When the transaction completes (or commits), the page to which it was writing becomes the permanent page, and is discarded if the transaction aborts. Recovery is fast, since it only involves discarding the modified pages into which the transactions in the active list are writing. The problem that this has is with the manner in which the physical pages are allocated on disk, and the corresponding bookkeeping (page-tables) needed to keep up with the allocation, which could slow the system down. The *disk scrambling* effect where logically contiguous database pages are not physically contiguous on the disk could also present problems. Logging avoids these problems by mapping each database page to only one static disk page (static mapping), with updates being made to that page, and a log of events to be undone during recovery also being maintained. This slows down the system during recovery, since time is required to scan the log and explicitly perform the undo.

Thus far, schemes for distributed systems have been considered which use pages as the *indivisible* unit of memory that is stored as part of a checkpoint and used for recovery. Lin and Ahamad (1990) proposed a checkpointing scheme for object-based distributed systems, which exploits the structure of objects to help reduce the number of processes that have to participate in checkpointing and rollback at a given time.

Their approach involves treating the system as a collection of objects, which may be located on different nodes or on the same node. Object-based systems use entities called *threads* to execute computations. Threads can span machine and object boundaries and can access multiple objects. Dependencies between objects are caused when a thread, which executes the code of one object, makes an invocation of another object's code, using data from the invoking object to execute the newly invoked object's code. On exiting the newly invoked object, some data is returned to the object from which the original invocation came. As a result of the bidirectional interobject flow of data, dependencies between objects are possible, which translates to dependencies between the nodes on which the objects are located.

Since objects are permanent entities that contain data, the authors propose the use of objects and object states as the chief component of checkpoint information, rather than threads, which are strictly temporal entities with a definite life span. Thus, when an object O takes a checkpoint, it records the state of O, as well as the list of objects that have dependencies with O, in the checkpoint in reliable storage. Since objects are accessed by various threads, which manipulate data inside the objects and which create dependencies between objects by invoking other objects, checkpointing has to ensure that such dependencies are also accommodated in the event of failure and subsequent rollback of the nodes on which the objects are located.

The various objects keep track of dependencies between themselves and other objects by maintaining two lists—one which keeps track of which objects should checkpoint with the object in question (the *in-list*), and the other, of which processes should roll back with it in the event of a failure (the *out-list*). Whether an invocation of data in another object is enough cause for both to have to checkpoint and recover simultaneously is dependent upon whether the operations in the interobject invocation were operations that modified data in the called object, or merely read data; and also whether any read data was data that had already been checkpointed by the called object, or modified by the object it belonged to since its last checkpoint. An interobject invocation that requests an object for data that the requester is going to modify should cause both objects to record that should both checkpoint together then onward, and also roll back together in the event that one of their nodes fails. Since there might be multiple calls to an object from different sources, until a requested process actually begins processing a request for modification of its own data from a foreign object, it does not bother to include the requesting object in either its in-list or its out-list. Again, until a requesting object knows for sure that its request has been heeded, it does not include the requested object in its in-list (since there is no point in checkpointing an object that has not been modified by the requesting object, as yet). In case of read operations on foreign data, if the read data is checkpointed data, no changes are required by either of the objects to their in-lists or out-lists. If the read data is dirty data, though, the requesting object is added to the out-list of the requested object, while the requested object is added to the in-list of the requester; this is so that if the requested object has sent the requester invalid data, both objects will roll back in the event of failure detection in the requested object's node and its subsequent recovery.

Whenever a process needs to checkpoint, it first notifies all objects in its in-list to take *tentative checkpoints*. All objects receiving this request first check if they have performed any services for the requesting object since their last checkpoints by checking their out-lists. If so, they agree to checkpoint and notify both the requester and all objects in their in-lists (this latter, to ensure that transitive dependencies between objects are also taken care of). If all such requested objects (both directly and transitively requested objects) agree to take checkpoints, they are made permanent checkpoints in the next phase of this two-phase checkpointing algorithm.

Similarly, when a rollback request is propagated to all the elements in the second list (the out-list), the elements first check to make sure that they have done some work with data obtained from the requesting object by checking their in-lists, and if the requesting object is contained in the in-list, the rollback request is heeded and propagated. Otherwise, it means that the requested object has not as yet been modified by an invocation from the requesting object and hence does not have to roll back. If all such requested objects reach a consensus on whether to roll back, the rollback is implemented in the second phase.

Both the checkpointing and rollback algorithms are two-phase algorithms. In the first phase, a checkpoint request is propagated to all objects with direct or transitive dependencies on the checkpointing object. If the requested object needs to checkpoint/roll back with the requesting object, it propagates the request to all those dependent on it, and otherwise ignores it. If all objects that were requested in the first phase, and agreed to it, were successful in checkpointing (or agreed to roll back if the request is a rollback request), then the second phase is when the checkpoints are committed (or the recovery done). This two-phase algorithm is essentially the same as an algorithm for checkpointing on distributed-memory systems.

The algorithm that was applied for checkpointing was the synchronous scheme. The chief advantage that is derived from the use of object-dependency information over the conventional memory-page information is that much fewer nodes, in general, are required to take part in the rollback stage. Since objects also encompass the threads which execute in them at a given time, a checkpoint initiated by an object will also record the state of any active threads in them. Once a new set of checkpoints is generated by reaching a consensus among all checkpointing nodes (or rather, the objects in them), the old set of checkpoints is discarded, and the in-lists and out-lists of all the objects that have checkpointed are cleared.

3.10 FORWARD RECOVERY SCHEMES

The basic feature common to all forward recovery schemes is that, upon detection of a failure, the system discards the current erroneous state and determines the correct state without any loss of computation. The different approaches used for forward recovery are summarized in the following sections. Basically, two different approaches exist: one relies on hardware redundancy, the other on software redundancy. The hardware redundancy approaches can be further classified into two categories: (i) static redundancy and (ii) dynamic redundancy approaches.

3.10.1 Static Redundancy Approaches

The approaches described next are very similar in principle: all use static redundancy to mask the failures. However, the implementation issues make these approaches quite different from a practical perspective.

Active masking redundancy. This approach uses an adequate level of replication to tolerate the failures, using voting on the outputs of all the replicas. The well-known TMR (triple-modular-redundant) systems use triplication to mask a single failure without any performance loss. For example, Tandem's Integrity S2 system used processor triplication reported in Jewett (1991a).

Active redundancy using fail-stop modules. In this approach, multiple modules of each processor actively execute each process. Each processor itself is assumed to be fail-stop. Thus, if one of the processors fails, it stops executing and the other processors executing the task continue functioning without any performance penalty, even in the presence of failures.

Stratus's *pair-and-spare* strategy discussed in Serlin (1984) is an example of this approach. In the Stratus system, each subsystem is duplicated, forming a pair. One of the replicas is identified as the spare. Each subsystem and its spare are, themselves, made self-checking by duplication. The hardware is thereby replicated four times. All four copies of the hardware are tightly synchronized.

When a fault is detected in a subsystem by its self-checking mechanisms, it disconnects itself as well as that the spare starts providing its service without any interruption or rollback.

Active redundancy using self-diagnostics. This approach is analogous to the above approach. However, instead of the concurrent self-checking mechanism, self-diagnosis tasks are used to identify the faulty processor.

The *reconfigurable duplication* mechanism, an example of this approach, is contained in Johnson (1989). In reconfigurable duplication, the process is replicated on two processors. Their outputs are continuously compared, any mismatch indicating a failure of at least one of the processors in the pair. After the fault is detected, each processor runs self-diagnostic tasks to determine if it has failed. Once the faulty processor is identified, the output of the fault-free processor can be accepted as correct. The use of self-diagnostic tasks instead of concurrent self-checking (as in the Stratus system) results in a computation overhead for determining the faulty processor after a fault is detected.

All the above schemes are redundancy intensive, with overhead as high as three to four times. The following describes forward error recovery schemes with checkpointing with potentially smaller hardware overhead.

3.10.2 Dynamic Redundancy Approaches

Forward recovery schemes based on dynamic redundancy and checkpointing, which try to avoid rollback even in the presence of failures, have been presented in Pradhan (1989) and Long, Fuchs, and Abraham (1990). To illustrate the basic principle behind roll-forward checkpointing schemes, consider a duplex system that detects failures by checkpointing the two modules in the system periodically and then comparing their states. When a failure is detected, a rollback scheme would restore the state of the two modules to the previous checkpoint. The roll-forward checkpointing schemes, instead, try to determine which of the two processing modules (PMs), if any, is fault-free. In the following, the roll-forward checkpointing scheme (RFCS) presented in Pradhan and Vaidya (1992) is discussed.

The RFCS scheme is a mechanism for identifying the faulty processing module (PM) in a duplex system by "retrying" the computation on a spare processing module. Once the faulty PM is identified, the state of the faulty PM is made consistent with the state of the fault-free PM in the duplex system. The computation is retried on a spare module, concurrent with continued execution of the task on the two modules in the duplex system.

Figure 3.17 depicts the execution of two copies of a task, named A and B. Assume that B fails in checkpoint interval I_j. Then the checkpoint signatures of A and B will mismatch at the end of interval I_j at time t_1. The mismatch at t_1 will activate concurrent retry of checkpoint interval I_j, on a spare, as follows. During this retry, both A and B continue to proceed forward into the next checkpoint interval I_{j+1}.

At the start of concurrent retry, the previous checkpoint (taken at time t_0) is loaded into a spare module, say module S. The executable code for the task is also loaded into the spare module. The checkpoint interval I_j, in which the fault occurred, is then retried on the spare module. Concurrently, A and B continue execution of the next checkpoint interval, I_{j+1}. As A and B were not in the same state

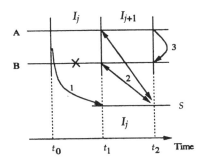

1 : Copy state to the spare
2 : Compare state of the spare with the state of A and B
3 : Copy state from A to B
✗   A fault

Figure 3.17: Concurrent retry in the RFCS scheme.

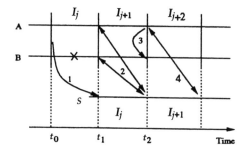

4: Compare state of the spare and   **Figure 3.18:** Concurrent retry in the
module A   RFCS scheme.

at time t_1, they are unlikely to be in the same state at the end of interval I_{j+1} (at time t_2).

After spare S completes interval I_j at time t_2, the state of S is compared with the state of A and B at time t_1. If A and S do not fail in I_j, then the state of S at t_2 will match with the state of A at t_1. When this match occurs, A is assumed to be fault-free at time t_1. Now, the state of B is made identical to the state of A at time t_2. Thus, if A did not fail in interval I_{j+1}, then A and B will both be in the correct state at t_2.

To determine whether A failed in I_{j+1}, the spare proceeds to execute interval I_{j+1} (Figure 3.18). When the spare completes this interval, its state is compared to the state of A at the end of I_{j+1}. If the two match, then A is assumed to have been fault-free in I_{j+1}; otherwise, the duplex system is rolled back. A complete discussion of the RFCS scheme is presented in Pradhan and Vaidya (1992) and Pradhan and Vaidya (1994a). These roll-forward checkpointing schemes also consider potential built-in fault detection capability in processing modules.

The RFCS scheme avoids rollback even in the presence of a single fault. The fault is thus tolerated without the performance penalty of a rollback.

Recently several variations of this scheme were proposed by Pradhan and Vaidya (1994). Assuming each module has certain built-in fault detection capability such as parity checks, exception detection capability, and the like, one can conceptualize four different scenarios, as shown in Table 3.6. In an optimistic recovery strategy, one trusts the built-in detection capability to the fullest extent. For example, consider a fault being detected in module B by the built-in detection

Table 3.6: Four Different Roll-Forward Schemes

Recovery Strategy	Resources Used	
	With Spare	No Spare
Optimistic	Roll-forward I	Rollback I
Pessimistic	Roll-forward II	Rollback II

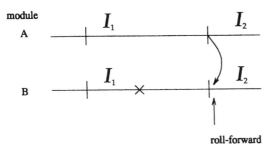

Figure 3.19: Optimistic scheme with or without spare.

mechanism, as shown in Figure 3.19. At the end of checkpoint interval I_1, the state of A may be copied into B and the process could roll forward. This will not require the use of a spare, even though it may be available. This scheme is, hereafter, referred to as Roll-forward I. In the pessimistic scheme, the spare is automatically activated and concurrent retry and recovery are performed, as described earlier, and shown in Figure 3.20a, referred to, hereafter, as Roll-forward II. It may be noted that although the module B has been already suspected to be faulty, a more conservative action was taken just in case A might have experienced a failure which escaped the built-in detection capability (of A during I_1). In this case, should A actually have been faulty during I_1 (thus corresponding to a double failure during I_1), the process will roll back when the spare disagrees with A after reexecuting I_1.

However, should there be no spares available, the optimistic scheme (Rollback I) will roll forward, as shown in Figure 3.19, whereas the pessimistic scheme (Roll-back II) will roll back both A and B to reexecute I_1, as in the standard checkpoint rollback scheme.

An analysis presented in Pradhan and Vaidya (1994) shows that significant performance gain can be achieved with a small sacrifice in reliability. Consider the reliability-performance trade-off curve shown in Figure 3.21. Given the three systems with different trade-offs, one would ideally prefer to have a system that exhibits the trade-off characteristic depicted in curve 1. This system will allow a small reduction in reliability to be traded off against a large gain in performance. The optimistic schemes described in this paper provide the potential for such schemes as shown in Figures 3.22 and 3.23.

Figure 3.22 illustrates the typical performance comparison indicated by analytical formulation (Pradhan and Vaidya, 1994). Here $\lambda = 10^{-6}$ is the assumed failure rate and $c = 0.8$ is the detection coverage. Generally, the mean completion time given a failure that has occurred is lower for the roll-forward scheme for both optimistic and pessimistic strategies. This is an important metric because without any failure, all the schemes perform similarly; therefore, the key question is how does a system perform after the system experiences a failure?

In computing reliabilities, one can assume different values of built-in coverage c ranging from 0 to 1, 0 indicating no built-in detection capability and 1 indicating perfect built-in capability. As can be seen when $c = 0$, the unreliability of

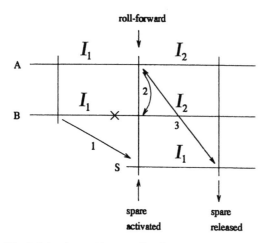

a) Pessimistic scheme with spare rolling forward with all single failures

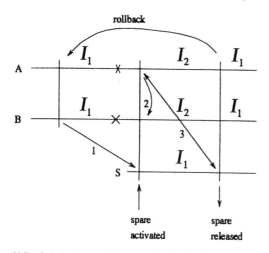

b) Pessimistic scheme with spare rolling back with double failures   **Figure 3.20:** Pessimistic schemes.

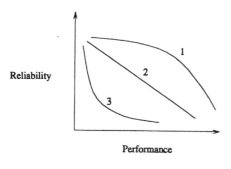

Figure 3.21: Three different roll-forward schemes.

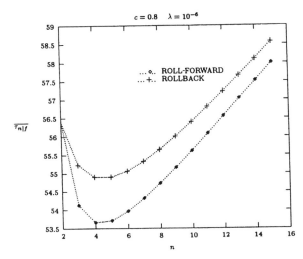

Figure 3.22: Performance comparison between optimistic and pessimistic schemes—mean completion time, given a fault.

Roll-forward I = Roll-forward II and Rollback I = Rollback II. In other words, when there is no built-in detection capability, the pessimistic and the corresponding optimistic scheme have identical reliabilities. Since there is no built-in detection, there is no way to identify the faulty module without comparison between modules. Now, as c increases, there is a difference between both these approaches as shown in Figure 3.23. Here the failure rate is assumed to be 10^{-3} and $n = 10$ is

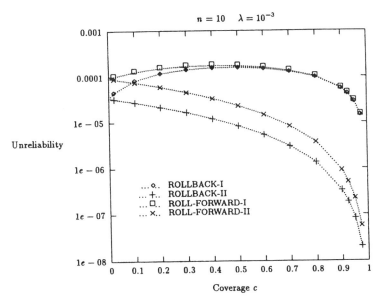

Figure 3.23: Reliability comparisons between optimistic and pessimistic schemes.

the number of checkpoint intervals. The pessimistic scheme suffers from less degradation in reliability than the optimistic scheme. However, this difference in unreliabilities is fairly small. Assuming one can tolerate this increased unreliability, one may prefer the optimistic scheme because of its superior performance, given a fault. On the other hand, if reliability is the primary concern, one may use the more conservative pessimistic schemes. Also, it may be noted that the effect of sparing may actually reduce reliability, given a fixed recovery strategy, but can improve performance. This trade-off is precisely what is demonstrated for various schemes in Pradhan and Vaidya (1994). The examples shown in Figures 3.22, 3.23, and 3.24 illustrate this.

One of the important advantages of a roll-forward scheme is in the minimal degradation in I/O performance. Consider the standard rollback scheme. Normally, the outputs will take place at the end of an interval after a comparison indicates no fault occurred during the interval. Consider, for example, a process which has output x at the end of I_1, y at the end of I_2, z at the end of I_3 and w at the end of I_4. Now, in the presence of a fault in I_1, the interval I_2 will be used for reexecuting I_1. Hence, all outputs after I_1 will experience one checkpoint interval delay, as shown in Figure 3.25.

Now, consider the roll-forward scheme. In the same scenario, the outputs will be temporarily delayed, as shown in Figure 3.24. The outputs x and y are the only ones delayed and all other outputs will occur at the regularly scheduled interval. Specifically, the output x will be delayed by two intervals, whereas y by only one. All the subsequent outputs will take place without *any* delay, as if there was no fault in the system, whatsoever. For example, outputs z, w, and v will occur at the end of I_3, I_4, and I_5, respectively, as shown in Figure 3.25. This is precisely the same time they are expected to occur when there are no faults, as shown in Figure 3.24(a). Other possible approaches to handling I/O in roll-forward schemes have been discussed in Vaidya and Pradhan (1992).

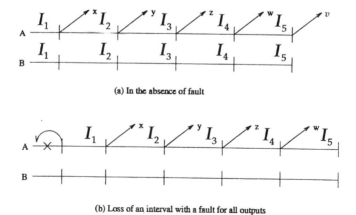

(a) In the absence of fault

(b) Loss of an interval with a fault for all outputs

Figure 3.24: Permanent delay in rollback scheme outputs in the event of a fault.

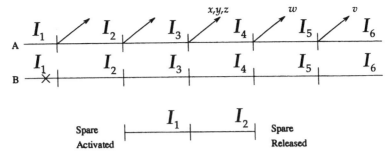

Figure 3.25: Temporary delay in roll-forward scheme outputs in the event of a fault.

A forward recovery scheme similar to RFCS was developed independently by Long, Fuchs, and Abraham (1990, 1991). In this approach also, a task is replicated on a pair of processors forming a duplex system. Whenever a fault is detected, the task is executed on four processors forming two duplex systems; each duplex system starts executing the task from one of the mismatching checkpoints. In parallel, the task is also executed starting from its previous checkpoint on a fifth processor. When this fifth processor completes a checkpoint interval, its checkpoint is compared with the two mismatching checkpoints. The result of these comparisons indicates which of the two mismatching checkpoints was correct, if any; Figure 3.26 depicts this scheme.

3.10.3 Software Redundancy-Based Approach for Forward Error Recovery

The above-described approaches primarily require hardware redundancy. Next, forward recovery schemes requiring a certain degree of software redundancy, as well as hardware redundancy, are described. There are two major differences between the schemes described below. First, the error detection is primarily performed by software acceptance tests. Although there is no guarantee that all tran-

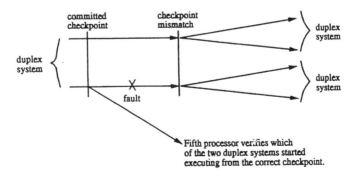

Figure 3.26: Forward recovery using checkpointing.

sient hardware faults in any single node will be detected as in the scheme proposed above, it does provide the capability of detecting certain software faults that will certainly escape the above-described schemes.

Recovery schemes using recovery blocks.   Recovery blocks are a language construct that support the incorporation of program redundancy into a fault-tolerant program in a concise and easily readable form; this scheme was introduced by Randell (1975). The syntax of the recovery block is as follows:

```
ensure  T
        by  B₁
        else by  B₂
        .
        .
        .
        else by  Bₙ
        else error
```

where T is the acceptance test, B_1 denotes the primary try block, and B_k denotes the $(k-1)$th alternate try block. All try blocks, primary and alternate, are designed to produce the same or similar computational results. The acceptance test is a logical expression whose output is 1, if the output of the execution of the try block meets the criterion for acceptability; that is, it tests the output to see if it is correct.

The concept of recovery blocks has been applied in a unifying manner to treat hardware and software faults in distributed real-time systems, depicted by Kim and Welch (1989). Distributed recovery blocks can be thought of as a means of achieving forward recovery (as opposed to rollback recovery), by attempting to recover from an error by using some other means to continue error-free execution of the program from the point of detection of the error, rather than trying to rollback and reexecute the program from a known error-free point. Kim and Welch (1989) describe a scheme for distributed recovery blocks starting with a very basic version and evolving into a more complicated, but more reliable, approach. Figure 3.27 shows the basic structure of the distributed recovery block. Their approach uses only two try blocks and involves two different computing nodes at any given time. The nodes are designated as the primary node X and the backup node Y. In the initial version, the primary node has only a single try block A, which is the primary execution block, while the backup node has the single alternate try block B, as well as the acceptance test unit. The acceptance test unit, itself, has two parts—the timer, to determine if the execution of the block has taken place within an acceptable time since the beginning of the execution by the block, and the logic acceptance test, whose function is to determine if the output of the try block is acceptable or not.

Both nodes receive the same input data, and the nodes concurrently execute

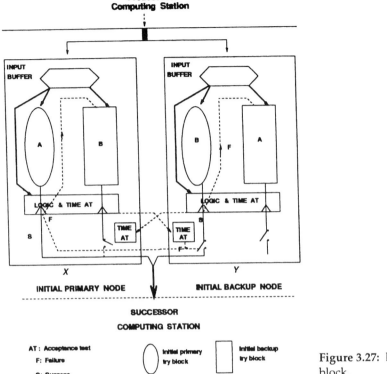

Figure 3.27: Distributed recovery block.

the same tasks. Once the computation is complete, the primary node's output is then fed to the acceptance unit and if its output fails either test (timing or logic), the backup node's output is tested and fed to the output, if it passes. If the primary unit's output passes the acceptance tests, it is fed to the output and the backup's output is discarded. This scheme suffers from the disadvantage that a fault in the backup node can crash both nodes.

Such a scenario can be resolved by duplicating the acceptance test unit and placing the duplicate copy in the primary node. Then, each node can check its output within the node itself, using the backup node only for alternate block results, in the event of failure.

A third approach introduces 100 percent redundancy into the scheme by duplicating all the resources used into a single node; that is, each node contains a copy of the primary and alternate try blocks, as well as the logic for the acceptance tests. However, while the primary node X uses block A as its primary block, the backup node Y uses B as its primary try block and A as its alternate try block. Whenever the primary node fails to produce a result out of its primary block that passes the acceptance tests, the backup node takes over and supplies the result, while at the same time becoming the primary node. In the meantime, the old primary node becomes the new backup node, attempting to reach a consistent state by retrying the execution of the previous computation through its alternate block. To prevent both the primary and secondary nodes from using the same try blocks for their primary blocks at the same time, the recovery block reconfiguration strategy dictates that the primary node always use the same block for its primary block (A), and the backup node always use block B. This means that whenever a primary node fails to produce a correct output from its primary try block, the backup node takes over, supplies the result from the execution of its previous primary try block, and then switches try blocks. In the meantime, the previous primary node becomes the new backup node, first trying to reach a state concurrent with the state of the primary node by retrying the previous (failed) computation through its alternate block, which becomes its new primary try block. While it is retrying the failed computation, any inputs coming to it must be buffered. An added advantage of this reconfiguration strategy arises from the fact that these blocks are designed so that block A is normally the more efficient one and is thus used maximally to generate the result. If the backup node fails before the primary node, it retries execution using its alternate block (A) and does localized recovery without disturbing the execution of the primary block. A problem with the reconfiguration strategy that can seriously degrade performance is that there will be frequent switches between the nodes if the primary try block (A) has a design error that causes it to fail the acceptance test. However, good software design can minimize that possibility. Figure 3.27 shows the basic structure of the distributed recovery block.

When extended to shared-memory multiprocessor systems, a straightforward application of this scheme will involve using pairs of processors (nodes) as primary backup pairs. This will result in throughput degradation of approximately 50 percent, which might be worse than the degradation from a recovery scheme that uses rollback recovery (given that errors are rare). A more balanced approach will be to queue the various data sets in multiple queues and allow idle nodes to choose from the queues the tasks that they would perform from primary blocks execution, acceptance test execution, and alternate block execution.

In this section, various recovery schemes have been discussed. The primary focus of all the schemes except the last one is recovery in the presence of transient hardware faults. The last scheme described provides a certain degree of protection against both transient hardware faults and software faults. More elaborate discussion of software fault tolerance is given in Chapter 7.

Most systems designed for availability do use checkpoint and rollback as the basis of recovery against hardware transient faults, as discussed in the next chapter. However, for various ultrareliable systems, the performance penalty of rollback is unacceptable and therefore, more appropriate for these masking and roll-forward schemes. A natural advantage of a multiprocessor system is to be able to reconfigure the system in the presence of a permanent fault to a smaller system without the faulty processor. Various techniques for reconfiguration are discussed next.

3.11 RECONFIGURATION IN MULTIPROCESSORS

The focus of most of the discussion above is on transient and intermittent faults. In the event, though, of a permanent fault, it is important that the faulty component be disconnected and the system be reconfigured.

In the first approach, the goal is to achieve a degraded level of performance after the identification and confinement of faults. This involves attempting to identify a subset of active processors connected by the same topology as the original topology with a smaller size. For example, if the original topology without failures is an $N \times N$ mesh, under failure, one tries to identify a working set of $M \times M$ processors, where $M < N$. In such schemes, the parallel applications that run on these multiprocessors use the property of the topology of the multiprocessor and can run on any size of the topology. Such an approach has been proposed in the various commercially available hypercubes from Intel, Ametek, and others. The simplest approach of software reconfiguration in hypercubes identifies the maximum size fault-free subcube in the hypercube, running the parallel applications on that smaller subcube as described by Graham, Harary, Livingston, and Stout (1987), Dutt and Hayes (1988), and Li and Fuchs (1990). The difficulty with this approach is that the performance degradation can be as high as 100 percent for the first fault in a hypercube, since one is forced to use a half-sized subcube.

A second approach to fault tolerance in static interconnection networks is simply to view the interconnection as a way to connect a large number of processors which may communicate by sending messages across the links. In such a situation, fault tolerance can easily be achieved by graceful degradation, by redistributing the computational load around failed processors and redirecting messages bound for, or using, the failed processors around them. In this case, the major research issue is to investigate novel fault tolerant routing algorithms that will allow messages to be routed among working processors, avoiding faulty processors. Such an approach has been proposed in many of the fault-tolerant multiprocessors such as cited by Katsuki, Elsam, Mann, Roberts, Robinson, Skowronski, and Wolf (1978), the CM* in Siewiorek, Kini, Mashburn, McConnel, and Hsao (1978), the Intel 432 in Johnson (1984), and the Tandem systems in Katzman (1978). This second approach is appropriate for scenarios where the applications that are executing on these multiprocessors do not need a specific topology of interconnect but need the processors to be connected.

The third and final approach is designing an augmented topology by adding spare processors and links to the original interconnection, such that under faults in processors and links, the original topology of working processors and links can be identified. In this approach, the reconfiguration is performed by substitution of faulty elements with spare ones such that the performance level is kept unchanged. The following sections discuss all three approaches of reconfiguration for various multiprocessor topologies.

Researchers in the parallel architecture area are continually working on newer topologies of interconnect. Clearly, the ideal interconnect from a perspective of parallel applications is having each node connected by a direct link to every other node. However, such a complete interconnect would require $O(n^2)$ connections, requiring n communication ports per processor. The objective of research in this area is development of architectures with low or bounded degrees of nodes; modular and scalable to large numbers of processors; low diameter (specified as the number of hops required to communicate between any two pairs of nodes); and ability to support a large number of useful communication patterns such as one-dimensional and two-dimensional arrays on the topology. Researchers in the fault tolerance area are investigating reconfiguration strategies in each of these static points to point networks. The following sections discuss reconfiguration strategies in various important interconnection networks.

3.11.1 Bus-Based Systems

The bus is the most common interconnection network where all the processors and memory modules are connected to a common resource. This is the cheapest form of interconnection; however, it produces a lot of contention on the single resource.

A number of bus-based fault tolerance multiprocessors have been developed over the last several years. The advantage of fault tolerance in a bus-based system is that processor modules and memory module pairs can be removed easily from such systems when a faulty processor or memory module is identified. Faults in the bus are handled by the use of redundant buses.

In a single bus system, a number of processors are connected to a number of memory modules over a single bus. In a redundant bus system, all the processors and memory modules are connected to a number of buses, described by Mudge, Hayes, and Winsor (1987), as shown in Figure 3.28. In a multiple bus system, several processors (up to P processors) may attempt to access several memory modules (up to M modules) simultaneously; hence, a policy must be implemented in hardware in the form of arbiters, which allocate the available buses (B buses) to the processors requesting access to the shared memory. Two sources of conflicts due to memory requests need to be handled. First, more than one request can be made to the same memory module. Such memory conflicts are resolved by the use of M 1-of-N arbiters, one per memory module. Second, the available bus capacity may be insufficient to accommodate all requests; hence, the memory requests selected by the M memory arbiters are allocated to the B buses by B-out-of-M arbiters.

When a bus becomes faulty, the system operates as a $B - 1$ bus system, assuming the system originally had B buses. The arbiters have to be configured to now operate on $B - 1$ buses.

Most commercial fault-tolerant multiprocessors used in the transactions processing market are based on bus-based designs. The Tandem Nonstop/16 and Cyclone/R fault-tolerant computers use dual redundant buses (called Dynabuses) to connect up to 16 processors. The Stratus XA/R Series 300 fault-tolerant

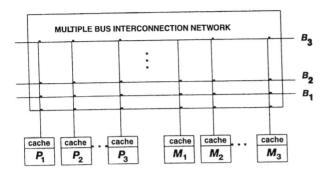

PROCESSORS   MEMORY BANKS   **Figure 3.28:** Multiple bus system.

multiprocessors use dual buses to connect up to 6 logical processors, where each logical processor is paired and spared using 4 physical processors. The Sequoia Series 400 fault-tolerant multiprocessors use dual redundant buses to connect up to 32 processors. The Stratus and Sequoia machines are shared-memory multiprocessors, whereas the Tandem machine is a distributed-memory multicomputer. Fault-tolerant bus topologies in which each processor is connected to a fixed number of buses and each bus is connected to a fixed number of processors, independent of the size of the system, are of significant interest. Such architectures allow for scalability, an essential requirement for multiprocessors. A technique is presented in Pradhan (1985) that allows interconnecting n processors using a fixed number of processors per bus, with each processor connected to exactly two buses. These topologies also provide a degree of fault-tolerance.

3.11.2 Crossbar-Based Systems

While the bus is the cheapest interconnection network where all the processors and memory modules are connected to a common resource, the opposite has a unique path from every processor to every memory. Such a connection can be implemented as an $N \times N$ crossbar switch using N^2 switches, quite expensive for large N. The crossbar switching connection allows simultaneous connection between all processor-memory pairs. Figure 3.29(a) shows an example of a crossbar connection connecting four processors to four memories. In general, an $N \times N$ crossbar shown can be implemented by N^2 switches, where all the arbitration logic is incorporated within the crossbar switch, itself. An equivalent way of constructing the $N \times N$ crossbar is viewing it as N individual $N \times 1$ multiplexers, with the N inputs being wired to each of the multiplexers. Each of the $N \times 1$ multiplexers can be implemented as a tree of 2×1 multiplexers having $N - 1$ such switches. Hence, the complexity of a $N \times N$ crossbar is, again, N^2 elements. Several such crossbars have been implemented, for example, the IBM Yorktown Simulation Engine with a 256×256 crossbar.

One means of providing higher reliability to such systems is through repli-

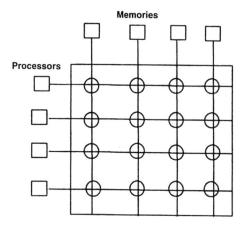

(a) Original crossbar system

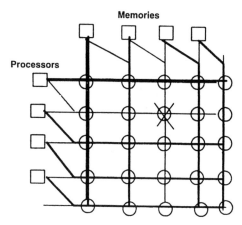

(b) Redundant crossbar system

Figure 3.29: Fault-tolerant crossbar system.

cation of the entire crossbar, that is, by keeping R copies of each of the N individual $N \times 1$ multiplexers, a rather costly scheme. Another way uses an extra row and column of switches, so as to use a $(N + 1) \times (N + 1)$ crossbar with each port connected to two rows or columns of switches. Under failure of a switch, the entire row and column of switches can be disconnected, and the spare column and row activated. The scheme is shown in Figure 3.29(b) with the dark lines depicting the reconfiguration of the crossbar under failure of a switch.

3.11.3 Multistage Interconnection Networks

While the crossbar switch allows multiple processor memory pairs to communicate simultaneously, it requires N^2 switches. Multistage interconnection networks (MIN) form a compromise in allowing for a large number of simultaneous requests, at the same time requiring only $log(N)$ stages of $N/2$ switches (each 2×2, or larger). Many interconnection networks for large-scale multiprocessors have been proposed. Multistage interconnection networks are well suited to the needs of tightly coupled shared-memory multiprocessors, a good balance between cost and performance. An example MIN comprised of a collection of multiple stages of (2×2) switches and links between switches is shown in Figure 3.30.

Several topologies of multistage interconnection networks have been proposed, such as the Omega, the Delta, the Cube, the Flip, and others cited by Adams, Agrawal, and Siegel (1987). Three basic forms of connections exist through a network. A one-to-one connection passes information from one network port to another through a route called a path. A permutation connection is a set of one-to-one connections such that no connection has the same source destination. A broadcast connection is when a single source carries a signal to multiple destinations.

Routing tags are a way of describing a path through the network and for providing distributed network flow control. For MINs, the tags often take the form of a multidigit integer, each successive digit encoding the switch setting for the switch in the next stage along a desired path.

Techniques for fault tolerance in MINs can be be categorized by whether they involve modifying the topology of the system. Some well-known methods of fault tolerance in MINs that do not modify the topology are the use of error correcting codes discussed in Lilienkamp, Lawrie, and Yew (1982), bit slice implementations of the network with error detection codes and spare bit slices described in Adams and Siegel (1982). The above techniques rely on the bit-slicing techniques to limit the extent of a single fault. Recently, some coding techniques

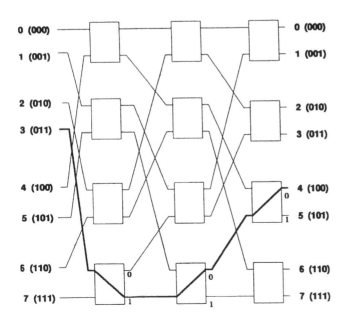

Figure 3.30: Multistage interconnection network.

have been applied using unidirectional error codes to detect errors arising out of VLSI fault models when the networks are not bit sliced but are implemented as a VLSI chip per switch, written of in Fuchs, Abraham, and Huang (1983). Many different techniques exist for changing the topology of the network to provide fault tolerance which include replication of the entire network, the addition of an extra stage of switches, varying the switch size, adding extra links between stages or with switches of the same stage, and adding extra ports.

Any fault tolerance scheme that uses the notion of modifying the network topology usually involves the detection and location of faults in the network, followed by a subsequent reconfiguration. Let us discuss some issues related to detection of faults in interconnection networks. Some researchers have proposed the use of offline or online testing of specific interconnection networks which apply a small number of tests independent of the size of the network, as in Falavajarni and Pradhan (1981), Agrawal (1982) or Feng and Wu (1981). The basic approach in these methods is first, to set all the switches in the network to a straight-through mode, applying a 1-out-of-2 coded input, that is, 01 or 10 input pattern to the different inputs of the network. Under no fault situation in the network can it be proven that the output ports will provide 10 or 01 patterns. Subsequently, all the switches in the network are set to crossover mode, and the same pattern of 10, 01 inputs are applied to the inputs ports, the corresponding output ports observed for 01, 10 patterns under no faults. Under any single fault, such as a stuck-at fault in the data lines or control lines of a switch, some of the outputs will provide an illegal output pattern, that is, 00 or 11 output. These patterns can be used to locate the fault, as well.

Testing approaches to fault detection detect only faults present during a test and are appropriate for permanent faults. To detect transient faults, though, techniques that use parity and error-correcting codes have been proposed for interconnection networks in Lilienkamp, Lawrie, and Yew (1982) and also in Fuchs, Abraham, and Huang (1983).

Once a fault in the MIN network has been detected through the use of testing or coding methods, numerous strategies for reconfiguration of the MIN networks have been proposed. They include replication of the entire network, the addition of an extra stage of switches, varying the switch size, adding extra links between stages or with switches of the same stage, and adding extra ports. The following gives an example of some of these approaches.

The extra-stage cube is an extension of the generalized cube multistage network. The generalized cube is an $N \times N$ multistage network with $log(N)$ stages, each stage consisting of $N/2$ switches which are 2×2 interchange elements. The switches in different stages are connected as a generalized cube connection, that is, the addresses of the switch links in the ith stage either are to the same addresses of the switch ports of the previous stage, or to an address that differs in the ith position. The extra-stage cube is formed from the generalized cube by adding an extra stage to the input inside of the network, along with some multiplexers and demultiplexers to bypass the first and last stages of the resultant MIN network. Figure 3.31a illustrates the extra-stage cube network for $N = 8$. It can be shown that there are two distinct paths of switches and links between any source and destination pair; hence, a single faulty switch or link can be tolerated. This is achieved by enabling or disabling selective stages of switches. Figure 3.31b shows a case where the third switch in stage 1 is faulty. If the processor at input port 1 is to be connected to memory at output port 4, then the two paths in the network

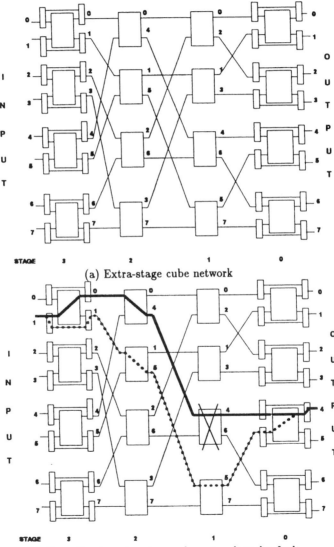

(a) Extra-stage cube network

(b) Rerouting in extra-stage cube network under fault

Figure 3.31: Extra-stage cube network.

are shown in bold continuous lines and bold dotted lines. Due to the fault switch, the dotted path will be selected. Similar methods of adding extra stages to other types of MIN topologies, to provide multiple redundant paths, have been proposed by Banerjee and Dugar (1989).

More recently, redundant paths have been proposed for MIN networks using intrastage links and making 3 × 3 switches, by Kumar and Reddy (1987) and also in Tzeng, Yew, and Zhu (1985). The basic idea in these approaches is to note that in each stage of a shuffle exchange MIN, there are subsets of switches (called conjugate subsets) that lead to the same subset of destinations. Switches in a conjugate subset are chained together in a loop using a third port of a 3 × 3 switch. Figure 3.32a shows an example of such a connection. When a switch is unable to process a request because of a faulty switch or link in the next stage, it can route the request via the auxiliary links to the next switch in the conjugate subset loop. The next switch can then make a connection to a nonfaulty switch of the next stage and lead to the same destination. Figure 3.32b shows an example rerouting from a processor connected at input port 9 to the memory connected to the output port 4, under a fault in the switch marked.

Numerous other proposals for fault tolerance of multistage interconnection networks exist. The reader is encouraged to read an excellent survey in Adams, Agrawal, and Siegel (1987) for more details.

3.11.4 Hypercube Networks

Hypercube multicomputers have recently offered a cost-effective and feasible approach to supercomputing by connecting a large number ($P = 2^d$) of processors with local memory, using direct links, according to the binary *d-cube* interconnection pattern discussed in Seitz (1985). Figure 3.33 shows the topology of a 16-processor (four-dimensional) hypercube. Numerous hypercube-based multiprocessors are commercially available from Intel Scientific Computers, NCUBE, Ametek, and others.

Several researchers have looked at the problem of fault tolerance in hypercube architectures using hardware approaches. Rennels (1986) proposed a reconfiguration scheme where the processors in a *d*-dimensional hypercube are augmented by an additional port in the $(d + 1)$th-dimension. The extra port is used to reach a spare, as shown in Figure 3.34a. The spare processor is to be effectively connected to the additional port of every processor of the hypercube, so that when a processor fails, it can take over the failed processor's tasks, activating the appropriate links to the faulty processor's neighbors in the hypercube topology. However, such a simple-minded approach would involve the spare processor having a degree of $N = 2^d$, clearly unacceptable. The solution to that problem was to use a set of VLSI crossbar switches to implement the connection. Consider a 16-processor hypercube, so each processor would normally have four ports. An extra port is added for fault tolerance. The 16 processors are subdivided into two groups of 8-processor subcubes. The eight connections coming out of each of the

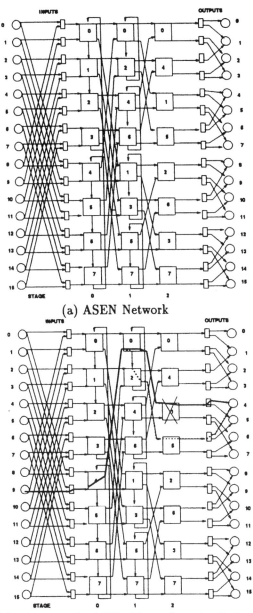

(a) ASEN Network

(b) Rerouting in ASEN Network under fault

Figure 3.32: Augmented shuffle exchange network (ASEN) for $N = 16$.

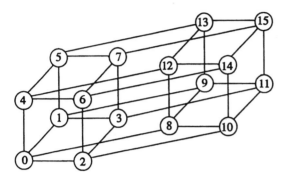

Figure 3.33: A 16-processor hypercube.

processors of a subcube are connected to a 8×5 crossbar chip. Each subcube of 8 processors has a corresponding crossbar switch (hence, a total of two crossbar chips are used). The outputs of the two crossbars are connected together to the five ports of the spare processor. When a processor in one subcube fails (e.g., processor 4), the spare needs to activate the four connections of the faulty subcube via the corresponding crossbar (e.g., to processors 0,5,6), and one link of the other crossbar switches (e.g., processor 12) in the other subcubes to which the faulty processor was connected, shown in Figure 3.34b. The above scheme was extended to use multiple spares where a spare processor was assigned to a subcube of processors, instead of the entire hypercube.

Recently, Banerjee, has reported two hardware approaches for reconfiguring a hypercube. (1990a). In the first hardware scheme for reconfiguration, it is assumed that spare processors can be attached to specific processors of the hypercube. In this approach, two types of nodes (P-nodes and S-nodes) are designated in the hypercube. Figure 3.35a shows an example 16-processor hypercube where four of the nodes (0,7,9, and 14, shown by double circles) are S-nodes, the rest being P-nodes. A P-node consists of a computation processor (CPU) connected through an internal bus to a local memory, and a message routing logic consisting of the DMA unit and a $(d + 1) \times (d + 1)$ crossbar switch for a 2^d-processor hypercube. An S-node consists of two copies of a CPU and local memory connected to two internal buses. The DMA and message routing logic is shared between the two processing units, one of which is active under normal conditions, the other a standby spare. Under failure of any processing element (CPU or local memory), either within the S-node or in a nearby P-node, the spare processor-memory/bus from the corresponding S-node is brought on line. The routing channels and the message routing logic of the S-node are shared between the active and spare processors through the internal buses.

A natural question that arises is how best to allocate the spare processing elements in the hypercube. Clearly, by allocating one spare for every processor, every node in the hypercube would become an S-node; hence, it would be easy to perform reconfiguration under faults if this scheme were not so expensive, requiring a hardware overhead of at least 100 percent. If a spare processor is as-

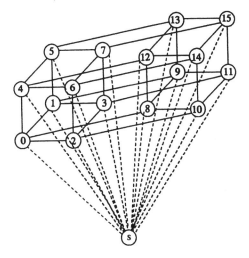

(a) Conceptual addition of spare to each processor through extra port

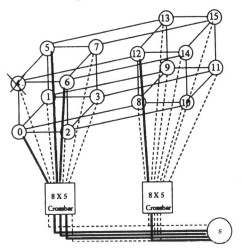

(b) Implementation of extra port connection using crossbar switches

Figure 3.34: Hypercube reconfiguration through extra port.

signed to a set of active processors, then the hardware overhead can be minimized. The spare embedding problem is to map the S-nodes onto a hypercube
topology such that each processor in the system is adjacent to (i.e., at most, one
hop away) at least one spare processor. Appropriate algorithms for cost-effective
embedding of spares in hypercubes have been developed. Figure 3.35a shows
an example embedding of four spares (S-nodes) on a 16-processor hypercube
(S-nodes shown as double circles).

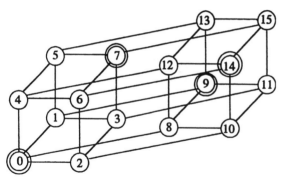

(a) Embedding of spares on hypercube

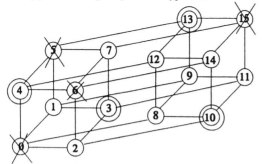

(b) Location of four faults in hypercube

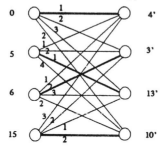

U Nodes   V Nodes
(Faults)   (Spares)

(c) Reconfiguration graph

Figure 3.35: Hypercube reconfiguration by node sparing.

Given a set of multiple faults in such a system, a reconfiguration strategy has been developed based on a bipartite graph model. The nodes of the bipartite graph correspond to faulty nodes and available spare nodes of the hypercube, and edges between them measure the distance between the nodes that need to be traversed between them. The reconfiguration algorithm which uses a weighted bipartite matching algorithm gives an optimal mapping of faulty nodes to spare nodes by minimizing the total dilation of mapping logical links across multiple physical links. Figure 3.35b shows an example hypercube with four faults located at nodes 0,5,6,15. Figure 3.35c shows the reconfiguration of a 16-processor hypercube under four failures. The fault in node 0 is replaced by a spare on 4, the fault in node 3 is replaced by a spare on 12, the fault in node 6 is replaced by a spare on 2, and the fault in node 15 is replaced by a spare on 10.

Fault-tolerant routing in hypercube networks.   It was mentioned earlier that one approach to fault tolerance in static interconnection networks is simply to view the interconnection as a way to connect a large number of processors which may communicate by sending messages across the links. In such a situation, fault tolerance can easily be achieved by graceful degradation, by redistributing the computational load around failed processors and redirecting messages bound for, or using the failed processors around them, as revealed in Salmon, Callahan, Flower, and Kolawa (1988), and Peercy and Banerjee (1992).

Numerous researchers have proposed rerouting algorithms for faulty hypercubes. First presented is the standard fixed routing procedure called the e-cube routing for hypercubes shown in Sullivan and Bashkow (1977). In the e-cube algorithm, the bit differences between the source and destination of a path are resolved from low dimension to high. Figure 3.36a shows an e-cube routing path in a 16-processor hypercube. Under faults in a hypercube, the messages have to reroute using a path such as the one shown in Figure 3.36b.

Chen and Shin (1988) have proposed an adaptive algorithm for routing. In this, each message carries a header, an ordered list of dimensions yet to traverse, and an n-bit tag. The list is initialized to the order of the dimensions that would be traversed by the e-cube routing. At each node in the path, the links are tried in the order given in the list until a fault-free one is found. The good link is taken, and that dimension is struck from the list. If all the dimensions in the list put the path on faulty links, then a spare dimension is chosen from outside the list. The link on that dimension is taken, and the list is appended by adding that dimension onto the end. The tag is used to mark dimensions derived from entirely blocked lists, or taken as spares so that a bouncing effect does not occur.

These rerouting algorithms will fail for more than $n - 1$ faulty nodes in a 2^n-processor hypercube. Chen and Shin (1990) proposed a depth-first search algorithm to deal with the problem of routing between any two connected nodes in a hypercube. In such a case, a set of faulty components encountered before has to be added to the message, and a more complicated procedure is required to guide the backtracking whenever it is forced to backtrack from a dead end. Instead of keeping track of the entire path traveled, the depth-first search routing can be implemented as a stack, in which case the operations required for backtracking are simplified. But, additional provisions are needed to ensure that each node will not be visited more than once, a procedure illustrated in Figure 3.36b. In the example, it is assumed that a message needs to be routed from node 0 (address 0000) to node 15 (address 1111). Since the node addresses differ in all dimensions, each dimension of the hypercube

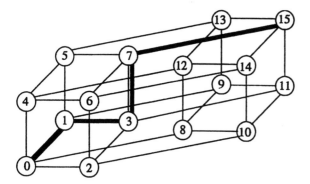

(a) E-cube routing on fault-free hypercube

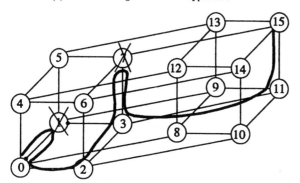

(b) Adaptive routing on faulty hypercube

Figure 3.36: Routing in fault-free and faulty hypercubes.

needs to be traversed. The e-cube routing routes the messages from lowest dimension to highest dimension in dimension order, and hence, would take the path (0-1-3-7-15). Since node 1 is faulty, the path (0-1) is blocked. So, the routing will backtrack from that solution and save dimension 0 on the stack, and try a path of the next dimension the addresses differ in, namely, dimension 1, and hence take path (0-2). From this node 2, it will try to go along dimension 0 again and take path (2-3). At this point, the dimensions 0 and 1 have been traversed. Next, dimension 2 will be attempted, namely path (3-7). However, since node 7 is faulty, that route will be backtracked, and dimension 2 will be kept on the stack. Next, dimension 3 is tried, which will lead to path (3-11). Until now, the dimensions 0,1,3 have been traversed. Finally, the dimension 2 that remains to be traversed will be attempted; hence, the path (11-15) will be selected. The final complete routing is (0-2-3-11-15).

Other rerouting algorithms for hypercubes have been proposed by Chow, Madan, and Peterson (1987), Gordon and Stout (1988), and Lee and Hayes (1988). It should be noted that a VLSI chip, called the hyperswitch, has been developed at the Jet Propulsion Laboratory to implement some of the above backtracking ideas in hypercube routing and has been used in a prototype fault-tolerant hypercube computer, discussed in Chow, Madan, and Peterson (1987). It may also be noted that generalizations of hypercubes and routing algorithms have been proposed in Bhuyan and Agrawal (1989). Hybrid networks using hypercubes and de Bruijn graphs are those proposed in Ganesan and Pradhan (1993) and Chen, Agrawal and Burke (1993). Robust, these hybrid networks overcome some of the shortcomings of hypercube which, therefore, make them attractive candidates for multiprocessor design.

3.11.5 de Bruijn Networks

Another class of networks that can provide fault tolerance is the de Bruijn network. A de Bruijn network can be defined for any number of nodes (Pradhan 1981). In a n node network every node i is connected to nodes $2i \bmod n$ and $(2i + 1) \bmod n$. Each node has 4 connections per node as shown in Figure 3.37. It may be noted that de Bruijn graph networks have inherent fault tolerance (Pradhan, 1981), unlike the shuffle exchange networks. In addition, the de Bruijn graph-based VLSI network has been shown to be more powerful in admitting computationally important subnetworks (Samanthan and Pradhan 1989). This is illustrated in Table 3.7 when it is compared to the shuffle exchange network. For example, both binary trees and end-to-end binary trees are easily admitted by de Bruijn networks with perfect dialation, as shown in Figures 3.37 and 3.38. Consider a 16-node de Bruijn network, as illustrated in Figure 3.37. In this network are embedded two complete binary trees, as shown in Figure 3.38a. The important point to note here is that the leaf nodes of these two trees are disjoint. For the first tree, the leaf nodes span 8 through 15, whereas for the second tree, they span nodes 0 through 7. Therefore, in the event of a node or link fault, one can still find a complete binary tree with just one less node—a minimal degradation. Interestingly, unlike shuffle exchange and hypercube, the de Bruijn graph admits end-to-end binary trees, as shown in Figure 3.38b for a 16-node de Bruijn graph. These networks admit simple partition and layout for VLSI implementation, Samantham and Pradhan (1989); Collins (1993). In the presence of faults, the de Bruijn network allows algorithmic routing and detour routing (Pradhan, 1985). Although no wide-scale use of the de Bruijn network as a multiprocessor network has been reported, an 8,192-node de Bruijn VLSI network has been implemented for use in the Galileo project (Collins, 1993).

Table 3.7: Summary of Parameters

Parameter	Hypercube	de Bruijn	Shuffle Exchange	Hyper-deBruijn
Nodes	$N = 2^{m+n}$	$N = 2^{m+n}$	$N = 2^{m+n}$	$N = 2^{m+n}$
Degree	$m + n$	4	3	$m + 4$
Diameter	$m + n$	$m + n$	$m + n$	$m + n$
Fault Tolerance	$m + n - 1$	1	0	$m + 3$
Embeddings				
Cycles	Even Cycles	Pancyclic	Not Pancyclic	Pancyclic
Mesh	Yes	No	No	Yes
Binary Tree	Two $(N/2 - 1)$-node trees	$(N - 1)$-node tree	No	$(N/2 - 1)$-node tree
Mesh of Tress	Yes	No	No	Yes

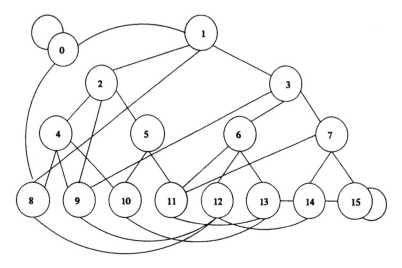

Figure 3.37: de Bruijn network of 16 nodes.

The network shown in Figure 3.39 illustrates the hyper-deBruijn network of Ganesan and Pradhan (1993), constructed by forming a Cartesian product of hypercubes and de Bruijn graph multiprocessor networks. The network derived from this product compares favorably with hypercubes, as shown in Table 3.7.

3.11.6 Mesh Networks

Recently, a number of two-dimensional mesh-based networks have been proposed, owing to their advantages of scalability, modularity, expandability, and degree boundedness. Figure 3.40 shows 16 processors arranged as a two-dimensional mesh. A modification of the mesh is a torus where there are also end-around connections for the processors at the extreme X and Y direction. Commercial multiprocessor products based on the mesh and torus have been announced from Ametek and Intel Scientific Computers. Mesh-based designs have been used in the ILLIAC IV computer, Intel Paragon, Cray T3D, and the Goodyear MPP massively parallel computer.

Fortes and Raghavendra (1984) proposed a fault tolerance strategy for mesh networks based on the philosophy of providing graceful degradation. For two-dimensional arrays of processors, they proposed the deletion of an entire row or column of processors on which a faulty processor belongs. Figure 3.41 shows the basic organization of the reconfiguration scheme with the help of the special switches shown in the bottom of the figure. Given a set of faulty processors, a set of rows and columns are deleted from the mesh to have a fault-free submesh. Such methods conventionally have been used in reconfiguring memory systems. Unfortunately, such a scheme degrades the performance significantly for a single

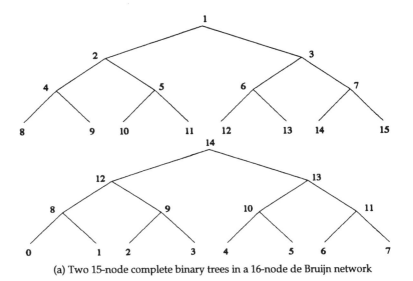

(a) Two 15-node complete binary trees in a 16-node de Bruijn network

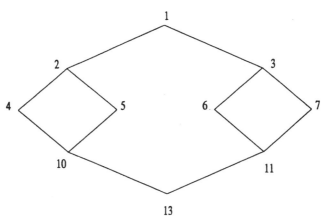

(b) End-to-end binary tree in a 16-node de Bruijn network

Figure 3.38: de Bruijn multiprocessor network.

fault, since it effectively wipes out a large number of active processors (a row or column) during reconfiguration. The spare utilization is, therefore, quite low in this approach.

Sami and Stefanalli (1986) have proposed a set of sparing techniques for two-dimensional arrays by using some complex node switching circuitry. In the direct reconfiguration method, in addition to the $N \times N$ array of normal processors, some extra rows and columns of processors are used. Reconfiguration is attempted along a specific direction by performing a global renaming of all processors in which logical indices of processors (i, j) are mapped onto physical indices

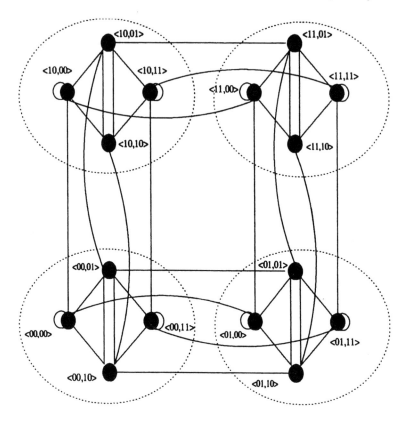

Figure 3.39: Hyper-de Bruijn network.

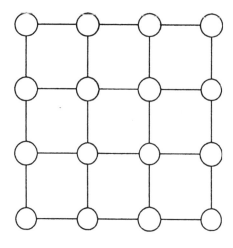

Figure 3.40: A 16-processor mesh.

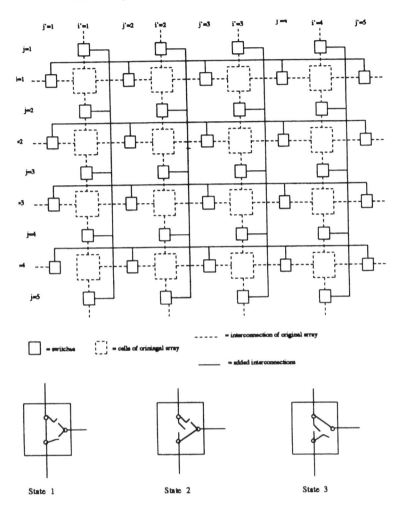

Figure 3.41: Mesh reconfiguration by row or column elimination.

(k, h) of working processors using a mapping function. Given a faulty processor (i, j), it is necessary to decide on a direction (horizontal or vertical) for reconfiguration; that is, whether the faulty cell will be replaced by the spare cell in the horizontal or vertical direction by a bypass link in the horizontal or vertical direction. The order in which horizontal and vertical reconfiguration steps are performed is critical. The strategy recommended was to classify the first fault in a column when scanning from bottom up, as a vertical fault, and all other faults as horizontal faults. If no row has more than one horizontal fault, reconfiguration is possible. Figure 3.42 shows an example of a direct reconfiguration on a 5×5 array of cells augmented by an extra row and an extra column. To support such reconfiguration, one needs to provide some additional links as switches.

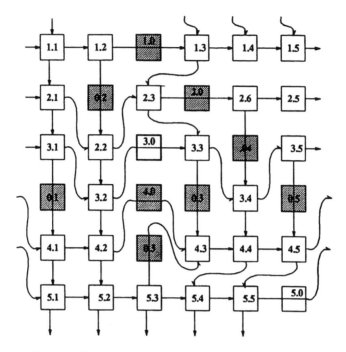

Figure 3.42: Mesh reconfiguration by logical mapping.

The above scheme can tolerate only certain fault patterns. In any row, only a single fault can be marked as a horizontal one, and in any column, only one fault can be marked as a vertical fault. Another approach that was proposed to increase the spare utilization was using the concept of *fault stealing*. The main approach is still the notion of global renaming. However, instead of restricting the search for the spares in the same row or column in which the fault occurs, as in the previous approach, one allows for stealing a spare from an adjacent row following some simple rules.

Numerous other reconfiguration methods for mesh networks have been proposed in Batcher (1980), Rosenberg (1983), and Belkhale and Banerjee (1992).

3.11.7 Tree Networks

While hypercube networks can connect P processors using a degree of $log(P)$ and maximum distance of $log(P)$, the mesh can connect P processors using a degree of 4, and maximum distance of $\sqrt{P}$. Tree networks can connect $P - 1$ processors using degree 3, and maximum distance $2.(log(P) - 1)$. Tree-based machines are configured as a binary tree where each node is connected to two children and to its parent in a recursive manner. Such an architecture is excellent for recursive parallel algorithms that use divide-and-conquer techniques. Several tree-based machines have been proposed for a variety of applications.

Numerous researchers have worked on fault tolerance in tree networks. One of the initial reconfigurable tree proposals was made by Hayes (1974) who developed optimal one-fault tolerant trees. The basic approach starts with a complete binary tree of m levels, using m spares, one per level. Some extra links are provided from the spares of a certain level to nodes of the binary tree of the next higher level such that under failure, the faulty node and its links are replaced by the spare and some redundant links.

Raghavendra, Avizienis, and Ercegovac (1984) have expanded on these proposals by adding sufficient redundant links to tolerate multiple failures. One spare is used per level of the tree on the right of the tree. Each node of the tree, including the spares; connects to its two children and also to the two children of its left neighbor and to one of the children of its right neighbor. Figure 3.43a shows the basic reconfiguration scheme. When a processor fails, all links of a processor to the right of it are readjusted to right neighbors. In order to decrease the complexity of the redundant connections, two decoupling networks can be used, as shown in Figure 3.43b. The schemes have been extended with multiple spares per level, where one spare is set per 2^i nodes.

3.12 OTHER ISSUES

In this section, we review three important additional areas in multiprocessor fault-tolerance theory and practice.

3.12.1 Bounds on Performance

One approach to fault tolerance in network-based parallel computers is to assign the computational load of a failed processor to a fault-free processor. All messages that are bound for the failed processor must be redirected to the fault-free processor. Further, all messages using the failed processor in transit should be redirected to use a path around the failed processor. It is inevitable that application programs on a parallel computer so reconfigured run slower than they would on the same parallel computer that is completely fault-free. A measure of this degradation in performance is called *slowdown*, defined to be the minimum value S, such that any computation that takes T steps on the fault-free computer can be performed in, at most, $S \times T$ steps in the reconfigured faulty computer. In general, the slowdown incurred will be a function of the number of faults in the system, how these faults are situated, and what algorithm is used to reconfigure the system.

The research in this area has attempted to answer fundamental questions regarding how various popular interconnection networks degrade in performance, due to the presence of faults. For instance, given a specific network (say a hypercube) and the location of all the faults in the network, what is the best way to reconfigure the network around faults, such that the slowdown incurred is mini-

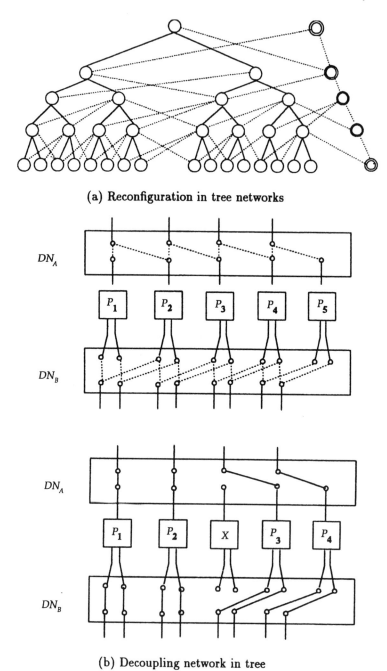

(a) Reconfiguration in tree networks

(b) Decoupling network in tree

Figure 3.43: Reconfiguration in tree networks.

mum? Or, given a specific network, what is the maximum number of faults that can occur, such that the slowdown incurred due to the faults is bounded by a fixed specified quantity?

Reconfiguring an N-leaf complete binary tree (or a fat tree) is considered in Leighton, Maggs, and Sitaraman (1992), Sitaraman (1993). The processors are the leaves of the tree and the nonleaf nodes are the communication switches. When processor failures occur, subtrees of height h that contain $h + 1$ or more failed processors are marked off as unusable. Even the fault-free processors in an unusable subtree will not be used. After the marking process, the computational load of each maximal unusable tree rooted at some node r is mapped to the subtree of the same size, rooted at the sibling of r. It has been shown that as long as the number of failed processors is smaller than $\log_2 N$, this reconfiguration process will not assign a fault-free processor the computational load of more than one failed processor. Consequently, the degradation in performance measured in terms of slowdown is no more than two.

Reconfiguring the hypercube when the hypercube nodes fail independently with some probability p is considered in Hastad, Leighton, and Newman (1987, 1989). The computational load of a failed node is mapped to a fault-free node in its neighborhood. Since the hypercube has sufficient connectivity, it is shown in Hastad, Leighton, and Newman (1987, 1989), that it is always possible to find a fault-free node in the neighborhood of each failed node. The resultant slowdown is only a constant factor. A similar result for the hypercube with a polyogarithmic number of worst-case faults is shown in Aielli and Leighton (1991).

Reconfiguring low-degree networks such as the butterfly (or omega), shuffle exchange, linear array, and two- and higher-dimensional meshes is dealt with extensively in Sitaraman (1993), Leighton, Maggs, and Sitaraman (1992), Cole, Maggs, and Sitaraman (1993). Due to their low connectivity, the reconfiguration algorithms for these networks are more complex. In particular, it may not be possible to find a fault-free processor in the vicinity of each faulty processor. A more complex reconfiguration technique, known as redundant computation is used to achieve graceful degradation in these networks. An important feature of this technique is that the computational workload of a failed processor is mapped to *more than one* fault-free processor.

The bisection width of an N-node network is the minimum number of nodes that must be removed so that the largest remaining connected component of the network is no more than $N/2$ in size. The bisection width is a measure of the fault tolerance of the network since if there are as many as the bisection width number of failed nodes, the network could be partitioned into small pieces. For instance, the bisection width of a $\log N$-dimensional butterfly network is N. If the N nodes in row $\log N/2$ of the butterfly fail, the butterfly is fragmented into $2\sqrt{N}$ pieces of approximately equal size! Of course, in practice, there is no cause for worry, since the number of faults will never be quite as large as the bisection width of the network. The perhaps surprising conclusion that can be drawn from the results in this area is that even if the number of faults in the network approaches the bisection width, many popular networks can be reconfigured around these faults, such that the degradation in performance is bounded and small.

3.12.2 Systems Level Diagnosis

A theoretical issue that has received much attention is the intrinsic ability of different architectures to perform system-level diagnosis in a multicomputer system. System-level diagnosis is a mechanism to identify the faulty components in a system. What is reviewed is how the system-level diagnosis approach proposed by Preparata, Metze, and Chien (1967) can be effectively used for diagnosis in a multicomputer system. This theory is extensively reviewed in Chapter 8, so only the basics are introduced here.

The system-level diagnosis approach is based on the premise that components in a system can test each other. Graph models are used to represent the system, nodes in the graph representing the system components, and arcs in the graph representing the diagnostic tests that can be performed in the system. For example, Figure 3.44 models a system (named S_3) consisting of three components represented by the three nodes u, v, and w. The arc (u, v) represents the fact that node u can test node v.

A large number of fault models and test paradigms have been studied in the literature. For the purpose of our discussion here, we will primarily concentrate on the model proposed by Preparata, Metze, and Chien (1967), hereafter called the PMC model. In the PMC model, each node in the system is assumed to be in one of two possible states: fault-free or faulty. Only permanent faults are considered in the PMC model. A test performed by a fault-free node always correctly determines the status of the tested node. However, the result of a test reported by a faulty node is unpredictable.

When a node v tests another node u and determines that u is faulty (fault-free) the outcome of the test is said to be 1(0). The collection of the outcomes of all

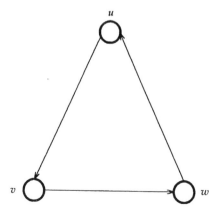

Figure 3.44: A three-node system S_3.

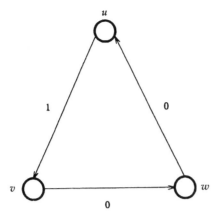

Figure 3.45: A syndrome.

the tests in a system is called a *syndrome*. For example, Figure 3.45 shows a syndrome for the three-node system S_3.

System S_3 is capable of locating a single faulty node. To see this, let us consider all possible fault situations and corresponding syndromes. Table 3.8 lists the eight possible fault situations. Such a table is called the *syndrome table.*

Observe that the syndromes for the no-fault situation and the three single-fault situations are distinct. Therefore, only if the number of faults is bounded by 1 can the faulty node always be identified correctly. However, if more than one fault occurs, it may not be possible to identify the faulty node(s) correctly. For instance, Figure 3.46 shows possible syndromes for fault set $\{u\}$ and $\{v, w\}$, respectively. Observe that both the syndromes are identical. Therefore, if more than one fault is allowed, then correct diagnosis cannot be performed in system S_3. System S_3 is said to be one-fault diagnosable or one-fault locating.

A system S is said to be *t*-fault diagnosable or *t*-fault locating if, given a syndrome, all the faulty nodes can be correctly located, provided the number of faulty nodes is, at most, t.

Although S_3 is not capable of locating more than one fault, it is capable of detecting up to two faults. Observe in Table 3.8 that the syndrome for one or two

Table 3.8: Syndrome Table for System S_3

Fault Nodes	(u, v)	(v, w)	(w, u)
none	0	0	0
u	x	0	1
v	1	x	0
w	0	1	x
u, v	x	x	1
v, w	1	x	x
w, u	x	1	x
u, v, w	x	x	x

x indicates that the value may be 0 or 1.

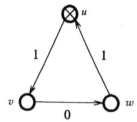 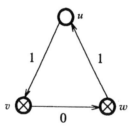

Figure 3.46: Two fault sets may produce the same syndrome.

faults is always distinct from the syndrome for the no-fault case. Therefore, up to two faults can be detected.

A system S is said to be t-fault detecting if, given a syndrome, existence of up to t faults is always detected.

As seen before, the syndrome for two faulty nodes may be identical to a syndrome which corresponds to a single faulty node in the system. Therefore, it should be noted that if we want to be able to locate the faulty node in S_3 when only one fault exists, then it is not possible to detect the presence of two faulty nodes. However, as was recently observed by Vaidya and Pradhan (1991), one can detect a large number of faults with a small reduction in the fault location capability of a system.

A system S is said to be t-fault locating/u-fault detecting if,

- given a syndrome, all the faulty nodes can be correctly located, provided the number of faulty nodes is, at most, t, and
- the existence of more than t faults is detected, provided the number of faulty nodes is, at most, u.

The approach of combining fault detection and fault location is termed *safe diagnosis*, as it allows for an alternate recovery mechanism to be invoked when the number of faults exceeds the system's fault location capability. Figure 3.47 shows a five-node system. By an analysis similar to that for S_3, it can be seen that S_5 is four-fault detecting. System S_5 can also be used as a two-fault locating system. However, when S_5 is used for two-fault location, the existence of three faults may result in incorrect diagnosis. By forming a syndrome table similar to Table 3.8, it can be seen that S_5 can also be used as a one-fault locating three-fault detecting system.

It has recently been shown that a large level of fault detection capability can be achieved by losing a small level of fault location capability, (Vaidya, 1991). For example, Table 3.9 compares the capability of a hypercube system when it is used only for fault location, with the capability of the hypercube system when some of its fault location capability is traded for a large fault detection capability. For example, one can detect 248 faulty nodes, in addition to locating faults in 7 out of the remaining 8 nodes, in a 256-node cube.

The systems shown in Figures 3.44 and 3.47 belong to a class of optimally diagnosable systems presented by Preparata, Metze, and Chien (1967). A system is optimally diagnosable if no other system with a lesser number of nodes and

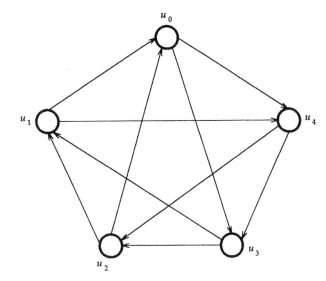

Figure 3.47: A five-node system.

links (arcs) can achieve the same fault location capability. An n node system in this optimal class is denoted as $D_{\delta t}$, where δ and t are parameters, such that δ and n are relatively prime and $t < n/2$. Let the nodes of a n node system be named u_0 through u_{n-1}. Then, in a $D_{\delta t}$ system, a node u_i is tested by a node u_j if and only if $j = (i + \delta m)$ modulo n, where $1 \le m \le t$. It can be shown that a $D_{\delta t}$ system is optimally t-diagnosable. A $D_{\delta t}$ system is also an optimal $(t - d)$-locating-$(n - t - 1 + d)$-detecting system, where $0 < d \le t$ with δ, n relatively prime, $D_{\delta t}$ isomorphic to D_{1t}.

The following reviews a different approach to fault detection without brute-force duplication. Like the above, although much research has been done on the following topic, no widespread use in real systems has yet been reported.

3.12.3 Algorithm-Based Fault Detection

It is clear from the discussion in Section 3.6 that general-purpose fault detection techniques in multiprocessors can require an overhead of about 100 percent in hardware or time. This is because when one uses P processors in a multiprocessor

Table 3.9: Comparison of Pure Fault Location
with Combined Fault Detection and Location

Number of Nodes	Only Fault Location	Safe Diagnosis	
		Location	Detection
32	5	4	27
64	6	5	58
128	7	6	121
256	8	7	248

to get P times the throughput of a uniprocessor, to achieve fault detection, one either must use twice the number of processors to keep the same throughput, or use the same number of processors and get half the throughput. For certain specific parallel applications running on these multiprocessors, it is often possible to use some algorithm-based schemes for error detection at much lower cost in hardware or time. Another advantage of algorithm-based techniques is that it is possible to gain a lot of fault tolerance at low cost with off-the-shelf hardware that has little or no concurrent error detection capability; most multiprocessors that are currently built fit that class.

Algorithm-based fault tolerance and detection were initially proposed for applications in array processors and systolic arrays, concerned with low-cost fault tolerance techniques specific to the algorithms being executed.

Conventional data encoding is performed at the word level, to protect against errors which affect bits in a word. Since a faulty module could affect all the bits of a word it is operating on, we need to encode the data at a higher level. This can be done by considering the set of input data to the algorithm and encoding this set. The original algorithm must then be redesigned to operate on this encoded data, and to produce encoded output data. The redundancy in the encoding would enable the correct data to be recovered or, at least, to recognize that the data are erroneous.

We illustrate the application of an algorithm-based checking technique by an example: the multiplication of two $N \times N$ matrices. In the checksum encoding, an extra row and an extra column are appended to the original matrix which are the sums of the elements of the columns and rows, respectively, (Huang, 1984). For each row or column in the matrix considered as a vector, $(a_1 a_2 \ldots a_N)$, the check element CS is appended to the vector where

$$CS = \sum_{i=1}^{N} a_i \tag{3.1}$$

Figure 3.48 shows an example of a 4×4 matrix, augmented by the row and column checksum encoding. When two such matrices are multiplied, the resultant matrix preserves the checksum property. If there is an error in the resulting matrix element (i, j), it will be identified by verifying the equality of the sum of the row elements with the checksum for row i, and by verifying the equality of the sum of the column elements with the checksum for column j. Suppose the matrix in Figure 3.48 is the result of a matrix multiplication, and element (2,2) is erroneous. Then, the error will be detected in a failed row 2 check, and a failed column 2 check. Once the erroneous element is identified, the correct element can be reconstructed by taking the sum of all elements of that row (column) except the erroneous element and subtracting this sum from the row (column) checksum.

This is illustrated in Figure 3.49 which shows a 5×4 row checksum encoded matrix, multiplied by a 4×5 column checksum encoded matrix on a 5×5 proces-

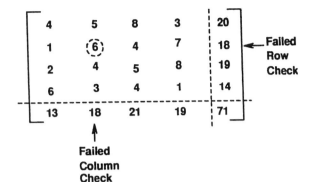

Figure 3.48: Checksum matrix encoding.

sor array, having row and column broadcasting capability to produce a 5×5 full checksum matrix. The operation of the array is as follows. For the matrix elements $a_{i,j}$ on the left-hand side of the array, the top four rows consist of the information part of the matrix A, and the fifth row is the summation vector; the elements $a_{i,j}$ are broadcast from the left boundary of the array to processors in the ith row at time j. For the matrix elements $b_{j,k}$ on the top of the array, the leftmost columns are the information part of the matrix B and the fifth column is the summation vector. The elements $b_{j,k}$ are broadcast from the top boundary of the array to processors in the kth column at time j. At time j, the processor $P_{i,k}$ performs the

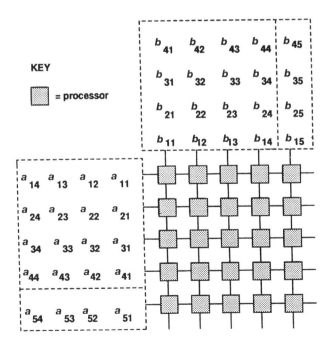

Figure 3.49: Checksum matrix multiplication on an orthogonal array.

product of $a_{i,j}$ with $b_{j,k}$ and accumulates the product in a register. Thus, after n steps, each processor calculates an element of the C matrix. Subsequently, one performs a verification of the checksum property for each row i and each column j. The verification of elements in row i is performed by processors in row $i + 1$. If the processor (i,j) in the array is faulty, it will affect the output element (i,j) of the matrix C; hence, the checks will fail for row i and column j, correctly identifying the faulty processor.

For an $N \times N$ array of processors, the original matrix multiplication can be performed in n time steps. The fault tolerant matrix multiplication needs an $(N + 1) \times (N + 1)$ array. The checksum verification can be performed in parallel among processors of the rows and columns using a tree-based summation, which would take $2logN/N$ steps. The redundancy overhead is $2/N$ in hardware and $2logN/N$ in time. For large values of $N > 100$, the overheads are less than 5 to 10 percent.

This scheme assumed a processor array of size $N \times N$ for performing a matrix multiplication of matrices of size $N \times N$. In reality, since the number of processors is limited (to say a $P \times P$ array), a partitioned matrix multiplication scheme has been proposed. The basic idea involves the partitioning of each matrix into an $N \times (P - 1)$ submatrix, and performing multiplication of partitioned submatrices with checksum rows or columns for each partition. To avoid the effect of a single faulty processor corrupting multiple data elements in the same row or column of the larger result matrix, each partitioned matrix multiplication was performed by rotating the matrix one row and column position at each step. Details of the algorithm can be found in Huang and Abraham (1984).

The idea of algorithm-based fault tolerance was proposed initially for systolic arrays. While these proposed techniques were interesting, none of the results were practically applicable, since there were not many commercially available systolic array processors for actual evaluation of the schemes. Recently, the application of the ABFT techniques to general-purpose multiprocessors such as hypercube mutiprocessors, (Banerjee, Rahmeh, Stunkel, Nair, Roy, Abraham and Balasubramanian 1990b) have been reported. While previous techniques of Algorithm-Based Fault Tolerance (ABFT) ignored the effects of finite precision roundoff errors on the encodings, the actual studies of ABFT reported on an Intel iPSC hypercube measuring the real error coverage in the presence of finite precision arithmetic. The schemes did not involve any hardware modifications or overhead.

We now describe the application of algorithm-based fault detection techniques for the matrix multiplication problem on a general purpose hypercube multiprocessor. The host computer of the hypercube partitions the matrix A into a number of rectangular strips by rows equal to the number of processors in the hypercube, and sends one strip to each processor. The complete matrix B is also sent to each processor. Each processor P_i performs the submatrix multiplication $C_i = A_i \times B$, using a sequential algorithm. At the end, each processor sends the submatrices of the result matrix back to the host.

The algorithm is modified to include system-level checks based on the checksum matrix encoding, as shown in Figure 3.50. The elements of each column of the matrix A are summed together to form the row $CC(A)$, called the column checksum of A. The matrix multiplications $C = A \times B$ and $D = CC(A) \times B$ are performed. The column checksum of matrix C, $CC(C)$, is computed and compared to D. In the absence of faults and round-off errors, $CC(C)$ and D should be identical.

The A strips are duplicated among processor pairs, such that the two processors (hereafter referred to as nodes) in a pair are mutual neighbors (or mates) in the hypercube. Node i computes the column checksum of the A strip of its neighbor $CC(A_{mate(i)})$, and then the D strip of its mate, $D_{mate(i)} = CC(A_{mate(i)}) \times B$. Node i then obtains the C strip of its mate, $C_{mate(i)}$. Node i checks its mate by comparing $CC(C_{mate(i)})$ to $D_{mate(i)}$, and sends the result (pass or fail) to the host. Finally, the host judges the computation error-free if all nodes "pass"; otherwise, it judges the computation erroneous.

If there is a fault in a node during the regular matrix multiplication computation, it will be detected by the row check with a high probability, since the checksum row for a strip C_i is calculated by the node that is the neighbor of node i. In fact, the above checksum encoding scheme was implemented on a 16-processor Intel iPSC hypercube (predecessor to the iPSC-2) for cubes of various sizes (4, 8, and 16 nodes), using randomly generated 64×64 matrices. It gave high error coverage (75 to 96 percent for bit-level errors, and 100 percent for word-level errors), while maintaining low time overheads (10 to 30 percent). Details of the implementation, as well as the experimental results, can be found in Banerjee, Rahmeh, Stunkel, Nair, Roy, Abraham, and Balasubramanian (1990).

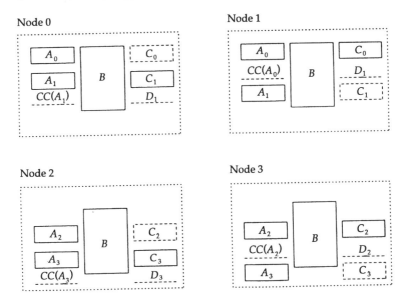

Figure 3.50: Algorithm-based fault detection for matrix multiplication on a general-purpose multiprocessor.

The algorithm-based fault tolerance techniques have been applied to a wide range of applications including matrix vector multiplication, Jou and Abraham (1984), matrix solvers, Luk (1985), Fast Fourier Transform, Jou and Abraham (1985); Choi and Malek (1988); Reddy and Banerjee (1990), QR Factorization (Reddy and Banerjee 1990), and adaptive filtering (Mueller-Thuns, McFarland and Banerjee 1989).

A relatively new area of research in the area of generating online system-level checks in general-purpose multiprocessors is the investigation of automated synthesis of algorithm-based fault detection schemes, by using a compiler-assisted approach. Balasubramanian and Banerjee (1990) Balasubramanian and Banerjee (1991) have reported on a compiler that identifies linear transformations in DO loops in FORTRAN programs, restructures programs to convert nonlinear transformations to linear transformations, and inserts system-level checks automatically by the compiler, based on the checksum encoding property described above.

3.13 CONCLUSIONS

This chapter provides a basic overview of principles and practices of fault-tolerant multiprocessor and distributed system design. Although most key fault-tolerant techniques have found applications in medium-performance systems such as Tandem, Stratus, and Sequoia, the high-performance systems have very minimal fault tolerance. In many of the high-performance systems such as CM-5 and Intel Paragon, the fault tolerance is primarily limited to techniques such as parity checking, retry, and simple reconfiguration schemes. As the demand for high availability for high-performance systems grows, some of the sophisticated techniques enumerated in this chapter may find application. Also, with the evolution of large-scale distributed systems, many of the fault-tolerant techniques described here will become essential features of many of these systems.

REFERENCES

[Adams82] Adams, G. B. III, and H. J. Siegel, "The Extra Stage Cube: A Fault Tolerant Interconnection Network for Supersystems," *IEEE Trans. Computers*, vol. C-31 (May 1982).

[Adams87] Adams, G., D. P. Agrawal, and H. J. Siegel, "A Survey and Comparison of Fault-Tolerant Multistage Interconnection Networks," *IEEE Computer* (June 1987), pp. 14–27.

[Agrawal82] Agrawal, D. P., "Testing and Fault Tolerance of Multistage Interconnection Networks," *IEEE Computer* (April 1982), pp. 41–53.

[Agrawal88] Agrawal, P., "Fault Tolerance in Multiprocessor Systems without Dedicated Redundancy," *IEEE Trans. Computers,* vol. 37, no. 3, pp. 358–362.

[Ahmed90] Ahmed, R., R. Frazier, and P.N. Marinos, "CARER: Cache-Aided Rollback Error Recovery Algorithm for Shared-Memory Multiprocessors," *Proc. 20th Int. Symp. Fault-Tolerant Computing,* June 1990, pp. 82–88.

[Aiello91] Aiello, W., and T. Leighton, "Coding Theory, Hypercube Embeddings, and Fault Tolerance," *Proceedings of the 3rd Annual ACM Symposium on Parallel Algorithms and Architectures,* July 1991, pp. 125–136.

[Akimoto88] Akimoto, Y., H. Tanaka, H. Ogi, H. Taoka, S. Nashida, "Autonomous Distributed Network Architecture for Control System," *IFAC Distributed Computer Control Systems,* Vitznau, Switzerland, 1988, pp. 21–27.

[Balasubramanian90] Balasubramanian, V., and P. Banerjee, "Compiler Assisted Synthesis of Algorithm-Based Checking in Multiprocessors," *IEEE Trans. Computers,* vol. 39, no. 4 (April 1990), pp. 436–447.

[Balasubramanian91] Balasubramanian, V., and P. Banerjee, "CRAFT: A Compiler for Synthesizing Algorithm-Based Fault Tolerance in Hypercube Multiprocessors," *Proc. Int. Conf. Parallel Processing (ICPP-91),* St. Charles, Ill., August 1991.

[Banerjee89] Banerjee, P., and A. Dugar, "The Design, Analysis and Simulation of a Fault-Tolerant Interconnection Network Supporting the Fetch-and-Add Primitive," *IEEE Trans. Computers,* 38(1) (January 1989), pp. 30–46.

[Banerjee90a] Banerjee, P., "Strategies for Reconfiguring Hypercubes under Faults," *Proc. 20th Int. Conf. Fault Tolerant Computing Systems,* June 1990. pp. 210–215.

[Banerjee90b] Banerjee, P., J. T. Rahmeh, C. B. Stunkel, V. S. S. Nair, K. Roy, J. A. Abraham, and V. Balasubramanian, "Algorithm Based Fault Tolerance on Hypercube Multiprocessors," *IEEE Trans. Computers,* vol. 39, no. 0 (September 1990), pp. 1132–1142.

[Batcher80] Batcher, K. E., "Design of a Massively Parallel Processor," *IEEE Trans. Computers,* C-29(9) (September 1980), pp. 836–840.

[Belkhale92] Belkhale, K. P., and P. Banerjee, "Reconfiguration Strategies for VLSI Processor Arrays and Trees Using a Modified Diogenes Approach," *IEEE Trans. Computers,* 41(1) (January 1992), pp. 83–96.

[Bernstein88] Bernstein, P. A., "Sequoia: A Fault-Tolerant Tightly Coupled Multiprocessor for Transaction Processing," *IEEE Computer* (February 1988), pp. 37–45.

[Bernstein88] Bernstein, P. A., "Sequoia: A Fault-Tolerant Tightly Coupled Multiprocessor for Transaction Processing," *Computer,* vol. 21, no. 2 (February 1988), pp. 37–45.

[Bhuyan89] Bhuyan, L. N., and D. P. Agrawal, "Generalized Hypercube and Hyperbus Structures for a Computer Network," *IEEE Trans. Computers,* vol. C-33 (April 1989), pp. 323–333.

[Bianchini90] Bianchini, R., Jr., K. Goodwin, and D. S. Nydick, "Practical Application and Implementation of Distributed System-Level Diagnosis Theory," (1990), pp. 332–339.

[Bianchini91] Bianchini, R., Jr. and Richard Buskens, "An Adaptive Distributed System-Level Diagnosis Algorithm and Its Implementation," (June 1991), pp. 222–229.

[Bowen91] Bowen, N. S., and D. K. Pradhan, "A Virtually Memory Translation Mechanism to Support Checkpoint and Rollback Recovery," *Supercomputing '91* (November 1991), pp. 890–899.

[Bowen92] Bowen, N., D. K. Pradhan, "Virtual Checkpoints: Architecture and Performance," *IEEE Transactions on Computers*, vol. 41 (May 1992), pp. 516–525.

[Bowen93] Bowen, N., and D. K. Pradhan, "Processor and Memory Based Checkpoint and Rollback Recovery," *Computer* (February 1993), pp. 22–31.

[Busken93] Buskens, R. W., and R. P. Bianchini, "Distributed On-Line Diagnosis in the Presence of Arbitary Faults," *Proc. 23rd Int. Symp. on Fault Tolerant Computing*, (June 1993), pp. 470–479.

[Chen88] Chen, M. S., and K. G. Shin, "Message Routing in an Injured Hypercube," *Proc. 3rd Conf. Hypercube Concurrent Computers and Applications*, (January 1988), pp. 312–317.

[Chen90] Chen, M. S., and K. G. Shin, "Depth-First Search Approach for Fault-Tolerant Routing in Hypercube Multicomputers," *IEEE Trans. Parallel Distributed Systems* (April 1990), pp. 152–159.

[Chen93] Chen, C., D. P. Agrawal, and J. R. Burke, "dBCube: A New Class of Hierarchical Multiprocessor Interconnection Networks with Area Efficient Layout," *IEEE Trans. Parallel and Distributed Systems*, vol. 4, No. 12 (December 1993), pp. 1332–1344.

[Cherequé92] Cherequœe, M., D. Powell, P. Reynier, J. L. Richer, and J. Voiron, "Active Replication in Delta-4," *Proc. FTCS-92*, Boston, Mass., (July 1992), pp. 28–37.

[Choi88] Choi, Y.-H., and M. Malek, "A Fault-Tolerant FFT Processor," *IEEE Trans. on Computers*, vol. C-37, no. 5 (May 1988), pp. 617–621.

[Chow87] Chow, E., H. Madan, and J. Peterson, "A Real-Time Adaptive Routing Network for the Hypercube Computer," *Proc. Real-Time Systems Symp.*, (December 1987), pp. 88–96.

[Cole1993] Cole, R., B. M. Maggs, R. Sitaraman, "Multi-Scale Emulation: A Technique for Reconfiguring Arrays with Faults," *25th ACM Symp. on Theory of Computing*, pp. 561–572.

[Collins93] Collins, O., S. Dolinar, R. McEliece and F. Pollara, "A VLSI Decomposition of the deBruijn Graph," *Journal of the Assoc. of Computing Machinery*, vol. 39, no. 4 (October 1992), pp. 931–948.

[Dimmer85] Dimmer, C. I., "The Tandem Non-Stop System," in *Resilient Computing Systems*, 1985.

[Dreil90] van Driel, C-J.L., R. J. B. Follon, A. A. C. Kohler, R. P. M. van Osch, J. M. Spanjers, "The Error-Resistant Interactively Consistent Architecture (ERICA)," *Proc. International Symposium on Fault-Tolerant Computing FTCS-20*, Newcastle-on-Tyne, 1990, pp. 474–480.

[Dutt88] Dutt, S., and J. P. Hayes, "On Allocating Subcubes in a Hypercube Multiprocessor," *Proc. 3rd Conf. Hypercube Concurrent Computers and Applications*, (January 1988), pp. 801–810.

[Falavarajan81] Falavarajani, K. M., and D. K. Pradhan, "Fault-Diagnosis of Parallel Processor Interconnection Networks," *Proc. 11th Annual International Symposium on Fault-Tolerant Computing*, (June 1981), pp. 209–212.

[Feng81] Feng, T-Y, and C-L Wu, "Fault-diagnosis for a Class of Multistage Interconnection Networks," *IEEE Trans. Computers*, vol. C-30 (October 1981).

[Fleisch89] Fleisch, B. D., and G. J. Popek, "Mirage: A Coherent Distributed Shared Memory Design," *Proc. 12th Symp. Operating System Principles*, 1989, pp. 211–223.

[Fortes84] Fortes, J. A. B., and C. S. Raghavendra, "Dynamically Reconfigurable Fault-Tolerant Array Processors," *Proc. 14th Fault-Tolerant Comp. Symp.*, (June 1984), pp. 386–392.

[Fuchs83] Fuchs, W. Kent, J. A. Abraham, and Kuang-Hua Huang, "Concurrent Error Detection in vlsi Interconnection Networks," *Proceedings of 10th Annual International Symposium on Computer Architecture*, (June 1983), pp. 309–315.

[Fujiwara90] Fujiwara, E., and D. K. Pradhan, "Error-Control Coding in Computers," *Computer*, (July 1990), pp. 63–72.

[Ganesan93] Ganesan, E., and D. K. Pradhan, "The Hyper-deBruijn Networks: Scalable Versatile Architecture," *Transactions on Parallel and Distributed Systems*, vol. 4, no. 9 (September 1993), pp. 962–978.

[Gordon88] Gordon, J. M., and Q. F. Stout, "Hypercube Message Routing in the Presence of Faults," *Proc. 3rd Conf. Hypercube Concurrent Computers and Applications*, (January 1988), pp. 318–327.

[Graham87] Graham, N., F. Harary, M. Livingston, and Q. Stout, "Subcube Fault Tolerance in Hypercubes," Technical report, University of Michigan, (September 1987).

[Harper88] Harper, R. E., J. H. Lala and J. J. Deyst, "Fault Tolerant parallel Processor Architecture Overview," in *Digest of Papers: 18th Int. Symp. Fault-Tolerant Comp.*, 1988, pp. 252–257.

[Harper91] Harper, R. E., and J. H. Lala, "Fault-Tolerant Parallel Processor," *Journal of Guidance, Control, and Dynamics*, vol. 14, no. 3 (1991) pp. 554–563.

[Hastad87] Hastad, J., T. Leighton, and M. Newman, "Reconfiguring a Hypercube in the Presence of Faults," *Proceedings of the 19th Annual ACM Symposium on Theory of Computing*, (May 1987), pp. 274–284.

[Hastad89] Hastad, J., T. Leighton, and M. Newman, "Fast Computation Using Faulty Hypercubes," *Proceedings of the 21st Annual ACM Symposium on Theory of Computing*, (May 1989), pp. 251–263.

[Hayes74] Hayes, J. P., "A Graph model for Fault-Tolerant Computing Systems," *IEEE Trans. Computers*, C-25(9) (January 1974), pp. 86–88.

[Hopkins78] Hopkins, A. L. III, T. B. Smith, and J. H. Lala, "FTMP: A Highly Reliable Fault-Tolerant Multiprocessor for Aircraft," *Proc. IEEE*, 66 (October 1978), pp. 1221–1239.

[Hossein84] Hosseini, S. H., J. G. Kuhl, and S. M. Reddy, "A Diagnosis Algorithm for Distributed Computing Systems with Dynamic Failure and Repair," *IEEE Transactions on Computers*, 33(3) (March 1984), pp. 223–233.

[Hsiao70] Hsiao, M. Y., "A Class of Optimal Minimum Odd-Weight-Column SEC-DED Codes," *IBM J. R&D*, vol. 14, (July 1970), pp. 395–401.

[Huang84] Huang, K. H., and J. A. Abraham, "Algorithm-Based Fault Tolerance for Matrix Operations," *IEEE Trans. Computers*, vol. C-33, no. 6 (June 1984), pp. 518–528.

[Hunt87] Hunt, D. B., and P. N. Marinos, "A General Purpose Cache-Aided Rollback Error

Recovery (CARER) Technique," *17th Symp. on Fault-Tolerant Computing*, (June 1987), pp. 170–175.

[Hwang84] Hwang, K., and F. A. Briggs, *Computer Architecture and Parallel Processing*, Mc-Graw-Hill, 1984.

[Iwasaki90] Iwasaki, K., and F. Arakawa. "An Analysis of the Aliasing Probability of Multiple-Input Signature Registers in the Case of a 2^m-ary Symmetric Channel," *IEEE Trans. Comput.-Aided Design*, 9(4) (April 1990), pp. 427–438.

[Janssen91] Janssens, B., and W. K. Fuchs, "Experimental Evaluation of Multiprocessor Cache-Based Error Recovery," *1991 International Conference on Parallel Processing*, (August 1991), pp. I-505–I-508.

[Jewett91] Jewett, D., "Integrity S2: A Fault-Tolerant Unix Platform," *Digest of Papers: The 21st Int. Symp. Fault-Tolerant Comp.*, 1991, pp. 512–519.

[Jewett91] Jewett, D., "A Fault-Tolerant Unix Platform," *Proc. International Symposium on Fault-Tolerant Computing FTCS-21*, Montreal, 1991, pp. 512–519.

[Johnson84] Johnson, D., "The Intel 432: A vlsi Architecture for Fault-Tolerant Computer Systems," *IEEE Computer* (August 1984), pp. 40–48.

[Johnson87] Johnson, D. B., and W. Zwaenpoel, "Sender-Based Message Logging," *Proc. 17th Int. Symp. on Fault-Tolerant Computing*, June 1987, pp. 14–19.

[Johnson89] Johnson, B. W., *Design and Analysis of Fault Tolerant Digital Systems*, Addison-Wesley, 1989.

[Jou84] Jou, Y. Y., and J. A. Abraham, "Fault-Tolerant Matrix Operations on Multiple Processor Systems Using Weighted Checksums," *SPIE Proceedings*, vol. 495 (August 1984).

[Jou85] Jou, J. Y., and J. A. Abraham, "Fault Tolerant FFT Networks," *Proc. 15th Int. Symp. on Fault Tolerant Computing*, Ann Arbor, Mich., (June 1985), pp. 338–343.

[Kaklamanis90] Kaklamanis, C., A. R. Karlin, F. T. Leighton, V. Milenkovic, P. Raghavan, S. Rao, C. Thomborson, and A. Tsantilas, "Asymptotically Tight Bounds for Computing with Faulty Arrays of Processors," in *Proceedings of the 31st Annual Symposium on Foundations of Computer Science*, (October 1990), IEEE Computer Society Press, pp. 285–296.

[Karpovsky91] Karpovsky, M. G., S. K. Gupta, and Dhiraj K. Pradhan, "Aliasing and Diagnosis Probability in MISR and STUPMS Using a General Error Model," in *Int. Test Conf.*, 1991, pp. 828–839.

[Katsuki78] Katsuki, D., E. S. Elsam, W. F. Mann, E. S. Roberets, J. G. Robinson, F. S. Skowronski, and E. W. Wolf, "Pluribus-An Operational Fault-Tolerant Multiprocessor," *Proceedings of the IEEE*, 66(10) (October 1978), pp. 1146–1159.

[Katzman78] Katzman, J. A., "A Fault-Tolerant Computing System," *Proc. 11th Hawaii Int. Conf. on system Sciences, Part III*, 1978, pp. 85–102.

[Kieckhafer88] Kieckhafer, R. M., C. J. Walter, A. M. Finn, and P. M. Thambidurai, "The MAFT Architecture for Distributed Fault Tolerance," *IEEE Trans. Computers*, 37(4) (April 1988), pp. 398–405.

[Kim89] Kim, K. H., and H. O. Welch, "Distributed Execution of Recovery Blocks: An Approach for Uniform Treatment of Hardware and Software Faults in Real-Time Applications," *IEEE Transactions on Computers*, 38(5) (May 1989).

[Kiski88] Kiskis, D., and K. G. Shin, "Implementation of TMR on a Hypercube Architecture," *Proc. 3rd Conf. Hypercube Concurrent Computers and Applications*, (January 1988), pp. 337–345.

[Koo87] Koo, R., and S. Toueg, "Checkpointing and Rollback Recovery for Distributed Systems," *IEEE Transactions on Software Engineering*, SE-13(1) (January 1987).

[Kumar87] Kumar, V. P., and S. M. Reddy, "Augmented Shuffle-Exchange Multistage Interconnection Networks," *IEEE Computer* (June 1987), pp. 30–40.

[Lamport82] Lamport, L., R. Shostak, and M. Pease, "The Byzantine Generals Problem," *ACM Trans. Prog. Lang. Syst.*, 4(3) (July 1982), pp. 382–401.

[Laprie85] Laprie, J. C., "Dependable Computing and Fault Tolerance: Concepts and Terminology," in *Digest of Papers: 15th Int. Symp. Fault-Tolerant Comp.*, (June 1985), pp. 2–11.

[Lee88] Lee, T. C., and J. P. Hayes, "Routing and Broadcasting in Faulty Hypercube Computers," *Proc. 3rd Conf. on Hypercube Concurrent Computers and Applications*, (January 1988), pp. 346–354.

[Lee93] Lee, I. and R. K. Iyer, "Faults, Symptoms, and Software Fault Tolerance in the Tandem GUARDIAN 90 Operating System," *Proc. 23rd Int. Conf. on Fault-Tolerant Computing*, 1993, pp. 20–29.

[Leighton92] Leighton, T., B. Maggs, and R. Sitaraman, "On the Fault Tolerance of Some Popular Bounded-Degree Networks," in *Proceedings of the 33rd Annual Symposium on Foundations of Computer Science*, (October 1992), IEEE Computer Society Press, pp. 542–552.

[Li86] Li, K., "Shared Virtual Memory on Loosely Coupled Multiprocessors," Technical Report, Graduate College, Yale University, 1986.

[Li90] Li, C. C., and W. K. Fuchs, "Graceful Degradation on Hypercube Multiprocessors using Data Redistribution," *Proc. of 5th Distributed Memory Computing Conference (DMCC90)*, (April 1990).

[Lilienkamp82] Lilienkamp, J. E., D. H. Lawrie, and P. Yew, "A Fault Tolerant Interconnection Network Using Error Correcting Codes," *Proc. Int. Conf. on Parallel Processing*, 1982, pp. 123–125.

[Lin90] Lin, L., and M. Ahamad, "Checkpointing and Rollback-Recovery in Distributed Object-Based Systems," *Proc. 20th Int. Symp. Fault-Tolerant Computing*, (June 1990), pp. 97–104.

[Lincoln93] Lincoln, P., and J. Rushby, "A Formally Verified Algorithm for Interactive Consistency Under a Hybrid Fault Model," *Proc. 23rd Int. Symp. on Fault Tolerant Computing*, (June 1993), pp. 402–411.

[Long90] Long, J., W. K. Fuchs, and J. A. Abraham, "A Forward Recovery Using Checkpointing in Parallel Systems," *Proceedings of the 1990 International Conference on Parallel Processing*, (August 1990), 1, pp. 272–275.

[Long91] Long, J., W. K. Fuchs, and J. A. Abraham, "Implementing Forward Recovery

Using Checkpoints in Distributed Systems," *IFIP 2nd Int. Working Conf. Dependable Computing for Critical Applications,* (February 1991).

[Lorie77] Lorie, R. A., "Physical Integrity in a Large Segmented Database," *ACM Transactions on Database Systems* vol. 2, no. 1 (March 1977), pp. 91–104.

[Luk85] Luk, F., "Algorithm-Based Fault Tolerance for Parallel Matrix So Ivers," *Proc. SPIE Real-Time Signal Processing VIII,* vol. 564 (June 1985),

[Meyer87] Meyer, F. J., and D. K. Pradhan, "Consensus with Dual Failure Modes," *Proc. FTCS-17,* Pittsburgh Pa., (July 1987), pp. 48–54.

[Meyer89] Meyer, F. J., and D. K. Pradhan, "Dynamic Testing Strategy for Distributed System," *IEEE Transactions on Computers,* vol. 38, no. 3 (March 1989), pp. 356–365.

[Meyer91] Meyer, F. J., and D. K. Pradhan, "Consensus with Dual Failure Modes," *IEEE Transactions on Parallel and Distributed Systems,* 2(2) (April 1991) pp. 214–222.

[Mudge87] Mudge, T. N., J. P. Hayes, and D. C. Winsor, "Multiple Bus Architectures," *IEEE Computer* (June 1987), pp. 42–48.

[Mueller-Thuns89] Mueller-Thuns, R. B., D. McFarland, and P. Banerjee, "Algorithm-Based Fault Tolerance for Adaptive Least Squares Lattice Filtering on a Hypercube Multiprocessor," *Proc. Int. Conf. on Parallel Processing* St. Charles, Ill., (August 1989), pp. 177–189.

[Ng91] Ng, T. P., *Checkpointing Algorithms for Shared Memory Systems,* Technical Report, Dept. of Computer Science, University of Illinois, Urbana-Champaign, 1991.

[Pease80] Pease, M., R. Shostak, and L. Lamport, "Reaching Agreement in the Presence of Faults," *Journal of the ACM* (April 1980), pp. 228–234.

[Peercy92] Peercy, M., and P. Banerjee, "Design and Analysis of Software Reconfiguration Strategies of Hypercube Multicomputers under Multiple Faults," *Proc. 22nd Fault Tolerant Computing Symp.,* (July 1992).

[Pradhan72] Pradhan, D. K., and S. M. Reddy, "Error Correcting Techniques for Logic Processors," *IEEE Transactions on Computers,* vol. C-21, no. 12 (December 1972), pp. 1331–1335.

[Pradhan80] Pradhan, D. K., and J. Stiffler, "Error-Correcting Codes and Self-Checking Circuits," *IEEE Computer,* Special Issue on Fault-Tolerant Computing, vol. 13, no. 3 (March 1980), pp. 27–38.

[Pradhan81] Pradhan, D. K., "Interconnctions Topologies for Fault-Tolerant Parallel and Distributed Architecture," *Proc. of 10th International Conference on Parallel Processing,* (August 1981), pp. 238–242.

[Pradhan82] Pradhan, D. K., and S. M. Reddy, "A Fault-Tolerant Communication Architecture for Distributed Systems," *IEEE Transactions on Computers,* (September 1982), pp. 863–870.

[Pradhan84] Pradhan, D. K., M. L. Schlumberger, and Z. Hanquan, "Fault-tolerant Multibus Architectures for Multiprocessors," *Proc. FTCS-14,* Kissimee, Fl., (June 1984), pp. 400–408.

[Pradhan85] Pradhan, D. K., "Dynamically Restructurable Fault-tolerant Processor Network Architectures," *IEEE Transactions on Computers,* vol. C-34, no. 5 (May 1985), pp. 434–447.

[Pradhan86] Pradhan, D. K., "Fault-Tolerant Computing: Theory and Techniques," vol. I, Prentice-Hall 1986.

[Pradhan89] Pradhan, D. K., *Redundancy Schemes for Recovery*, Technical Report, TR-89-CSE-16, ECE Department, University of Massachusetts, 1989.

[Pradhan90] Pradhan, D. K., and E. Fujiwara, "Error Computing Codes in Fault-Tolerant Computers," *Computer*, vol. 23, no. 7 (July 1990), pp. 62–72.

[Pradhan91] Pradhan, D. K., and S. K. Gupta, "A New Framework for Designing and Analyzing BIST Techniques and Zero Aliasing Compression," *IEEE Transactions on Computers*, vol. 40, no. 6 (June 1991), pp. 743–763.

[Pradhan92] Pradhan, D. K., and N. H. Vaidya, "Roll-Forward Checkpointing Scheme: Concurrent Retry With Nondedicated Spares," *IEEE Workshop on Fault Tolerant Parallel and Distributed Systems*, (July 1992), pp. 166–174.

[Pradhan94a] Pradhan, D. K., and N. Vaidya, "Roll Forward Checkpointing Scheme: A Novel Fault-Tolerant Architecture," *IEEE Transactions on Computers*, vol. 43(10), (October 1994), pp. 1163–1174.

[Pradhan94] Pradhan, D. K., and N. Vaidya, "Performance and Reliability Trade-offs in Roll-forward Schemes", *Proc. FTCS-24*, Austin, Texas, (June 1994).

[Preparata67] Preparata, F. P., G. Metze, and R. T. Chien, "On the Connection Assignment Problem of Diagnosable Systems," *IEEE Transactions on Computers*, 16(6) (December 1967), pp. 848–854.

[Raghavendra84] Raghavendra, C. S., A. Avizienis, and M. Ercegovac, "Fault-Tolerance in Binary Tree Architectures," *IEEE Trans. Computers*, C-33 (June 1984), pp. 568–572.

[Ramanathan90] Ramanathan, P., K. G. Shin, and R. W. Butler, "Fault-Tolerant Clock Synchronization in Distributed Systems," *Computer* (October 1990), pp. 33–42.

[Randell75] Randell, B., "System Structure for Software Fault Tolerance," *IEEE Trans. Software Eng.*, SE-1(2) (June 1975), pp. 220–232.

[Reddy90] Reddy, A. L. N., and P. Banerjee, "Algorithm-Based Fault Detection for Signal Processing Applications," *IEEE Trans. on Computers*, vol. 39, no. 10 (October 1990), pp. 1304–1308.

[Rennels86] Rennels, D. A., "On Implementing Fault Tolerance in Binary Hypercubes," *Proc. 16th Int. Symp. on Fault-Tolerant Computing*, (July 1986), pp. 344–349.

[Reuter80] Reuter, A., "A Fast Transaction-Oriented Logging Scheme for UNDO Recovery," *IEEE Transactions on Software Engineering* vol. SE-6, no. 4 (July 1980), pp. 348–356.

[Rosenberg83] Rosenberg, A. L., "The Diogenes Approach to Testable Fault-Tolerant vlsi Processor Arrays," *IEEE Trans. Computers*, C-32(1) (October 1983), pp. 21–27.

[Salmon88] Salmon, J., S. Callahan, J. Flower, and A. Kolawa, "Moose: A Multitasking operating system for hypercubes," *Proc. 3rd Conf. Hypercube Concurrent Computers and Applications*, (January 1988).

[Samanthan89] Samantham, M. R., and D. K. Pradhan, "The deBruijn Multiprocessor Networks: A Versatile Parallel Processing Network for VLSI," *IEEE Transactions on Computers*, vol. 38, no. 4 (April 1989), pp. 567–581.

[Sami86] Sami, M., and R. Stefanalli, "Reconfigurable Architectures for vlsi Processing Arrays," *Proc. IEEE*, 74(5) (May 1986), pp. 712–722.

[Seitz85] Seitz, C. L., "The Cosmic Cube," (January 1985).

[Serlin84] Serlin, O., "Fault-Tolerant Systems in Commercial Applications," *IEEE Computer* (August 1984), pp. 19–30.

[Sequoia92a] Sequoia Systems Incorporated, *Series 400 Technical Summary*, (June 1992).

[Sequoia92b] Sequoia Systems Incorporated, "The Series 400," Sequoia Product Report, 1992.

[Siewiorek78] Siewiorek, D. P., V. Kini, H. Mashburn, S. McConnel, and M. Hsao, "A Case Study of c.mmp, cm*, and c.vmp. i. Experiences with Fault Tolerance in Multiprocessor Systems," *Proc. IEEE*, 66 (October 1978), pp. 1178–1199.

[Sistla89] Sistla, A. P., and J. L. Welch, "Efficient Distributed Recovery Using Message Logging," *Proc. 8th ACM Symposium on Principles of Distributed Computing*, (1989), pp. 223–238.

[Sitaraman93] Sitaraman, R., "Communication and Fault Tolerance in Parallel Computers, "Ph.D diss.; Technical Report CS-TR-414-93, Department of Computer Science, Princeton University, Princeton, N.J., (June 1993).

[Stratus92a] Stratus Computer Incorporated, "XA/R Series 300," Stratus Product Report, 1992.

[Stratus92b] Stratus Computer Incorporated, "Stratus FTX," Stratus Product Report, 1992.

[Strom85] Strom, R. E., and S. Yemini, "Optimistic Recovery in Distributed Systems," *ACM Transactions on Computers*, (August 1985), pp. 204–226.

[Strom88] Strom, R. E., D. F. Bacon, and S. A. Yemini, "Volatile Logging in *n*-Fault-Tolerant Distributed Systems," *Proc. 18th Int. Symp. Fault-Tolerant Computing*, (June 1988), pp. 42–50.

[Sullivan77] Sullivan, H., and T. R. Bashkow, "A Large Scale Homogeneous Machine," *Proc. of 4th Ann. Symp. on Computer Architecture*, 1977, pp. 105–114.

[Svobodova84] Svobodova, L., "Resilient distributed Computing," *IEEE Trans. Software Engineering*, SE-10 no. 3 (May 1984), pp. 257–267.

[Tandem90] Tandem Computers Incorporated, "NonStop Cyclone," Tandem Product Report, 1990.

[Tandem93] Tandem Computers Incorporated, "NonStop Cyclone/R," Tandem Product Report, 1993.

[Thambidurai88] Thambidurai, P., and Y. K. Park, "Interactive Consistency with Multiple Failure Modes," *Proc. 7th Symp. on Reliable Distributed Systems*, (October 1988), pp. 93–100.

[Tohma86] Tohma, Y., in D. K. Pradhan, *Fault-tolerant Computing: Theory and Techniques*, Vol. I, 1986, Prentice Hall.

[Tzeng85] Tzeng, N-F, P-C Yew, and C-Q Zhu, "A Fault Tolerant Scheme for Multistage Interconnection Networks," *Proc. 12th Int. Conf. Computer Architecture*, (June 1985), pp. 368–375.

[Vaidya91] Vaidya, N. H., and D. K. Pradhan, "Voting in Fault-Tolerant Systems: Reliability and Safety Issues," Technical Report TR-91-CSE-7, ECE Department, Univ. of Massachusetts, (June 1991).

[Vaidya92] Vaidya, N. H., and D. K. Pradhan, "A Fault Tolerance Scheme for a System of Duplicated Communicating Processes," *IEEE Workshop on Fault-Tolerant Parallel and Distributed Systems,* Amherst, Massachusetts, (July 1992).

[Vaidya93] Vaidya, N. H., and D. K. Pradhan, "Fault-Tolerant Design Strategies for High Reliability and Safety", *IEEE Transactions on Computers,* vol. 42, no. 10 (October 1993),

[Vaidya95] Vaidya, N. H., and D. K. Pradhan, "Degradable Byzantine Agreement," *IEEE Transactions on Computers,* vol. 44, no. 1, (January 1995), pp. 146–150.

[Wensley78] Wensley, J. H., L. Lamport, J. Goldberg, M. W. Green, K. N. Levitt, P. M. Melliar-Smith, R. E. Shostak and C. B. Weinstock, "Sift: Design and Analysis of a Fault-Tolerant Computer for Aircraft Control," *Proc. IEEE,* 66(10) (October 1978), pp. 1240–1255.

[Wu90] Wu, K-L., and W. K. Fuchs, "Recoverable Distributed Shared Virtual Memory," *IEEE Transactions on Computers,* 39(4) (April 1990),

[Wu90] Wu, K-L., W. K. Fuchs and J. H. Patel, "Error Recovery in Shared Memory Multiprocessors Using Private Caches," *IEEE Transactions on Parallel and Distributed Systems,* vol. 1, no. 2 (April 1990), pp. 231–240.

[Zorpette90] Zorpette, G., "The Power of Parallelism," *IEEE Spectrum* (September 1990), pp. 28–33.

PROBLEMS

3.1. What specific fault-tolerant architectural support would you recommend in designing a SIMD computer and a MIMD computer? Discuss your choices. From the point of view of performance degradation, which techniques discussed in the chapter are most applicable to the SIMD and MIMD computers?

3.2. Extend the Byzantine algorithm to tolerate both single benign faults and single Byzantine faults (see [Meyer, 1987]). Discuss the complexity of your algorithm with the OM algorithm.

3.3. Assuming that the voter is unreliable, develop a reliability-safety trade-off table for a five-module system. Assume voter reliability of 0.99. Assuming each module has a built-in fault detection capability to detect the fault, design a voter for a 4-out-of-5 scheme.

3.4. Construct the H matrix for a Hsiao code with 11 data bits and design the encoder and decoder logic. Compare this decoder logic design against standard SEC/DED Hamming code decoder.

3.5. Compare the two checkpoint schemes discussed—processor cache and virtual—from the point of view of performance overhead. Discuss a scheme similar to that implementated in Sequoia for handling faults during checkpointing in a virtual checkpoint scheme.

3.6. Develop a Markov model for the RFCS scheme and plot reliability and failure rate trade-offs. Assume the spare has a reliability higher than the two primary modules since it is not used continuously, and compare the reliability and overhead of the standard TMR with the RFCS scheme.

3.7. Compare the performance overheads of pessimistic and optimistic recovery schemes. Discuss ways to reduce these overheads.

3.8. A hypercube of N processors has $log(N)$ connections per processor. Design a new reconfiguration scheme for a hypercube that uses one spare processor and uses no more than $2.log(N)$ links per processor and which can tolerate single processor faults. (*Hint:* Lay out processors of a hypercube in a line and identify pairs of processors in each hypercube dimension. For each dimension, connect all pairs of processors and the spare processor in a ring, such that you can configure $N/2$ pairs of fault-free processors among $N + 1$ processors in each dimension.)

3.9. You are given a shuffle exchange multistage interconnection network that connects 32 processors to 32 memories using 2×2 switches. Each source is connected to each destination through a unique path. Show the unique path from source 10010 to destination 11000. Design a fault-tolerant interconnection network that uses two extra stages of switches. How many paths exist from each source to each destination? Show the paths for source 10010 to destination 11000. Consider a second design of a fault-tolerant network by duplicating the entire network. Show the two redundant paths from source 10010 to destination 11000. A third design of a fault-tolerant network is to design the network using three stages of 4×4 switches. You will note that some redundant bits are present in this network to route from each source to each destination. Compare the effectiveness of each of these schemes.

3.10. Several commercial distributed-memory multicomputers are built around the two-dimensional toroidal mesh topology. In the fault-free case, routing in these networks is performed under the X-first, Y-next algorithm, which can be proven to be deadlock free. Under faults, develop a fault-tolerant routing algorithm that routes around faults using shortest paths, if they exist in the network, and uses nonshortest paths when they do not exist.

3.11. Design and implement an algorithm-based fault tolerance scheme for the Gaussian elimination method for solving dense linear systems of equations on a commercial multicomputer such as an Intel iPSC hypercube or a Connection Machine CM-5. Use row and column checksum encoding. Assume there is no need for pivoting.

3.12. Design and implement an algorithm for checkpointing and recovery in message-passing multicomputers. Compare between synchronous and asynchronous methods of checkpointing and vary the checkpointing frequency. Examine some real message-passing applications to see if you can avoid domino effects of rollback and recovery.

3.13. One of the methods of reconfiguration in a hypercube described in the chapter used an embedding of spare processors in specific modes of a hypercube. Develop a similar method for two-dimensional and three-dimensional meshes. Develop an embedding such that each processor is, at most, one hop away from a spare node. Then, given a fault pattern (choose at random), develop the reconfiguration method by assigning faulty processors to available spares, using the bipartite graph model described in the chapter.

3.14. Develop an algorithm-based fault tolerance scheme for a single processing or image processing algorithm of your choice. Use a checksum encoding or a property inherent to the algorithm to detect faults.

3.15. Consider the hyper-DeBruijn graph, shown in Figure 3.39. Derive different fault detection and fault location capabilities that can be found for this network, using system diagnosis theory. Consider both centralized and distributed diagnosis environments.

4

Case Studies in Fault-Tolerant Multiprocessor and Distributed Systems

Dhiraj K. Pradhan

4.1 INTRODUCTION

The last three chapters reviewed various design concepts, and also examined certain architectural issues. This chapter provides an in-depth examination of eight different fault-tolerant architectures. Two of these are prototypes; the other five architectures are commercially available systems two of which have already been briefly discussed in Chapter 2. These architectures have been carefully selected as representative in order to provide an overview of a wide range of techniques commonly used in the real world. As will be apparent, many of the techniques discussed earlier have already been used in medium-performance fault-tolerant systems.

Tandem, CLX, Cyclone, Cyclone IR, Dynabus, EXPANO, Guardian, NonStop, Himalaya, and TorusNet are trademarks of Tandem Computers Incorporated. Stratus, Continuous Processing, and FTX are registered trademarks of Stratus Computer Incorporated, and RSN and XA/R are trademarks of Stratus Computer Incorporated. Sequoia is a registered trademark, and TOPIX is a trademark of Sequoia Systems Incorporated. MC68040 is a registered trademark and VME Bus is a trademark of Motorola Incorporated. All other brand and product names are trademarks or registered trademarks of their respective companies.

236

4.2 CASE STUDY 1: TANDEM MULTICOMPUTER SYSTEMS

4.2.1 Introduction

Tandem Computers, Inc. has been developing fault-tolerant multicomputer systems since the 1970s. Among its most recent offerings are the Cyclone and Himalaya families of reliable parallel processing systems. The following presents two of these systems: the NonStop Cyclone and the Himalaya K10000.

4.2.2 NonStop Cyclone

The NonStop Cyclone (Tandem, 1990; Tandem, 1993), shown in Figure 4.1, can be classified as a Multiple Instruction Multiple Data stream (MIMD), loosely coupled, distributed-memory, shared-bus multiprocessor (Hwang and Briggs, 1984).

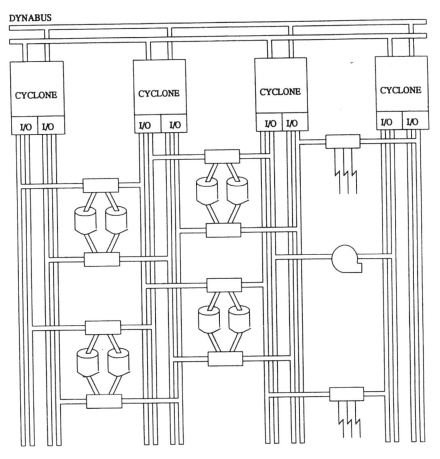

Figure 4.1: Tandem NonStop Cyclone system.

First introduced in 1989, the Cyclone system was designed with the primary objective of preventing a single hardware or software failure from disabling the system. Its processors execute independently, running Tandem's proprietary, fault-tolerant, load-balancing, GUARDIAN 90 operating system. The GUARDIAN 90 operating system maintains idle backups of user processes on separate processors, transparently, in case of failure (Lee and Iyer, 1993). It also provides load balancing to minimize idle components and increase performance. A fully configured Cyclone system contains 16 processors, 2GB of main memory, and 64 I/O channels. However, further expansion is available through Tandem's FOX network and EXPAND networking software, which can connect up to 255 Cyclone systems in a single distributed, fault-tolerant network.

System architecture.   The Cyclone's processors were designed around an advanced, *superscalar*, CISC architecture (Horst, Harris, and Jardine 1990). This architecture uses dual eight-stage pipelines and an instruction-pairing technique to allow simultaneous operations on multiple instructions. Additional features include separate 64KB instruction and data caches, and the use of dynamic branch prediction algorithms for the minimization of costly pipeline "bubbles." Error-correcting memory arrays, totaling up to 128MB, comprise the main memory for each Cyclone processor.

The Cyclone's architecture uses multiple, physically separate *sections*. Each section houses up to four processors interconnected by a proprietary, fault-tolerant bus called Dynabus. Dynabus is composed of redundant interprocessor buses, which have an aggregate throughput of 40MB/sec. Up to four sections can be interconnected using another proprietary, fault-tolerant interprocessor bus called Dynabus+, shown in Figure 4.2. Dynabus+ uses fiber optics to achieve the same aggregate bandwidth as Dynabus over a much greater distance, up to 50 meters. This eases installation by allowing sections of the Cyclone system to be placed in different locations within a room, or in different rooms altogether. However, regardless of their location, the sections must be powered by the same external source. By isolating Dynabus+ from Dynabus, processors can communicate simultaneously within separate sections at the maximum bandwidth provided by Dynabus.

Each Cyclone processor can support one or two I/O subsystems consisting of two I/O channels each. Each channel supports up to 32 I/O controllers, which work with a variety of devices or communications lines. Each I/O subsystem can transmit data at a burst rate of 5MB/sec. for an aggregate bandwidth of 10MB/sec. per processor. The Cyclone also uses direct memory access (DMA) I/O channels, so no processor cycles are required to move data from a channel to memory or vice versa.

Hardware fault tolerance.   The NonStop Cyclone employs redundant hardware throughout its subsystems to reduce the possibility of a single point of failure. Using multiple processors, redundant buses and I/O controllers, mirrored disks, and multiple power supplies, Tandem has ensured that failure of a

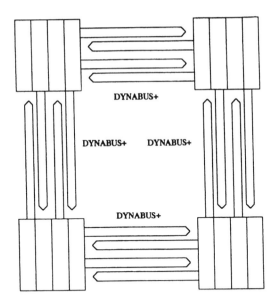

DYNABUS+

DYNABUS+   DYNABUS+

DYNABUS+

SYSTEM

Figure 4.2: Four separate sections connected by Dynabus+.

single major component will not bring the system down. Components that do fail are guaranteed to "fail fast," and terminate operation immediately after detection of an error to reduce the possibility of error propagation. Components are also designed to be replaced online by on-site personnel, increasing availability while reducing the chance for a fatal second failure.

The availability of multiple processors and memories, online diagnostics, and various coding techniques allows continuous operation in the event of a processor or memory failure. Hardware self-checking logic is used to detect when a processor has failed. When a failed processor is detected, the GUARDIAN 90 operating system distributes the processor's applications to the remaining processors, transparently, where they continue to execute unabated. Main memory, located on each processor card, is protected by coding techniques, embedded in hardware, which corrects single-bit errors and detects double-bit errors. Control store and cache memory arrays automatically recover from transient failures, but a spare RAM chip is available for use in case of a permanent failure.

Reliable interprocessor communication is handled by Tandem's Dynabus and Dynabus+. Dynabus is composed of two independent, 20MB/sec. buses capable of simultaneous operation, which are used to connect processors within a section, as shown in Figure 4.1. Dynabus+ uses four unidirectional optic fibers, resulting in redundant, bidirectional links, which are used to connect sections together, as shown in Figure 4.2. In addition to the reliability gained by redundant links, Dynabus+ has the additional advantage of fiber optic cabling, which reduces the risk of errors caused by electromagnetic interference.

Extra I/O subsystems and channels are used to improve I/O performance and connectivity. Each Cyclone processor has two I/O subsystems, each with two I/O channels, dual-ported controllers, and mirrored disks. Each I/O subsystem has redundant channels, and each channel is capable of solely supporting an I/O controller and its attached device. The I/O controllers are dual-ported, with each port connected to two channels from separate I/O subsystems within different processors, as shown in Figure 4.1. This thorough level of redundancy ensures that if a processor, I/O subsystem, or channel fails, an alternate is readily available to take over access of the supported device. When a failure occurs, the operating system is designed to transfer access away from the failed component to its alternate, transparently, without losing any data that may be in transit. The Cyclone's disks, one of the most critical devices, employ similar techniques for protection of their data. Each logical disk is actually a physical pair of disks and is mirrored to ensure that there is a redundant copy of stored data. Each physical disk is dual-ported, with each port connected to separate I/O controllers. Disks are replaceable online, with new drives configured and updated automatically by the system.

The design of the Cyclone system incorporates several other techniques that improve reliability and availability, including high-speed impingement air cooling, integrated backplanes, and field-replaceable units. Excessive heat and radical temperature changes greatly reduce the life expectancy of electronic components. To reduce the chance of such failures, the Cyclone employs impingement cooling, which blows air directly down onto components to eliminate overheating to maintain a consistent temperature throughout the platform. Excessive internal cabling is also a problem, since cables restrict air flow and hamper maintenance. Thus, the Cyclone uses highly integrated backplanes which greatly reduce the amount of internal cabling. The backplanes also enable the implementation of components onto individual, on-site replaceable, hot-pluggable cards, which Tandem calls *field-replaceable units* (FRUs). Processors, I/O controllers, fans, and power supplies are all implemented as FRUs. This is made possible through the operating system's support of transparent switching and reconfiguration of redundant resources.

Software fault tolerance.   The NonStop Cyclone system runs Tandem's proprietary GUARDIAN 90 operating system (Lee and Iyer, 1993). GUARDIAN 90 augments the fault-tolerant hardware by providing error detection and recovery from hardware and software failures using consistency checks, special protocols, redundant data, and backup processes.

The GUARDIAN 90 operating system detects failures using kernel and nonkernel consistency checks, and the "I'm alive" message protocol. Consistency checks, such as the comparison of redundant data structures and kernel-level assertions, are designed to catch local software and hardware failures (Lee and Iyer, 1993). In the event that an error is detected, the operating system is designed to immediately halt the processor to ensure data integrity. Other processors can detect a halted processor using the "I'm alive" protocol. The "I'm alive" protocol keeps each processor in the system up-to-date about the status of every other processor by exchanging messages. Every second, each processor in the system sends a special "I'm alive" message over every bus to all other processors in the system. Every two seconds, each processor checks to see if it has received a message from every other processor. If a message has not been received from a particular processor during that period, it is assumed to be down.

For critical applications, the GUARDIAN 90 operating system creates and maintains a duplicate backup process on a separate processor. If the primary process fails or falls victim to a hardware failure, the GUARDIAN 90 operating system automatically switches to the backup. In order to reduce overhead, the backup process is implemented as a passive replica of the primary process, becoming active only when the primary process fails. Consistency between the primary and backup processes is maintained through periodic checkpointing messages. Prior to performing a critical function, such as changing information in a database through an output commit, the primary process sends a checkpoint message to its backup. Contained within the message are data and status information necessary to complete the critical operation if the primary process fails. If it should happen that the backup process cannot be activated, the GUARDIAN 90 operating system halts the entire processor.

4.2.3 Himalaya K10000

The Himalaya K10000, shown in Figure 4.3, is a loosely coupled, massively parallel multicomputer composed of fault-tolerant multiprocessor sections connected in a three-dimensional torus topology (Horst, 1994). Introduced in 1993, the K10000 was designed to satisfy the ever-increasing performance, reliability, and availability requirements that large commercial applications demand. The K10000's intersection network, shown in Figure 4.4, gives customers the option of purchasing a system with as few as 4 processors, one full section, or as many as 4,080 processors. The loosely coupled, sectioned architecture also allows customers to easily upgrade the system as needed. The K10000 is similar in design to the NonStop Cyclone, but their processor architectures and section interconnections differ sharply. However, like the majority of Tandem's systems, the K10000 was built with the overall objectives of eliminating single points of failure and preventing the propagation of errors; to this end, almost every component is replicated and fail-fast. Its most notable features are its CPU architecture and three-dimensional torus network, called TorusNet.

The K10000 builds on the framework established in the Cyclone family of systems. However, unlike the Cyclone's single superscalar CISC processor, the K10000 system uses two cross-coupled 150 MHz R4400 RISC processors. The K10000's processors reside on a single CPU board, and are viewed as a single "logical" processor. Processor *cross-coupling* is the practice of forcing two processors into executing the same instruction and then comparing their results. In the K10000, if a fault is detected by the comparator logic, then the CPU board is immediately shut down. Thus, error latency and propagation are reduced at the cost of twice the number of processors. The K10000 CPUs are also distinguished by their large complements of cache, main memory, and I/O channels. Each CPU

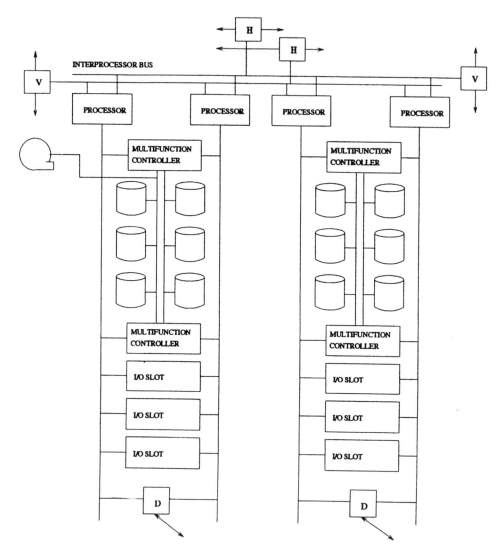

Figure 4.3: Tandem Himalaya K10000 system.

has 32KB of primary cache, 4MB of secondary cache, and up to 256MB of main memory. In addition, each CPU supports an I/O subsystem with four independent I/O channels.

TorusNet, Tandem's proprietary reliable, fiber-optic network, was designed for connecting sections within the K10000. As shown in Figure 4.3, each section contains redundant vertical and horizontal TorusNet, fiber optic controllers (labelled V and H respectively), connected directly to the section's interprocessor bus. The horizontal controllers are capable of connecting four sections in a ring, called a *node*. The vertical controllers are capable of connecting up to 14 nodes in

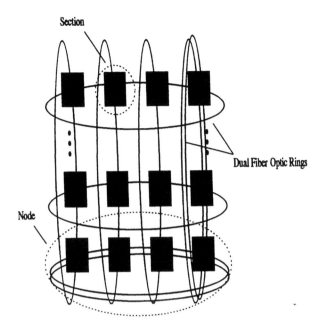

Figure 4.4: Himalaya K10000's intersection network.

a two-dimensional torus, called a *domain*. A third pair of controllers, called the *depth* controllers (labelled D), are standard LAN or WAN controllers that are capable of connecting 16 domains together for a total of 4,080 processors. The redundant controllers and links provide protection from any single controller, link, or power supply failure from disconnecting the system and disrupting service. Furthermore, the fiber optic cabling provides sufficient bandwidth and noise resistance for interconnecting large numbers of processors.

4.3 CASE STUDY 2: TANDEM INTEGRITY S2

4.3.1 Introduction

The Tandem Integrity S2 was designed to meet the need for a reliable UNIX-based computing system (Jewett, 1991). Prior to the Integrity S2's conception, fault-tolerant systems typically utilized proprietary operating systems. However, the majority of commercial applications were, and still are, being written for UNIX-based systems. Thus, Tandem developed the Integrity S2, a fault-tolerant system which supports UNIX applications. Requirements that Tandem made regarding the Integrity S2 were that it has to provide source-level application portability, support for an industry-standard peripheral bus, and data integrity throughout the entire system. The resultant system is comprised of a TMR core of

R4000 RISC processors with duplexed memories and I/O subsystems. Redundant power supplies and batteries provide UPS protection, and low-level system software provides fault detection and recovery within a transparent layer between the hardware and the MIPS-ported UNIX OS. The following review of this unique architecture presents the hardware and its fault-tolerant strategies, the fault-tolerant aspects of the system software, and system performance benchmarks.

4.3.2 Architecture

A block diagram of the Integrity S2 architecture is shown in Figure 4.5. Elements within the system are divided into hot-pluggable customer replaceable units. The overall system consists of seven primary components: central processor units (labeled CPC in Figure 4.5); triple-modular-redundant (TMR) controllers (labeled TMRC); I/O packetizers (labeled IOP); reliable system buses (labeled RSB); reliable I/O buses (labeled RIOB); NonStop V+ buses; and I/O controllers (not shown).

The triplicate central processor units comprise the main processing core of the system. Each unit is replaceable by the customer and consists of an R4000 RISC processor, and R4010 floating point co-processor, a 33MHz oscillator, 128KB

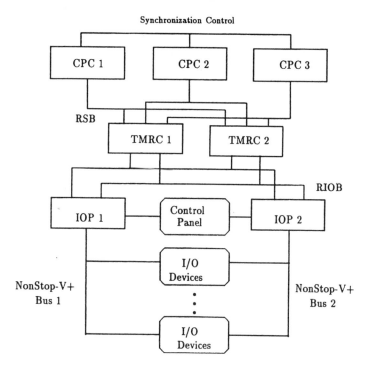

Figure 4.5: The Integrity S2 architecture.

split instruction and data caches, and an interface onto a reliable system bus. In addition, each unit contains a write buffer, various peripherals, and synchronization and interrupt handling logic. On board each processor has a direct memory access (DMA) component which contains at least 8MB of DRAM local store, hardware write protection logic, and its own interface onto the reliable system bus. The DMA component is responsible for transferring pages of memory from the global store to the local memory store. The triplicate reliable system buses transport information between the processing units and the duplexed TMR controllers. The duplexed TMR controllers are responsible for the TMR voting and the global store. Each contains 128MB of global memory, the TMR voters, interrupt registers, and interfaces to the reliable system and I/O buses. The duplexed reliable I/O buses transport information between the TMR controllers and the I/O packetizers. The duplexed I/O packetizers provide the interface between the TMR controllers and the peripherals on the NonStop-V+ buses. Their primary purpose is to translate reliable I/O bus operations to NonStop-V+ operations and vice versa. They also contain registers for holding interrupts issued by the peripherals on the bus. The duplexed NonStop-V+ buses transport information between the I/O device controllers and the I/O packetizers. The I/O controllers comprise the interface between the I/O devices and the NonStop-V+ buses. They are responsible for the translation of NonStop-V+ bus operations to the industry standard VME bus interface upon which the devices reside.

4.3.3 Fault Tolerance Strategies

One of the primary design goals of the engineers at Tandem was to ensure data integrity throughout the system. To accomplish this, the Integrity S2 implements many fault-tolerant strategies at all levels of its architecture. The following sections present many of these strategies.

Processing core.   The processing core is composed of three central processing units in a TMR configuration. The TMR configuration provides protection from a single module failure or uncorrelated permanent, transient, or intermittent faults by voting on the information passing to and from the global store. The processing units themselves do not have self-checking logic or other fault-tolerant features but rely solely on the data integrity and fault tolerance provided by the TMR voting.

TMR voting is performed when the processors come to a point in their instruction streams that necessitates access of a resource beyond the boundary of their units, at which point they simultaneously generate the same request onto the reliable system buses for passage to the duplexed TMR controllers. Each TMR controller then votes on the command, address, and data fields of the request and informs the processing units of any discrepancies via the status and exception mechanisms of the reliable system buses. If there is a failure within one of the processing units or reliable system buses, then the voting mechanisms could be blocked waiting on the requisite data. To avoid this, the TMR controllers employ timers that limit the amount of time spent waiting on a result. In addition, since requests are buffered by the processing units, a bus arbiter is included on each unit that ensures that reads and writes occur synchronously to eliminate voting errors.

Each processor has its own clock, and therefore, operates independently of the others. This makes it possible for each processor to execute different instruction streams when voting is not important, such as during the boot process and certain failure and reintegration procedures. However, when voting is desired, the processors must execute the same instruction stream synchronously. Since the processors have their own clock, they cannot be synchronized in lockstep fashion but, instead, are logically aligned by instruction. Thus, the processors are synchronized in a virtual time domain where the passage of time is counted by instruction, as opposed to the physical time domain where time is counted by clock cycle. Therefore, it is possible to have each processor at a different virtual time at the same point in physical time. To maintain their virtual time synchronization, several techniques are employed.

Processor synchronization is accomplished during voted read instructions and periodic rendezvous. Voted read instructions inherently align the processors since there is only a single logical copy of the data, and all the processors must receive it at the same virtual time. However, since the processors can execute within their cache for a long time, it is possible that a processor could stray far enough such that the TMR controllers time out while waiting on its result. Thus, periodic rendezvous are established through the use of a set of counters on each processing unit. As each instruction is executed, a processing unit's counter is incremented until it reaches a synchronization point, at which time, the processor is suspended until the other processors reach the same point.

The handling of interrupts produces another problem for virtual time domain synchronization. Since the handling of an exception can cause state changes within a processor or initiate voted reads or writes, it is imperative that the processors are interrupted at the same virtual moment. Thus, interrupts are also handled by virtue of instruction counters to ensure that they occur upon the same instruction boundary across all processors.

The DMA engines on the processing units protect data integrity by generating checksums over each block of data they transfer. These checksums are then used by the operating system to check end-to-end data transfers.

Global memory and voting. The duplexed TMR controllers contain the global memory, TMR voters, and interrupt registers. The controllers are organized in a hot sparing configuration. During operation, one controller is designated as the primary and drives its output on the buses. The other controller is considered a hot spare and, although it performs the exact same operations, its output is disconnected from the bus. Thus, in the event of a failure of the primary, the spare can be switched onto the bus without a loss of data. To handle failures, the controllers contain self-checking logic for fail-fast operation. Thus, if the primary controller's self-checking logic detects an error, it is disconnected and replaced by the spare.

The global memory on the TMR controllers is protected by parity, with a parity bit per byte of data. The memory is word-oriented, and the even parity of the word address of the datum is hashed into every byte of data parity to detect addressing failures in the memory controller.

The TMR voters on the controllers contain two parts, a majority voter and a vote analyzer. The majority voter performs a bitwise majority vote on the data from the processing units. The vote analyzer determines if one of the inputs is faulty, so that the appropriate processing unit can be flagged for repair. To detect errors in the voters, each TMR controller actually contains a pair of voters whose outputs are compared.

The registers and static RAMS on the TMR controllers are protected by even byte parity, and the EPROMs by checksum. All of the data paths are protected by even parity hashed among the four data bytes comprising the word of data being transferred.

I/O subsystem.   The duplexed I/O packetizers are responsible for the translation of bus operations from the reliable I/O buses to the NonStop-V+ buses. The packetizers are self-checking and fail-fast, and each can provide full operation in case the other one fails. The data paths of the packetizers are protected by even parity hashed among the datum, similar to what is used in the TMR controllers.

Since it is possible for an I/O controller to directly access global memory, the I/O packetizers contain a mechanism to prevent illegal access and to isolate the global memory from peripheral faults. Each packetizer contains a direct mapped cache table, called the Access and Validation RAM (AVRAM), that maps virtual VME bus addresses, generated by the I/O controllers, to physical, reliable I/O bus addresses. When the AVRAM is translating a request, it verifies that the controller has access to read or write the requested reliable I/O bus address by checking the protection bits in the AVRAM. Thus, global memory integrity is maintained even in the face of a faulty I/O controller.

Likewise, to prevent global memory faults from propagating to the I/O devices, the I/O packetizers present a picture of a singular global memory by detecting erroneous data and compensating. Thus, if the primary TMR controller provides faulty data, the I/O packetizers submit a request for the same data to the spare TMR controller.

Power subsystem.   The power subsystem provides fault-tolerant operation through the use of redundant batteries and power supplies. The duplexed 24VDC batteries drive two independent power buses and supply continuous operation in the face of brownouts and temporary power during a power outage. The duplexed 36VDC power supplies drive two additional independent power buses and supply the primary power during operation. Each customer replaceable unit is connected to all four power buses through DC-DC converters which extract the necessary voltage. Thus, the system can tolerate one power supply failure and still provide continuous operation. If both power supplies fail, or if there is a power outage, then the redundant batteries supply power for a graceful system shutdown.

4.4 CASE STUDY 3: STRATUS XA/R SERIES 300 SYSTEMS

4.4.1 Introduction

Stratus Computer, Inc. started producing fault-tolerant computing systems in 1981 and is acknowledged as being the first to provide purely hardware-based fault tolerance (Webber and Beirne, 1991). Since that time, its effective "pair-and-spare" approach has made Stratus one of the primary contenders in the fault-tolerant computing arena. In the Stratus approach, system boards are duplicated. On each board there are identical pairs of circuits which execute the same operations and continually compare results. If a comparison fails, the faulty board is immediately isolated from the systems while its duplicate continues to operate unabated. The XA/R Series 300 family of systems is one of the most recent offerings from Stratus (Stratus, 1992a). The Series 300 systems, designed for the lucrative online transaction processing market, utilize RISC technology to provide high levels of performance in a scalable MIMD, tightly coupled, shared-memory, shared-bus, symmetric multiprocessing environment (Hwang and Briggs, 1984). Two operating systems are offered with the Series 300 systems: the UNIX-based FTX system, or the proprietary VOS system (Stratus, 1992b).

4.4.2 System Architecture

The XA/R Series 300 systems are composed of one or more *modules* connected via Stratus's redundant, intermodule bus called StrataLINK. Each module, shown in Figure 4.6, is independent and complete, containing duplexed processor, memory, and I/O boards, a battery backup system and redundant power supplies, and supported devices. System boards communicate across a proprietary fault-tolerant bus, integrated into the backplane of the module's cabinet. On top of the hardware, Stratus provides users with their choice of operating systems: the UNIX SVR4 compliant FTX or Stratus's proprietary VOS.

The Series 300 processors are based on the Intel i860 family of 64-bit RISC microprocessors. Depending on the model, a single module can have from one to six "logical" processors containing redundant sets of either 32MHz i860XR or 48MIIz i860XP physical microprocessors. External cache is included on each processor board to augment the i860's own internal cache.

Main memory is shared and can be installed in increments of 32MB or 128MB.

All I/O in the Series 300 modules is handled by redundant, dedicated I/O

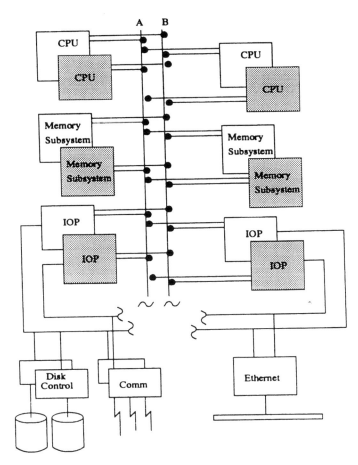

Figure 4.6: Stratus XA/R Series 300 module.

processing subsystems. Each I/O subsystem is composed of a duplexed pair of boards which host a group of up to 14 I/O adapters across a proprietary fault-tolerant bus. Each I/O board contains a dedicated Motorola M68030 microprocessor, 4MB of RAM, and a DMA engine. Each proprietary I/O adapter has its own microprocessor, which is responsible for diagnosis, reconfiguration, and recovery. Available adapters include those for networking (IEEE 802.3, IEEE 802.5, and X.21), asynchronous terminals, universal serial communications (RS232, RS422, RS423, and V.35), SCSI disks, tapes, printers, StrataLINK, and Stratus's Remote Service Network.

StrataLINK is Stratus's proprietary intermodule bus. It is composed of duplexed boards driving redundant 1.4MB/sec. coaxial links. The VOS operating system uses StrataLINK to present the collection of interconnected modules as a unified system. In addition, VOS supports message passing between processes across StrataLINK.

A fully configured module has six logical processors, 512MB of main memory, 105GB of disk storage, and 8 I/O subsystems capable of supporting 112 I/O adapters. Using StrataLINK, up to 32 systems may be loosely interconnected as one large multiprocessing system, for a total of up to 192 processors.

4.4.3 The Pair-and-Spare Approach

Stratus's architecture centers around the pair-and-spare approach to fault tolerance. In the general *pair-and-spare* approach, a system is composed of a pair of identical primary components and any number of spare components. All of the components receive the same inputs and feed their outputs into a switch. The switch selects the outputs of two of the components and feeds them into a comparator. Initially, the switch chooses the outputs from the primary pair of components, while the spares are held on standby. If the comparator detects a disagreement in the components' outputs, the faulty component is identified and taken offline. A spare is then activated to take its place.

Advantages of the pair-and-spare approach are that errors are detected immediately with high probability and prevented from propagating beyond the system's boundary. However, a problem with this approach is how to determine which component failed. If diagnostics are used, then there is a disruption in service until the failed component is convicted. To overcome this problem, Stratus permanently pairs components together such that if an error is detected, both components are taken offline. The spare components are not held on standby but operate in synchrony with the primary components, driving their outputs onto the bus. Thus, if a comparison fails, the suspect components may be quietly taken offline while their "partner" components continue to operate unabated.

General system board. The XA/R Series 300 system boards are self-checking and fail-fast. Each primary system component is duplicated onto separate halves of a single system board, as shown in Figure 4.7. Both halves, labeled A and B in Figure 4.7, are designed to operate independently, but in synchronous lockstep. Synchronization logic ensures that the boards perform the exact same operations on the exact same input every clock cycle. During each cycle, on-board, redundant comparator logic compares the outputs from the two halves. If there is a mismatch, the comparators immediately disable output to the bus, take the board offline, raise a flag, and light a LED on the front of the board. Otherwise, the comparators enable the bus interface and allow the board to drive its output onto the bus. Since the bus interface is beyond the comparator logic, its failure cannot be detected by the board. Thus, additional logic, described later, is employed to detect a faulty bus interface. In order to reduce the possibility of a power supply failure, each system board also contains its own power regulator. Incorporating power regulation into each system board reduces the complexity of the critical power supplies, increasing overall system reliability.

Almost every system board in an XA/R Series 300 system has an identical partner board. Partner boards may either operate in synchronous lockstep or as

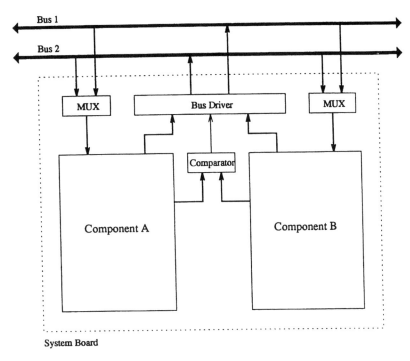

Figure 4.7: Stratus system board.

logical pairs. Partner boards that operate in lockstep perform identical operations each clock cycle. Thus, at any one time, four circuits may place data onto the bus. To compensate, the outputs of the circuits are logically ORed by the bus. The processor and memory boards operate in synchronous lockstep. Partner boards that operate as logical pairs do not execute in lockstep but rely on the operating system for synchronization. Unlike the boards that operate in synchronous lockstep, the failure of a logically paired board may affect its partner by increasing its workload. Disk, network, and communications boards operate as logical pairs.

Processors, memory and I/O.   The processors and memory control logic are self-checking and operate in synchronous lockstep with their partner boards, as described previously. However, additional techniques are employed to protect the memory arrays. Each memory array is duplexed, with one array located on each partner board, and is protected by error-correcting codes. Additional protection is provided by "scrubber" logic, which continually and methodically checks memory locations for latent errors, correcting them as it goes.

Each I/O processing subsystem is composed of a duplexed pair of self-checking system boards. Attached to each subsystem is a proprietary fault-tolerant bus, which hosts logically paired I/O adapters. The bus is composed of redundant, independent buses, each protected by parity. The I/O adapters also contain special logic to monitor the bus for errors.

Main bus and power subsystem.   The main bus, shown in Figure 4.6, is actually two independent buses, each capable of handling the full load. The buses are integrated into the backplane of the XA/R Series 300 cabinet and are socketed for connection to each board. Both buses are protected by parity, which is monitored by detection logic located on the memory boards. The detection logic continually monitors the parity signals that cross the redundant buses. If an error is detected on one of the buses, the detection logic signals all boards to cease use of the suspect bus. However, every system board is connected to both buses, so the loss of one bus does not disable the module.

Each Series 300 module has redundant power supplies and battery backups to protect against power disturbances or supply failures. The redundant power supplies drive independent rails which supply either all the even or odd slots in the cabinet's backplane. Therefore, partner boards, which are inserted adjacent to one another in the cabinet, are powered by separate supplies. This practice ensures that the module can continue to operate in the presence of a power supply failure. To protect from brownouts and blackouts, battery backups are available to power the module long enough for a proper shutdown. When a power failure is detected, the batteries are brought online and the mechanical subsystems are shut down, but the module continues to operate. If the failure continues beyond a preset time threshold, which represents the dividing line between a brownout and a blackout, the module goes into hibernation. The volatile state of each of the system boards is first saved into memory, and then all remaining power is dedicated to supplying the memory boards. The module can remain in this state of hibernation for a long period of time, preventing the loss of data due to extended power failure.

4.4.4 System Software

The Series 300 systems can run the VOS or FTX operating systems. VOS is Stratus's proprietary operating system, tuned for the Series 300 systems. FTX is Stratus's implementation of UNIX SVR4, with extensions for fault tolerance. Both provide support for multiple users, symmetric multiprocessing, batch and interactive sessions, and online hardware replacement. The nature of the Stratus architecture virtually eliminates the need for software-based fault-tolerant techniques such as checkpointing, process shadowing, and interprocess "I'm alive" messaging. However, two proprietary software packages perform critical roles in maintaining continuous processing on the XA/R Series 300 systems: the Maintenance and Diagnostics software, and the Remote Service Network.

The Maintenance and Diagnostics (MD) software is responsible for tracking, diagnosing, and reporting hardware failures and system board reintegration configuration. If a board fails, it is up to the MD software to determine the cause of the failure and take appropriate action. Initially, the MD software computes the board's mean time between failure (MTBF) based on its previous failures. If the calculated MTBF is lower than a preset low-water mark, then the board is assumed to be intermittently faulty and is marked for replacement. Otherwise, the MD software prompts the board to perform its self-tests. If the tests are successful, the failure is classified as transient and the board is brought back into service. However, if the tests fail, the board is known to be permanently faulty and is marked for replacement.

The Remote Service Network (RSN) software is used to communicate with Stratus's Customer Assistance Center (CAC) in the event the MD software determines that a component needs to be replaced. As soon as the decision is made, the MD software notifies the RSN software, which immediately calls the CAC and reports the failure. The RSN software is then used by the CAC staff to confirm the report remotely. Once the failure has been confirmed, the CAC dispatches a replacement part via express shipping. Very often, the system administrator does not know that a part has failed until its replacement arrives. The quick response provided by the RSN software is crucial to maintaining availability, since it is possible that a second board failure could cripple the system.

4.5 CASE STUDY 4: SEQUOIA SERIES 400 SYSTEM

4.5.1 Introduction

Sequoia Systems, Inc. began shipping fault-tolerant systems in 1987. Throughout its existence, Sequoia has focused its attention on businesses which are critically dependent on online transaction processing. The Series 400 systems, first introduced in 1991, use multiple modules of duplexed, self-checking, "off-the-shelf" components in a tightly coupled multiprocessing architecture to provide flexible, scalable, and highly available processing (Sequoia, 1992a).

The Series 400 system uses multiple self-checking processor, memory, and I/O elements running in parallel to achieve high performance and high availability. Elements typically contain a pair of cross-coupled components which perform operations simultaneously and compare results to detect errors. The Series 400 architecture, shown in Figure 4.8, can be classified as a MIMD, tightly coupled, shared-memory, shared-bus, symmetric multiprocessor (Hwang and Briggs, 1984). All processors run Sequoia's proprietary, UNIX-based, fault-tolerant operating system called *TOPIX*. TOPIX is capable of executing applications designed for SYSV and BSD versions of UNIX, providing them with automatic and transparent fault protection. A fully configured Series 400 system consists of multiple system and peripheral cabinets containing 32 processor elements, 16 memory elements of 256MB each (totaling 4GB), and 30 I/O elements (Sequoia, 1992b).

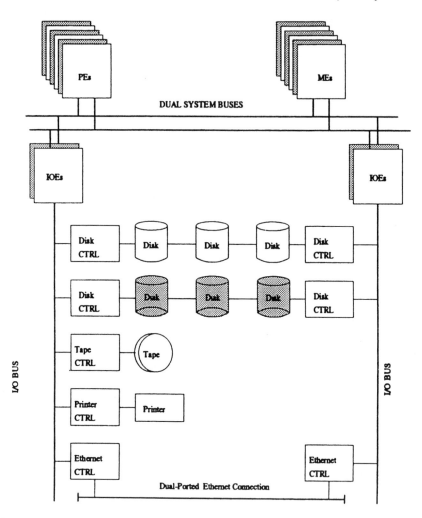

Figure 4.8: Components of a Sequoia system.

4.5.2 System Architecture

Each processor element, shown in Figure 4.9, uses dual Motorola M68040 microprocessors. The M68040 is a 32-bit, 33 MHz microprocessor containing an on-chip floating point unit, separate 4KB instruction and data caches, and separate instruction and data memory management units. The M68040 can address a virtual memory address space of up to 4GB. The dual processors are augmented with a second-level 4MB, four-way set-associative, nonwrite-through cache; a PROM containing system diagnostic and fault recovery code; a bootstrap loader; and duplexed comparator logic.

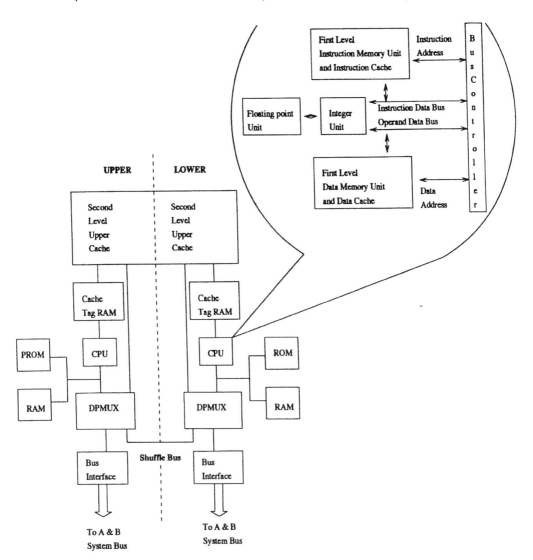

Figure 4.9: Functional block diagram of a processing element.

Each memory element, shown in Figure 4.10, contains up to 256MB of memory organized into one shared array. This array is divided, using independent addressing logic, into two virtual arrays which shadow each other. The addressing logic is designed such that the most significant bit of an address selects one of the virtual arrays, and the remaining bits form the offset address into that array. The base addresses of each of the virtual arrays is stored in physical address registers that can be dynamically reconfigured by the operating system. Each memory ele-

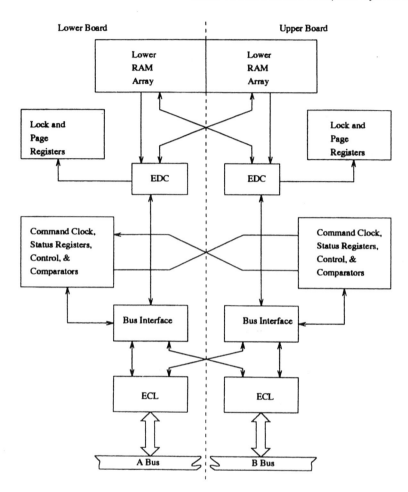

Figure 4.10: Functional block diagram of a memory element.

ment also contains duplexed error detection and memory access logic that independently address the virtual arrays. In addition, hardware test-and-set locks are included, which are used by the operating system to control simultaneous access to shared resources. Every 16MB of memory has 1,024 test-and-set locks.

Each I/O element consists of a duplexed bus adapter and a duplexed multibus adapter. The bus adapter is connected to the local memory bus and resides within the system cabinet. Its primary function is to buffer data passing between the processor elements in the system cabinet, and the multibus adapter in the peripheral cabinet. The bus adapter contains four channels, each having 4KB of buffer space, that are independently accessible by the multibus adapter and processor elements. These four channels form two 8KB fault-tolerant channels, which the bus adapter uses to double-buffer data; while a processor element is accessing one channel buffer, the multibus adapter accesses the other, and then the channels are switched. This activity results in better I/O performance. The multibus adapter, housed in the peripheral cabinet, contains its own duplexed Motorola M68010 microprocessors. These processors run a special operating system that is tuned for the movement of data between memory and the device controllers, located on the adapter's IEEE multibus. The bus adapter and multibus adapter are connected by the external bus, which has a maximum aggregate bandwidth of 5MB per second and allows 400 feet of separation between the two cabinets.

The main duplexed bus used to connect processors, memory, and I/O elements is composed of two 40-bit, 10 MHz buses. These buses are capable of an aggregate peak throughput of 80MB/sec. During normal operation, the two buses operate in parallel. However, if a fault is detected somewhere in the system, only one bus, called the "executive bus," transfers data. A processor chooses the executive bus in advance, using separate lines dedicated for this purpose.

4.5.3 Hardware Fault Tolerance

The Series 400 system implements various fault detection and isolation mechanisms throughout its hardware design. Such mechanisms include the use of error-control codes, the comparison of redundant operations, and protocol monitoring. The duplexed element boards usually have a combination of shared circuitry and redundant circuitry. Shared circuitry is usually protected by error-control codes, whereas redundant circuitry performs continuous comparison of redundant operations. Most elements contain both shared and redundant circuitry. All elements within the Series 400 system use one or more of these mechanisms. If a mechanism detects a failed element, the element is electrically isolated from the system and flagged for repair.

The redundant circuitry in the processor elements, such as the processors and comparators, detect faults by continuously comparing results. The shared circuitry, such as the local cache, uses parity for fault detection. Additionally, each processor element maintains a 128-byte status block in the main memory that describes its operational status. This block is updated every 100 ms and periodically cross-checked by another processor element to ensure that it is operating correctly. The detection of any error results in the automatic and immediate electrical isolation and flagging of the element from the system. Thus, the elements are "fail-fast."

The memory arrays on the memory elements are protected with a double-error detection (DED) and single-error correction (SEC) code. This SEC/DED code requires an additional 8 bits for each 32-bit data word. When a read is issued to a memory element, the error detection and correction (EDC) logic flags single-bit, double-bit, or multiple-bit errors in the element's status registers. If the error is not single-bit, the element removes itself from the physical address space. The EDC logic is protected through duplication and comparison. Finally, to ensure data integrity in the presence of memory element failure, modifiable data is written to two separate memory elements.

The components of an I/O Element, the bus adapter and multibus adapter, are protected separately. However, both contain duplexed boards with shared and redundant circuitry incorporating parity checking and comparison of redundant operations. All peripherals are dual-ported and connected to different I/O elements in order to tolerate the failure of a single I/O element. In addition, file mirroring, writing files to two separate disk drives, is used to enable recovery from hard-disk failure.

Redundant power supplies and battery backup units reduce downtime due to power supply failures or blackouts. The main cabinet's power supply also provides filtering, conditioning, and regulation to reduce the possibility of dirty power damaging components.

4.5.4 Software Fault Tolerance

The Series 400 systems run Sequoia's TOPIX operating system. TOPIX is a high-level, UNIX-based operating system that is compatible with both the AT&T System V.3 and Berkeley, as well as X/Open XPG2 compliant. TOPIX provides support for symmetric multiprocessing, dynamic load balancing, test-and-set locking, trapping of software errors, fault detection, and fault recovery.

Each processor element in the Series 400 runs the TOPIX kernel from a single image in shared memory. In order to allow concurrent access to kernel data, access must be synchronized among the processor elements. Thus, the operating system uses the hardware test-and-set locks, located on the memory elements, to coordinate access to shared resources and maintain consistency of the kernel data. However, in order to recover from a failure, the operating system must maintain a consistent image of the entire system. Kernel support for fault recovery must ensure that a process can be recovered without the loss of data or program continuity, regardless of when a fault occurs. Such fault recovery is dependent on the kernel's ability to always maintain memory resident processes in an internally consistent state.

The TOPIX kernel maintains a consistently recoverable state through periodic "checkpointing." The kernel checkpoints the system by flushing the nonwrite-through caches and registers of the processor elements to the main memory. During execution, dirty pages are stored in the local nonwrite-through cache of each processor element. At regular intervals, or when a processor element is holding a lock it is no longer using, the kernel flushes the caches and registers to the main memory, effectively saving a "snapshot" of the state of the system. If a failure occurs, the kernel rolls back to the previous checkpoint and reexecutes. The kernel protects against failures occurring during the flush operation by flushing data to the backup memory element first. Thus, if a failure occurs during flushing, the kernel can roll back to the checkpoint in the uncorrupted primary element. If the component that failed was a processor element, the kernel divides and relocates the failed element's workload to the remaining operational processor elements. This relocation capability can also be used for dynamic load balancing, improving performance.

The TOPIX operating system incorporates built-in self-checking in the form of executable assertions. When an instruction that is covered by executable assertions is performed, the assertions which cover it are compared with the results of the instruction. If the results violate the assertions, the operating system initiates fault recovery. Additional features of TOPIX include enhanced security protection of sensitive database information, support for remote diagnosis, online expansion, and automatic recovery and reintegration of modules.

Table 4.1 presents a comparison of the fault-tolerant systems discussed so far.

4.6 CASE STUDY 5: THE ERROR-RESISTANT INTERACTIVELY CONSISTENT ARCHITECTURE (ERICA)

4.6.1 Introduction

ERICA is a (4,2)-concept computer that matches hardware redundancy with a (4,2)-error-correcting code to provide a highly reliable system at a relatively low cost (Driel, Follon, Kohler, Osch, and Spanjers, 1990). This architecture was developed by Phillips for use in its switching systems. Its appeal stems from the fact that it is comparable in reliability to that of a Quad Modular Redundancy (QMR) or pair-and-pair system, at a cost roughly equivalent to that of a TMR or doubled system. The following sections present this unique architecture. The first section discusses the philosophy of the (4,2)-concept. The second section presents details of the hardware.

4.6.2 The (4,2)-Concept

The (4,2)-concept approach to modular redundancy is one example of the more general (n,k)-concept. An (n,k)-concept computer has n redundant processors and k redundant memories that operate in synchrony and logically behave as a highly reliable simplex system. It is comprised of n modules, with each module containing a processor, a decoder, an encoder, and a memory slice that is $(k/n)*w$-bits wide, where w is the word size in bits. Data integrity is attained through the use of an (n,k)-error correcting code that is generated for each word of data prior to storage. Thus, a (4,2)-concept computer has four redundant processors and two redundant memories organized into four modules, as shown in Figure 4.11. Each module has a memory slice that stores one-half of a memory word, also called a *symbol*. For a system with 16-bit words, this results in a 32-bit code word comprised of four 8-bit symbols.

When a data word is written to memory, each processor passes the word through its unique encoder, reducing it to a symbol. This symbol is then placed into the module's memory slice. The collection of all the modules' symbols com-

Table 4.1: Comparison of Fault-Tolerant Systems

	NonStop	Integrity S2	Stratus	Sequoia
Architecture	Loosely coupled message-passing multiprocessor.	Uniprocessor with triplicated PEs.	Tightly coupled shared-memory multiprocessor.	Tightly coupled shared-memory multiprocessor.
Operating system	NonStop Kernel/ Guardian.	UNIX.	VOS, FTX (UNIX-based).	TOPIX (UNIX-based).
Fault tolerance scheme	Self-checking modules with check-pointing among duplicate processes.	TMR with self-checking duplexed voter.	Pair-and-spare hardware scheme.	Self-checking modules with a consistent image of process in memory.
Fault tolerance in memory	1-bit error correction and 2-bit error detection of data. Address error detection.	Even bit parity and memory array duplication. Local memory: Memory array triplication.	Single-bit error correction.	Single-error correction and double-error detection, ECC logic is self-checking. Duplex memory elements.
Fault tolerance in bus	Checksum on bus transactions.	Even parity hashed on 4 data bytes.		Error detection mechanism.
Application domain	OLTP.	OLTP and general purpose.	OLTP and general purpose.	OLTP.
Service-ability	Online service and maintenance.	Online service and maintenance.	Online service and maintenance.	On-line service and maintenance.
Overhead	Only one process is active which runs on duplex processors. A dormant copy of the process resides in another PE.	Three processors execute the same process.	Two duplex PEs execute same process.	A duplex PE executes a process with a consistent image of the process in main memory.

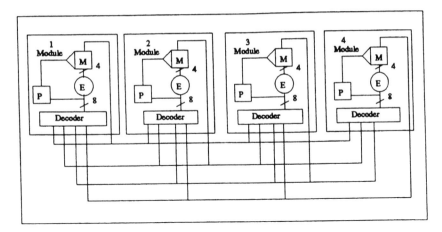

Figure 4.11: The (4,2)-concept computer.

prise the code word for the specific data word. When the data word is to be read from memory, the modules exchange their symbols so that each module's decoder receives all 4 symbols comprising the entire 32-bit code word. The decoder then extracts the original data word and passes it to the processor. If the code word is corrupted, the decoder utilizes the redundancy in the (4,2)-code to reconstruct the original data, provided that the corruption is not beyond what the (4,2)-code is capable of correcting. The code used in ERICA is capable of the following (Driel, Follon, Kohler, Osch, and Spanjers, 1990):

- correction of any single-symbol error
- correction of any double-bit error
- correction of one missing symbol and any single-bit error

Thus, it is apparent that the code can reconstruct the original data, even in the presence of a single module failure.

Because of the modularity of the architecture, errors due to faults within a module do not propagate to other modules. Thus, a module is called a *fault isolation area*. However, because errors can fool correctly working modules it is possible that an error may not be detected immediately, causing inconsistent behavior between modules. To avoid this, a Byzantine General's algorithm, encoded in hardware, is used to ensure agreement between correctly working modules. Thus, a (4,2)-concept computer can safely tolerate one Byzantine module failure.

4.6.3 The Architecture

ERICA is an implementation of a (4,2)-concept computer that has two logical processors, a control processor and a user processor, and 12MB of memory. This translates to a physical system of eight processors and 24MB of memory. Below is a description of a single module of the system, shown in Figure 4.12, followed by a discussion of the data flow through a module. A brief look at ERICA's I/O handling is then presented, followed by a presentation of the (4,2)-bus handling.

Module composition.   A single module consists of two Motorola M68010 16-bit 8MHz microprocessors operating as the user processor and the control processor, 6MB of memory separated into user memory and control memory, two 16-bit buses for the control processor and user processor, several 8-bit encoders, a two-channel I/O handler, a boot ROM, a special store as a workspace for (4,2)-concept-specific tasks, an interrupt and synchronization handler, and a (4,2)-bus handler incorporating a decoder and a hardware implementation of the Byzantine General's algorithm.

The **user processor** executes application programs and the **control processor** manages interrupts, I/O, and (4,2)-concept-specific tasks following an error. Both processors have their own bus and, therefore, are capable of operating independently. All data passing from a processor to a bus can either pass straight through or via two parallel 8-bit encoders. Although one 16-bit encoder could have been used, separate 8-bit encoders were chosen to take advantage of the capability of the processors to operate on 8-bit or 16-bit data. Similarly, other components in the module are sliced into 8-bit implementations and paired to provide greater flexibility. Likewise, data passing from the boot ROM to the control bus is always encoded. The buses' only data interconnection is through the (4,2)-bus handler, but the interrupt and resynchronization handler is also present on

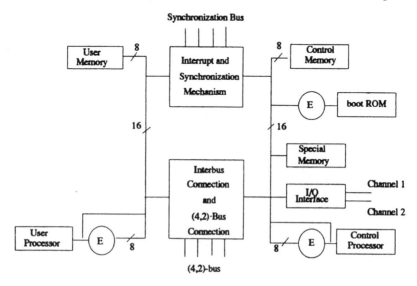

Figure 4.12: The ERICA architecture.

both buses. The only other module present on the user processor's bus is the **user memory**, which is the store for user programs.

Present on the control processor's bus is the control memory, the boot ROM, the special memory, and the I/O interface. The **control memory** is used to store information about the state of the decoder, Byzantine General's logic, and any other information specific to the control of the module. All data stored into the control memory is encoded/decoded in the same fashion as that stored in the user memory to maintain consistency across modules. The **special memory** contains uncoded data that is the result of (4,2)-specific operations and experiments. The **boot ROM** contains code necessary to initialize the machine upon startup. Between the boot ROM and the control bus is a pair of encoders, similar to those used by the processors, that transform all data read from the boot ROM into 8-bit symbols. These symbols are then combined and decoded in the same manner that is used for storing and retrieving data from the memories to ensure data consistency within the boot ROM. The **I/O interface** links the control bus to either of two I/O channels. If the control processor detects a failing channel, the faulty channel can be disabled by the control processor at the I/O interface. The **(4,2)- bus** is 32-bits wide and is responsible for distributing the symbols between the modules. The **(4,2)-bus handler** links the module to the (4,2)-bus. It contains the decoder and the Byzantine General's logic.

Processor operation.   The user processor stores information through encoders, across the user bus, and into the user memory. Since the M68010 is a 16-bit microprocessor, two encoders operate in parallel to encode the 16-bit data word into an 8-bit symbol. Retrieval of information by the user processor is a multistep process. First, the 8-bit symbol is passed from the user memory across the user bus into the (4,2)-concept handler and out onto the (4,2)-bus. Within the handler, the symbol is then combined with the symbols received from the other modules, and the resulting 32-bit code word is passed to the decoder. The decoder extracts the original 16-bit data word, correcting errors if necessary, and passes it across the user bus to the user processor.

The control processor stores and retrieves information from its control memory in the same fashion as the user processor. However, the control processor is responsible for many more tasks. Primarily, the control processor is responsible for managing the interrupt-driven I/O, as well as for controlling the operation of the decoder, the Byzantine General's logic, and any other (4,2)-concept-specific task. The control processor is also responsible for reading the boot ROM on startup and for executing startup routines.

I/O handling.   ERICA interfaces with all I/O devices through two channels located within each module. Access to these channels is provided by the I/O interface unit on the control bus and is handled by the control processor. The I/O devices are standard M680*0 devices and are slaves of ERICA. In order to provide fault isolation from I/O devices, ERICA utilizes interrupt-driven I/O instead of polled I/O, voting on output data and consistency checking on input data.

Interrupt-driven I/O prevents abeyance of normal operation by allowing the control processor within a module the freedom to choose when I/O channels are enabled so that a failed channel does not immediately affect operation. In addition, all control and address lines are unidirectional from the module to the channels. As a matter of fact, the only line that can disturb operations is the interrupt request line, which is unidirectional from the channels to the module. The interrupt request line is used to signal the module when service is demanded by a device. For example, in the case of a read, the control processor enables a channel on which the appropriate device waits and sends out address and control information. When the device has fetched the appropriate data, it issues an interrupt on the interrupt request line of that channel to which it is connected. At an appropriate time, the control processor executes the interrupt handler and removes the data. Some time later, it acknowledges the interrupt and disables the channel. To prevent malicious interrupt activity, once a failed channel is detected its interrupt request line is disabled.

Since all of the modules are operating synchronously, voting is performed on the address and control information before delivery to the appropriate device. The voting is performed for each channel by a set of cards that interface to two separate buses on which the I/O devices wait. Thus, if a channel were to fail, then the correct information could still be delivered to the I/O device.

Upon receipt of the data from the I/O device, the Byzantine General's logic is used to ensure the consistency of the data across all the modules. When the I/O device fetches the data, the data is passed through a set of boards that distribute it to all of the module's channels. If a channel is faulty, then one module will have inconsistent data. To avoid this, all data received from I/O devices is passed through the Byzantine General's logic prior to reception by the control processor. Thus, data consistency is ensured across all modules in the case of channel failure.

(4,2)-bus handling. The (4,2)-bus handler is the interface between the module and the (4,2)-bus. It is responsible for decoding and correcting the 32-bit code words, and for the detection and location of faulty modules to ensure consistency of operation between the correctly working modules. It contains two primary components: a decoder and a Byzantine General's chip, as shown in Figure 4.13. These components are connected to the (4,2)-bus, as well as to an internal bus which connects the user and control buses. Each component is handled by the control processor, which manipulates operations through directly addressable registers within each component. These registers are used to select the components for operation and to maintain "state" information, or the mode of the system, such as information about errors detected or symbols to be erased. The following is a discussion of the operations of these two components.

The decoder receives the 32-bit code word across the four 8-bit symbol lines

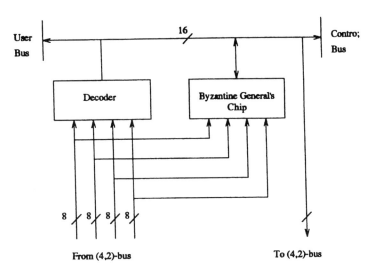

Figure 4.13: The (4,2)-bus handler.

of the (4,2)-bus and extracts the original 16-bit data word. If there are errors in the code word, the decoder uses the redundancy in the (4,2)-code to extract the correct data and flags the errors within its internal error register. If a module has failed, then the error registers of all the correctly working modules' decoders should show the same error flags. To ensure that the errors were due to a module failure and not a transient, the control processor distributes the decoder's error register to its peer modules via the Byzantine General's chip. If, indeed, a module has failed, then the register data is stored into the decoder's mode register. The mode register instructs the decoder to ignore the symbol coming from the failed module in future decoding operations. Thus, a failed module's output symbol, once uniformly detected as faulty, is effectively removed from contention by each of the correctly working modules.

The Byzantine General's chip is a hardware implementation of the Byzantine General's algorithm that is used to form an agreement among all the modules, even in the presence of a maliciously failed module. The basic layout of the Byzantine General's chip can be seen in Figure 4.14. It contains two separate channels of data flow, the bypass data transfer channel, and the voted data transfer channel. Which channel will be used is set by the control processor through the use of one of the internal control registers. The bypass data channel is used primarily to broadcast a bitstream signal from one module to the other modules. The voted data channel is used to vote on the broadcast signals in a manner defined in the Byzantine General's algorithm; it consists of four 3-input voters and one 4-input voter which perform bitwise voting and are designed to erase an input signal as determined by a control register. The decision to erase an input is based on the contents of a mode register that is equivalent to the mode register

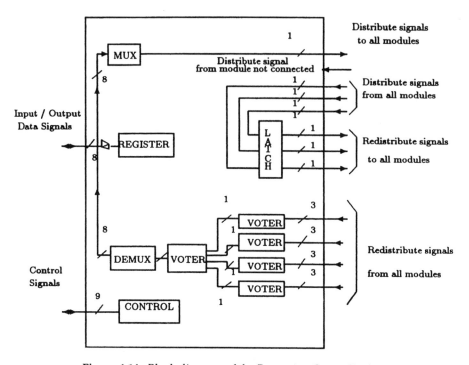

Figure 4.14: Block diagram of the Byzantine General's chip.

used in the decoder. The voters feed a demultiplexer which passes the word of data out onto the control and user buses, or into a multiplexer for distribution to the other modules. Similar to the processor encoders, the Byzantine General's chip is sliced into two 8-bit chips to provide 8-bit and 16-bit processing capability.

4.7 CASE STUDY 6: FAULT-TOLERANT PARALLEL PROCESSOR

4.7.1 Introduction

The fault-tolerant parallel processor (FTPP) architecture, developed by the Charles Stark Draper Laboratory, combines fault tolerance with parallel processing to provide high reliability and high throughput (Harper and Lala, 1991). The FTPP architecture utilizes a Byzantine-resilient hard-core network to connect processing elements into a parallel processor cluster and then combines clusters to form an even layer parallel multiprocessor. The attractiveness of this architecture over others lies in its Byzantine resilience, "off-the-shelf" component construction, mixed redundancy, and parallel hybrid redundancy management. The following sections contain a discussion of Byzantine resilience, a presentation of the FTPP's architecture, and a brief look at some prototypes.

4.7.2 Byzantine Resilience

The FTPP architecture is built around the concept of *Byzantine resilience:* the ability to tolerate any arbitrary hardware failure mode.

Designing a system to be Byzantine-resilient allows the detachment of the user from the implementation details of the fault tolerance techniques. For the FTPP system, the redundant hardware and hardware management are transparent to the user, thus allowing distributed applications to be developed and debugged on simplex systems without consideration of fault tolerance. Likewise, as an aid to the user, the FTPP message-passing system can be unambiguously represented in the form of a Byzantine-resilient virtual circuit abstraction. The Byzantine-resilient virtual circuit abstraction is simply a theoretical black-box model of the FTPP's network, which programmers may refer to when designing distributed programs for the FTPP. The abstraction provides assurance of interprocessor message ordering and validity, even in the presence of Byzantine faults, so that the programmer need not worry about faults when designing a distributed application. For example, a Byzantine-resilient virtual circuit abstraction for a typical triplex configuration on the FTPP provides the following guarantees:

> Messages sent by nonfaulty members of a source triplex are correctly received by nonfaulty members of a destination triplex.

> Messages are received by members of a nonfaulty triplex in the order that they are sent.

The difference in the absolute times of arrival of a corresponding message to members of a triplex does not exceed an upper bound.

4.7.3 Architecture

Network elements.   Since the processing elements in a Byzantine-resilient multiprocessor must be connected by at least $(2f + 1)$ disjoint paths, their connectivity becomes intolerably complex as the system is scaled upward. Likewise, the additional processing overhead incurred by the handling of fault tolerance specific functions has been shown to consume as much as 60 percent of the processor's throughput. Thus, the designers of the FTPP developed special hardware components called *network elements* that reduce the number of interconnections between processing elements, reduce processor overhead due to fault tolerance specific functions, and provide numerous other advantages as well.

Network elements reduce the number of interprocessor connections by allowing multiple processors to share links through the use of time-division multiplexing (TDM). A network element basically has two interfaces: an interconnection network interface and a bus interface, as shown in Figure 4.15. The interconnection network interface is a collection of point-to-point TDM links that connect the network element to its peers. The bus interface is an industry standard bus onto which proces-

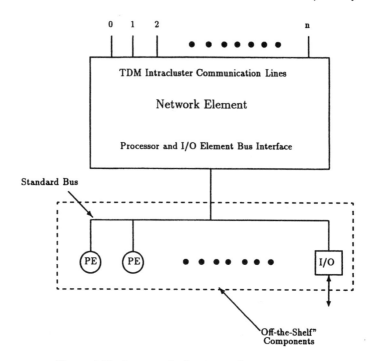

Figure 4.15: A network element and its subscribers.

sor and I/O *subscribers* are connected. Each network element services an exclusive group of subscribers that, together, form a primary fault-containment region. In addition to simple message passing, the services provided by the network elements are those necessary for fault tolerance such as voting, interactive consistency, and synchronization.

The use of network elements has other advantages as well. The provision of a standard bus interface allows the FTPP to be constructed from *"off-the-shelf"* components; this is a significant advantage over systems using proprietary components because it reduces production cost, increases flexibility, and facilitates maintenance. In particular, upgrading or repairing the system can be as simple as swapping old component cards for new ones. The use of a standard bus also makes possible *n*-version fault tolerance by allowing the use of heterogeneous components. For example, one network element may service Intel processors, while another services Motorola processors.

Clusters. A *cluster* is a collection of network, processing, and I/O elements. The network elements within a cluster are fully connected via point-to-point links and form a Byzantine-resilient hard core for their subscribers. This unique design allows the processing elements within the system to be configured into mixed and parallel hybrid redundancy.

A cluster's processing elements can be organized into any number of possible configurations such as quadruplex, triplex, and simplex. For example, Figure 4.16 shows a cluster of 12 processing elements in a mixed redundancy configuration. The cluster contains one quadruplex (Q1), two triplexes (T1 and T2), and two simplexes (S1 and S2). Since members of a Byzantine-resilient computational group must not reside within the same primary fault containment region, each member of group Q1 is connected to a different network element. Likewise, the members of T1 and T2 also reside within unique regions. However, S1 and S2 may reside within any region. Figure 4.17, on the other hand, shows a cluster of four triplex groups. Configuring a cluster this way provides the programmer with a virtual multiprocessor of four very reliable Byzantine-resilient, fault-masking, fully connected processors.

The configuration of a cluster can be dynamically altered to compensate for such events as component failures or changes in the demand for reliable computation. For example, if a component in group Q1 of the cluster in Figure 4.16 were to fail, then the cluster could be reconfigured so that one of the simplex processors would take the place of the failed component within the redundant group. Likewise, the group could be degraded to a triplex, as well.

Ensembles.   Since network elements are bound in speed and bandwidth, a system consisting of a large number of processors cannot be realized utilizing a single cluster. Thus, similar clusters of an appropriately small number of proces-

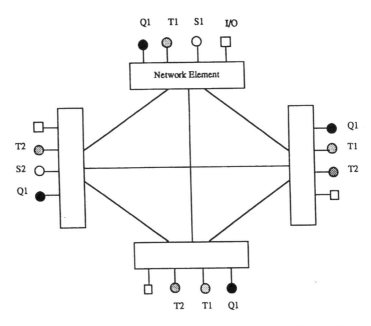

Figure 4.16: A cluster of 12 processing elements in mixed redundancy.

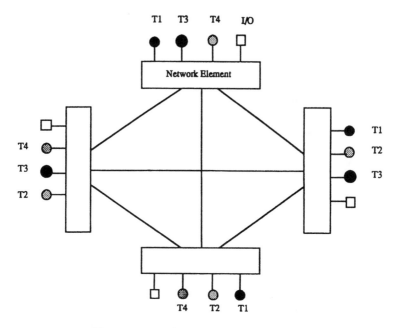

Figure 4.17: A four-triplex group cluster.

sors can be combined to form a larger system, called an ensemble, through the use of special intercluster I/O elements.

An intercluster I/O element (IOE) is a component dedicated to the task of intercluster communication. In an ensemble, each network element has, as one of its subscribers, an IOE connected to corresponding IOEs in neighboring clusters via point-to-point links. Unlike network elements within a cluster, the IOEs are not required to be fully connected. The aggregate IOEs of a cluster form a redundant group and synchronously execute an intercluster message passing protocol to ensure timely and orderly delivery of messages between clusters. For example, Figure 4.18 shows an ensemble of two clusters, each containing 24 processing elements divided equally among six network elements, as might be used for a multiprocessor of 16 triplex groups. Each network element has one IOE as a subscriber for a total of six IOEs per cluster. Thus, there are six redundant point-to-point links for intercluster messages.

Synchronization. A fundamental problem in fault-tolerant computing, synchronization between collaborating components is necessary to perform techniques such as comparison of outputs, failure detection, and voting. Unfortunately, synchronization is also difficult to achieve, especially between processing elements in a loosely coupled multiprocessor like the FTPP. One solution is to distribute a global clock pulse to the processing elements. However, although

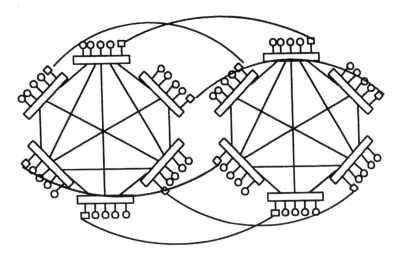

Figure 4.18: An ensemble of 16 triplex groups.

feasible for a small system, signal skew prohibits its use in a large system. In addition, synchronization using a global clock signal would limit the level of processor heterogeneity. To overcome this hurdle, the FTPP uses message passing to synchronize its network elements and functional synchronization to synchronize processes running within a redundant group.

In order to achieve Byzantine-resilient computation, the network elements that form the hard core of a cluster must be tightly synchronized. To achieve tight synchrony, each network element uses the occasion of a message exchange to adjust its local clock. At some point in the message exchange protocol, each network element sends a copy of the same message to each of its peers. Since each network element executes the exact same microcode, a network element can adjust its clock by calculating the skew between the time it started to send the message and the time its peers started to send the same message.

Processes of a redundant processing group must also be synchronized within a known skew of each other. To this end, processes are synchronized through the use of functional synchronization. Functional synchronization is the use of instructions, embedded into the code of a process by hand or by a compiler, that initiate synchronization. When such an instruction is reached, the process sends a message into the network core addressed to itself. Since the elements of the core are synchronized within a tolerably small skew of each other, the members of the redundant process group all receive the message within the same skew and are effectively synchronized. There are many advantages to this form of synchronization, but notable among them are its conservation of bandwidth, its suitability for heterogeneous processing elements, and its potential transparency to the programmer through the use of automated compiler-based code insertion.

Table 4.2: FTPP Prototypes

Cluster Name and Year	PE Model and Number/Cluster	Performance of a 192-PE FTPP	Network Element Features
C1 (1989)	M68020 (12.5 MHz) 16/Cluster	115-345 MIPS (RAW VAX)	64 Mbit/s Metal interconnect
C2 (1989)	M68030 (20 MHz) 4/Cluster	184-552 MIPS (RAW VAX)	64 Mbit/s Fiber-optic interconnect
C3 (1993)	M68040/80960/DSP32C 40/Cluster	Depends on PE suite	100 Mbit/s Fiber-optic interconnect

4.7.4 Prototypes

Table 4.2 presents the three FTPP prototypes, creatively named C1, C2, and C3, that have been developed, to date, at the Charles Stark Draper Laboratory. The processing elements for each prototype are "off-the-shelf" and commonly available. Likewise, the network elements utilize the popular VME bus interface.

4.8 CASE STUDY 7: THE MAFT DESIGN FOR ULTRARELIABLE SYSTEMS

The SIFT and FTMP architectural models initiated the evolutionary path for the present generation of ultrareliable systems. The objectives of both FTMP and SIFT are to provide sustained system operation through the worst-case fault scenarios. Both SIFT and FTMP use redundancy as a means to achieve the fault tolerance and reliability objectives; however, the nature and implementation of the redundancy management techniques distinguish each approach. FTMP primarily utilizes hardware fault tolerance methods, with synchronization, task replication, voting, and control functions implemented in hardware. SIFT uses the alternative software approach, depending on algorithm-based system operations of synchronization, scheduling, and redundancy management. A characteristic feature of SIFT is that much effort was expended to formally validate and demonstrate proofs of correctness for system operations.

However, neither the SIFT nor the FTMP is designed as a truly distributed system, and, because they were initially developed as proof-of-concept demonstrators, little emphasis was placed on system performance and efficiency issues. The SIFT model incurs an overhead penalty for its executive functions, requiring as much as a 70 to 80 percent outlay on the system's computational capability. Although FTMP provides for most functions in hardware, the executive functions can still result in up to a 60 percent overhead on the processor utilization.

Alleviating these limitations on efficiency, performance, and system size serves as the motivation for the next generation system designs. Following on the FTMP approach is the FTP system, which is targeted towards enhancing system efficiency. The efficiency of FTP exceeds that of both SIFT and FTMP; though unlike the multiprocessing FTMP and SIFT systems, FTP is a uniprocessor employing redundant processing channels to provide for fault tolerance. The throughput of the redundant system is equal to uniprocessor throughput. The FTP serves as one of the primary building blocks for the distributed AIPS system, the commonality of the designs of FTMP, FTP, and AIPS being the hardware fault tolerance approach. A subsequent system, FTPP, presents a semihierarchical approach to large system design, though based on the same hardware fault tolerance approach. The FTPP design emphasizes performance issues; however, it does not provide the same level of validated Byzantine-resilient operation as the FTMP, especially for synchronization-based operations.

4.8.1 The MAFT Philosophy

Differing from the hardware intensive approaches for the architecture family of FTMP, FTP, AIPS, and FTPP (Harper and Lala, 1991), and the software-intensive SIFT approach, the MAFT design exemplifies a hybrid hardware-assisted software model. Also, the uniqueness of MAFT is that it provides fault-tolerant capability against mixed-mode faults (Meyer and Pradhan, 1987; Walter, 1990).

MAFT is a distributed system designed to combine ultrareliable system operations with high performance in a real-time environment. The MAFT approach draws its genetic origins from the software SIFT model and shares the SIFT characteristic of providing formal validation of system operations.

All primary system operations (synchronization, voting, scheduling, and error management) are algorithm-based, though assisted by hardware implemented functions. These functions, if implemented in software, would add overhead and degrade performance and would be less transparent to the user. A MAFT feature is that the correctness of these primary operations is ensured by the use of Byzantine fault-tolerant algorithms. Fault tolerance is provided by executing redundant copies of tasks on different nodes. The design emphasis is to enhance the efficiency of operations and system performance without compromising the Byzantine fault resilience. The operational approach is to partition the system into functional blocks and provide formal validation for the constituent system blocks.

4.8.2 System Model

Architecture.   MAFT is an event-triggered, synchronous distributed system based on message passing protocols. Each MAFT module consists of a set of fully interconnected autonomous units. System growth and performance in larger systems is maintained by using MAFT as a building block within a larger cluster-based model, with the partial connectivity between clusters (Suri, Hugue, and Walter, 1992). A fully connected network implies restrictions on system growth; however, as MAFT constitutes only a building block within a larger cluster-based model, with the intercluster interconnection being not fully connected, this facet does not inhibit the system growth and performance. To minimize the influence of the executive function overhead on the computational part of the section, each constituent MAFT node is a processor pair comprising an *OC (operations controller)* and *AP (applications processor)* unit. Figure 4.19 illustrates the MAFT block architecture. Processor segregation occurs by function: An OC is a dedicated data-driven ASIC unit that handles the entire set of system executive functions—synchronization, task scheduling, voting, error management, and reconfiguration. The intent is to make this system's redundancy management operations core as domain independent as possible. The AP unit is devoted entirely to application (or computational) tasks as delegated to it by the OC. The AP operations involve reading the external inputs, performing task computations and delivering output results to the actuators under the supervision of the OC. An AP sends the computed results to its OC, which processes the information through interactions with the other OCs as per the task fault tolerance and scheduling requirements. The voted result is then delivered to the AP for output over the I/O network. This partitioning of the system operations implies a restricted involvement of the AP with the OC operations. This

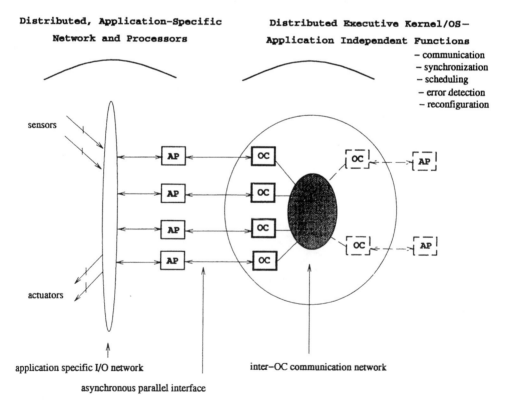

Figure 4.19: System architecture of a MAFT module.

also limits an AP's influence on the system OS functions and permits matching the APs specifically to the application requirements. The usage of heterogeneous AP units, as required for a specific application, is also supported in MAFT. An OC communicates with its AP using an asynchronous parallel interface. Again, to minimize the executive function overhead on the AP, this interface is simply seen as an I/O port by the AP. An application-specific I/O network links the APs to the sensors and actuators.

Architecturally, the system is a simple aggregation of OC and AP units with a software OS overlay implemented on the OC's determining the system capabilities and operations, as compared with the hardware intensive functionality of FTMP, FTP, AIPS, and FTPP.

The hybrid fault-effects model in MAFT.   Existing ultrareliable systems are fixed-fault severity models, considering each instance of fault occurrence to be the worse case Byzantine fault instance. Although, MAFT is also designed as a Byzantine-resilient ultrareliable system, it permits a flexible choice of a fault set, (Meyer and Pradhan, 1987), (Suri, Hugue, and Walter, 1992), as required for different applications. Considerable debate exists regarding the need to protect against Byzantine faults, since the protocols required to tolerate such faults are more expensive to implement, relative to the perceived probability of occurrence of such faults. Conversely, the protocols that treat all faults as Byzantine do not take advantage of the presence of less pernicious faults. Unlike previous models, the hybrid fault-effects model (HFM) permits a choice of mixed aspects of a fault effect (Walter, Suri, and Hugue, 1994). Fault classification is done by fault effect. The faults are partitioned according to the *nature* and *symmetry*. The hybrid fault types are *symmetric/asymmetric* benign, and *symmetric/asymmetric* malicious faults model scenarios in which an occurrence probability can be assigned to each hybrid fault type. By distinguishing among different fault types and their probabilities of occurrence, more realistic system models and algorithms which are capable of handling a continuum of fault types can be developed. Also, strategies to assess the impact of ignoring certain fault types are developed.

The HFM facilitates the process of selecting the fault set to be tolerated, which, in turn, is used to justify design decisions. For example, to enhance the Byzantine fault coverage from one to two faults, the number of system nodes must be increased from four to seven. Under the classic Byzantine model, a system of five or six nodes actually yields a lower reliability estimate than even a four-node system. However, it has been shown that a system's reliability and its resilience to non-Byzantine faults are enhanced when the HFM is used, justifying the addition of redundant resources without increasing the complexity of the algorithm.

Classical synchronization conditions—approximate and exact agreement—are proven to hold under the HFM, demonstrating the underutilization of potential fault coverage endemic in existing algorithms. The HFM can be integrated into virtually all existing MAFT synchronization and distributed agreement algorithms, thus enhancing the fault coverage of the basic algorithms. If the fault tolerance techniques implemented in a system do not support the segregation and handling of mixed faults, then the HFM reverts to the single fault-type models, with no improvement. The developed hybrid algorithms differ from existing algorithms because dynamic fault tolerance is needed to exploit the ability to detect certain types of faults locally. Thus, we combine the benefits of perfect fault detection with the increased coverage of the more complex models.

An important attribute of MAFT is the capability of diagnosing the hybrid faults using an online algorithm (Walter, Suri, and Hugue, 1994). This differs from other approaches which rely on the system to be taken offline and require full availability of the system for testing. In performing diagnosis online for a more complete fault set, MAFT achieves a greater efficiency of resource management, which translates into lower operational and repair costs.

4.9 CASE STUDY 8: SPACE SHUTTLE SYSTEM

4.9.1 Introduction

The space shuttle is an *ultra-reliable* system that uses modular redundancy effectively both in hardware and software. Also, it is an early example of the use of design diversity to achieve software fault-tolerance (see Chapter 7). Its *data processing system* (DPS) performs its functions through the use of specialized hardware components and a self-contained, redundant flight software system, Jenkins and NASA (1995). The primary functions of the data processing system include:

> support the guidance, navigation, and control (GN&C) of the vehicle, process vehicle data for the flight crew and for transmission to the ground, and allow ground control of some vehicle systems via transmitted commands, monitor, and control vehicle subsystems.

The DPS consists of the following systems, as shown in Figure 4.20.

1. Five General-Purpose Computers (GPCs)
2. Two magnetic tape Mass Memory Units
3. A time-shared computer data bus network consisting of serial digital data buses to accommodate the data traffic between the GPCs and shuttle vehicle systems

Out of five identical general-purpose computers abroad the orbiter control space shuttle vehicle systems are IBM AP-101S computers. The GPCs consists of a Central Processor Unit (CPU) and an Input/Output Processor (IOP) in one avionics box. The GPCs can perform more than 1 million benchmark tests per second.

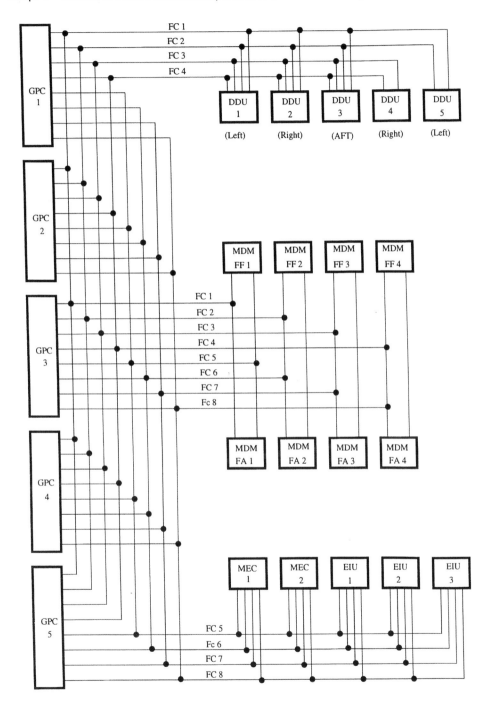

Figure 4.20: The Data Processing System (DPS) of the Space Shuttle.

Each GPC contains a main memory consisting of 256,000 32-bit words. Each of the five GPCs abroad the orbiter weighs 64 pounds, and requires 550 watts of electrical power.

The GPCs have CMOS memory with a battery pack to preserve the state when the GPC is powered off. Because the CMOS memory can be altered by radiation which the shuttle encounters in orbit, the memory was designed with error correcting and detecting codes. Whenever the GPC is powered, a hardware process called "scrub" continually checks the GPC's memory for alterations, such as a bit flip induced by a radiation particle. Scrub is capable of correcting *single* bit errors and detecting *multiple* bit errors. Scrub checks all of the GPC's memory in 1.7 seconds. Each memory location is also checked prior to being referenced by the GPC.

4.9.2 Fault-tolerant Features

Every aspect of the shuttle is designed with redundant systems (when possible). The goal of the shuttle is to withstand any two failures and still maintain crew safety. This goal is met with very few exceptions. For the computer system, there are two levels of redundancy. The first level of redundancy is through the use of multiple computers running the same software. The second level is through the use of two completely independent sets of software that provide design diversity to overcome untested software bugs that were causes of some of the early space mission problems.

The software stored and executed by GPCs is the most sophisticated and complex set of programs ever developed for aerospace use. The programs are designed to accommodate almost every aspect of space shuttle operations, including orbiter checkout, prelaunch activities, countdown, launch, ascent, on-orbit flight, entry, landing, and aborts.

A redundant mode is used for the critical phases of the mission, such as launch, ascent, entry, landing, and aborts. The principle software used to operate the vehicle during a mission is the primary avionics software system (PASS). It contains all the programming needed to fly the vehicle through all phases of the mission, as well as managing all vehicle and payload systems.

During these critical phases of flight, four of the five GPCs are loaded with the same PASS software to perform all GN&C functions simultaneously and redundantly. As a safety measure, the fifth GPC contains a different version developed independently. This is designed to take control of the vehicle if a generic error in the PASS software or other multiple errors should cause a loss of vehicle control. This software is called the Backup Flight Systems (BFS). In the less dynamic phases of on-orbit operations, the BFS is not activated.

If two or more GPCs are running together, they are said to form a redundant set, since they receive the same vehicle inputs, process the same information, and produce identical outputs. Each GPC performs about 325,000 operations per second during critical phases. While each computer in the redundant set produces the same outputs, only one computer will actually send its commands and data to the appropriate group of hardware. This group is called a "string". Each piece of hardware on a string can be accessed by more than one computer. Thus, if one computer fails, the hardware on its string is not lost; it can be reassigned to an alternate computer.

Each computer in a redundant set operates in synchronized steps and cross-checks results of processing about 500 times per second. Synchronization refers to the software scheme used to ensure simultaneous intercomputer communications of necessary GPC status information among the primary avionics computers.

If a GPC operating in a redundant set fails to meet two redundant synchronization codes in a row, the remaining computers will vote it out of the redundant set. Or if a GPC has a problem with its multiplexer interface adapter receiver during two successive reads of response data, and does not receive the data, they, in turn, will vote the GPC out of the set. A failed GPC is halted as soon as possible.

If errors occur and the PASS computers begin to fail, the shuttle commander has the responsibility to engage the BFS. At this point, all PASS computers are halted and the sole BFS computer is in command of the shuttle. The mission would then have to be aborted and a return to earth made as quickly as possible.

Placing the backup flight system (BFS) GPC in standby does not stop BFS software processing or preclude BFS engagement; it only prevents the BFS from commanding. During non-critical flight periods in orbit, only one or two GPCs are used for GN&C tasks and another for systems management and payload operations. A GPC on orbit can also be "freeze-dried"; that is, it can be loaded with the software for a particular memory configuration and then moded to standby. It can then be moded to halt and placed in a reduced power mode. Thus it can be seen that the space shuttle uses a wide variety of techniques to achieve both reliability and safety. As can be seen the quad redundancy instead of standard TMR provides an added degree of safety by making the system free from both single and double point failures. Also, having two versions of the program—one as primary and the other as backup—provides robustness against latent software bugs. Over the years space shuttle safety record speaks for the overall robustness of the system.

4.10 REMARKS

This chapter reviewed eight different systems. They span a wide variety of applications ranging from Tandem commercial transaction processing to the ultra reliable space shuttle system. It is clear that low-cost techniques such as duplication and checkpointing form the basis of fault-tolerance of highly available systems such as Tandem and Sequoia. On the other hand, massive redundancy such as triplication and quadredundancy techniques tend to be widely used in ultra-reliable systems. But it is interesting to note that with reduced cost of hardware, the line between low cost and high cost techniques is getting somewhat blurred.

It is projected that future fault-tolerant system design will not be limited by hardware costs, but more by performance penalties incurred by fault-tolerance. Therefore, static redundancy roll forward schemes will dominate over performance sacrificing retry and rollback schemes. Also the fault-tolerant concepts developed for specialized ultra-reliable systems will continue to migrate to more general commercial systems. This is clearly evident from the family of Tandem architectures which uses both TMR and duplex organizations.

REFERENCES

[Dreil90] van Driel C-J. L., R. J. B. Follon, A. A. C. Kohler, R. P. M. van Osch, J. M. Spanjers, "The Error-Resistant Interactively Consistent Architecture (ERICA)," *Proc. International Symposium on Fault-Tolerant Computing FTCS-20*, Newcastle-on-Tyne, 1990, pp. 474–480.

[Harper91] Harper R. E., and J. H. Lala, "Fault-tolerant Parallel Processor," *Journal of Guidance, Control, and Dynamics*, vol. 14, no. 3, (1991), pp. 554–563.

[Horst90] Horst R., R. Harris, and R. Jardine, "Multiple Instruction Issue in the NonStop Cyclone Processor," *Proc. 17th Int. Symp. on Computer Architecture*, (May 1990).

[Horst94] Horst R., "Massively Parallel System You Can Trust," *COMP-CON94 Digest of Papers*, San Francisco, (February 1994).

[Huang84] Huang, K. H. and J. A. Abraham, "Algorithm-Based Fault Tolerance for Matrix Operations," *IEEE Trans. Computers*, vol. C-33, no. 6, (June 1984), pp. 518–528.

[Hwang84] Hwang, K., and F. A. Briggs, *Computer Architecture and Parallel Processing*, McGraw-Hill, 1984.

[Jenkins95] Jenkins, D. R., "Space Shuttle: The History of Developing the National Space Transportation System," ISBN 0-9633974-1-9.

[Jewett91] Jewett D., "A Fault-Tolerant Unix Platform," *Proc. International Symposium on Fault-Tolerant Computing FTCS-21*, Montreal, (1991), pp. 512–519.

[Kieckhafer88] Kieckhafer, Roger M., Chris J. Walter, Alan M. Finn, and Philip M. Thambidurai, "The MAFT Architecture for Distributed Fault Tolerance," *IEEE Trans. Computers*, 37(4) (April 1988), pp. 398–405.

[Lee93] Lee, I., and R. K. Iyer, "Faults, Symptoms, and Software Fault Tolerance in the Tandem GUARDIAN 90 Operating System," *Proc. 23rd Int. Conf. on Fault-Tolerant Computing*, (1993), pp. 20–29.

[Meyer87] Meyer, F. J., and Dhiraj K. Pradhan, "Consensus with Dual Failure Modes," *Proc. FTCS-17*, Pittsburgh, (July 1987), pp. 48–54.

[Meyer89] Meyer, F. J., and Dhiraj K. Pradhan, "Dynamic Testing Strategy for Distributed System," *IEEE Transactions on Computers*, vol. 38, no. 3, (March 1989), pp. 356–365.

[NASA95] Data Processing Systems Section, "DPS Flight Controller Training Manuals," NASA-Johnson Space Center, Houston, TX, 77058.

[Sequoia92a] Sequoia Systems Incorporated, *Series 400 Technical Summary*, (June 1992).

[Sequoia92b] Sequoia Systems Incorporated, "The Series 400," Sequoia Product Report, 1992.

[Stratus92a]Stratus Computer Incorporated, "XA/R Series 300," Stratus Product Report, 1992.

[Stratus92b] Stratus Compute Incorporated, "Stratus FTX," Stratus Product Report, 1992.

[Suri92] Suri, N., M. Hugue, and C. Walter, "Reliability Modeling of Large Fault-Tolerant Systems," *Proc. International Symposium on Fault-Tolerant Computing FTCS-22*, Boston, pp. 212–220.

[Tandem90] Tandem Computers Incorporated, "NonStop Cyclone," Tandem Product Report, 1990.

[Tandem93] Tandem Computers Incorporated, "NonStop Cyclone/R," Tandem Product Report, 1993.

[Walter90] Walter, C., "Identifying the Cause of Detected Errors," *International Symposium on Fault-Tolerant Computing FTCS-20*, Newcastle upon Tyne 1990, pp. 48–55.

[Walter94] Walter, C., N. Suri, and M. Hugue, "Continual On-Line Diagnosis of Hybrid Faults," *Fourth International Conference on Dependable Computing for Critical Applications*, San Diego, 1994, pp. 150–167.

[Webber91] Webber, S., and J. Beirne, "The Stratus Architecture," *Proc. 21st Intl. Symp. Fault-Tolerant Comp.*, (1991), pp. 79–85.

PROBLEMS

4.1. Classify the systems described in this chapter in terms of reliability, availability, and effectiveness in recovery from failures.

4.2. Enumerate what precise features Tandem multicomputer systems are designed specifically for fault tolerance. Discuss how scalability features interplay with fault tolerance features in these systems.

4.3. Compare Tandem Integrity with ERICA with respect to robustness and cost-effectiveness.

4.4. Derive a simple combinatorial series-parallel reliability expression for the Tandem integrity system. Develop a Markov model for this system and study the various reliability and failure rate trade-offs of realistic range of failures rates.

4.5. Define and compare the fault isolation region in FTTP and MAFT. Compare the FTPP approach to the MAFT approach for Byzantine fault resilience.

4.6. Discuss the pros and cons of rollback recovery versus roll-forward recovery, as implemented in Stratus and Sequoia, respectively.

4.7. Design a hypothetical 16-processor shared-memory multiprocessor to provide graceful degradation in the presence of all single failures. Discuss what specific features of your design directly relate to shared memory features.

4.8. Critique one of the commercial systems described here and suggest improvements.

5

Experimental Analysis of Computer System Dependability

Ravishankar K. Iyer and Dong Tang

5.1 INTRODUCTION

So far we have discussed various design methodologies for realization of fault-tolerant systems. Crucial to the success of any design methodology is validation of the design with respect to dependability specifications. Two basic approaches exist—experimental and analytical. The following two chapters provide an in-depth overview of experimental and analytical techniques respectively.

In computer science more than in the physical sciences, the experimenter must decide what data to gather and analyze, sometimes without the benefit of guidance, experience, or easily available intuition. How to obtain general models from experiments or measurements made in a particular environment is by no means clear. This chapter discusses the current research in the area of experimental analysis of computer system dependability. The discussion centers around methodologies, major developments, and major directions of the research in the area.

Experimental evaluation of the dependability of a system can be performed at different phases of the system's life. In the *design phase,* computer-aided design (CAD) environments are used to evaluate the design via simulation, including simulated fault injection. Such fault injection tests the effectiveness of fault-tolerant mechanisms and evaluates system dependability, providing timely feedback to system designers. Simulation, however, requires accurate input parameters and validation of output results. Although the parameter estimates can be obtained from past measurements, this is often complicated by design and technology changes. In the *prototype phase*, the system runs under controlled workload conditions. In this stage, controlled physical fault injection is used to evaluate the system behavior under faults, including the detection coverage and the recovery capability of various fault tolerance mechanisms. Fault injection on the real system can provide information about the failure process, from fault occurrence to system recovery, including error latency, propagation, detection, and recovery (which may involve reconfiguration). But this type of fault injection can only study artificial faults; it cannot provide certain important dependability measures, such as mean time between failures (MTBF) and availability. In the *operational phase,* a direct measurement-based approach can be used to measure systems in the field under real workloads. The collected data contains a large amount of information about naturally occurring errors/failures. Analysis of this data can provide understanding of actual error/failure characteristics and insight into analytical models. Although measurement-based analysis is useful for evaluating the real system, it is limited to detected errors. Further, conditions in the field can vary widely, casting doubt on the statistical validity of the results. Thus, all three approaches—simulated fault injection, physical fault injection, and measurement-based analysis—are required for accurate dependability analysis.

In the design phase, simulated fault injection can be conducted at different levels: the electrical level, the logic level, and the function level. The objectives of simulated fault injection are to determine dependability bottlenecks, the coverage of error detection/recovery mechanisms, the effectiveness of reconfiguration schemes, performance loss, and other dependability measures. The feedback from simulation can be extremely useful in cost-effective redesign of the system. This chapter will discuss different techniques for fault injection simulation. We also introduce different levels of simulation tools.

In the prototype phase, while the objectives of physical fault injection are similar to those of simulated fault injection, the methods differ radically because real fault injection and monitoring facilities are involved. Physical faults can be injected at the hardware level (logic or electrical faults) or at the software level (code or data corruption). Heavy ion radiation techniques can also be used to inject faults and stress the system. This chapter will illustrate the instrumentation involved in fault injection experiments using real examples, including several fault injection environments.

In the operational phase, measurement-based analysis must address issues such as how to monitor computer errors and failures and how to analyze measured data to quantify system dependability characteristics. Although methods for the design and evaluation of fault-tolerant systems have been extensively researched, little is known about how well these strategies work in the field. A study of production systems is valuable not only for accurate evaluation but also for identifying reliability bottlenecks in system design. This chapter addresses several issues in measurement-based analysis, including workload/failure dependency, modeling and evaluation based on data, software dependability in the operational phase, and fault diagnosis.

The measurement-based analysis results discussed in this chapter are based on over 200 machine-years of data gathered from IBM, DEC, and Tandem systems. The evaluation methodology discussed includes the use of the measured hardware and software error data to jointly characterize the interdependence between performance and dependability, correlation analysis to quantify correlated failures and their impact on dependability, Markov reward modeling of measured systems from data to evaluate the loss of system service due to errors and failures, and algorithms that use online error logs to perform automatic fault diagnosis and failure prediction.

Before discussing methodologies and developments for the design, prototype, and operational phases, we present an overview of the relevant statistical techniques used in this area. The techniques cover the estimation of parameters and confidence intervals; distribution characterization, including function fitting; and multivariate analysis methods, including clustering analysis, correlation analysis, and factor analysis. Importance sampling, a statistical technique to accelerate Monte Carlo simulation, is also introduced. These techniques are later used in the analysis of data obtained from fault injection or from operational systems.

In discussing the experimental analysis approaches used in the three phases, a wide range of dependability issues are addressed, including error latency, error propagation, error detection, error recovery, error correlation, workload/error dependency, availability, reliability, performability, and reward rate. In addition to presenting methodologies and major developments in each of the phases, we critique the relative merits and research issues for the different approaches. Most evaluation techniques introduced are illustrated by case studies of their uses on actual systems.

5.2 STATISTICAL TECHNIQUES

In this section, we introduce several statistical techniques commonly used to analyze the data collected from fault injection experiments and operational systems. The discussion is not intended to be comprehensive. For a comprehensive study of statistical methods, the reader is referred to the advanced texts in statistics, such as (Kendall, 1977 and Dillon, 1984). In particular, we discuss parameter estimation, distribution characterization, and some relevant multivariate analysis techniques. A statistical technique to accelerate Monte Carlo simulation is also discussed. Most of these techniques are widely used in every phase of the experimental evaluation of dependability.

5.2.1 Parameter Estimation

The most important characteristics of a random variable are its distribution, mean, and variance. In practice, means and variances are usually unknown parameters. Thus, how to estimate these parameters from data needs to be addressed.

Point estimation.   *Point estimation* is often used in experimental analysis. Examples include the estimation of the detection coverage from fault injections and the estimation of mean time between failures (MTBF) from field data. Each fault injection and each failure occurrence can be treated as an experiment. In this analysis, each experiment (e.g., injection of a fault) is assumed to be independent.

Given a collection of n experimental outcomes, $x_1, x_2, \ldots x_n$, of a random variable X, each x_i can be considered as a value of a random variable X_i. These X_i's are independent of each other and identical to X in distribution. The set $\{X_1, X_2, \ldots, X_n\}$ is called a *random sample* of X. Our purpose is to estimate the value of some parameter θ (θ could be $E[X]$ or $Var[X]$) of X using a function of X_1, $X_2, \ldots, X_n$. The function used to estimate θ, $\tilde{\theta} = \tilde{\theta}(X_1, X_2, \ldots, X_n)$, is called an *estimator of* θ, and $\tilde{\theta}(x_1, x_2, \ldots, x_n)$ is said to be a *point estimate* of θ.

An estimator $\hat{\theta}$ is called an *unbiased estimator* of θ, if $E[\hat{\theta}] = \theta$. The unbiased estimator that has the minimum variance, that is, it minimizes $Var(\tilde{\theta}) = E[(\tilde{\theta} - \theta)^2]$ among all $\tilde{\theta}$'s, is said to be the *unbiased minimum variance estimator*. It can be shown that the sample mean

$$\overline{X} = \frac{1}{n} \sum_{i=1}^{n} X_i \tag{5.1}$$

is the unbiased minimum variance linear estimator of the population mean μ, and the sample variance

$$S^2 = \frac{1}{n-1} \sum_{i=1}^{n} (X_i - \overline{X})^2 \tag{5.2}$$

is, under some mild conditions, an unbiased minimum variance quadratic estimator of the population variance σ^2. If an estimator $\tilde{\theta}$ converges in probability to θ, that is,

$$\lim_{n \to \infty} P(|\tilde{\theta}(X_1, X_2, \ldots, X_n) - \theta| \geq \epsilon) = 0 \tag{5.3}$$

where ϵ is any small positive number, it is said to be *consistent*.

Method of maximum likelihood.   If the functional form of the probability distribution function (p.d.f.) of the variable is known, the *method of maximum likelihood* is a good approach to parameter estimation. In many cases, approximate functional forms of empirical distributions can be obtained. In such cases, the maximum-likelihood method can be used to determine distribution parameters.

The maximum-likelihood method is to choose an estimator based on the assumption that the observed sample is the most likely to occur among all possible samples. The method usually produces estimators that have minimum-variance and consistency properties. But if the sample size is small, the estimator may be biased.

Assuming X has a p.d.f. $f(x \mid \theta)$, where θ is an unknown parameter, the joint p.d.f. of the sample $\{X_1, X_2, \ldots, X_n\}$,

$$L(\theta) = \prod_{i=1}^{n} f(x_i \mid \theta) \tag{5.4}$$

is called the *likelihood function* of θ. If $\bar{\theta}(x_1, x_2, \ldots, x_n)$ is the point estimate of θ that maximizes $L(\theta)$, then $\bar{\theta}(X_1, X_2, \ldots, X_n)$ is said to be the *maximum-likelihood estimator* of θ.

The following example illustrates the method. Let X denote the random variable "time between failures" in a computer system. Assuming X is exponentially distributed with an arrival rate λ, we wish to estimate λ from a random sample $\{X_1, X_2, \ldots, X_n\}$. By Eq. (5.4),

$$L(\lambda) = \prod_{i=1}^{n} \lambda e^{-\lambda x_i} = \lambda^n e^{-\lambda \sum_{i=1}^{n} x_i}$$

How do we choose an estimator such that the estimated λ maximizes $L(\lambda)$? An easier way is to find the λ value that maximizes $lnL(\lambda)$, instead of $L(\lambda)$. This is because the λ that maximizes $L(\lambda)$ also maximizes $lnL(\lambda)$, and $lnL(\lambda)$ is easier to handle. In this case we have

$$lnL(\lambda) = n \, ln(\lambda) - \lambda \sum_{i=1}^{n} x_i$$

To find the maximum, consider the first derivative

$$\frac{d[lnL(\lambda)]}{d\lambda} = \frac{n}{\lambda} - \sum_{i=1}^{n} x_i$$

The solution of this equation at zero,

$$\tilde{\lambda} = \frac{n}{\sum_{i=1}^{n} x_i}$$

is the maximum-likelihood estimator for λ.

Method of moments.   Sometimes it is difficult to find maximum-likelihood estimators in closed form. One example is the p.d.f. of the gamma distribution $G(\alpha, \theta)$

$$g(x) = \frac{1}{\Gamma(\alpha)\theta^\alpha} x^{\alpha-1} e^{-x/\theta}$$

The estimation of α and θ is complicated by the existence of the gamma function $\Gamma(\alpha)$. The gamma distribution, however, is useful for characterizing interval times in the real world. As shown in Section 5.5.3, the software time to error (TTE) for the measured operating system fits a multistage gamma distribution. In such cases, the *method of moments* can be used if an analytical relationship is found between the moments of the variable and the parameters to be estimated.

To explain the method of moments, we introduce the simple concepts of *sample moment* and *population moment*. The kth $(k = 1, 2, \ldots)$ sample moment of the random variable X is defined as

$$m_k = \frac{1}{n} \sum_{i=1}^{n} X_i^k \tag{5.5}$$

where $X_1, X_2, \ldots, X_n$ are a sample of X. The kth population moment of X is just $E[X^k]$.

Suppose there are k parameters to be estimated. The method of moments is to set the first k sample moments equal to the first k population moments, which are expressed as the unknown parameters, and then to solve these k equations for the unknown parameters. The method usually gives simple and consistent estimators. However, some estimators may not have unbiased and minimum variance properties. The following example shows details of the method.

Consider the above gamma distribution example. We wish to estimate α and θ, based on a sample $\{X_1, X_2, \ldots, X_n\}$ from a gamma distribution. Since $X \sim G(\alpha, \theta)$, we know

$$E[x] = \alpha\theta, \qquad E[x^2] = \alpha\theta^2 + \alpha\theta$$

The first two sample moments, by definition, are given by

$$m_1 = \frac{1}{n} \sum_{i=1}^{n} x_i = \overline{X}, \qquad m_2 = \frac{1}{n} \sum_{i=1}^{n} x_i^2 \approx S^2 + \overline{X}^2$$

Setting $m_1 = E[X]$ and $m_2 = E[X^2]$ and solving for α and θ, we obtain

$$\tilde{\alpha} = \frac{\overline{X}^2}{S^2}, \qquad \tilde{\theta} = \frac{S^2}{\overline{X}}$$

These are the estimators for α and θ from the method of moments.

Interval estimation.   So far, our discussion has been limited to the point estimation of unknown parameters. The estimate may deviate from the actual parameter value. To obtain an estimate with a high confidence, it is necessary to construct an interval estimate such that the interval includes the actual parameter value with a high probability. Given an estimator $\bar{\theta}$, if

$$P(\bar{\theta} - e_1 < \theta < \bar{\theta} + e_2) = \beta \tag{5.6}$$

the random interval $(\bar{\theta} - e_1,\ \bar{\theta} + e_2)$ is said to be $100 \times \beta$ *percent confidence interval* for θ, and β is called the *confidence coefficient* (the probability that the confidence interval contains θ).

Confidence Intervals for Means. In the following discussion, the sample mean $\bar{X}$ is used as the estimator for the population mean. As mentioned before, it is the unbiased minimum variance linear estimator for μ. We first consider the case in which the sample size is large. By the central limit theorem, $\bar{X}$ is asymptotically normally distributed, no matter what the population distribution is. Thus, when the sample size n is reasonably large (usually 30 or above, sometimes 50 or more if the population distribution is badly skewed with occasional outliers), $Z = (\bar{X} - \mu)/(S/\sqrt{n})$ can be approximately treated as a standard normal variable. To obtain a $100\,\beta$ percent confidence interval for μ, we can find a number $z_{\alpha/2}$ from the $N(0, 1)$ distribution table such that $P(Z > z_{\alpha/2}) = \alpha/2$, where $\alpha = 1 - \beta$. Then we have

$$P(-z_{\alpha/2} < \frac{\bar{X} - \mu}{S/\sqrt{n}} < z_{\alpha/2}) = 1 - \alpha$$

Thus, the $100(1 - \alpha)$ percent confidence interval for μ is approximately

$$\bar{X} - z_{\alpha/2}\frac{S}{\sqrt{n}} \le \mu \le \bar{X} + z_{\alpha/2}\frac{S}{\sqrt{n}} \tag{5.7}$$

If the sample size is small (considerably smaller than 30), the above approximation can be poor. In this case, we consider two commonly used distributions: normal and exponential. If the population distribution is normal, the random variable $T = (\bar{X} - \mu)/(S/\sqrt{n})$ has a student t distribution with $n - 1$ degrees of freedom. By repeating the same approach performed above with a t distribution table, the following $100\,(1 - \alpha)$ percent confidence interval for μ can be obtained:

$$\bar{X} - t_{n-1;\alpha/2}\frac{S}{\sqrt{n}}\mu < \bar{X} + t_{n-1;\alpha/2}\frac{S}{\sqrt{n}} \tag{5.8}$$

where $t_{n-1;\alpha/2}$ is a number such that $P(T > t_{n-1;\alpha/2}) = \alpha/2$. Theoretically, Eq. (5.8) requires that X have a normal distribution. However, we will show later that the estimator is not very sensitive to the distribution of X when the sample size is reasonably large (15 or more).

If the population distribution is exponential, it can be shown that $\chi^2 = 2n\bar{X}/\mu$ has a chi-square distribution with $2n$ degrees of freedom. Thus, the chi-square distribution table should be used. Because the chi-square distribution is not symmetrical about the origin, we need to find two numbers, $x^2_{2n;1-\alpha/2}$ and $x^2_{2n;\alpha/2}$, such that $P(\chi^2 > x^2_{2n;1-\alpha/2}) = \alpha/2$ and $P(\chi^2 < x^2_{2n;\alpha/2}) = \alpha/2$. The obtained $100(1 - \alpha)$ percent confidence interval for μ is

$$\frac{2n\overline{X}}{x^2_{2n;1-\alpha/2}} < \mu < \frac{2n\overline{X}}{x^2_{2n;\alpha/2}} \tag{5.9}$$

Confidence Intervals for Variances.   The estimation of confidence interval for variances is more complicated than that for means, because the sample variance cannot be simply approximated by a unique distribution (such as normal distribution) regardless of the population distribution. However, irrespective of the population distribution, $\lim_{n\to\infty}$ Var $[S^2] = 0$. Thus, a good confidence interval can be expected as long as the sample size n is large. Next, our discussion will focus on the two commonly used distributions: normal and exponential.

If X is normally distributed, the sample variance S^2 can be used to construct the confidence interval. It is known that the random variable $(n-1)S^2/\sigma^2$ has a chi-square distribution with $n-1$ degrees of freedom. To determine a $100(1-\alpha)$ percent confidence interval for σ^2, we follow the procedure for constructing Eq. (5.9) to find the numbers $x^2_{n-1;1-\alpha/2}$ and $x^2_{n-1;\alpha/2}$ from the chi-square distribution table. The confidence interval is then given by

$$\frac{(n-1)S^2}{x^2_{n-1;1-\alpha/2}} < \sigma^2 < \frac{(n-1)S^2}{x^2_{n-1;\alpha/2}} \tag{5.10}$$

Our experience shows that this equation, like Eq. (5.8), is not restricted to the normal distribution when the sample size is reasonably large (15 or more).

If X is exponentially distributed, Eq. (5.9) can be used to estimate the confidence interval for σ^2, because for the exponential random variable σ^2 equals μ^2. Since all terms in Eq. (5.9) are positive, we can take square for them. The result gives a $100(1-\alpha)$ percent confidence interval for σ^2:

$$\left(\frac{2n\overline{X}^2}{x^2_{2n;1-\alpha/2}}\right) < \sigma^2 < \left(\frac{2n\overline{X}}{x^2_{2n;\alpha/2}}\right)^2 \tag{5.11}$$

Confidence Intervals for Proportions.   Often, we need to estimate the confidence interval for a proportion or percentage whose underlying distribution is unknown. For example, we may want to estimate the confidence interval for the detection coverage after fault injection experiments. In general, given n Bernoulli trials with the probability of success on each trial being p and the number of successes being Y, how do we find a confidence interval for p? If n is large (particularly when $np \geq 5$ and $n(1-p) \geq 5$ (Hogg, 1983), Y/n has an approximately normal distribution, N (μ, σ^2), with $\mu = p$ and $\sigma^2 = p(1-p)/n$. Note that Y/n is the sample mean, which is an estimate of μ or p. By Eq. (5.7) the $100(1-\alpha)$ percent confidence interval for p is

$$\frac{Y}{n} \pm z_{\alpha/2}\sqrt{p(1-p)/n} \tag{5.12}$$

This equation can be used to determine the number of injections required to achieve a given confidence interval for an estimated fault detection coverage. Let n represent the number of fault injections and Y the number of faults detected in the n injections. Assume that all faults have the same detection coverage, which is approximately p. Now we wish to estimate p with the $100(1 - \alpha)$ percent confidence interval being e. By Eq. (5.12), we have

$$e = z_{\alpha/2}\sqrt{p(1-p)/n} \qquad\qquad (5.13)$$

Solving the equation for n gives us

$$n = \frac{(z_{\alpha/2})^2 p(1-p)}{e^2} \qquad\qquad (5.14)$$

where n is the number of injections required to achieve the desired confidence interval in estimating p.

For example, assume detection coverage $p = 0.6$, confidence interval $e = 0.05$, and confidence coefficient $1 - \alpha = 90$ percent. Then the required number of injections is

$$n = \frac{1.645^2 \times 0.6 \times 0.4}{0.05^2} = 260$$

5.2.2 Distribution Characterization

Mean and variance are important parameters that summarize data by single numbers. Probability distribution provides more information about data. Analysis of distributions can help one understand the data in detail and arrive at simple conclusions regarding the underlying models. For example, if the time to failure and the recovery time for a system are all exponential, then the model is clearly a Markov model; otherwise, it could be one of several types of semi-Markov models. We now discuss empirical distribution functions and function fitting in this subsection.

Empirical distribution.   Given a sample of X, the simplest way to obtain an empirical distribution of X is to plot a histogram of the observations. The range of the sample space is divided into a number of subranges called *buckets*. The lengths of the buckets are usually the same, although this is not essential. Assume that we have k buckets, separated by $x_0, x_1, \ldots, x_k$, for the given sample of size n. In each bucket, there are y_i instances. Clearly, the sample size n is $\sum_{i=1}^{k} y_i$. Then, y_i/n is an estimation of the probability that X takes a value in bucket i. The histogram is an *empirical probability distribution function* (p.d.f.) of X or the *empirical distribution*. It is easy to construct the *empirical cumulative distribution function* (c.d.f.) from the histogram, as follows:

$$F_k(x) = \begin{cases} 0, & x < x_0 \\ \sum_{l=1}^{i} \dfrac{y_l}{n}, & x_{i-1} \leq x < \\ 1, & x_k \leq x \end{cases} \qquad (5.15)$$

The key problem in plotting histograms is determining the bucket size. A small size may lead to such a large variation among buckets that the characterization of the distribution cannot be identified. A large size may lose details of the distribution. Given a data set, it is possible to obtain very different distribution shapes by using different bucket sizes. One guideline is that if any bucket has less than five instances, the bucket size should be increased or a variable bucket size should be used. In our experience, ten or more buckets are sufficient in most cases, depending on the sample size.

Distribution function fitting.   Analytical distribution functions are useful in analytical modeling and simulations. Thus, it is often desirable to fit an analytical function to a given empirical distribution. Function fitting relies on knowledge of statistical distribution functions. Given an empirical distribution, step 1 is to make a good guess of the closest distribution function(s) by observing the shape of the empirical distribution. Step 2 is to use a statistical package such as SAS to obtain the parameters for a guessed function by trying to fit it to the empirical distribution. Step 3 is to perform a significance test of the goodness-of-fit to see if the fitted function is acceptable. If the function is not acceptable, we go to step 1 to try a different function.

Now we discuss step 3—the significance test. Assume that the given empirical c.d.f. is F_k, defined in Eq. (5.15), and the hypothesized c.d.f. is $F(x)$, obtained from step 2. Our task is to test the hypothesis

$$H_0 : F_k(x) = F(x)$$

Two commonly used goodness-of-fit test methods are the *chi-square test* and the *Kolmogorov-Smirnov test*. We now briefly introduce these two methods.

Chi-Square Test.   The chi-square test assumes the distribution under consideration can be approximated by a multinomial distribution. Let

$$p_i = F(x_i) - F(x_{i-1}), \quad i = 1, \ldots, k$$

where pi is the probability that an instance falls into bucket i. If we define

$$P[x_{i-1} \leq X_i < x_i] = p_i, \quad i = 1, \ldots, k$$

then $X_1, X_2, \ldots, X_k$ have a multinomial distribution that is equivalent to the original distribution $F(x)$. Thus, for a sample size of n, the expected instances falling into bucket i is np_i by the above distribution. The sum of error squares divided by the expected numbers

$$q_{k-1} = \sum_{i=1}^{k} \frac{(y_i - np_i)^2}{np_i} \tag{5.16}$$

is a measure of the closeness of the observed number of instances, y_i, to the expected number of instances, np_i, in bucket i. If q_{k-1} is small, we tend to accept H_0. The smallness can be measured in terms of statistical significance if we treat q_{k-1} as a particular value of the random variable Q_{k-1}. It can be shown that if n is large ($np_i \geq 1$), Q_{k-1} has an approximate chi-square distribution with $k-1$ degrees of freedom, $\chi^2 (k-1)$. If H_0 is true, we expect that q_{k-1} falls into an acceptable range of Q_{k-1}, so that the event is likely to occur. The boundary value, or critical value, of the acceptable range, $\chi_\alpha^2 (k-1)$ is chosen such that

$$P[Q_{k-1} > \chi_\alpha^2(k-1)] = \alpha$$

where α is called the *significance level* of the test. Thus, we should reject H_0 if $q_{k-1} > \chi_\alpha^2 (k-1)$. Usually, α is chosen to be 0.05 or 0.1.

Kolmogorov-Smirnov Test. The Kolmogorov-Smirnov test is a nonparametric method in that it assumes no particular distribution for the variable in consideration. The method uses the empirical c.d.f., instead of the empirical p.d.f., to perform the test, which is more stringent than the chi-square test. The Kolmogorov-Smirnov statistic is defined by

$$D_k = sup_x[F_k(x) - F(x)] \tag{5.17}$$

where sup_x represents the least upper bound of all pointwise differences $F_k(x) - F(x)$. In calculation, we can choose the midpoint between x_{i-1} and x_i, for $i = 1, \ldots, k$, to obtain the maximum value of $F_k(x_i) - F(x_i)$. It is seen that D_k is a measure of the closeness of the empirical and hypothesized distribution functions. It can be derived that D_k submits to a distribution whose c.d.f. values are given by the table of Kolmogorov-Smirnov Acceptance Limits (Hogg, 1983). Thus, given a significance level α, we can find the critical value d_k from the table such that

$$P[D_k > d_k] = \alpha$$

The hypothesis H_0 is rejected if the calculated value of D_k is greater than the critical value d_k. Otherwise, we accept H_0.

5.2.3 Multivariate Analysis

In reality, measurements are usually made on more than one variable. For example, a computer workload measurement may include usages on the CPU, memory, disk, and network. A computer failure measurement may collect data on multiple components. *Multivariate analysis* is the application of methods that deal with multiple variables. These methods, which include cluster analysis, correlation analysis, and factor analysis (to be discussed), identify and quantify simultaneous relationships among multiple variables and are valuable tools for computer systems analysis.

Cluster analysis. *Cluster analysis* is helpful in identifying patterns in data. Specifically, it can help in reading a large number of points plotted in *n*-dimensional space into a few identifiable states called *clusters*. A common use is in characterizing workload states in computer systems by identifying the points in a resource usage plot that are "similar" by some measure and grouping them into a cluster. Assume we have a sample of p workload variables. We call each instance in the sample a *point* characterized by p values. In this case, the measure of similarity is the Euclidean distance. Let $x_i = (x_{i1}, x_{i2}, \ldots, x_{ip})$ denote the ith point of the sample. The Euclidean distance between points i and j,

$$d_{ij} = \left| x_i - x_j \right| = \left(\sum_{l=1}^{p} (x_{il} - x_{jl})^2 \right)^{1/2}$$

is usually used as a similarity measure between points i and j.

There are several different clustering algorithms. The goal of these algorithms is to achieve small *within-cluster* variation relative to the *between-cluster* variation. A commonly used clustering algorithm is the *k-means* algorithm. The algorithm partitions a sample with p dimensions and n points into k clusters, C_1, $C_2, \ldots, C_k$. The mean, or centroid, of C_j is denoted by $\bar{x}_j$. The error component of the portion is defined as

$$E = \sum_{j=1}^{k} \sum_{x_i \in C_j} \left| x_i - \bar{x}_j \right|^2 \tag{5.18}$$

The goal of the *k*-means algorithm is to find a partition that minimizes E.

The clustering procedure is as follows. Start with k groups, each of which consists of a single point. Each new point is added to the group with the closest centroid. After a point is added to a group, the mean of that group is adjusted to take the new point into account. After a partition is formed, search for another partition with smaller E by moving points from one cluster to another cluster until no transfer of a point results in a reduction in E.

A problem associated with clustering algorithms is the presence of outliers in the sample. Outliers can be an order of magnitude greater than any of the other points (which are usually more than 95 percent) of the sample and can be scattered over the sample space. As a result, the generated clusters may not characterize the features of the sample well. For example, most generated clusters contain only one or two outliers, with all other points groupable into only a few clusters. One way to deal with this problem is to specify in the algorithm the minimum number of points that form a cluster, typically 0.5 percent of the sample size. Another way is to define an upper bound for the radius (maximum distance between the centroid and any point in a cluster) of any generated cluster. A recommended range for the upper bound is 1.0 to 1.5 standard deviations of the sample (Artis, 1986).

Correlation analysis.   The correlation coefficient, $Cor\ (X_1, X_2)$, between the random variables X_1 and X_2 is defined as

$$Cor(X_1,\ X_2) = \frac{E[(X_1 - \mu_1)(X_2 - \mu_2)]}{\sigma_1 \sigma_2}$$ (5.19)

where μ_1 and μ_2 are the means of X_1 and X_2, and σ_1 and σ_2 are the standard deviations of X_1 and X_2, respectively. If we use ρ to denote the correlation coefficient, then ρ satisfies $-1 \le \rho \le 1$. The correlation coefficient is a measure of the linear relationship between two variables. When $|\rho| = 1$, we have $X_1 = aX_2 + b$, where $b > 0$ if $\rho = 1$, or $b < 0$ if $\rho = -1$. In this extreme case, there is an exact linear relationship between X_1 and X_2. When $|\rho| \ne 1$, there is no exact linear relationship between X_1, and X_2. In this case, ρ measures the goodness of the linear relationship $X_1 = aX_2 + b$ between X_1 and X_2. Usually, a ρ value of 0.5 or above is considered reasonably high. *Correlation analysis* can be used to quantify error or workload dependency between two components in a system.

Given random variables, X_1, X_2, and X_3, and correlation coefficients between each pair, ρ_{12}, ρ_{23}, and $\rho_{13,}$ we know these variables are related to each other by ρ_{12}, ρ_{23}, and ρ_{13}. Since X_1 is related to X_2, and X_2 is related to X_3, a partial dependence between X_1 and X_3 may be due to X_2. The partial correlation coefficient defined below quantifies this partial dependence:

$$\rho_{13.2} = \frac{\rho_{13} - \rho_{13}\rho_{23}}{\sqrt{(1 - \rho^2_{12})(1 - \rho^2_{23})}}$$ (5.20)

The partial correlation coefficient can be considered as a measure of the common relationship among the three variables.

If a random variable, X, is defined on time series, the correlation coefficient can be used to quantify the time serial dependence in the sample data of X. Given a time window $\Delta t > 0$, the *autocorrelation coefficient* of X on the time series t is defined as

$$Autocor(X, \Delta t) = Cor(X(t), X(t + \Delta t))$$ (5.21)

where t is defined on the discrete values (Δt, $2\Delta t$, $3\Delta t$, ...). In this case, we treat $X(t)$ and $X(t + \Delta t)$ as two different random variables, and the autocorrelation coefficient is actually the correlation coefficient between the two variables. That is, $Autocor\ (X, \Delta t)$ measures the time serial correlation of X with a window Δt.

Factor analysis. The limitation of correlation analysis is that the correlation coefficient can only quantify dependency between two variables. However, dependency may exist within a group of two or more variables or even among all variables. The correlation coefficient cannot provide information about this multiple dependency. *Factor analysis* is a statistical technique to quantify multiway dependency among variables. The method attempts to find a set of unobserved common factors that link together the observed variables. Consequently, it provides insight into the underlying structure of the data. For example, in a distributed system, a disk crash can account for failures on those machines whose operations depend on a set of critical data on the disk. The disk state can be considered to be a common factor for failures on these machines.

Let $X = (x_1, \ldots, x_p)$ be a normalized random vector. We say that the k-factor model holds for X if X can be written in the form

$$X = \Lambda F + E \tag{5.22}$$

where $\Lambda = (\lambda_{ij})$ $(i = 1, \ldots p; j = 1, \ldots, k)$ is a matrix of constants called *factor loadings*, and $F = (f_1, \ldots, f_k)$ and $E = (e_1, \ldots, e_p)$ are random vectors. The elements of F are called *common factors*, and the elements of E are called *unique factors* (error terms). These factors are unobservable variables. It is assumed that all factors (both common factors and unique factors) are independent of each other and that the common factors are normalized.

Each variable x_i $(i = 1, \ldots, p)$ can then be expressed as

$$x_i = \sum_{j=1}^{k} \lambda_{ij} f_j + e_i$$

and its variance can be written as

$$\sigma_i^2 = \sum_{j=1}^{k} \lambda_{ij}^2 + \psi_i$$

where ψ_i is the variance of e_i. Thus, the variance of x_i can be split into two parts. The first part

$$h_i^2 = \sum_{j=1}^{k} \lambda_{ij}^2$$

is called the *commonality*. It represents the variance of x_i that is shared with the other variables via the common factors. In particular $\lambda_{ij} = Cor(x_i, f_j)$ represents the extent to which x_i depends on the jth common factor. The second part, ψ_i, is called the *unique variance*. It is due to the unique factor e_i and explains the variability in x_i not shared with the other variables.

5.2.4 Importance Sampling

Importance sampling has long been used to reduce sampling size while keeping estimates obtained from the sample at a high level of confidence (Kahn, 1953). Specifically, it allows the analysis of rare events (such as failures or errors) with a high degree of accuracy when Monte Carlo techniques are used for numerical solutions. The method has been recently used to reduce the number of runs in Monte Carlo simulations for evaluating computer dependability (Goyal, 1992; Choi, 1993b). In the following, we first give an overview of the method and then discuss its applications in the Monte Carlo simulation of discrete-time Markov chains (DTMCs).

Overview of the method.   Assume that a random variable X has p.d.f. $f(x)$ and that $Y = h(X)$ is a function of X. Our goal is to estimate the expected value of Y,

$$\theta = E[Y] = E[h(X)] = \int_{-\infty}^{+\infty} h(x)f(x)dx \qquad (5.23)$$

through sampling. That is, we generate a sample $\{x_1, x_2, \ldots, x_n\}$ according to $f(x)$, therefore generating $\{y_1, y_2, \ldots, y_n\}$. We then calculate

$$\tilde{\theta} = \overline{Y} = \frac{1}{n}\sum_{i=1}^{n} y_i = \frac{1}{n}\sum_{i=1}^{n} h(x_i)$$

It may be very expensive to generate a statistically significant sample of X. For example, if $y_i = h(x_i) = 0$ for most generated x_i, we may need an extremely large size of sample to estimate θ with a high level of confidence. However, if we can, in sampling, select the rare x_i's that are considered important for estimating θ much more frequently while keeping the estimate unbiased, the sample size will be greatly reduced. This is the essence of the importance sampling method.

To do importance sampling, we change the p.d.f. of X from $f(x)$ to $g(x)$ such that the x's of importance in our parameter estimation have higher occurrence probabilities in $g(x)$. We use X' to represent the variable that has p.d.f. $g(x')$. By Eq. (5.23), we have

$$\theta = \int_{-\infty}^{+\infty} h(x)f(x)dx = \int_{-\infty}^{+\infty} h(x)\frac{f(x)}{g(x)}g(x)dx = \int_{-\infty}^{+\infty} h(x)\Lambda(x)g(x)dx \qquad (5.24)$$

where

$$\Lambda(x) = \frac{f(x)}{g(x)} \tag{5.25}$$

is called the *likelihood ratio*. Let $Y' = h(X)\Lambda(X)$. Then Eq. (5.24) becomes

$$\theta = \int_{-\infty}^{+\infty} y'g(x)dx = E[Y'] \tag{5.26}$$

Thus, instead of sampling from $f(x)$ to estimate the expected value of Y, the experiment is changed to sampling from $g(x')$ to estimate the expected value of Y'. That is, we generate a sample $\{x_1', x_2', \ldots, x_n'\}$ according to $g(x')$, therefore generating $\{y_1', y_2', \ldots, y_n'\}$, and then calculate

$$\tilde{\theta} = \overline{Y} = \frac{1}{n}\sum_{i=1}^{n} y_i' = \frac{1}{n}\sum_{i=1}^{n} h(x_i')\Lambda(x_i')$$

The variance of the above estimator is

$$Var(Y') = E[(Y' - \theta)^2] = \int_{-\infty}^{+\infty} \frac{h(x)f(x)^2}{g(x)}g(x)dx - \theta^2$$

To achieve the minimum variance, we should have

$$g(x) = \frac{h(x)f(x)}{\theta}$$

But θ is the unknown parameter to estimate. A heuristic is that the shape of $g(x)$ should follow the shape of $h(x)f(x)$ as closely as possible.

Applications in DTMC simulation.   In many cases, the operation of a computer system can be modeled by a discrete-time Markov chain (DTMC) (Trivedi, 1982). If the built DTMC is very large (such that it exceeds the available storage) or the functional simulation (simulation of the execution of machine instructions, algorithms, etc.) is used above a DTMC, the Monte Carlo simulation method is perhaps the only feasible way to solve the model. In dependability models, system failures are usually rare events with extremely small probabilities. To obtain statistically significant results, large simulation runs are required, which can be very time consuming. In such a case, importance sampling can reduce simulation runs, usually by orders of magnitude.

Assume we have a DTMC $\{Y_s, s \geq 0\}$ with a set of states $\{S_1, S_2, \ldots, S_m\}$ and a transition matrix $[p_{ij}]$. For each simulation run, we have a path $x_i = S_{i_0}, S_{i_1}, \ldots, S_{i_k}$. The occurrence probability of path x_i is (Goyal, 1992)

$$P(x_i) = p_{i_0}p_{i_0 i_1} \cdots p_{i_{k-1} i_k}$$

where each p_{ij} is an element in $[p_{ij}]$. All possible paths constitute the probability space of a random variable $X = \{x_1, x_2, x_3, \ldots, \}$.

To reduce simulation runs, we change the transition probability matrix from $[p_{ij}]$ to $[p'_{ij}]$ such that the paths that are important in our dependability evaluation are more likely to be sampled. After the change, the occurrence probability of path x_i is

$$P'(x_i) = p'_{i_0} p'_{i_0 i_1} \cdots p'_{i_{k-1} i_k}$$

Assume the dependability measure to evaluate is $\theta = E[h(X)]$. Then θ can be estimated using a sample, $\{x_1, x_2, \ldots, x_n\}$, obtained from simulations by

$$\tilde{\theta} = \frac{1}{n} \sum_{i=1}^{n} h(x_i) \Lambda(x_i) \tag{5.27}$$

where

$$\Lambda(x_i) = \frac{P(x_i)}{P'(x_i)} = \frac{p_{i_0} p_{i_0 i_1} \cdots p_{i_{k-1} i_k}}{p'_{i_0} p'_{i_0 i_1} \cdots p'_{i_{k-1} i_k}} \tag{5.28}$$

The remaining question is how to determine $[p'_{ij}]$. Several heuristics categorized as *failure biasing* have been proposed in the literature (Lewis, 1984; Goyal, 1992). Here we introduce one of the commonly used heuristics. Assume that in state S_i, transitions out of the state go either to a set of failure states, F (e.g., the system suffers one more component failure), or to a set of recovery states, R (e.g., the system recovers from a component failure). (S_i itself can be treated as either in F or in R.) It is obvious that we have

$$\sum_{j \in F} p_{ij} + \sum_{j \in R} p_{ij} = 1$$

Define a parameter b such that p''_{ij}'s satisfy

$$\sum_{j \in F} p'_{ij} = b, \quad \sum_{j \in R} p'_{ij} = 1 - b \tag{5.29}$$

Then we determine each p'_{ij} in state S_i by

$$p'_{ij} = \begin{cases} b \dfrac{p_{ij}}{\sum_{k \in F} p_{ik}} & j \in F \\[4mm] (1-b) \dfrac{p_{ij}}{\sum_{k \in R} p_{ik}} & j \in R \end{cases} \tag{5.30}$$

The parameter b is usually chosen to be 0.5 (Goyal, 1992). Since the sum of the original probabilities to failure states is often very small, then by Eq. (5.29), the selection of b can significantly increase these probabilities, making these transitions much more likely to occur in simulations.

5.3 DESIGN PHASE

In the design phase of a system, simulation is an important experimental means for performance and dependability analysis. Compared to analytical modeling, simulation has the capability to model complex systems to a high degree of fidelity without being restricted to assumptions made to keep an analytical model mathematically tractable. However, simulation for dependability analysis involves the injection of faults into the system under study at three levels of abstraction: the electrical level, the logic level, and the function level. The issues studied usually include, but are not limited to, fault propagation, fault latency, and fault impact such as coverage, reliability, availability, and performance loss. Figure 5.1 shows fault injection at the different levels.

Transient faults account for more than 80 percent of the failures in computer systems (Siewiorek, 1978; Iyer, 1986). These faults result from physical causes, such as power transients, capacitive or inductive crosstalk, or cosmic particle interventions (Yang, 1992).

Electrical-level fault injection emulates transient faults by changing the electric current and voltage inside a circuit. The faulty current and voltage can cause errors in logic values at the gate level. The gate-level errors can then propagate to other functional units and output pins of the chip. Electrical-level simulation can be used to study the impact of transient faults in a circuit or chip. The simulation, however, can be very time consuming and memory bound, since it has to track

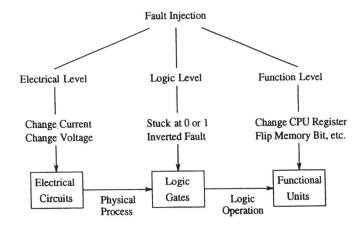

Figure 5.1: Simulated fault injections at different levels.

the propagation of faults from circuits to gates, to functional units, and eventually out to the pins.

Logic-level fault injection simulates the abstractions of physical fault models to logic gates in order to study large VLSI circuits or systems. Commonly used fault models include stuck-at-0, stuck-at-1, bridging faults, and inverted faults. These models are generally considered to be representative of faults occurring at the gate level. Although simulation at the logic level ignores the physical processes underlying gate faults, it still needs to trace the impact of gate-level faults to higher levels. For the same reason that electrical-level simulation cannot be effectively used to study large VLSI systems, logic-level simulation cannot effectively study large computer systems.

Function-level fault injection simulation is usually used to study dependability features of large computers or networks. Faults are injected into various components of the system under study. Functional fault models are used in the simulation, while detailed processes of fault occurrence at lower levels are ignored. Functional models representing the manifestation of faults can be extracted from results obtained from electrical- or logic-level fault injection or from field measurements. For example, "flipped memory bit" and "CPU register error" are two typical fault models. Analytical dependability models of computer systems are usually built at this level. Compared to analytical modeling, simulation is capable of representing detailed architectural features, realistic fault conditions, and intercomponent dependencies.

There are several common issues that apply to fault injection at all levels. The first is: What is the appropriate fault model at the chosen level of abstraction? While there is no easy answer to this question, filed data and experience are valuable guides. The second issue is: For a given fault model (e.g., one bit flip in memory) and fault type (e.g., transient fault), where should the fault be injected? A straightforward approach is to randomly choose a location from the injection space (e.g., all gates in a VLSI chip, or all memory bits). This scheme is easy to implement, but many faults may have similar impact (e.g., all faulty bits in an ALU may have the same effect) and many faulty locations may not be exercised. Another approach is to inject faults into a few representative locations under selected workloads so as to provide a directional evaluation of the system. This technique can be used to study fault impact in terms of locations or workloads.

The third issue involves workloads. The impact of faults on system dependability is workload-dependent. Hence, it is important to analyze a system while it is executing representative workloads. These workloads can be real applications, selected benchmarks, or synthetic programs. If the goal of study is to investigate fault impact on a mission task, the real applications running in the mission should be used in the simulation. If the goal is to study fault impact on general workloads, several representative benchmarks should be selected for the simulation. If the objective is to exercise every functional unit and location, neither real applications nor benchmarks may be appropriate. In this case, synthetic workloads may have to be designed for achieving the goal. The workload issue complicates simulation models and increases simulation time. It is essential to develop techniques to represent realistic workloads while maintaining reasonable simulation times.

The last issue is simulation time explosion. This occurs in two cases: (1) When too much detail is simulated, such as modeling physical processes in fault injections at the electrical level, and (2) when extremely small failure probabilities require large simulation runs to obtain statistically significant results (the theory is discussed in Section 5.2.1). Several techniques, including mix-mode simulation (Saleh, 1990; Choi, 1992), importance sampling (Goyal, 1992; Choi, 1992), hybrid simulation (Bavuso, 1987; Goswami, 1993a), and hierarchical simulation (Goswami, 1992) have been used to address the time explosion problem.

Table 5.1 summarizes features and representative studies in simulated fault injection at different levels. We discuss these studies in the following three sections.

5.3.1 Simulated Fault Injection at the Electrical Level

There are several reasons for simulating fault injection at the electrical level. First, fault injection at this level can be used to study the impact of physical causes that lead to faults and errors. Second, studies show that simple stuck-at fault models are not always representative of physical failures (Banerjee, 1982; Beh, 1982; Kim, 1988). Third, some circuits are of a mixed analog/digital nature which cannot be fully characterized by logic-level fault models. Thus, there is a growing need for fault simulators that can handle electrical transient faults and permanent physical failures for the purposes of both circuit testing and dependability evaluation.

Mixed-mode approach.   The basic simulation methodology used in fault injections at the chip level is *mixed-mode* approach. The fault-free portions of the

Table 5.1: Summary of Simulated Fault Injection

Category	Electrical Level	Logic Level	Function Level
Approach	Alter electrical current and voltage in circuits	Inject stuck-at or inverted faults to logic gates	Inject faults to CPU, memory, I/O devices, etc.
Target under study	VLSI chip Software running on the chip	VLSI chip Computer system Software	Computer system Network system Software
Studies	Fault simulation (Yang, 1992) HS1602 (Duba and Iyer, 1988) FOCUS (Choi et. al., 1992)	BDX930 (McGough, 1981) BDX930 (Lomelino, 1986) IBM RT PC (Czeck, 1991) EMAX (Kanawati, 1993)	Trace-driven (Chillarege, 1987) NEST (Dupuy, 1990) DEPEND (Goswami, 1992) REACT (Clark and Pradhan, 1993a) MEFISTO (Jenn, 1994)

circuit are simulated at the logic level while the faulty portions of the circuit are simulated at the electrical level. A representative mixed-mode fault simulator is SPLICE1 (Saleh, 1984). The electrical analysis in SPLICE1 is based on the method of iterated timing analysis (ITA), which incorporates a nonlinear relaxation method with event-driven selective tracing. ITA has been shown to be accurate and fast; it can provide a speedup of up to two orders of magnitude. The logic analysis in SPLICE1 is performed using a relaxation-based method and MOS-oriented models.

In fault injection that is based on mixed-mode simulation, a circuit model description is read and modified by adding a current source at the fault injection node.[1] During each iteration, the scheduled node events in the current time step (simulated run time, or virtual simulation time) are processed, and new events are scheduled and queued in the event list. For each fan-in element in the processed node, the element type (electrical, switch-level, logical) is determined. If the element type is electrical, then additional analysis is performed to determine whether the node is an injection site (i.e., analog signals are dealt with). The *fault injection time window* is the period between the fault injection time t and $t + dt$, where dt is the duration of the fault. If the node is an injection site and if the virtual simulation time is within the fault injection time window, the current source representing the transient is activated and additional current is added to the total current calculation. The additional current value is determined from a function representing the current source for the particular virtual simulation time. The total current is used to calculate the fault voltage level at the processed node.

Figure 5.2 illustrates the overall simulation and fault injection approach. A simple CMOS AND gate with buffered output is illustrated in the figure. The dotted boxes indicate normal voltage waveforms for the circuit. The dashed boxes contain waveforms resulting from a transient injection at the location marked by X. Notice that waveforms within the electrical-level analysis behave in an analog fashion but are discrete in the logic-level analysis.

Dynamic mixed mode.   Recently, a more efficient technique for performing transient fault simulation has been developed (Yang, 1992). The representation of a subcircuit that is subjected to transient fault injections is dynamically switched among different analysis modes (i.e., electrical and logic levels) during the simulation. The subcircuit is evaluated at the logic level until a fault is injected. When a transient fault is injected, the voltage level of the target node is upset and behaves in an analog fashion. Electrical-level analysis is used to evaluate this analog fault behavior. The analysis continues until the faulty voltage waveform stabilizes into a discrete signal. At this point, the subcircuit is evaluated with logic-level analysis until another transient occurs.

The dynamic approach is shown conceptually in Figure 5.3. For example, for

---

[1]A *node* is defined as a point in a conductive interconnection between electrical and/or logical elements.

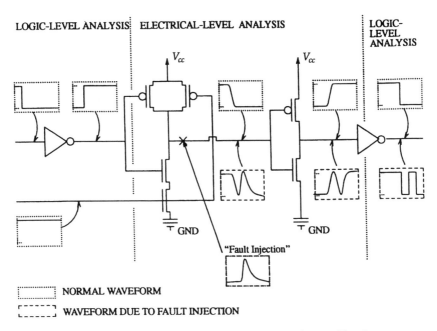

LOGIC-LEVEL ANALYSIS   ELECTRICAL-LEVEL ANALYSIS

LOGIC-
LEVEL
ANALYSIS

V_{cc}

V_{cc}

$\top$ GND

$\top$ GND

"Fault Injection"

NORMAL WAVEFORM

WAVEFORM DUE TO FAULT INJECTION

Figure 5.2: Illustration of fault injection at electrical level.

the schematic circuit diagram shown, if a transient fault occurs in subcircuit S3, one can determine that subcircuits S2, S3, and S4 must be simulated at the electrical level to capture the effects of the transient. Therefore, these subcircuits must be simulated at the electrical level. In the dynamic approach, unlike static mixed-mode simulation, all subcircuits begin the simulation at the logic level. When a transient occurs in subcircuit S3 at time t_1, the simulation mode changes to electrical-level analysis until the effect of the transient disappears. When the effect of the fault injection propagates to subcircuits S2 and S4, these two subcircuits are also forced to perform circuit simulation starting at time points t_2 and t_3, respectively. The electrical-level simulation of these subcircuits terminates after a short time, when the transients in each subcircuit have settled, and switch back to logic-level simulation. Since subcircuits S1, S5, S6, and S7 are not affected by the fault injection, they remain at the logic level throughout the simulation period. This approach is better able to reduce costly electrical-level analysis by exploiting the nature of the digital circuits while capturing the desired behavior of transients.

We now describe an automated environment for electrical-level fault injection. The design integrates a fault injection engine, a tracing facility, and graphical and statistical analysis packages into a user environment.

FOCUS—A chip-level simulation environment.   FOCUS is a simulation environment for fault sensitivity analysis of IC chips (Choi, 1992). In this environment, a range of user-specified electrical-level transient faults are automatically

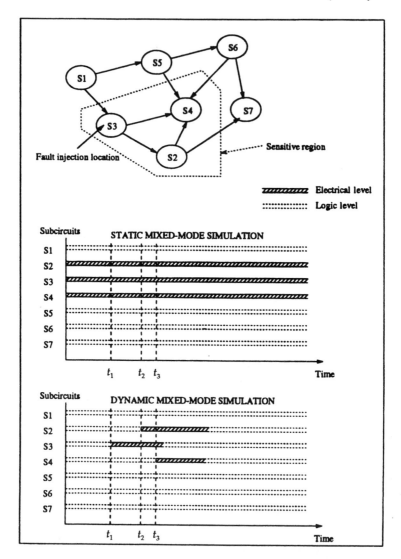

Figure 5.3: Static and dynamic mixed-mode simulation.

injected at the circuit level, and fault propagation is measured at the gate and higher levels. SPLICE1 is used as the fault simulation engine. Figure 5.4 depicts the overall experimental environment. The environment takes as input a net-list of the hardware description of the system and converts it into a simulation model. The user provides the fault description data, and specified faults are injected during the simulated run time of the target system. Faults that get propagated and detected are traced by the tracing facility, and the graphical analysis and impact analysis are performed on the fault data.

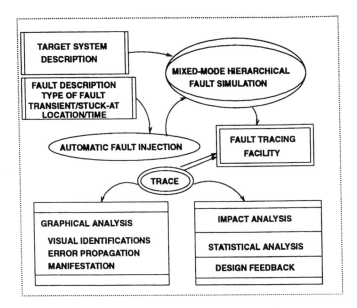

Figure 5.4: The FOCUS experimental environment.

The *fault injection process* is implemented as a run-time modification of the circuit, whereby a current source is added to a target node, thus altering the voltage level of the node over the time interval of the injected current waveform. The experimental environment allows both transient and permanent (single or multiple) fault injections. Since the injected current source is specified as a mathematical function, the resulting transients can be of varying shapes and duration. For example, electrical power surge, in-chip alpha particle intervention, lightning, and bridging faults can be modeled. The user can control the location of a fault, the time and duration of a fault, and the shape of the current source.

The *tracing facility* monitors all switching activities in the target system, including fault propagation through each gate or transistor, for all processed events. The trace data for each event consists of the time of the event, the hierarchical node name, and the new and previous voltage levels (for electrical nodes) or logic levels (for logic nodes).

The *graphical analysis facility* is used to visualize the error activity in different functional units of the processor and the fault propagation on the major interconnects and at the external pins. The *statistical analysis tools* provide impact analysis of the target system and generate the models necessary to depict the fault behavior in the system (e.g., I/O pin error distribution, latch error distribution, and internal fault propagation model).

The application of FOCUS is illustrated by analyzing a microprocessor used in commercial aircraft for real-time control of jet-engine functions. The 16-bit microprocessor consists of six major functional units. The arithmetic and logic unit

(ALU), which contains six registers, can perform double precision arithmetic operations. The control unit, which issues signals to control ALU operations, is made up of combinational logic and several registers. The decoder unit decodes I/O signals, the multiplexer unit provides the discrete lines and buses, and the *countdown unit* drives chip-wide clock signals. The *watchdog unit* provides protection against faults by resetting the processor in the event of a parity error or in the event the application software is timed out by a software sanity timer. The signal to synchronize the dual system is also provided by this unit. The chip runs at 12.08 MHz and is implemented in a three-micron technology CMOS gate-array made of 2688 blocks of four N-channel and four P-channel transistors. The system incorporates a variety of fault-tolerant design features at multiple levels, including software checks, parity checks, memory test, and error counting. The objective of the study is to investigate the impact of charge-level transients on latch, pin, and functional levels.

An experimental analysis of the susceptibility of the microprocessor to upsets due to current and voltage transients was conducted using simulated fault injection (Duba, 1988; Choi, 1990). The parameters used in the simulations were extracted from the actual microprocessor design and circuit layout. The application code running on the simulated processor exercised all the functional units at which transient fault injections were made. Fault injections were made at seven randomly chosen nodes in six functional units. For each node, current transients were injected at five charge levels: 0.5, 1.0, 2.0, 3.0, and 4.0 pC. Each charge level was injected at five time-points during the execution of the application code sequence. This amounted to over 1,000 simulated fault injections. Transients below 3.0 pC had no significant impact on the circuit.

The error data was generated by comparing each faulted simulation with a fault-free simulation. An *error event* was defined as either a logic state change or a voltage level change large enough to cause a node to be faulted at a future time. Error events were classified into three categories: (1) *logic upsets*—voltage transients large enough to constitute logic level errors; (2) *latch errors*—errors in the first-level latches; and (3) *pin errors*—errors at the chip I/O pins.

Nearly 80 instruction cycles (90300 ns) of the application code were executed on the target system during each simulation run. The application code was carefully selected to ensure that all of the functional units were executed. A total of 2,100 simulations were performed to obtain stable results. During the simulation, all nodes (including all latches and external I/O pins) in the circuit were monitored and processed. Table 5.2 summarizes the overall impact of transients in the range 0.5 to 9.0 pC. In the table, a *first-order error* is defined as one that occurs during the first clock cycle following a transient fault injection; *second- and higher-order errors* are those occurring during the second and subsequent clock cycles.

Figure 5.5 shows the propagation of the latch errors in time. In the figure, the *x*-axis represents the clock cycles from the fault injection time, and the *y*-axis represents the total latch error count for each clock cycle. It can be seen that,

Table 5.2: Impact of Transients Injected to the Target System

Type	Injections Involved	Percent of Total Injections	Resultant Errors
First-Order Latch Errors	470	22.4	2,149
Second- and Higher-Order Latch Errors	120	5.7	1,829
First-Order Pin Errors	255	12.1	1,168
Second- and Higher-Order Pin Errors	90	4.3	839
Functional Errors	193	9.2	747

given a certain number of latch errors in the first clock cycle, the number of latch errors degenerates significantly until the fourth clock cycle. At approximately the fifth clock cycle, the number of errors rapidly multiplies. This is because at this time, the error signal enters a unit with a large number of latches and high fan-out, such as the ALU registers. After the sixth cycle, the number of errors degenerates significantly until finally disappearing after the eighth cycle. Thus, the impact of latch errors lasts, at most, up to eight clock cycles from the time of fault injection.

5.3.2 Simulated Fault Injection at the Logic Level

Simulated fault injection at the logic level is similar to that at the electrical level in that both are circuit-level simulations. The difference is in the fault models used. Logic-level fault simulation uses abstract logical models for both faults and circuit functions to evaluate the behavior of a system. In contrast to the evaluation of the physical models used at the electrical level, logic-level simulation performs binary operations that represent the behavior of a given device. It takes binary input vectors and evaluates the output of the device for a given input pattern. Each signal in the circuit is represented by a member in a set of Boolean values depicting the steady-state conditions of the physical circuit. For example, set {1,0,X} is often used to describe high-, low-, and unknown-voltage values for

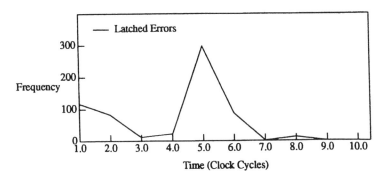

Figure 5.5: Latch error occurrence in time.

logic gates. Fault injection at this level simply forces a node to either be stuck-at-1 or stuck-at-0, or it inverts a logic value. Fault injection location and time can be set arbitrarily. Hence, with logic-level simulation, one obtains outputs with discrete values and possibly with some approximate timing information. Typically, outputs of the faulty and nonfaulty systems are compared to determine whether a fault has been detected.

For MOS technology, a gate-level logic simulator is inadequate to handle circuits containing pass transistors, ratioed logic, buses, and other features that exhibit bidirectional signal flow and/or charge-sharing effects. To handle such transistor networks without resorting to expensive electrical-level analysis, *switch-level* simulation is used in (Bryant, 1984). Switch-level analysis allows bidirectional signal flow and different levels of signal strengths. For example, a discrete set $\{0,1,\ldots,9\}$ can be used to model different signal strengths or voltage levels. At this level, transistor-level fault modeling can also be easily incorporated.

This type of fault simulation has been widely used for evaluating the coverage of a given set of test vectors for testing manufacturing defects in a chip. Typically, a set of test vectors is generated either randomly or manually by an automatic test pattern generator (ATPG). The test vectors are then submitted to the fault simulator to determine how many faults they can detect. In this case, the test vectors become the workload or the inputs to the system. In the beginning of such a simulation, a stuck-at fault is injected, and the faulty circuit is simulated while a given test is applied at the primary inputs of the circuit. A similar run is performed again without any fault injection. The logic values at the primary outputs of the faulty circuit are then compared to the outputs of the fault-free run to determine if there is any difference in the outputs. If the injected fault altered logic values at the outputs compared to the clean run, then the fault is assumed to be detected. If a fault is detected, there is no reason to continue the simulation for that specific fault. This process of test generation and fault simulation is iterated until satisfactory fault coverage (the percentage of faults detected of all theoretically detectable faults) is achieved. This application has been used in industry to evaluate and assist test generation (Ruehli, 1983; Rogers, 1985).

The use of fault simulation to perform dependability analysis at the design phase is more complicated. Here we are concerned with both permanent and transient faults and the time at which a fault is introduced. Fault sensitivity analysis of very large circuits through simulated fault injection and subsequent fault propagation can identify critical dependability bottlenecks. To characterize a highly dependable VLSI system, we need to evaluate, simultaneously, the fault behavior of all components as well as their combined behavior.

Stuck-at faults can be simulated using conventional logic-level fault simulators that are widely available. A stuck-at fault injection is performed by forcing the state of a node to a specified value for the duration of the simulation. By selectively tracing/detecting a set of internal and external nodes, fault propagation can be monitored. Fault behavior in a system can then be modeled and analyzed by studying the fault propagation trace.

Transient faults are injected by altering the logic values of the target node for a specified time during the simulation. For example, the output of a gate is set to 1 when it should normally be 0. This faulty logic is forced on the output for a specified time period. Logic-level transient injection can be performed in two different ways. The above bit-flip effect can be performed on the combinational part of the circuit using a timing simulator. The created "pulse" can then propagate and may become latched or disappear. Another approach is to change the state of a machine by flipping a bit in a register or in a memory element in the system. These approaches, however, may not always reflect the actual device-level transient behavior at the logic level, because a transient can propagate in multiple paths and result in more than one latch error.

To evaluate system dependability based on realistic fault models, a fault-behavior dictionary approach can be taken (Choi, 1993). The approach is illustrated in Figure 5.6. A fault-behavior dictionary generated from electrical-level fault analysis can serve as a fast lookup table for a logic-level concurrent or parallel simulation. First, an electrical-level fault-behavior dictionary for a given chip is generated by extensive fault simulation. In this step, gates around the fault-injection location are extracted, and a subcircuit consisting of these gates is formed. This subcircuit is exercised by exhaustively applying all input combinations while fault injection is performed. Faulty behavior at each of the subcircuit outputs is analyzed and recorded in a dictionary. The resulting entry in the dictionary consists of the input vector, fault injection time, and fault location. Second,

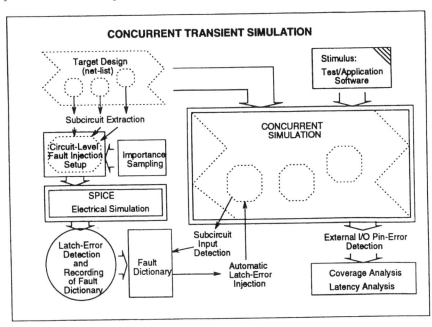

Figure 5.6: Concurrent transient simulation.

concurrent run-time fault injections of the generated logical error at the subcircuit level are performed using the fault dictionary. A concurrent simulator can be used to propagate, in a single simulation pass, the effects of multiple injected errors.

Both transient and permanent faults can be injected using switch-level or gate-level logic simulation. The overall simulation approach for fault injection at the logic level consists of the following steps:

1. Obtain the net-list of a design and devise appropriate simulation models to emulate the given design.
2. Simulate the model using a logic-level simulator.
3. During the simulation, run a given workload depicting the application or test software (by applying test vectors to the primary inputs).
4. Save the behavior of the system under fault-free conditions by tracing all the changes in the evaluated logic events of monitored nodes for comparison with the subsequent fault injection runs.
5. Run the same workload again and inject a fault to a selected node during the simulation period and trace.
   - *For a stuck-at fault:* Force the state of the selected node to either 1 (for stuck-at-1 fault) or 0 (for stuck-at-0 fault) and evaluate the circuit. Hold the state to the stuck-at fault value throughout the simulation.
   - *For a transient fault:* Force the state of the selected node to a logic value that is the reverse of the normal state (i.e., force a 0 if the normal state is a 1, and vice versa). Hold the state to the reverse value on the node for one or more clock cycles. Let the fault effect propagate by evaluating the circuit with the corrupted logic state. Release the forced state when a new signal/event arrives at that node.
6. Monitor the behavior of the system under fault conditions.
7. Compare the traces from the faulty and fault-free runs and identify the differences to determine where and when the fault has propagated.
8. Use collected statistical measurements to determine dependability parameters (e.g., detection coverage) and the fault impact (e.g., minor program error or system failure).

These fault injection steps should be repeated many times for a given workload. If the experiment is intended to estimate single measures (e.g., detection coverage), the number of injections required for achieving a given confidence interval can be determined using Eq. (5.14). If the purpose is to obtain distributions (e.g., error latency distribution), the fault injections should not be stopped until the constructed distribution is stable, that is, the two consecutive distributions constructed are not statistically different. Importance sampling can be used to significantly reduce simulation runs.

Two early studies in fault injection at this level analyzed a digital avionic miniprocessor, BDX-930, as the target system. The first study investigated the impact of faults at gates and pins on the output results of programs, with emphasis on the fault latency and fault coverage issues (McGough, 1981). The second study investigated error propagation from the gate level to the pin level (Lomelino, 1986). A recent study explored the behavior of transient faults that occur during the normal execution of a processor (Czeck, 1991). The study quantified faults that can be emulated by software-implemented fault injection (to be discussed). We discuss these studies in the following two subsections.

Study of Bendix BDX-930.   An early study in this field was the simulated fault injection to the Bendix BDX-930, a digital avionic miniprocessor, to investigate fault latency and coverage (McGough, 1981). The BDX-930 was composed of bit slice processors (AMD2901) and was used in a number of flight control avionic systems. Fault tolerance was achieved by replication of the processing and voting in software. A gate-level emulator of the BDX-930 was developed for this study. The run speed of the emulator was 25,000 times slower than the BDX-930 when hosted on a PDP-10.

The methodology used in the study was: Given a software program running on the processor, inject a single stuck-at or inverted fault at a gate or pin selected randomly and observe the time to detection. Assume that a detection occurs whenever there is a difference between the outputs of the faulty and fault-free processors executing the same program. The experiment is repeated 600 to 1,000 times to construct an empirical latency distribution. Six programs were selected to repeat the above experimental procedure. In addition, a typical avionic flight control system self-test program was written for this study and executed to determine fault detection coverage.

Results showed that most of the detected faults were detected during the first execution of the program. Subsequent repetitions did not significantly increase the propagation of detected faults. A large percentage of faults (about 60 percent for the gate-level faults and 30 percent for the pin-level faults) remained undetected after as many as eight repetitions of the program. The fault coverage of the self-test program was found to be 87 percent for the gate-level faults and 98 percent for the pin-level faults.

The above study emphasized the impact of faults at gates and pins on the output results of programs. Another study on the Bendix BDX-930 computer investigated error propagation from the gate level to the pin level (Lomelino, 1986). In this study, a single AMD2901 processor chip in the BDX-930 was selected for fault injection and error data collection. The processor was simulated using an event-driven, gate-level logic simulator developed at NASA Langley (Migneault, 1985). The simulator was driven by a self-test program developed for the BDX-930 which provides a high probability of detecting error activity.

In the simulation, the single stuck-at fault model was applied to 150 selected gates for fault injection. The gates were distributed throughout the nine function units of the AMD2901. Error data was collected by first simulating a fault-free circuit, then simulating the circuit with a single injected fault, and finally comparing the output of two simulations. Four sets of simulation experiments, consisting of 150 simulations per set, were conducted. Results showed that 78.7 percent of faults produced error propagation detected within the chip and that 66.7 percent of faults produced errors that propagate to the output pins, within the first 100 clock cycles. The error distribution at the output pins was found to be sensitive to the locations of faults. The results also showed that the error activity increases with the increase of concurrent microinstruction activity.

Study of IBM PC RT.   In (Czeck, 1991), a simulation model of the IBM RT PC was used to inject transient, gate-level faults for exploring the behavior of transient faults that occur during the normal execution of a processor. The emulated hardware functional units in the processor included instruction prefetch buffer (IPB), microinstruction fetch (MIF), data fetch and storage (DFS), ALU and shifter (ALU), and ROMP storage channel interface (RSCI). The simulation model included original error detection mechanisms (EDM) that reside in the IBM RT PC (such as illegal instruction traps and memory access violation) and additional error detection mechanisms provided in this study for evaluating their effectiveness (such as timeout and control flow monitoring).

Figure 5.7 shows possible error manifestations after a fault injection. In the figure, *minor errors* are those differences in the internal processor state between the faulty and fault-free simulation runs that have not been detected by an EDM. *Monitoring errors* are those uncovered by the "duplicate and compare" EDM that monitors bus addresses and data. *Severe errors* are those resulting in the change of a microinstruction and the instruction address registers, which lead to a change in the control flow of the program. *Fatal errors* have triggered a system resident EDM and caused an abnormal termination of the application task. *Results overdue* occurs when the task executes longer than a predetermined time limit and the execution is halted. *Overwritten* means that the injected fault does not manifest to a minor error or that a mirror error is overwritten by correct data.

Three workloads were selected for this study: an iterative matrix multiplica-

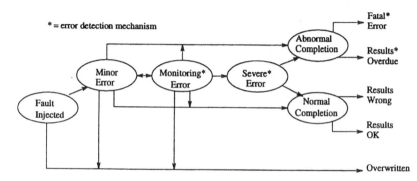

Figure 5.7: Error manifestations in the IBM PC RT simulation model.

tion, a recursive Fibonacci program, and an iterative Fibonacci program. These workloads were considered to be representative of the characteristics of instruction set architectures and diversity in program structure. For each workload and each fault location, 1,000 faults were injected. The following experimental methodology was used:

1. For each workload, the fault-free behavior of the workload is extracted from the internal state of the processor and saved for comparison during the subsequent fault injection experiments.
2. A fault location is selected such that the fault in the location has a high probability of producing an error and locations for different injections do not yield the same error behavior.
3. The fault injection time is set to the start of the workload execution. The fault injection time will be advanced by one cycle for each successive fault injection experiment.
4. The fault is injected for a duration of one clock cycle at the location and time selected.
5. For each successive clock cycle, the internal processor state of the faulty processor is compared with that obtained in step 1. Differences are recorded for offline analysis.
6. The faulty behavior is monitored at each clock cycle until the program execution is completed or a severe error causes the monitor to cease.
7. The simulation run is restarted at step 3 and the time of next fault injection will be advanced by one clock cycle.

It was found that 40 percent to 55 percent of injected faults do not produce an error. Among the faults that manifest to errors, approximately two-thirds of them can be emulated by the software-implemented fault injection approach (to be discussed). The other one-third of these faults manifest to errors in CPU components (e.g., microinstruction control registers) that are not accessible to software. At the system level, the fault behavior showed a strong dependency on the workload structure and the instruction sequencing rather than on the instruction mix. Error detection latency was found to follow a Weibull distribution with a decreasing detection rate. The distribution represents two error occurrence processes: a fast process in which fault manifestation and error propagation occur within a small time window and a slow process in which dormant faults and errors are activated gradually by the workload.

The next section introduces a tool that uses a hardware simulation engine to simulate permanent stuck-at faults at the gate/switch level and extracts a high-level error model automatically.

EMAX.   EMAX is a high-level error model automatic extractor. It simulates user-selected, permanent, stuck-at faults that may occur inside a processor chip

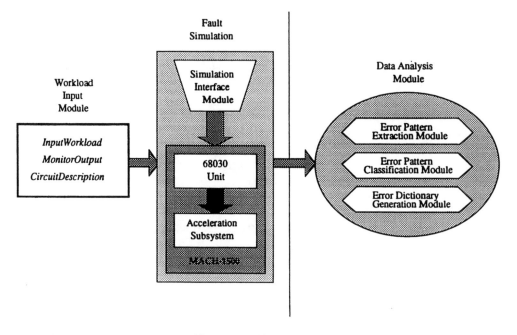

Figure 5.8: The EMAX modules.

at the gate and/or the switch level and generates the output patterns produced by faulty circuits (Kanawati, 1993). See Figure 5.8. It is designed to investigate the representativeness of faults/errors applied at the pins or at the system level for the faults inside VLSI chips. Based on the error patterns, cost-effective, high-level fault/error injection patterns are developed for validating fault-tolerant system designs.

EMAX consists of a workload input module, a fault simulation module, and a data analysis module. The workload input module takes as input workload patterns and circuit descriptions. The fault simulation module uses a hardware simulation engine, the Zycad MACH-1500, to speed up the simulation experiments. The data analysis module includes three submodules, an error pattern extractor module, an error pattern classification module, and a fault dictionary module. It reads the output fault records generated by the MACH-1500, extracts error patterns for every fault, divides error patterns into classes, and builds a fault dictionary.

The application of EMAX was illustrated by analyzing a processor. The processor has seven instructions; two of the instructions require two execution phases and the others need four phases. Faults were injected at every node defined in the net-list of the processor. During the experiments, less than 16 percent of injected faults caused errors. Thirteen error types were observed, seven of which involved more than one component and one of which caused a processor halt. Execution phases of instructions were taken into account. The majority of errors during phase 1 were address line errors that caused the processor of fetch wrong instructions. As a result, data line errors were observed during the next phase of execution. The majority of the errors in phase 2 were also address line errors that caused the processor to fetch wrong instructions. The errors propagated to phase 3 as address errors and control line errors, which eventually propagated to phase 4 as data line errors and address line errors. Overall, 73 percent of errors were address line errors while fetching an instruction, 13 percent were address line errors while fetching an operand, and each of the other error types contributed less than 5 percent of the errors.

5.3.3 Simulated Fault Injection at the Function Level

Function-level fault injection simulation is used to study overall computer and network systems rather than their individual components. These studies typically consider the hardware, the software, their interactions, and the interdependence between the various components of the system. There are several outstanding issues in developing functional simulation models at the system level: (1) a lack of well-established system-level fault models, (2) a large and varied component domain, (3) the effort and time required to develop a functional simulation model, (4) the impact of the software on system dependability, and (5) simulation time explosion.

The first issue, a lack of well-established system-level fault models, is partly due to the second, a large and varied component domain. At the gate level, the basic components are gates with single functions and well-defined interconnections. At this level, it is possible to establish a fault model, such as the single stuck-at fault model, that can be consistently applied to all gates to model their fault behavior. At the system level, the basic components include CPUs, communication channels, disks, software systems, and memory. These components have complex inputs, perform multiple functions, and have varied physical attributes (e.g. hardware and software) and complex interconnections. In addition to the diversity of the components that make up a system, two similar components (such as two CPUs) can have different functions and behavior. This makes it difficult to establish a single fault model that can be applied consistently to all components.

For this reason, various types of fault models are required, depending on the type of component being studied. The fault models are functional fault models that simulate system-level manifestations of gate-level faults. For instance, a single bit-flip is typically used to simulate a memory or register fault. Various fault models can be used for communication channels. Messages traversing the channel can be corrupted or destroyed, or the channel can be made inoperative. A fault in a processing node can be modeled as a service interrupt caused by CPU, memory, disk, or software faults in the node. More detailed fault models for a processor or other system components can be derived from lower-level simulations using the fault-dictionary approach discussed earlier. For instance, a gate-level simulation of a processor can be injected with faults while executing a typical workload. The effect of the faults on the workload can be stored in a fault dictionary that contains, for each gate-level fault injected, the types of effects and the probability of these effects. This dictionary can then serve as a fault model for system-level simulations.

The third issue, the effort and time required to develop a functional simulation model, is especially significant when simulating large complex systems. Two factors contribute to the problem. One is the time and effort needed to describe the detailed functionality of the system components. The other is the time and effort required to inject faults, initiate repairs, abort, reschedule and synchronize events, and maintain a whole host of fault statistics. As the number of components in the system becomes large, a well-formulated, structured, and automated approach is needed to contend with the complexity. A solution is a tool that includes a library of software "objects" that provide the framework needed to conduct simulated fault injection studies and that can be easily customized to meet user-specific needs.

The fourth issue is the impact of the software on system dependability. Dependability studies have tended to focus on a system's hardware components. But as hardware becomes more reliable, software is becoming a more dominant factor (Gray, 1990). The effectiveness of functional detection and repair schemes depend upon several application-specific measures, such as detection latency and error propagation times. To study the impact of the software on system dependability, methods should allow the designer to incorporate the software into the overall dependability study. The simulation tool should permit the execution of actual user programs and relevant operating system features.

The fifth issue, simulation time explosion, is extremely important. This occurs when the system modeled has very small failure probabilities requiring large simulation runs to obtain statistically significant results. This is especially a problem with functional simulation: Its primary benefit, detailed modeling, further contributes to simulation time explosion. Acceleration techniques used at the system level can reduce simulation time explosion. Hierarchical and hybrid simulation methods have been shown to be very effective (Goswami, 1992; 1993a). The basic approach of these techniques is to (1) break down a large, complex model into simpler submodels, (2) analyze submodels individually, (3) combine the results from step 2 to build a simplified system model, and (4) analyze the system model to obtain the solution. If the models in step 1 and step 3 are both simulation models, the approach is called *hierarchical simulation*. If the models in step 1 are simulation models and the model in step 3 is an analytical model, the approach is called *hybrid simulation*. As long as the interactions among the subsystems are weak, this decomposition approach provides valid results. The approach is ideally suited for dependability analysis because dependability models can usually be broken into two submodels—a fault occurrence submodel and an error handling submodel—whose interactions are typically weak.

Since there are many analytical modeling tools, including Petri-net-based simulation tools, what is the need for functional simulation tools for system-level dependability analysis? What additional information and capabilities can they provide? The answer is that analytical modeling tools use only probabilistic models to represent the behavior of a system. In essence, the effect of a fault on the system is predefined by a set of probabilities and distributions. Functional simulation tools not only use stochastic modeling; they also permit behavioral modeling, which does not require that the effect of the faults be predefined.

An example that demonstrates this capability is a distributed system using a centralized, prediction-based, load-balancing scheme demonstrated in Figure 5.9. The system is evaluated under faulty conditions.

The load-balancing software that makes task placement decisions and maintains the database is executed on a simulated distributed system. Communication faults were injected to destroy and corrupt fields of the status messages sent to the CPU maintaining the database. Faults were also injected into the CPU containing the load-balancing software to erase its database. The effect of these faults is to corrupt the database and impair the placement decisions made by the load-balancing software. If a purely probabilistic modeling tool was used for this study, the user would have to prespecify

- the probability that a fault will corrupt the database,
- how each fault will corrupt the database,
- which portions of the database will be corrupted,
- the extent of corruption, and
- how each corruption will impair the placement decision made by the load-balancing software.

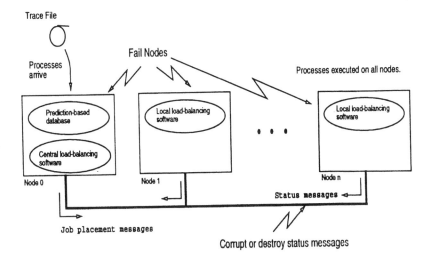

Figure 5.9: Distributed system executing load-balancing software.

These factors are extremely difficult to obtain without executing the actual software. Because the simulation executes the actual software, these parameters are the results of (and not inputs to) the fault injection experiment. Only the fault arrival rates and the types of faults injected need to be specified. Thus, the simulation results can identify the failure mechanisms, obtain failure probabilities, and quantify the effect of faults. It can be used to pick out the key features that must be modeled and help to determine and specify both the structure of, and the parameters to, analytical models.

A singular feature that distinguishes behavioral modeling from probabilistic modeling is the ability of behavioral modeling to reveal design flaws in the software. For example, the simulation helped to uncover a design feature of the software that caused erratic increases in system response time only when status messages were destroyed. Once the software was modified, the erratic increase in response time ceased. Clearly, such results cannot be obtained with analytical modeling tools.

An additional advantage of functional simulation is that it allows the use of any type of time to failure (TTF) distributions. Unlike analytical modeling, in which only a few types of distributions are commonly used for the tractability of models, the simulation method can handle any form of distribution, empirical or analytical.

In recent years, several function-level simulation tools that can be used for fault injection have been or are being developed. NEST, DEPEND, REACT, and MEFISTO are four representative tools. NEST is a function-level testbed that specializes in modeling and evaluating distributed network systems (Dupuy, 1990). Although the tool is not designed for fault injection, users can make node or link failures by deleting or adding nodes and links or changing their features while the simulation is running. DEPEND, developed at the University of Illinois, exploits the properties of the object-oriented paradigm to provide a general-purpose, system-level dependability analysis tool that can evaluate various types of fault-tolerant architectures (Goswami, 1992). The object-oriented feature of DEPEND makes the tool capable of modeling multiple levels of functional units to meet a wide range of applications. REACT, a software testbed that performs automated life testing of a variety of multiprocessor architectures through simulated fault injections, was developed at the University of Massachusetts and the Texas A&M University (Clark, 1993a). Several system, workload, and fault/error models, which are representative of multiprocessor architectures and conditions, are embedded in the testbed. MEFISTO, developed at LAAS-CNRS in France and Chalmers University in Sweden, is an integrated environment for applying fault injection into VHDL simulation models encompassing various levels of abstraction (Jenn, 1994). In the following, we discuss these tools.

NEST–A Network Simulation Testbed.   NEST (NEtwork Simulation Testbed) is a graphical environment running on the UNIX system for modeling, executing, and monitoring distributed network systems and protocols (Dupuy, 1990). Using a set of graphical tools provided by NEST, the user can develop simulation models of communication networks. The model includes node functions (e.g., routing protocols) and communication link behaviors (e.g., packet loss or delay features), typically coded in C. These user procedures are linked with run-time routines embedded in NEST and executed by the NEST simulation server. The user can reconfigure a modeled network system through graphical interaction or programming. Built-in graphical tools allow users to program custom monitors and observe the simulation results on-line.

Figure 5.10 shows the overall architecture of NEST. NEST consists of a simulation server and several client monitors. The simulation server is responsible for running simulations. The generic client monitors are used to configure simulation models and control their executions. The custom client monitors are used to observe simulation behavior and display results. Clients can reside on separate machines so that the server is dedicated to time-consuming simulations.

Node functions are used to model distributed communicating processes running at network nodes (e.g., protocols and database transactions). NEST executes node processes and their communication calls using a set of embedded primitives for sending, broadcasting, and receiving packets. The motion of a packet over links is simulated by passing it through the link functions. Link functions are used to model the behavior of communication links (e.g., packet loss and link jamming). Link functions are also used to monitor and collect performance statistics of link traffic. The simulation server schedules the execution of the node and link processes to meet the delay and timing specified by the user.

The user can create and modify a network description (node and link functions and connections) using the NEST graphical tools. Once the user has defined a simulation scenario, it is sent to the simulation server to be executed. One of NEST's key feature is its ability to reconfigure a scenario during the simulation

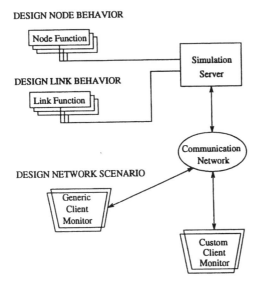

Figure 5.10: Overall architecture of NEST.

run. The user may delete or add nodes and links (thus failures can be emulated) or change their features while the simulation is running. The impact of these changes may be instantly observed and interpreted. Such dynamically reconfigured simulations can be used to study the impact of node/link failure and recovery on the modeled network system.

NEST has been used to evaluate IPLS (a distributed Incremental Position Location System), topology recognition and broadcasting connectivity tables for the ARPAnet and Internet, various dynamic load-balancing schemes, and an experimental multiprocessor operating system.

DEPEND—A System Dependability Analysis Environment.   DEPEND is an integrated design and fault injection environment (Goswami, 1992). It provides facilities to model fault-tolerant architectures and conduct extensive fault injection studies. It is ideally suited for evaluating specific fault-tolerant mechanisms, detailed fault scenarios such as latent errors, and software behavior due to hardware faults. It is a functional, process-based (Kobayashi, 1978; Schwetman, 1986) simulation tool. The system behavior is described by a collection of processes that interact with one another. A process-based approach was selected for several reasons. It is an effective way to model system behavior, repair schemes, and system software in detail. It facilitates modeling of intercomponent dependencies, especially when the system is large and the dependencies are complex, and it allows actual programs to be executed within the simulation environment. Both hierarchical and hybrid simulation techniques have been used in DE-PEND.

DEPEND exploits the properties of the object-oriented paradigm, specifically, modular decomposition and modular composability (Meyer, 1988), to model different levels of components and to implement a variety of fault models. *Modular decomposition* consists of breaking down a problem into small elements, whereas *modular composition* favors production of elements that can be freely combined with each other to provide new functionality. If, for instance, the fault injection process is divided into two elements or objects—an object that determines when to inject and interrupt the system and an object that determines the response to a fault (the fault model)—then the two criteria are met. The first object, called a *key object*, is common to all fault injection methods. It encapsulates the various mechanisms used to determine the arrival time of a fault and interrupt the system. The second object, the *fault model*, is specific to the component being injected and to the type of fault injection study. The two are combined via function calls. Thus, by specifying different fault model objects, one key object, such as the injector object, can be used for all types of fault injections. Key objects are designed to be parameterized. That is, the user can specify various fault arrival distributions or trace files. This same approach is used to model components that are similar but not identical. Common aspects are encapsulated in an object that then invokes other objects to provide more specific functionality. Furthermore, because users can specify specific behaviors (e.g., their own fault model objects), the tool is not limited to any predefined set of fault models or component types.

A library of objects that provide the skeletal foundation necessary to model an architecture and conduct simulated fault injection experiments is provided. This reduces the time and effort needed to build simulation models. In addition to decomposition, composition, and parameterization, the concept of *inheritance* (Meyer, 1988) makes it possible to provide a library with a minimum set of objects that can be readily specialized to model a wide range of architectures and fault injection experiments. With inheritance, users can reuse the properties of an existing object and develop more specialized objects with minimum effort. There are two types of objects: elementary objects and complex objects. Elementary objects provide basic functions such as injecting faults and compiling statistics. Complex objects created from several elementary objects simulate fundamental components found in most fault-tolerant architectures such as CPUs, self-checking processors, N-modular redundant processors, communication links, voters, and memory.

The steps required to develop and execute a model are shown in Figure 5.11. The user writes a control program in C++ using the objects in the DEPEND library. The program is then compiled and linked with the DEPEND objects and the run-time environment. The model is executed in the simulated parallel run-time environment. Here, the assortment of objects, including the fault injectors, CPUs, and communication links, execute simultaneously to simulate the functional behavior of the architecture. Faults are injected and repairs are initiated according to the user's specifications, and a report containing the essential statistics of the simulation is produced.

DEPEND allows users to specify different fault models. In addition, DEPEND provides default fault routines for each object to minimize user design time. For instance, the default fault model for a communication medium simulates the effects of a noisy communication channel. Fields in the messages passed along the communication link are actually corrupted or the message is destroyed.

The *fault injector* is a fundamental object in DEPEND. It encapsulates the

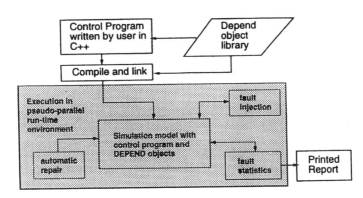

Figure 5.11: The DEPEND environment.

mechanism for injecting faults. To use the injector, a user specifies the number of components, the TTF distribution for each component, and the fault subroutine that specifies the fault model. In addition to user-specified distributions, the injector provides constant time, exponential, hyperexponential, and the Weibull distributions. The injector also provides a workload-based injection scheme that varies the fault arrival rate based on a specified workload. The user provides a workload function, a set of workload states, and an exponential fault arrival rate for each state. For example, the workload function may be the utilization of a server. With this approach the fault arrival rate will fluctuate with the utilization of the server. The fault injector will periodically poll the workload function to update a state transition diagram to maintain a history of the workload behavior. This history is used to inject a large number of faults during peak workload conditions and fewer faults when the workload is low. This technique models the workload/failure dependency observed in (Butner, 1980) and (Castillo, 1981).

In addition to executing actual C++ and C programs, DEPEND provides an abstract software modeling environment to simulate program behavior during the early design stages when actual code does not exist. The environment represents application programs by decomposing them into graph models consisting of a set of nodes, a set of edges that probabilistically determine the flow from node to node, and a mapping of the nodes to memory. The graph models are then mapped to virtual memory and executed while errors are injected into the program's memory space. The environment provides application-dependent parameters, such as detection and propagation times, and permits meaningful application-dependent evaluation of function-and system-level error detection and recovery schemes. This environment has been used to analyze memory-scrubbing schemes within the context of application programs (Goswami, 1993c). The application-dependent coverage values obtained were compared with those obtained by traditional schemes that assume uniform or random memory access patterns. The coverage values obtained using the traditional approach were found to be up to 100 percent larger than those obtained with the software graph model. The findings demonstrate the need for application-dependent evaluation—especially when evaluating the dependability of application-specific systems.

DEPEND has been applied to evaluate several computer systems. In (Goswami, 1991), DEPEND was used to simulate the UNIX-based Tandem Integrity S2 fault-tolerant system and evaluate how well it handles near-coincident errors caused by correlated and latent faults. Issues such as memory scrubbing, reintegration policies, and workload-dependent repair time were evaluated. The accuracy of the simulation model was validated by comparing the results of the simulations with measurements obtained from fault injection experiments conducted on a production Tandem Integrity S2 machine. DEPEND has also been used to study the CM5 connection machine, the Parsytec high-performance computer being developed by the European Esprit project, the Space Station Data Management System, and other systems.

REACT—A Software Testbed for Analyzing Multiprocessors. The REli-able Architecture Characterization Tool (REACT) is a software testbed for analyzing a variety of fault-tolerant multiprocessor systems (Clark and Pradhan, 1993a; 1993b). It was developed to meet the need for a generalized simulation package that can evaluate high-level dependability metrics more precisely than feasible with analytical approaches. Most other fault-injection tools are oriented toward simulating systems over very short intervals of time to measure the effects of error propagation or the latency and coverage of detection mechanisms. REACT, on the other hand, has the capability to evaluate reliability or availability as functions of time and analyze failure modes over the operational life of a system.

REACT abstracts a system at the architectural level and performs life testing through simulated fault injection to measure dependability. This involves conducting a certain number of experiments or trials in which the operation of an initially fault-free system is simulated, while randomly occurring faults are injected into its components. Systems are operated until they either fail or reach a particular censoring time. Failure statistics are collected during each trial which are later aggregated over the entire simulation run in order to compute system dependability metrics.

REACT can analyze multiprocessor systems that utilize N-modular redundancy, duplication and comparison, standby sparing or error-control coding to achieve fault tolerance. Figure 5.12 depicts the system model employed by REACT. This class of architectures consists of one or more processor modules (P) interconnected via buses (B) to one or more memory modules (M) through a block of *fault tolerance mechanisms.* The fault tolerance mechanisms supply the hardware necessary to detect, correct, or mask errors during memory accesses and reconfigure the system when modules fail. Predefined functional-level abstractions are used to model individual processors and memories. The number of processor and memory modules, their interconnection, and the operation of the fault tolerance mechanisms are all user-specified. This framework provides the flexibility needed to represent many different architectures, without the complexity of developing custom simulation models for each.

REACT can automatically inject both permanent and transient faults into the processors, memories, and the fault tolerance mechanisms of a system. Fault occur-

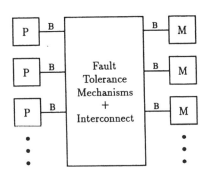

Figure 5.12: Class of architectures REACT can analyze.

rence times are sampled from a Weibull distribution. Behavior of each type of faulty component within the system is independently governed by a stochastic model that accounts for both fault and error latency. These models were derived, in part, from the results of other low-level fault-injection experiments. Repair times for failed components are assumed to have a log-normal distribution after a fixed logistics delay. The time required to reintegrate a repaired component back into the system and to reboot the system after a critical failure are constant and user-specified.

A synthetic workload is assumed for which processors continually perform *instruction cycles* consisting of several possible memory references and the simulated execution of an instruction. Real code and data are not used by REACT, but errors are allowed to propagate throughout the system as if the application program were actually being executed. The workload model is specified by a mean instruction execution rate, the probabilities of performing a memory read and write access per instruction, plus a locality-of-reference model that determines which locations are accessed.

An example of how faults are modeled in REACT is illustrated by the processor fault model. Processor operation in the presence of faults is governed by the stochastic model shown in Figure 5.13. Ovals in this diagram represent

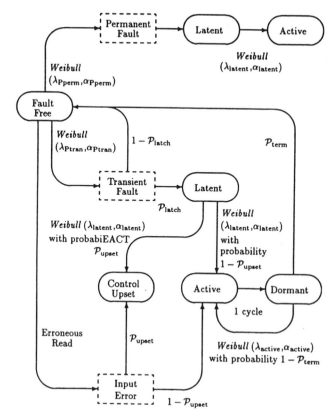

Figure 5.13: Processor fault model.

valid processor states, while arcs indicate what state changes may take place. Dashed boxes are temporary nodes that are passed through when moving into a valid state. All processors initially start in the fault-free state. Permanent faults occur at Weibull ($\lambda_{P_{perm}}$, $\alpha_{P_{perm}}$)-distributed interarrival times and become latent. No errors are generated by latent processor faults. A permanent fault will remain latent for a period of time specified by a Weibull (λ_{latent}, α_{latent}) distribution and then become active. A processor is considered to be failed and will produce errors during every instruction cycle when it is in the active state due to a permanent fault. It can only leave this state and return to the fault-free state if it is repaired and resynchronized.

Transient processor faults occur at Weibull (λ_{Ptran}, α_{Ptran}) distributed interarrival times. A transient is assumed to generate a single logic upset that must be latched to become latent. If not latched with probability P_{latch}, the processor will immediately return to the fault-free state. A latent transient fault will upset the control flow of an executing program with probability P_{upset}, after a Weibull (λ_{latent}, α_{latent})-distributed period of time. This will cause the processor to diverge from the correct instruction stream and enter the control upset state. It is assumed that the processor will remain in the control upset state, producing errors during every instruction cycle until it is resynchronized. If the latent transient does not result in a control flow upset, it will become active after a Weibull (λ_{latent}, α_{latent})-distributed length of time. An active transient fault is assumed to produce errors during one instruction cycle and then move into the dormant state. With termination probability P_{term}, the processor will immediately return to the fault-free state. Otherwise, it will hold in the dormant state for a period of time that is Weibull (λ_{active}, α_{active})-distributed. After the holding time in the dormant state expires, the transient will again become active and repeat the same sequence of state changes. This cyclic behavior is intended to represent multiple errors being sourced from a single fault that eventually disappears. Register and cache faults may exhibit such behavior when they are read several times before being overwritten.

When a processor reads an error from memory (through the fault tolerance mechanisms), its state may become corrupted. All input errors will be latched internally, so they are assumed to have an immediate effect on the processor. Based on the probability P_{upset}, an input error will put the processor in either the control upset or active state. The input error is assumed to behave like a transient fault once the processor has entered either of these states.

Processor errors can affect both the addresses and (write) data generated during an instruction cycle. The probabilities of an error affecting only an address ($P_{addr-error}$) or data ($P_{data-error}$) are specified by the user. Addresses and data are simultaneously affected by an error with probability ($1 - P_{addr-error} - P_{data-error}$). An erroneous address is assumed to access a random memory location. Erroneous data take on a random value.

The effectiveness of REACT was demonstrated through the analysis of several alternative multiprocessor architectures. Specifically, two dependability trade-offs associated with triple-modular-redundant (TMR) systems were investigated. Processor and memory modules are triplicated in a TMR system, and a majority voter is used to mask erroneous outputs from any one processor or memory at a time. The performance penalty of voting and the expense of triplicating modules, especially memory, are the major drawbacks of a TMR design. The first study explored the reliability-performance trade-off made by voting unidirectionally, instead of bidirectionally, on either memory read or write accesses (Clark and Pradhan, 1992). The second study examined the reliability cost trade-off made by duplicating, rather than triplicating, memory modules and comparing their outputs via error detecting codes (Clark, 1993b). The effects of different failure rates, fault types, and workload conditions on dependability were considered. Both studies showed that in many cases little reliability is sacrificed for potentially large performance increases or cost reductions, in comparison to the traditional TMR design.

The MITRE reliability and maintainability center has developed a simulation program based on REACT. The simulator was used to evaluate availability and other reliability metrics for a proposed Navy fixed, very low frequency transmitter that could not be accurately modeled using traditional analytical approaches.

MEFISTO—Fault Injection into VHDL Models. The growing use of VHDL in the development process of digital systems and its inherent abstraction capabilities (Dewey, 1992) make it a privileged language to support the integration of fault injection as early as possible and throughout the successive validation phases of the design process of fault-tolerant systems in a coherent simulation framework. The Multi-level Error/Fault Injection Simulation Tool (MEFISTO) is an integrated environment for applying fault injection into VHDL simulation models encompassing various levels of abstraction. This tool is the result of an ongoing collaborative research effort between LAAS-CNRS in France and Chalmers University in Sweden (Jenn, 1994) and is aimed at developing and using an integrated environment that supports the application of fault injection in VHDL models.

MEFISTO is intended for (1) estimating the coverage of fault tolerance mechanisms, (2) investigating mechanisms for mapping results from one level of abstraction to another, and (3) validating fault and error models applied during fault injection experiments carried out on the implementation of a fault-tolerant system (e.g., software implemented or pin-level fault injection).

MEFISTO supports several techniques for injecting faults into VHDL models. Specific components called *saboteurs* can be inserted in the VHDL model of the target system or some of the system's components, or processes can be mutated. MEFISTO can also use the command language of the underlying simulation engine (the VantageSpreadsheet environment) to modify the variables and signals of the target VHDL model. Users define and execute a *fault injection campaign*, which is made up of a series of *fault injection experiments*. A campaign consists of three phases: setup, simulation, and data processing.

The first set of experiments carried out with MEFISTO consisted of injecting transient faults on two architectures of a simple 32-bit processor: one behavioral and one structural. The structural (RTL) model was composed mainly of a finite state control machine, an ALU, a program counter, a register file, and several buffers and latches. The behavioral model consisted mainly of a VHDL process containing a large case statement that initiates the bus cycle appropriate with the operation code of the fetched instruction. Two fault injection campaigns with two different workloads (bubble-sort and heap-sort sorting programs) were run on each model. These experiments proved useful in (1) studying the impact of the fault injection techniques (i.e., signal and variable manipulation) on the experimental results and (2) analyzing the mapping between two sets of fault classes chosen at the two levels of abstraction considered.

Remaining simulation issues.   While there has been much progress in developing functional simulations for designing and evaluating dependable systems, several important questions remain unanswered. The main question is that of fidelity to the actual system. How much more accurate is a simulation than an analytical model? For example, to what degree of detail must we model detection and recovery mechanisms in order to evaluate their effectiveness using simulation? Analytic tools use probabilistic models to represent the behavior of the system; in essence the effect of a fault on the system is predefined by a set of probabilities and distributions. Simulation tools vary in range from using stochastic modeling to permitting behavioral modeling, which does not require that the effect of the faults be predefined. From both a research and a user perspective, there is a need of methods to establish the fidelity of the simulation in the absence of an actual system. Other unresolved issues include how to determine the accuracy of the assumed fault models with respect to fault behavior and how to establish this accuracy, how to model software faults, and how to model workloads and interactions.

5.4 PROTOTYPE PHASE

During the prototype phase of a fault-tolerant system, physical fault injection is feasible for use to evaluate fault, error, failure, and fault tolerance characteristics of the developed system. Fault injection is usually applied to fault-tolerant systems or components because the injected faults, if activated, would almost always crash a system without fault-tolerant mechanisms. However, fault injection can be used in nonfault-tolerant systems if the system control flow can be well traced and the system state information can be obtained when a crash occurs.

A fault injection environment typically contains the following components: target system, controller and monitor, fault injector, data collector, and data analyzer, as shown in Figure 5.14. The target can be a VLSI chip, a computer system, or a networked system.

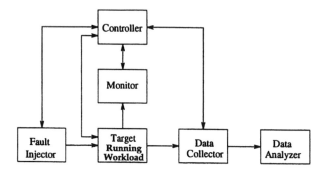

Figure 5.14: Components in a fault injection environment.

Faults are injected into the target while the system is exercised using benchmarks or synthetic workloads that emulate the system's operational environment. The controller is a software program, on the target or on another computer, that controls the overall fault injection experiment. The fault injector contains information on the type of fault(s) to be injected and their location. It also contains appropriate hardware or software logic to ensure that faults are injected into the right component at the right time. The monitor keeps track of normal and abnormal executions of the workload and initiates data collection whenever necessary. The data collector and analyzer perform on-line data collection and off-line data processing and analysis, respectively.

The fault injector can be implemented by hardware, software, or radiation. Correspondingly, fault injection can generally be divided into three types: *hardware-implemented*, *software-implemented*, and *radiation-induced*. Table 5.3 lists features and representative studies in these categories. The monitor can be imple-

Table 5.3: Categories of Fault Injections

Category	Hardware-Implemented	Software-Implemented	Radiation-Induced
Approach	Inject faults to IC pins by hardware instrumentation	Inject faults to components by special software	Inject faults by applying radiation rays to target
Advantages	No distrubance to workload High time resolution	Wide choices of FI locations/models Low cost	Can induce transient faults inside IC evenly
Disadvantages	Limited access points High cost	Workload disturbance Low time resolution	Fault injection points are uncontrollable
Studies	FTMP (Lala, 1983) FTMP (Shin, 1984, 1986) FTMP (Finelli, 1987) MESSALINE (Arlat, 1990a)	Accelerated Injection (Chillarege, 1989) FIAT (Segall, 1988), (Barton, 1990) FERRARI (Kanawati, 1992) HYBRID (Young, 1992) DEFINE (Kao, 1994) SFI (Rosenberg, 1993)	Z-80 (Cusick, 1985) MC6809E (Karlsson, 1989) MC6809E (Gunneflo, 1989)

mented by hardware, software, or by a combination of hardware and software (hybrid). If the fault injector is implemented by software and the monitor is implemented by hardware or by both hardware and software, the system is called a *hybrid* fault injection environment. Before discussing in detail each type of fault injection, we give a brief review of the formal methodology described in Arlat (1990a).

In Arlat (1990a), a formal methodology is proposed to characterize fault injection. The methodology consists of a tuple of four sets: **FARM,** where **F** is a set of faults, **A** is a set of activations, **R** is a set of readouts, and **M** is a set of derived measures. **F** and **A** constitute the input domain, and **R** and **M** constitute the output domain. The methodology can be applied to three levels of models: (1) axiomatic or analytical models, such as reliability block diagrams, fault trees, Markov chains, and Petri nets, (2) empirical models which incorporate more detailed behavioral and structural descriptions that may require the simulation approach to process them, and (3) physical models which correspond to hardware and/or software prototypes. The physical prototypes can be software-only prototype, hardware-only prototype, or hardware-and-software prototype. Physical models are more related to the fault injections discussed in this section.

In physical models, the **F** set is based on physical faults. In the case of software-only and hardware-only prototypes, the **A** set consists of a set of test patterns for exercising the injected faults. In the case of hardware-and-software prototypes, the **A** set may vary significantly, depending on the target systems. For general systems, representative programs can be used as a solution. A fault injection experiment is characterized by a triple (f, a, r), where f is a fault in **F,** a is an activation trajectory in **A,** and r is an experiment outcome in **R**. The measures in **M** can be obtained from a series of fault injection experiments.

5.4.1 Hardware-Implemented Fault Injection

Hardware-implemented fault injection is a method of introducing faults in the hardware of a computer system with the aid of additional hardware instrumentation. The method is well suited for studying dependability characteristics that require high time resolution and cannot be easily achieved by other fault injection methods, such as fault latency in the CPU. Two main techniques are used to accomplish hardware-implemented fault injections.

The first approach involves the use of active probes attached to the desired hardware injection points. The currents through these injection points can be altered, thereby influencing the corresponding logic values. The types of faults attainable with probes are usually limited to stuck-at faults. However, it is also possible to introduce bridging faults by placing the probes across multiple hardware points. Care must be taken with the use of active probes that force values onto injection points, because damage to the target hardware can result from an inordinate amount of current.

The second technique involves the insertion of additional hardware into the target computer system. Whereas the first method uses active probes that are external to the target system, this method introduces additional hardware that becomes part of the target system. The most common approach requires the interpolation of a socket between a chip and the circuit board. This socket is able to inject stuck-at faults or open faults, where the chip pin is essentially tri-stated. In addition, more complex logical faults can be forced onto these pins. For instance, the pin signals can be inverted, ANDed, or ORed with adjacent pin signals or even with previous signals on the same pin.

In theory, the domain of possible injection locations is limited only by the physical constraints of the target system that prevent the introduction of probes or other hardware. Since the target system is usually a complete prototype computer system, fault injection below the chip pin level is impractical. Thus, most injections focus on the pins of chips. Also, active probes can be attached to certain circuit board locations, such as buses or other signal lines.

In addition to the range of possible injection locations, a major concern of any fault injection environment is what fault types or models are available. We have already discussed some types of faults achievable with probes and sockets: stuck-at, open, bridging, or complex logical functions. Another important aspect of fault types is the duration of the fault, which can be either permanent, transient, or intermittent. Permanent faults are simply held on the injection point until an error detection occurs. In contrast, transient faults are placed on the injection point only for an active period, after which they are removed. Thus, the possibility exists that the transient fault may never even be latched into a chip (i.e., the fault never produces an error), especially if the active period is less than the system clock period on a synchronous machine. Intermittent faults are injected in the same manner as transient faults, but they are also repeated, either randomly or according to some function. Both injection methods discussed previously are capable of creating any of the three temporaral fault types.

In the following sections, we will discuss two representative hardware-implemented fault injection environments: FTMP (Lala, 1983) and MESSALINE (Arlat, 1990a).

FTMP. Several studies centered around the fault-tolerant multiprocessor (FTMP) fault injection instrumentation (Lala, 1983; Shin, 1986; Finelli, 1987). FTMP is a computer architecture that evolved over a ten-year period in connection with several critical aerospace applications. The architecture, as mentioned in Chapter 2, was designed to have a failure rate of the order of 10^{-10} per hour. The basic blocks of the architecture are independent processor cache modules and memory modules that communicate through redundant buses. The modules are dynamically grouped into several TMR triads or assigned to spare status. Jobs can be scheduled to any processor triad. All transactions between processor modules and memory modules in a triad are voted bit-by-bit. When a fault occurs, the faulty module is isolated and the faulty triad reconfigured. Fault detection, diagnosis, and recovery are handled in such a way that application programs are not involved.

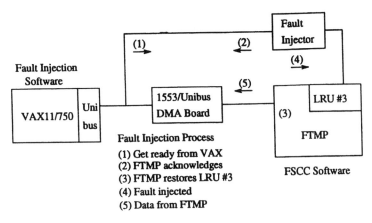

Figure 5.15: FTMP fault injection environment.

Figure 5.15 shows the diagram of the FTMP fault injection instrumentation developed at the Charles Stark Draper Laboratory (Lala, 1983; Finelli, 1987). In an FTMP computer, there are several line replaceable units (LRUs), each containing a processor, clock generator, power subsystem, and bus interface circuits. LRU 3 is constructed for connection of the fault injector. All chips in LRU 3 are connected to sockets that allow them to be removed for insertion of the fault injection implant. Each fault injection implant contains circuitry that can interrupt and reconnect the pins in the sockets. Several different types of faults, such as stuck-at-0 and stuck-at-1 can be injected into the pins by the implants. These implants are controlled by a VAX 11/750 computer. A special version of the System Configuration Control (FSCC) program running in the FTMP communicates with the Fault Injection Software (FIS) running in the VAX 11/750 through one of the FTMP I/O ports and a 1553/UNIBUS data link.

Faults are normally injected on one pin at a time. When an injection occurs, the FIS program chooses a fault and a pin, applies the fault to the pin, and records the injection time. Once the FTMP detects and identifies the fault and reconfigures the system, it sends this information along with the time of each event, back to FIS. Upon receiving the information, FIS removes the fault by restoring the pin to its normal state and notifies the FTMP. The FTMP then puts the victim module back into an active state and notifies FIS that it is ready for another fault injection. This process is repeated after a random delay.

In the experiments conducted at the Charles Stark Draper Laboratory (Lala, 1983), a total of 21,055 faults were injected, and 17,418 (83 percent) were detected. All of the detect faults were identified correctly, and the system subsequently recovered successfully from each of these faults by replacing the faulty module. That is, the coverage in the FTMP was 100 percent, which validated the FTMP architecture and implementation.

Another study using the FTMP fault injection instrumentation was reported in Shin (1984), with emphasis on the investigation of fault latency. Results showed that the hazard rate of fault latency is monotonically decreasing. Two distributions with monotonically decreasing hazard rates, Weibull and gamma distributions, were then used to fit the experimental results. The study also investigated the effect of fault latency on the probability of having multiple faults. It was shown that there exists an optimal fault latency in minimizing the multiple fault probability.

Later, fault injection experiments on the same instrumentation were conducted at the NASA Langley Research Center (Finelli, 1987) to investigate two issues: fault sampling methods and fault recovery distributions. For each fault injection, two choices must be made: the fault location (pins) and the fault type (e.g., stuck-at-1, stuck-at-0, inverted signal). Thus, the possible fault set (the collection of all different injected faults) can be very large. Exhaustive fault injection is costly and time consuming. It is necessary to find appropriate sampling methods to reduce the time and cost of testing. The study compared the effects (detection behavior) of different faults and grouped these faults into several subsets according to the similarity in their effects. The results showed that the effects are not homogeneous across the fault set. This indicates that stratified sampling methods, based on the fault subsets, should be developed for fault injection. The study also showed that the fault recovery time is not exponentially distributed.

MESSALINE.   MESSALINE (Arlat, 1990a) is a flexible, pin-level fault injection tool developed at LAAS-CNRS in Toulouse, France. The general architecture of MESSALINE and its environment are given in Figure 5.16. The injection, activation, and collection modules are implemented in hardware on an Intel 310 microcomputer. The software management module resides on a Macintosh II computer, which provides a flexible user interface.

The fault injection mechanism for MESSALINE uses active probes and

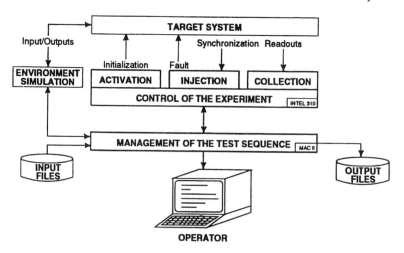

Figure 5.16: General architecture of MESSALINE.

socket insertion. Thus, fault types such as stuck-at, open, bridging, and complex logical functions can be injected. Because the duration and frequency of faults can be controlled, the fault injector can introduce permanent, transient, and intermittent faults. Signals collected from the target system can provide feedback to the injector. Also, a device is associated with each injection point to sense when and if each fault is activated and produces an error. MESSALINE has facilities to inject up to 32 injection points simultaneously.

The application of MESSALINE has been shown in two experiments involving (1) a subsystem of a centralized, computerized interlocking system (called PAI) for railway control applications and (2) a distributed system corresponding to an implementation of the dependable communication system of the ESPRIT Delta-4 Project.

In the case of the PAI system, permanent stuck-at-0, stuck-at-1, and open circuit faults were injected to various memory and CPU chips. The results indicated that CPU errors were more difficult to detect than memory errors. The error detection mechanisms were analyzed individually, and it was discovered that the diagnosis software accounted for most of the error coverage. The elimination of hardware detection would have decreased the overall coverage by less than 3 percent.

The distributed communication system was injected with intermittent stuck-at-0 and stuck-at-1 faults. The actual faults were injected into the network attachment controllers (NAC), which provide the connection for each node to the local area network. Results showed that over 67 percent of all errors caused the injected NAC to be correctly identified and extracted. Also, 24 percent of the errors did not cause a detectable error. Thus, in over 91 percent of the injections, the distributed system was able to correctly handle the error. These experiments demonstrate the utility and flexibility of the MESSALINE fault injection tool.

5.4.2 Software-Implemented Fault Injection

While hardware-implemented fault injection requires special hardware instrumentation and interface to circuits of the target systems, software-implemented fault injection provides a cheap and easy-to-control methodology. In software-implemented fault injection, no extra hardware instrumentation is needed, and users can choose fault locations in both hardware and software accessible to machine instructions. In addition, the software approach allows the emulation of software defects by an appropriate code change. Several techniques have been proposed to emulate different types of hardware and software faults through software-implemented fault injection.

Software-implemented fault injection is achieved by changing the contents of memory or registers, based on specified fault models. Hardware faults in the CPU, memory, bus, and network can lead to software errors and affect software executions (produce hardware-induced software errors). Injections to emulate these errors are implemented as execution of incorrect instructions and access of incorrect data. By *software faults*, we mean software design/implementation defects (e.g., incorrect initialization of a variable or failure to check a boundary condition), which may change software states to unexpected states. If software data is corrupted by either hardware or software faults, we call these *software errors*.

At least two related issues need to be addressed for software-implemented fault injection. The first issue is which fault models should be used to simulate hardware and software faults. We have discussed hardware fault models at the function level in Section 5.3.3. Similar to models for hardware-implemented fault injection, models for software-implemented fault injection should be built based on engineering experience and field measurements. The second, and related, issue is who owns the memory location or which process is executing when a fault is injected into a memory location or a register. In other words, what is the target of the fault injection?

Several fault models and implementation techniques are listed in Table 5.4. All these techniques are similar in that they change program or memory words. To inject software faults, the text segment needs to be modified. Some typical software faults are a variable that is used before it is initialized; a module's interface is defined or used incorrectly; statements are in wrong order or omitted (Sullivan, 1991). As a result of executing faulty software code, the data segment may be corrupted, causing software errors. Software errors can also be directly injected by changing the data segment.

When software injection is used to emulate hardware faults, it is usually assumed that the faults are transient in nature. For example, the faulty bits in memory or CPU registers can be overwritten by subsequent instructions. However, the software approach can be used to emulate permanent faults by repeatedly injecting the same fault into a location whenever there is an access to the location. For example, to emulate a permanent stuck-at-0 fault at a particular bit in a memory word, the bit is changed to 0 after every write operation to the word. To emulate a permanent stuck-at-1 fault at a bus address line, the corresponding bit in the effective address (in the program counter or in a CPU register) is set to 1 before any access to the bus. Clearly this emulation is expensive, involving the monitoring and execution of many additional instructions.

Table 5.4: Techniques Used for Software Fault Injection

Type	Method
Software Fault	Modify the text segment of the program
Software Error	Modify the data segment of the program
Memory Fault	Flip memory bits
CPU Fault	Use a trap to modify the memory area of the saved CPU registers
Bus Fault	Use traps before and after an instruction to change the code or data used by the instruction and then restore them after the instruction is executed
Netword Faults	Modify or delete transmission messages

Unlike hardware-implemented fault injection, which is difficult to gear toward specific workload areas, software fault injection can be targeted toward user applications, the operating system, or both. If the target is a user application, the fault injector is inserted into the user application or it can be an extra layer between the user application and the operating system. If the target is the operating system, the fault injector has to be embedded in the operating system, because it is very difficult to add an extra layer between the machine and the operating system.

Although the software approach is flexible, it has some restrictions. First, the approach cannot inject faults to locations not accessible to software. We mentioned in Section 5.3.2 that approximately one-third of the errors produced in logic-level fault injections cannot be emulated through the software approach (Czeck, 1991). Second, the software instrumentation may disturb the workload running in the target system and even change the structure of original software, although careful design of the injection environment can alleviate the perturbation to the workload. Third, the poor time resolution of the approach may cause fidelity problems. For the long latency faults, such as memory faults, the low time resolution may not be a problem. For the short latency faults, such as bus and CPU faults, the approach may fail to capture the error behavior (e.g., propagation). This problem can be solved by using a hardware monitor, i.e., the hybrid approach. The hybrid approach combines the versatility of software-implemented fault injection and the accuracy of hardware monitoring. It is well suited for measuring extremely short latencies. However, the hardware monitoring involved in this approach can decrease flexibility (e.g., limited observation points and buffer size of the monitor) and increase cost.

There have been several studies using the software approach. In Chillarege (1989), a *failure-acceleration* method is used to inject the overlay software faults into an IBM commercial transaction processing system. The failure process is said to be accelerated when the fault model is not altered and (1) the fault latency is decreased; (2) the error latency is decreased; (3) the probability of a fault causing a failure is increased. An overlay occurs when a program writes into an incorrect area. It is estimated that about one-third of software errors can be mapped into the overlay model. The failure acceleration method is intended to minimize fault latency and to expose the fault impact on the system immediately after the fault injection by using the overlay model and by increasing the workload level.

The study found that a total loss of the primary service occurred in only 16 percent of all detected faults. A class of errors termed *potential hazards* was quantified to be at least 22 percent. Potential hazards do not affect the short-term availability and will cause a catastrophic failure when there is a significant change in the operating state of the system. At least 41 percent of errors were identified as potential candidates for the category *failure prevention and error repair*. These errors do not affect the short-term availability and experience adequate times for repair action, thus providing an opportunity for using inexpensive techniques to achieve high coverage.

Table 5.5: Comparison of Software-Implemented Fault Injection Tools

Tool	FIAT (Segall, 1988)	FERRARI (Kanawati, 1992)	HYBRID (Young, 1992)	DEFINE (Kao, 1994)	SFI (Rosenberg, 1993)
Hardware	PC RT	SPARC	Tandem S2	Sun	Harts
Injection target	O.S. User	User	O.S. User	O.S. User	O.S. User
Monitor	Software	Software	Hybrid	Software	Software
Fault types	Memory CPU Communi-cation	Memory CPU Bus Control flow	Memory CPU Cache	Memory CPU Bus Communi-cation Software	Memory CPU Communi-cation
To evalu-ate	Detection Latency Recovery	Detection Latency	Detection Latency Recovery	Detection Propagation	Detection Recovery

In recent years, interest in developing software-implemented fault injection tools has increased. Several environments have been published in literature: FIAT (Segal, 1988), FERRARI (Kanawati, 1992), HYBRID (Young, 1992), DEFINE (Kao, 1994), and SFI (Rosenberg, 1993). Table 5.5 lists features of these tools, which will be discussed in the following subsections.

FIAT. A number of fault injection studies at Carnegie-Mellon University have centered around FIAT (Fault Injection Automated Testing), a software-implemented fault injection environment (Segal, 1988; Bargon, 1990; Czeck, 1991). The FIAT hardware implementation consists of IBM RT PCs connected by a token ring network. The FIAT software structure is divided into two parts: the *fault injection manager* (FIM) and the *fault injection receptor* (FIRE). FIM is a global control program responsible for all phases of the experiment. FIRE, under the control of FIM, collects the experimental results and sends appropriate information to FIM for offline analysis. Figure 5.17 shows the process of a typical fault injection experiment.

FIAT has been used to study the impact of faults on the application workload level (Barton, 1990). Two representative programs, a matrix multiplication task and a selection sort task, were chosen as application workloads. To achieve fault tolerance, each task was executed on two different processors, and the results were compared. Three fault types were injected in the experiment: zero-a-byte, set-a-byte, and 2-bit compensating. The zero-a-byte or set-a-byte sets a consecutive 8 bits anywhere within a 32-bit word to 0 or 1. The 2-bit compensating complements 2 bits in a word such that the parity code would not detect it as an error. Faults were injected into all locations within a workload, with a total of over 130,000 faults injected.

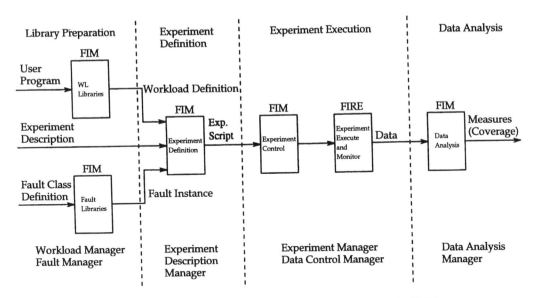

Figure 5.17: Typical fault injection experiment in FIAT.

Results showed that there are a limited number of system-level fault manifestations. The mean error detection coverage for different workloads and fault types is approximately 50 percent to 60 percent. Error detection latency was found to follow a normal distribution. This result conflicts with those presented in Shin (1986), and Finelli (1987), where the latency was shown to follow either gamma, Weibull, or log-normal distributions. This difference may be explained by the differences in the experimental environment and detection mechanisms. In Shin (1986) and Finelli (1987), the hardware-implemented fault injection technique is used, and the resolution of detection time is on the order of milliseconds, while the time resolution of the software-implemented FIAT is on the order of seconds, which may skew the results.

FERRARI.   FERRARI (Fault and ERRor Automatic Real-time Injector), another software-implemented fault injection environment, was recently developed at the University of Texas (Kanawati, 1992). The purpose of FERRARI is to evaluate complex systems by emulating most hardware faults in software. It is implemented on SPARC workstations in an X-window environment. It consists of four software modules: the *initializer and activator, the user information,* the *fault and error injector,* and the *collector and analyzer.* These four modules are controlled by the *manager module,* which coordinates the operation of the four modules.

The initialization and activation module prepares the target program for fault injection by extracting information, such as the starting address, the program size, the execution time, the output of an error-free program, and the addresses used by the program. The user information module receives experiment parameters provided by the user. These parameters include

- duration, location, time, and bit position of the fault,
- user-specified or pseudorandom selection of the fault,
- fault type (XOR, set, or reset a bit; zero or set a byte),
- fault and error classes (hardware, control flow, user-defined), and
- dependability properties to measure (coverage, latency).

The fault and error injection module is responsible for injecting different types of transient or permanent faults, such as address line faults, data line faults, and faults in condition code flags. The data collection and analysis module records experiment results, such as information about error detection, error latency, and failures, and it determines statistics of these measures at the end of the experiment.

The main fault and error injection mechanism involves using software traps. At the appropriate time or program location, the program to be injected is trapped. The selected fault or error is then injected. For transient errors, the current instruction is executed and then the injected error is removed. For permanent faults, the injected fault is not removed. Instead, the program is trapped for the next n instructions, where n is the duration of the fault in instruction cycles. Table 5.6 lists the fault and error classes that FERRARI can inject.

To demonstrate the capabilities of FERRARI and to study the behavior of the target system under faulty conditions, over 600,000 fault injection runs were conducted on SUN4 SPARC workstations under different applications. Results showed that the error coverage is highly dependent on the fault type. The highest coverage was obtained when errors were injected into the task memory image. This is because the injected errors are likely to be exercised repeatedly if the corrupted instructions are in a loop. An important finding is that a considerable number of undetected errors are those that corrupted input/output routines and system libraries. These routines may tend to be ignored when error detection techniques are embedded in the user code.

Table 5.6: Selected Fault and Error Classes Supported by FERRARI

CPU and Control Flow	Memory and Bus
Corrupted register	Address line error when an operand is fetched
Program counter error	Address line error when operand is stored
Instruction type fault	Data line error when an opcode is fetched
Illegal branch	Data line error when an operand is fetched
Condition code flag error	Data line error when an operand is stored

HYBRID.   To enhance the low resolution of detection time in purely software-implemented fault injection environments, error detection mechanisms can be implemented with the combination of hardware and software. This approach is used in HYBRID, a hybrid fault injection environment developed at the University of Illinois (Young, 1992). In HYBRID, faults are injected via software, and the impact is measured by both software and hardware.

The environment consists of a fault injection system, a hybrid monitor system (implemented by both hardware and software) to measure the effects of injected faults, and a supervisory system to automate the measurements. Figure 5.18 illustrates how these systems are physically situated. The *fault injector* and *software monitor* execute on the *test system*, while the *supervisor program* executes on the *control host*. Probes attach the hardware monitor to the address/data backplane of the test system so that the monitor can analyze and record the signals generated. Communication between the supervisor and the hardware monitor takes place over an RS-232 or GPIB connection.

The function of the environment is to perform experiments that repeatedly inject faults and record observations. The environment introduces faults into the test system during the execution of a *target program*, measures the effects of that fault, and returns the test system to conditions present prior to fault injection. These operations form a single *observation loop*. Faults can be injected into any location that has a physical address, such as CPU registers, cache, local memory, mass storage, and network controllers. Faults can also be injected into locations allocated to a single, executing user program or even into the kernel, and propagation can be characterized down to the instruction level.

The fault injection environment was used to study dependability characteristics of a Tandem Integrity S2 fault-tolerant computer system (Jewett, 1991) described in Chapter 4. High degrees of accuracy in measuring latency (within 20 ns) were obtained. Measurements of the sensitivity of different instructions to faults indicated a 5 percent chance that a faulted MIPS RISC instruction will not fail when executed. Modeling of multilevel error propagation showed that error detections were due to multiple corruptions of state in as many as 57 percent of reads from wrong addresses and 37 percent of writes to wrong addresses. The median latency associated with error detection by an individual CPU was on the

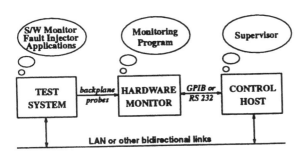

Figure 5.18: Physical layout of HYBRID.

order of 10 µs, and the median delay between detection and the start of CPU shutdown was on the order of 100 ms. Kernel fault injection studies show that a fault in the kernel is 2.6 times as likely to bring down a CPU as a fault elsewhere.

DEFINE.   DEFINE is a UNIX-based distributed fault injection environment developed at the University of Illinois (Kao, 1994). Its predecessor, FINE (Kao, 1993), is a single-machine fault injection environment. The significance of DEFINE is twofold. First, it can emulate software faults as well as hardware errors. Second, it can trace fault propagation through software modules. The software faults that can be injected by DEFINE include initialization (missing or incorrect), assignment (missing or incorrect), condition check (missing or incorrect), and function (incorrect) faults. Injectable hardware errors include CPU (ALU, shifter, opcode decoder, or registers), memory (text segment or data segment), bus (address lines or data lines), and communication errors (missing messages or corrupted messages).

Figure 5.19 shows the DEFINE environment. DEFINE consists of a *target system*, a *fault injector*, a *software monitor*, a *workload generator*, a *controller*, and several *analysis utilities*. The target system is a group of connected machines consisting of servers and clients. The controller, fault injector, software monitor, and workload generator are running on another machine (host machine) which is connected to the target system. The local fault injector and message recorder are embedded in the kernel so that faults can be injected there and their propagation can be monitored. Fault injection is implemented by modifying the system trap

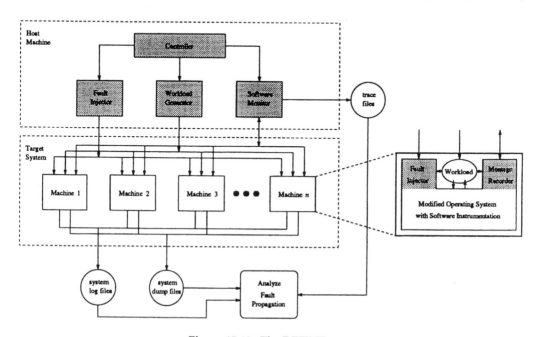

Figure 15.19: The DEFINE environment.

handling routines and hardware clock interrupt handling routines, so the fault injector can be considered an extra layer between the operating system and the machine. The fault injector uses hardware clock interrupts to control the time of fault injection and activation and uses software traps to inject all the faults except communication faults and memory faults in the data/stack segments. The software monitor traces the execution flow and key variables of the kernel. Software probes are inserted into functions in the kernel to record the execution flow and the values of arguments and key variables. The synthetic workload generator issues various system calls to activate injected faults. The distribution of generated system calls can be specified by users to emulate real workloads or to deliberately accelerate the activation of injected faults. The controller assigns experiment specifications to the fault injector and the monitor, and it initiates experiments. The analysis utilities provide assistance in analyzing fault propagation. The target of the study is the UNIX kernel, a nonstopped, highly parameterized, complex service program with high impact and a broad spectrum of workloads.

Two experiments were conducted by applying DEFINE to investigate fault propagation and to evaluate the impact of various types of faults. The first experiment was on SunOS 4.1.2 (on a SPARCstation IPC). Results showed that memory faults and software faults usually have a very long latency, while bus faults and CPU faults tend to crash the system immediately. Nearly 90 percent of detected errors are detected by hardware. About half (47 percent) of the detected errors are data errors. These data errors are detected when the system tries to access an area it has no privilege to access. In the software fault propagation, incorrect control flow is the major impact for the first level of propagation, while data corruption is the major impact for the subsequent propagation. Analysis of fault propagation among the UNIX subsystems revealed that only about 8 percent of faults propagate to other UNIX subsystems. The second experiment was on six Sun workstations (one as server and the others as clients). Experimental results show that fault propagation from servers to clients occurs more frequently than from clients to servers. The majority of no-impact faults are dormant. The fault impact depends on the workload.

SFI.   SFI is designed for validating dependability mechanisms on an experimental distributed real-time system HARTS (Rosenberg, 1993; Han, 1993). (See Figure 5.20). It introduces a new fault type, *intermittent*, in addition to permanent and transient faults. The interarrival time between intermittent faults can be deterministic or can follow a specified exponential distribution. Injectable errors include memory (code, global variables, or heap), communication (lost, altered, or delayed messages), and processor errors (adder or multiplier).

SFI consists of the SFI Experiment Generator (SEG) and the SFI Control Modules (SCM). The SEG takes as input a user-supplied experiment description to drive fault injection experiments. The SCM consists of fault injection routines that will be included into executable files by the SEG. Memory errors are injected by changing the contents of the selected address. Communication errors are in-

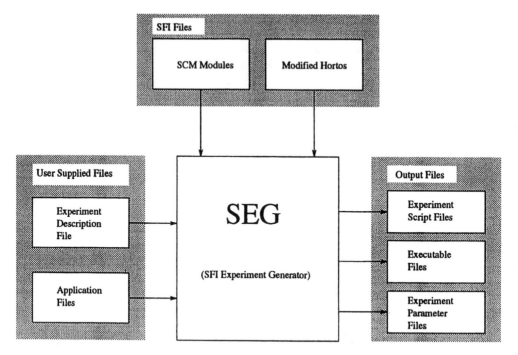

Figure 5.20: The relationship of SFI files.

jected by modifying the communication protocols to mimic the desired behavior. Processor errors are injected by changing the assembly code during compilation.

Two experiments of HARTS were conducted to investigate the effect of intermittent message losses between two adjacent nodes and the effect of routing using failure data. In the first experiment, a model of communication between two nodes was developed to predict the effect of intermittent message losses. Experimental results showed that the predicted values of average round-trip delay, average number of attempts per message, and frequency of number of attempts matched the observed values very well. The second experiment investigated three routine methods with or without failure information. The first method uses transmission time of a message on each link only. The second method considers transmission time and the average number of timeouts on each link. The third method uses the delivery time of test messages that are sent out by each node to its neighbors periodically. Results showed that none of the methods is best under poor traffic operating conditions.

5.4.3 Radiation-Induced Fault Injection

Neither hardware-implemented nor software-implemented fault injection has a way to produce transient faults at random locations inside ICs. Radiation-induced fault injection provide such a capability. One way to do this is to expose the chip to the heavy-ion radiation from a *Californium*[252] (*Cf*[252]) source (Gunneflo, 1989; Karlsson, 1989). The heavy ions emitted from the source are capable of creating transient faults when they pass through a depletion region in the IC. One advantage of this method is that it can produce transient faults at random locations evenly and can cause either a single-bit flip or multiple-bit flips, leading to large variation in the errors seen on the output pins of the IC.

In the fault injection experiments reported in Gunneflo, (1989) and Karlsson (1989), the *Cf*[252] method was used to investigate error coverage and detection latency for error detection schemes for the MC6809E eight-bit microprocessor. The intention of the experiments was to characterize the effects of transient faults that originate inside a CPU. The MC6809E is fabricated in NMOS, a technology sensitive to heavy ion radiation. The error detection schemes under study are suitable for implementation with a watchdog processor that checks the behavior of the main processor on the external bus. The developed experimental system is called FIST (Fault Injection System for Study of Transient Fault Effects). Figure 5.21 shows the FIST diagram.

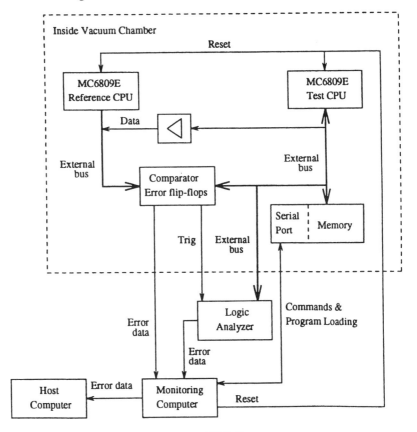

Figure 5.21: FIST diagram.

The heavy-ion radiation is implemented using a commercially available 37×10^3 Becquerel (1 μC_i) Cf^{252} source. The Cf^{252} source is mounted inside a vacuum chamber together with a small computer system. One of the system boards is placed on a mechanical fixture movable in three dimensions for accurate positioning of the CPU beneath the Cf^{252} source. The system has two MC6809E CPUs, which operate synchronously using the same clock. One CPU is exposed to heavy-ion radiation. The other is used as a reference to detect errors via comparison on the output from the two CPUs. When errors are detected by the comparison logic, the logic analyzer is triggered to record the external bus signals. The monitoring computer is responsible for data acquisition and control of experiments.

A fault injection experiment is conducted in the following way. Before the experiment starts, the monitoring computer fetches from the host computer a load file that contains the test program to be executed. The test program is then loaded from the monitoring computer to the MC6809E system. After the loading, the test program is started with a "go" command from the monitoring computer. When a mismatch is detected, the monitoring computer fetches the recorded error data from the logic analyzer and the error flip-flops in the MC6809E system and transfers them to the host computer. Finally, the MC6809E system is reset, and the test program is reloaded for the next experiment.

It was found from fault injection experiments that 78 percent of all errors affected control flow (i.e., caused the processor to diverge from the correct sequence) and 17 percent caused errors in data. Results also showed that 30 percent of all errors were multiple-bit errors on the output pins, although the origin of each of these errors was only one single heavy ion. The error recordings obtained from the experiments were also used as input to simulation models of different error detection mechanisms to evaluate these error detection mechanisms without implementing them. The coverage of several detection mechanisms was investigated. It was found that the best mechanism was the one that detects access to the memory outside permitted areas and that the combination of two mechanisms gave a better coverage than any one mechanism alone. It was also found that the type of the test program had a considerable influence on the results of error detection mechanisms.

5.5 OPERATIONAL PHASE

When a computer system is in normal operation, various types of errors can occur both in the hardware and in the software. There are many possible sources of errors, including untested manufacturing faults and software defects, wearing out of devices, transient errors induced by radiation, power surges, or other physical processes, operator errors, and environmental factors. The occurrence of errors is also highly dependent on the workloads running on the system. A distribution of operational outages from various error sources for several major commercial systems are reported in Siewiorek (1992).

There is no better way to understand dependability characteristics of a complex computer system than by direct measurement and analysis. Here, measuring a real system means monitoring and recording naturally occurring errors and failures in the system while it is running under user workloads. Analysis of such measurements can provide valuable information on actual error/failure behavior, identify system bottlenecks, quantify dependability measures, and verify assumptions made in analytical models.

Given field error data collected from a real system, a measurement-based study consists of four steps, as shown in Figure 5.22: (1) data processing, (2) model identification and parameter estimation, (3) model solution if necessary, and (4) analysis of models and measures. Step 1 consists of extracting necessary information from field data (the result can be a form of compressed data or flat data), classifying errors and failures, and coalescing repeated error reports. In a compute system, a single problem commonly results in many repeated error observations occurring in rapid succession. To ensure that the analysis is not biased by these repeated observations of the same problem, all error entries that have the same error type and occur within a short time interval (e.g., five minutes) of each other should be coalesced into a single record. The output of this step is a form of coalesced data in which errors and failures are identified. This step is highly dependent on the measured system. Coalescing algorithms have been proposed in Tsao (1983), Iyer (1986) and Hansen (1992).

Step 2 includes identifying appropriate models (such as Markov models) and estimating various measures of interest (such as MTBFs and TBF distributions) from the coalesced data. Several models have been proposed and validated using real data. These include workload-dependent cyclostationary models (Castillo, 1981), a workload hazard model (Iyer, 1982a), and error/failure correlation models (Tang, 1992a). Statistical analysis packages such as SAS (SAS, 1985) or measurement-based dependability analysis tools such as MEASURE+ (Tang, 1993b) are useful at this stage. Step 3 solves these models to obtain dependability measures (such as reliability, availability, and transient reward rates). Dependability and performance modeling and evaluation tools such as SHARPE (Sahner, 1987) can be used in this step. Step 4, the most creative part of this study, involves

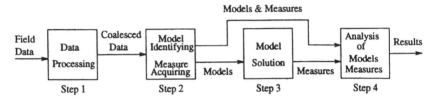

Figure 15.22: Measurement-based analysis.

a careful interpretation of the models and measures obtained from the data, for example, the identification of reliability bottlenecks and impact on availability of design enhancement. The analysis methods can vary significantly from one study to another study, depending on project goals.

Measurement-based dependability analysis of operational systems has evolved significantly over the past 15 years. These studies have addressed one or more of the following issues: basic error characteristics, dependency analysis, modeling and evaluation, software dependability, and fault diagnosis. Table 5.7 provides a quick overview of the issues addressed in the literature.

Early studies in this field investigated transient errors in DEC computer systems and found that more than 95 percent of all detected errors are intermittent or transient errors (Siewiorek, 1978; McConnel, 1979). The studies also showed that the interarrival time of transient errors follows a Weibull distribution with a

Table 5.7: Measurement-Based Studies of Computer System Dependability

Category	Issues	Studies
Data	Analysis of time-based tuples	(Tsao, 1983), (Hansen, 1992)
Coalescing	Clustering based on type and time	(Iyer, 1986), (Lee, 1991), (Tang, 1993a)
Basic	Transient faults/errors	(Siewiorek, 1978), (McConnel, 1979), (Iyer, 1986)
Error	Error/failure bursts	(Iyer, 1986), (Hsueh, 1987), (Tang, 1993a)
Characteristics	TTE/TTF distributions	(McConnel, 1979), (Iyer, 1985b), (Lee, 1993a)
	Hardware failure/workload dependency	(Butner, 1980), (Castillo, 1981), (Iyer, 1982a)
Dependency	Software failure/workload dependency	(Castillo, 1982), (Iyer, 1985b), (Mourad, 1987)
Analysis	Correlated failures and impact	(Tang, 1990), (Wein, 1990), (Tang, 1992a)
	Two-way and multiway failure dependency	(Dugan, 1991), (Lee, 1991), (Tang, 1991)
Modeling	Performability model for single machine	(Hsueh, 1988)
and	Markov reward model for distributed system	(Tang, 1993a)
Evaluation	Two-level models for operating systems	(Lee, 1993a)
	Error recovery	(Velardi, 1984), (Hsueh, 1987)
Software	Hardware-related & correlated software errors	(Iyer, 1985a), (Tang, 1992b), (Lee, 1993a)
Dependability	Software fault tolerance	(Gray, 1990), (Lee, 1992), (Lee, 1993b)
	Software defect classification	(Sullivan, 1991), (Sullivan, 1992)
Fault	Heuristic trend analysis	(Tsao, 1983), (Lin, 1990)
Diagnosis	Statistical analysis of symptoms	(Iyer, 1990)
	Network fault signature	(Maxion, 1990a), (Maxion, 1990b) (Maxion, 1993)

decreasing error rate. This distribution was also shown to fit the software failure data collected from an IBM operating system (Iyer, 1985b). A recent study of failure data from three different operating systems showed that time to error (TTE) can be represented by a multistage gamma distribution for a single-machine operating system and by a hyperexponential distribution for the measured distributed operating systems (Lee, 1993a).

Several studies have investigated the relationship between system activity and failures. In the early 1980s, analysis of measurements from IBM (Butner, 1980) and DEC (Castillo, 1981) machines revealed that the average system failure rate was strongly correlated with the average workload on the system. The effect of workload-imposed stress on software was investigated in Castillo (1982) and Iyer (1985b). Recent analyses of DEC (Tang, 1990; Wein, 1990) and Tandem (Lee, 1991) multicomputer systems showed that correlated failures across processors are not negligible, and their impact on availability and reliability are significant (Dugan, 1991; Tang, 1991, 1992a).

In Hsueh (1988), analytical modeling and measurements were combined to develop measurement-based reliability/performability models using data collected from an IBM mainframe. The results showed that a semi-Markov process is better than a Markov process for modeling system behavior. Markov reward modeling techniques were further applied to distributed systems (Tang, 1993a) and fault-tolerant systems (Lee, 1992), to quantify performance loss due to errors/failures for both hardware and software.

A census of Tandem system availability indicated that software faults are the major source of system outages in the measured fault-tolerant systems (Gray, 1990). Analyses of field data from different software systems investigated several dependability issues including the effectiveness of error recovery (Velardi, 1984), hardware-related software errors (Iyer, 1985a), correlated software errors in distributed systems (Tang, 1992b), software fault tolerance (Lee, 1992, 1993b) and software defect classification (Sullivan, 1991, 1992). Measurement-based fault diagnosis and failure prediction issues were investigated in Tsao (1983), Iyer (1990), Lin (1990), Maxion (1990a, 1990b, 1993).

In the following subsections, we discuss issues and representative studies involved in measurements, data processing, preliminary analysis of data, dependency analysis, modeling and evaluation, software dependability, and fault diagnosis.

5.5.1 Measurements

There are numerous theoretical and practical difficulties associated with making measurements. The question of what and how to measure is a difficult one. A combination of installed and custom instrumentation is typically used in most studies. From a statistical point of view, sound evaluations require a considerable amount of data. In modern computer systems, especially in fault-tolerant systems, failures are infrequent and, in order to obtain meaningful data, measurements must be made for a long period of time. Also, the measured system must be exposed to a wide range of usage conditions for the results to be representative. In an operational system, only detected errors can be measured.

There are two ways to make measurements: online automatic logging and human manual logging. Many large computer systems, such as IBM and DEC mainframes, provide error-logging software in the operating system. This software records information on errors occurring in the various subsystems, such as the memory, disk, and network subsystems, as well as other system events, such as reboots and shutdowns. The reports usually include information on the location, time, and type of the error, the system state at the time of the error, and sometimes error recovery (e.g., retry) information. The reports are stored chronologically in a permanent system file. The main advantage of the online automatic logging is its ability to record a large amount of information about transient errors and to provide details of automatic error recovery processes which cannot be done manually. Disadvantages are that an online log does not usually include information about the cause and propagation of the error or about offline diagnosis. Also, under some crash scenarios, the system may fail too quickly for any error messages to be recorded.

Table 5.8 shows a sample of extracted error logs from a VAXcluster multi-

Table 5.8: A Sample of Extracted Error Logs from a VAXcluster[a]

Entry	System ID	Logging time	Subsystem and unit	Interpretation
5815	Earth	20-DEC-1987 20:23:13.22	I/O, H0$DUA51:	Disk drive error
7005	Earth	4-JAN-1988 11:45:07.12	I/O, H3$MUA1:	Tape drive error
12979	Europa	8-JAN-1988 14:14:28.63	CI, EUR$PAA0:	Path #0 went from good to bad
13005	Europa	8-JAN-1988 16:23:17.41	CI, EUR$PAA0:	Error logging data gram received
13734	Europa	19-JAN-1988 17:31:30.74	CI, EUR$PAA0:	Virtual circuit timeout
3260	Mercury	24-DEC-1987 04:54:52.06	Memory, TR #2	Corrected memory error
10939	Jupiter	1-APR-1988 09:57:39.40	Unknown Device	
14209	Jupiter	16-MAY-1988 13:37:04.97	CPU, SBI	Unexpected read data fault
13941	Mars	25-FEB-1988 02:13:20.25	CPU, IBOX	Machine check
20937	Mars	18-APR-1988 16:46:39.75	BugCheck	Bad memory deallocation request size/address
27958	Mars	14-MAY-1988 20:57:46.48	BugCheck	Insufficient nonpaged pool to remaster locks
37790	Saturn	20-JUL-1988 18:51:49.15	BugCheck	Unexpected system service exception

[a]The sample is intended to illustrate the different types of erros logged. Therefore, the entry numbers are not consecutive.

computer system. Often, the meaning of a record in a log can differ between versions of the operating system and between machine models. One reason is that error detection and recording routines are written and modified over time by different groups of people. For example, a careful study of VAX error logs and discussion with the field engineers indicate that the operating system on different VAX machine models might report the same type of error into different categories. Thus, it is important to distinguish these errors in the subsequent error classification.

Since the information provided by online error logs may not be complete, it is valuable to have operator logs compensate for the missing information. An operator log should include information on system crashes, failure diagnosis, component replacement, and hardware and software updates.

5.5.2 Data Processing

Usually, online logs contain a large amount of redundant and irrelevant information in various formats. Thus, data processing must be performed to classify this information and to put it into a flat format to facilitate subsequent analyses. The first step in data processing is *error classification*. This process classifies errors in the measured system into types based on the subsystems and components in which they occur. There is no uniform or "best" error classification, because different systems have different hardware and software architectures. But some error types, such as CPU, memory, and disk errors, are seen in most systems. Table 5.9 lists an error classification (major error types) for VAXcluster systems (Tang, 1992b, 1993a).

After error classification, the following data processing can be broadly divided into two steps: *data extraction* and *data coalescing*. Data extraction selects useful entries such as error and reboot reports (throwing away uninteresting entries such as disk volume change reports) from the log file and transforms the data set into a flat format. The design of the flat format depends on the necessity of the subsequent analyses. The following is a possible format:

entry number	logging time	error type	device ID	error description fields

Table 5.9: Major Error Types in VAXcluster

System	Type	Description
Hardware	CPU	CPU or bus controller errors
	Memory	Memory ECC errors
	Disk	Disk, drive, and controller errors
	Network	Local network and controller errors
Software	Control	Problems involving program flow control or synchronization
	Memory	Problems referring to memory management or usage
	I/O	Inconsistent conditions detected by I/O management routines

In online error logs, a single fault in the system can result in many repeated error reports in a short period of time. To ensure that the subsequent analyses will not be distorted by these repeated reports, entries that correspond to the same problem should be coalesced into a single event, or *tuple* (Tsao, 1983). A typical data-coalescing algorithm merges all error entries of the same error type that occur within a ΔT interval of each other into a tuple. The algorithm is as follows:

```
IF <error type> = <type of previous error>
        AND <time away from previous error> ≤ΔT
THEN <put error into the tuple being built>
ELSE <start a new tuple>
```

A tuple reflects the occurrence of one or more errors of the same type in rapid succession. It can be represented by a record containing information such as the number of entries in the tuple and the time duration of the tuple.

Different systems may need different time intervals in data coalescing. A recent study (Hansen, 1992) defined two kinds of mistakes that can be made in data coalescing: *collision* and *truncation*. A collision occurs when the detection times of two faults are close enough (within ΔT) such that they are combined into a tuple. A truncation occurs when the time between two reports caused by a single fault is greater than ΔT such that the two reports are split into different tuples. If ΔT is large, collisions are likely to occur. If ΔT is small, truncations are likely to occur. The study found that there is a time interval threshold beyond which collisions are rapidly increased. Based on this observation, the study proposed a statistical model that can be used to select an appropriate time interval. In our experience, collision is not a big problem if the error type and device information are used in data coalescing as shown in the above coalescing algorithm. Truncation is usually not considered to be a problem (Hansen, 1992). Also, there are techniques (Iyer, 1990; Lin, 1990) to deal with truncation which have been used for fault diagnosis and failure prediction (see Section 5.5.7).

5.5.3 Preliminary Analysis

Once coalesced data is obtained, the basic dependability characteristics of the measured system can be identified by a preliminary statistical analysis. Commonly used measures in the analysis include error/failure frequency, time to error or time to failure distribution, and error/failure/hazard rate function. In the following discussion, data from several commercial systems are used to illustrate analysis methods.

Basic statistics.   It is important but easy to obtain basic statistics from the measured data such as frequency, percentage, and probability. These statistics provide an overall picture of the measured system. Often, dependability bottlenecks can be identified by analysis of these statistics. Table 5.10 shows the

Table 5.10: Error/Failure Statistics for the VAXcluster

Category	Error		Failure		Recovery Probability
	Frequency	Percentage	Frequency	Percentage	
I/O	25,807	92.87 ± 0.30	105	42.86 ± 6.20	0.996 ± 0.001
Machine	1,721	6.19 ± 0.28	5	2.04 ± 1.77	0.970 ± 0.002
Software	69	0.25 ± 0.06	62	25.31 ± 5.44	0.101 ± 0.071
Unknown	191	0.69 ± 0.10	73	29.80 ± 5.73	0.618 ± 0.069
All	27,788	100.0	245	100.0	0.991 ± 0.001

error/failure statistics for a measured VAXcluster (Tang, 1993a). In the table, I/O errors include disk, tape, and network errors. Machine errors include CPU and memory errors. Software errors are software-related errors. The 95 percent confidence intervals for the percentage and probability estimates shown in the table are calculated using the method for proportions discussed in Section 5.2.1.

Two bottlenecks can be identified from the table. First, the major error category is I/O errors (93 percent), that is errors from shared resources. This category of error has a very high recovery probability (0.996). However, these errors still result in nearly 43 percent of all failures. This result indicates that, although the system is generally robust with respect to I/O errors, the shared resources still constitute a major reliability bottleneck due to the sheer number of errors. Improving such a system may require using an ultrareliable network and a disk system to reduce the raw error rate, not just providing high recoverability.

Second, although software errors constitute only a small part of all errors (0.3 percent), they result in significant failures (25 percent). This is because software errors have a very low recovery probability (0.1). This software failure estimation is conservative because there are significant unknown failures (30 percent). Some of these unknown failures could also be attributed to software problems. Thus, software-related problems are severe in the measured system.

Empirical TTE distributions and hazard rates.   TTE/TTF probability distributions and error/failure hazard rates are commonly used to investigate how errors and failures occur across time. It is relatively easy to obtain empirical TTE/TTF distributions from data. Figure 5.23 shows the empirical TTE distribution function, $f(t)$, for a measured VAXcluster system (Tang, 1993a). Notice that

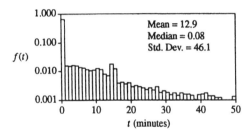

Figure 5.23: VAXcluster empirical TTE distribution.

the logarithmic coordinate is used for $f(t)$ because of the big contrast between the largest and smallest values. It is seen that about 67 percent of the TBEs are less than one minute. Most of these instances are "time between errors of two different machines" because errors of the same type occurring within a five-minute interval of each other on the same machine have been coalesced into a single-error event. This fact implies that errors are likely to occur on the different machines in the measured system within a very short period of time.

The *hazard rate* characterizes error/failure intensity in time. It is the probability that an error (failure) will occur within the coming unit of time, given that no error (failure) has occurred since the start of the system or the last error (failure) occurrence. The mathematical definition of the hazard rate (Ross, 1985) is as follows:

$$h(t) = \frac{Pr\{error\ in\ (t,\ t+dt)\}}{Pr\{no\ errors\ in\ (0,t)\}dt} = \frac{f(t)}{1-F(t)}. \tag{5.31}$$

Figure 5.24 shows the empirical failure hazard rates computed from the VAXcluster failure data. The high hazard rate near the origin, that is, the high probability that the second failure will occur within a short time after a failure occurrence, indicates that failures in the VAXcluster tend to occur in bursts. The most likely time for a second failure is the first two hours after a failure occurrence. An early study of transient errors (McConnel, 1979), which fitted a Weibull distribution with a decreasing failure rate to the interarrival time of transient errors, implied the existence of failure/error bursts. Failure bursts have been observed in several other studies (Tsao, 1983; Iyer, 1986; Hsueh, 1987; Bishop, 1988).

Analytical time to error distributions. A realistic analytical form of TTE distributions is essential in modeling and evaluating computer system dependability. Often, for simplicity or due to lack of information, the TTE is assumed to be exponentially distributed. Early measurement-based studies found that the Weibull distribution with a decreasing failure rate is representative of the time between failures (TBF) in a measured DEC computer system (McConnel, 1979) and for a measured IBM-VM/SP operating system (Iyer,1985b). A recent comparative study of the dependability of the Tandem GUARDIAN, DEC VAX VMS, and IBM MVS operating systems showed that the software TTE in a single ma-

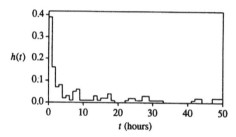

Figure 5.24: VAXcluster empirical failure hazard.

chine can be represented by a multistage gamma distribution, and the software TTE in multicomputers can be represented by a hyperexponential distribution (Lee, 1993a). In this section, we discuss these distributions.

Figure 5.25 depicts the probability density function for disk errors in the Carnegie Mellon University (CMU) Andrew files system (Siewiorek, 1992). Analysis shows that the instantaneous error rate (hazard function) for this data is a decreasing function of time. The data is seen to best fit a Weibull distribution, that is, the probability density function, $f(t)$, is given by

$$f(t) = \alpha \lambda t^{\alpha-1} exp[-\lambda t^{\alpha}]$$

and the hazard (error rate) function is given by

$$h(t) = \alpha \lambda t^{\alpha-1}$$

where α is the shape parameter and λ is the scale or rate parameter. Note that if $\alpha = 1$, then the hazard function reduces to a constant (i.e., $f(t)$ reduces to the exponential). The Weibull function has been found to describe a wide variety of hardware and software errors; it is superimposed upon the actual data presented in Figure 5.25. Note that α is usually much less than 1, which means the hazard function is decreasing.

Before presenting TTE distributions for the three operating systems studied in Lee (1993a), we first explain how a TTE distribution is obtained from a multicomputer system, because two of the three operating systems were running on multicomputer systems. In a multicomputer system, typically, all the constituent machines work in a similar environment and run the same version of the operating system. The whole system can be treated as a single entity in which multiple instances of an operating system are running concurrently. Every software error

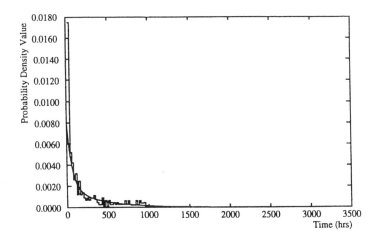

Figure 5.25: Distribution of Andrew disk errors.

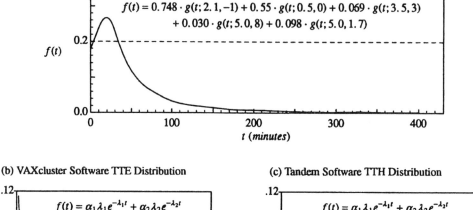

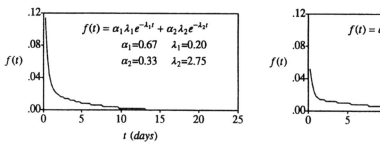

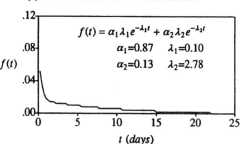

Figure 5.26: Analytical software TTE distributions extracted from data.

in the system is sequentially ordered, and a distribution is constructed. The constructed TTE distribution reflects the software error characteristics for the whole system. We will call this distribution the *multicomputer software TTE distribution*.

Figure 5.26 gives the analytical TTE or time to halt (TTH) distributions extracted from data by using SAS for the three measured systems. All the three empirical distributions failed to fit simple exponential functions. The fitting was tested using the Kolmogorov-Smirnov or chi-square test (see Section 5.2.2) at a 0.05 significance level. The two-phase hyperexponential distribution provided satisfactory fits for the VAXcluster and Tandem multicomputer software TTE distributions. An attempt to fit the MVS TTE distribution to a phase-type exponential distribution led to a large number of stages. As a result, the following multi-stage gamma distribution was used:

$$f(t) = \sum_{i=1}^{n} a_i g(t; \alpha_i, s_i)$$

where $a_i \geq 0$, $\sum_{i=1}^{n} a_{i=1}$, and

$$g(t; \alpha, s) = \begin{cases} 0 & t < s, \\ \dfrac{1}{\Gamma(\alpha)}(t-s)^{\alpha-1}e^{-(t-s)} & t \geq s \end{cases}$$

It was found that a five-stage gamma distribution provided a satisfactory fit, which means that the software TTE distribution on the MVS has a complicated mode.

Figures 5.26b and 5.26c show that the multicomputer software TTE distribution can be modeled as a probabilistic combination of two exponential random variables, indicating that there are two dominant error modes. The higher error rate, λ_2, with occurrence probability α_2, captures both the *error bursts* (multiple errors occurring on the same operating system within a short period of time) and the *concurrent errors* (multiple errors on different instances of an operating system within a short period of time) on these systems. The lower error rate, λ_1, with occurrence probability α_1, captures regular errors and provides an interburst error rate.

Error bursts can be explained as repeated occurrences of the same software problem or as multiple effects of an intermittent hardware fault on the software. Software error bursts have also been observed in laboratory experiments reported in Bishop (1988). The study showed that, if the input sequences of the software under investigation are correlated rather than independent, one can expect more "bunching" of failures than those predicted using a constant failure rate assumption. In an operating system, input sequences (user requests) are highly likely to be correlated. Hence, a defect area can be triggered repeatedly.

5.5.4 Dependency Analysis

Many underlying dependencies exist among measured parameters and components. Examples are the dependency between workload and failure rate, and the dependency or correlation among failures on different components. Understanding and quantifying such dependencies is important for developing realistic models and hence better designs. The workload/failure dependency issue was studied in the early 1980s, and the correlated failure issue has been investigated more recently.

Dependency between workload and failure was addressed in two approaches: *statistical quantification* of the dependence between workload and failure rate (Butner, 1980; Iyer, 1985b) and *stochastic modeling* of failures as functions of workload (Castillo, 1981). Both approaches demonstrated the strong correlation between workload and failure rate. The results indicated that dependability models cannot be considered representative unless the system workload is taken into account. Based on this result, several workload-dependent analytical models have been proposed (Meyer, 1988; Aupperle, 1980; Dunkel, 1990).

Recent measurements on VAXclusters (Tang, 1990; Wein, 1990), and Tandem machines (Lee, 1991) found that correlated failures exist significantly in distributed systems. Further, the studies also showed that even a small correlation can have major impact on system dependability (Dugan, 1991; Tang, 1991; Tang, 1992a). Neither traditional models that assume failure independence or those that are believed to take correlation into account are representative of the actual occurrence process of correlated failures observed in measured systems (Tang, 1993b).

In the following subsections, dependency analysis is illustrated by discussing two issues: (1) dependency between workload and failure, and (2) dependency among errors/failures on different components in a computer system.

Workload/failure dependency. An early study (Castillo, 1981) introduced a workload-dependent cyclostationary model to characterize system failure processes. The basic assumption in the model was that the instantaneous failure rate of a system resource can be approximated by a function of the usage of the resource considered. Specifically, the failure rate of a particular resource, $\lambda(t)$, is assumed to be

$$\lambda(t) = au(t) + b \tag{5.32}$$

where $u(t)$ is a usage function of the resource, which in turn, consists of a deterministic, periodic function of time, $m(t)$, and a modified, stationary Gaussian process, $z(t)$:

$$u(t) = m(t) + z(t) \tag{5.33}$$

The failure arrivals were assumed to follow a Poisson process. Thus, the failure process involves two stochastic processes: a Poisson process and a Gaussian process. Such a process was defined as a *doubly stochastic process*. The model was applied to a PDP-10 machine running a modified version of the standard TOPS-10 operating system. It was shown that the TTF distribution predicted by the model and the one observed from the real system have a very good fit at the significance level 0.36 in a χ^2 test.

Castillo (1982) introduced a workload dependent software probabilistic model to predict the differences in manifestations of hardware transient and software errors as a function of system workload. The model was applied to a modified version of the TOPS-10 operating system running on a PDP-10 machine. The central argument behind this study was that the observed software failure rate depends on the instantaneous complexity of the data to be processed while the system failure rate due to hardware transients is insensitive to the data complexity. If a system doubles its average fraction of time spent in the kernel mode, its failure rate due to hardware transients increases linearly. Thus, deviations from this expected linearity can be attributed to software errors.

In Iyer (1982a), a load hazard model was introduced to measure the risk of a failure as the system activity increases. The proposed model is similar to the hazard rate defined in Eq. (5.31). Given a workload variable X, the load hazard is defined as

$$z(x) = \frac{Pr[\text{failure in load interval } (x, \ x + \Delta x)]}{Pr[\text{no failure in load interval } (0, \ x)]\Delta x} = \frac{g(x)}{1 - G(x)} \tag{5.34}$$

where $g(x)$ is the p.d.f. of the variable "a failure occurs at a given workload value x" and $G(x)$ is the corresponding c.d.f. That is,

$$g(x) = Pr[\text{failure occurs} \mid X = x] = \frac{f(x)}{l(x)} \tag{5.35}$$

where $l(x)$ is simply the p.d.f. of the workload in consideration

$$l(x) = Pr[X = x] \tag{5.36}$$

and $f(x)$ is the joint p.d.f. of the system state (failure state or nonfailure state) and the workload

$$f(x) = Pr[\text{failure occurs } \& X = x] \tag{5.37}$$

A constant hazard rate implies that failures are occurring randomly with respect to the workload. An increasing hazard rate on the increase of X implies that there is an increasing failure rate with increasing workload.

The load hazard model was applied to the software failure and workload data collected from an IBM 3081 system running the VM operating system. Based on the collected data, $l(x)$, $f(x)$, $g(x)$, and $z(x)$ were computed for each workload variable. Figure 5.27 shows the $z(x)$ plots for three selected workload variables:

1. OVERHEAD—fraction of CPU time spent on the operating system
2. PAGEIN—number of page reads per second by all users
3. SIO (Start I/O)—number of input/output operations per second

The regression coefficient, R^2, which is an effective measure of the goodness of fit, is also shown in the figure.

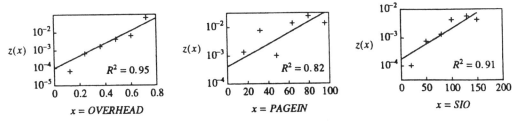

Figure 5.27: Workload hazard plots for the IBM 3081 system.

The hazard plots show that the workload parameters appear to be acting as stress factors, that is, the failure rate increases as the workload increases. The effect is particularly strong in the case of the interactive workload measures OVERHEAD and SIO. The correlation coefficients of 0.95 and 0.91 show that the failure closely fits an increasing load hazard model. The risk of a failure also increases with increased PAGEIN, although at a somewhat lower correlation (0.82). Note that the vertical scale on these plots is logarithmic,

The second step is calculating correlation coefficients using Eq. (5.19) based on the data matrix. Each time, we pick up two columns (X_i and X_j) to calculate $Cor(X_i, X_j)$. This step can be automated by using a statistical package such as SAS. Table 5.11 lists the average correlation coefficients of the 21 pairs of machines in a VAXcluster for different types of errors and failures (Tang, 1993a). Generally, the error correlation is high (0.62) and the failure correlation is low (0.06). Disk and network errors are strongly correlated, because the processors in the system heavily use and share the disks and the network concurrently.

We have seen that the failure correlation coefficient in Table 5.11 is low (0.06). An important question is: Does such a low correlation have impact on dependability? Two independent studies, Dugan (1991) and Tang (1991), showed that even a small correlation can have significant impact on system unavailability through different approaches. Here, we discuss the approach used in Dugan (1991).

In Dugan (1991), another type of correlation coefficient, which is different from that discussed above, was introduced to quantify the correlation between the ith and $(i + 1)$th failure. Let A and B be random variables representing failures of the first and second components, respectively. A (B) takes a value of 1 if the first (second) component is in the failure state. Otherwise, it takes a value of 0. (So A and B are similar to X_i in the matrix discussed above.) The *steady-state linear correlation coefficient* between A and B was defined as

$$\rho_{AB} = \frac{E[(A - m_A)(B - m_B)]}{\sqrt{E[(A - m_A)^2]E[(B - m_B)^2]}} \tag{5.38}$$

where m_A and m_B are the time average (mean) of A and B, respectively. Given the failure rate of the first component λ_1, ρ_{AB} can be used to determine the failure rate of the second component by

$$\lambda_2 = \frac{\mu(\lambda_1 + \lambda_1 \rho_{AB} + \mu \rho_{AB})}{\mu - \lambda_1 \rho_{AB} - \mu \rho_{AB}} \tag{5.39}$$

where μ is the recovery rate of components 1 and 2.

Table 5.11: Average Correlation Coefficients for VAXcluster Errors

	Error					Failure
All	CPU	Memory	Disk	Network	Software	All
0.62	0.03	0.01	0.78	0.70	0.02	0.06

Table 5.12: Effect of Correlation on Unavailability for Systems with Two to Four Components

ρ_{AB}	0	0.0001	0.001	0.01
2-Component System	4.84×10^{-8}	7×10^{-8}	4.28×10^{-7}	2.27×10^{-6}
3-Component System	1.06×10^{-11}	3.63×10^{-10}	6.71×10^{-9}	1.97×10^{-7}
4-Component System	2.34×10^{-15}	2.93×10^{-11}	1.40×10^{-9}	8.64×10^{-8}

The study applied the methodology to solve Markov models of two-, three-, and four-component systems subject to permanent, intermittent, and transient correlated failures under a range of assumed correlation coefficients. Table 5.12 lists the evaluated unavailability for systems with two, three, and four components under several different correlation coefficients, given a set of component failure and recovery rates. The results showed that a correlation coefficient as small as in a range from 0.0001 to 0.01 can increase unavailability of a system by several orders of magnitude.

If errors/failures on more than two components are related, the correlation coefficient is not enough to quantify the dependence among these components (multiway correlation). In such a case, the factor analysis method introduced in Section 5.2.3 can be used to uncover the multiway correlation. In the following, the application of factor analysis is illustrated using the processor failure data (Lee, 1991) collected from a Tandem fault-tolerant system (Chapter 2).

Similar to the correlation analysis discussed above, the first step is building an $m \times n$ data matrix based on measurements, where n is the number of components in the system and m is the number of measured time intervals. The element (i, j) of this matrix has a value of 1, if processor j halts during the ith time interval; otherwise, it has a value of 0. The jth column of the matrix represents the sample halt history of processor j, while the ith row of the matrix represents the state of the eight processors in the ith time interval. The matrix is called a *processor halt matrix*.

In Lee (1991), the factor analysis approach was applied to data collected from an eight-processor Tandem fault-tolerant system (i.e., $n = 8$). The time interval (Δt) used was 30 minutes. Results obtained by applying the SAS procedure FACTOR to the processor halt matrix are shown in Table 5.13. The numbers in

Table 5.13: Factor Pattern of the Tandem Processor Halts

Processor	Factor 1	Factor 2	Factor 3	Factor 4	Commonality
1	0.997	−0.004	−0.069	0.023	1.00
2	0.000	0.000	0.000	0.000	0.00
3	0.061	0.012	0.853	−0.133	0.75
4	0.001	0.999	−0.011	0.021	1.00
5	0.982	−0.000	0.188	−0.018	1.00
6	−0.001	0.447	−0.005	0.009	0.20
7	0.047	−0.002	0.862	0.506	1.00
8	−0.007	0.762	0.090	0.641	1.00
Var.	1.965	1.781	1.519	0.685	
Var. %	24.6	22.3	19.0	8.6	

the middle of the table are factor loadings, and the last column shows commonality. The bottom two rows show the amount of variances explained by the common factors and their percentages to the total variance.

According to Dillon (1984), factor loadings greater than 0.5 are considered significant. However, in reliability analysis, factor loadings lower than 0.5 can be significant. The results show that there are four common factors. Factor 1 captures the dependence between processor 1 and processor 5 and accounts for 24.6 percent of the total variance. Factor 2 captures the multiway dependence among processors, 4, 6, and 8, although the contribution of processor 6 is small (0.447^2, i.e., 20 percent of its variance is explained by this factor). Factor 2 explains 22.3 percent of the total variance. Factor 3 captures the dependence between processor 3 and processor 7 and contributes 19 percent to the total variance. Factor 4 captures the dependence, although it is lower (with factor loadings 0.506 and 0.641), between processor 7 and processor 8 and accounts for 8.6 percent of the total variance.

5.5.5 Markov Reward Modeling

Many natural and social phenomena can be modeled by Markov or semi-Markov stochastic processes (Trivedi, 1982). In the computer area, the Markov process is one of the most frequently used models in performance and dependability evaluation. Compared to combinatorial models, Markov models have several advantages, such as the ability to handle time-dependent failure rate, performance degradation, and interactions among components. In the area of analytical modeling of computer systems, performability models (MeyerJ, 1980, 1992), availability models (Goyal, 1987), and Markov reward models (Reibman, 1989; Trivedi, 1992) have all been addressed. Typically, Markov models are built based on certain assumptions (such as independent failures on different components) using individual component parameters (such as failure and recovery rates). The evaluated results are highly dependent on the input parameters and on the model assumptions. A substantial amount of the research addresses the questions of solving a given model. However, how to identify an accurate model to start with remains unclear. Also, the assumptions made in building analytical models need to be validated by measurement-based analysis.

In measurement-based modeling, Markov models are identified from data and therefore called *measured models* (Tang, 1993b). No additional assumptions (more than the Markov property) are made in the construction of these models. Measured models provide the best evaluation for real systems as well as insight into the development of representative analytical models. Thus, it is valuable to identify appropriate models from measured data. In the following sections, measurement-based Markov reward modeling techniques are illustrated by a system model generated for a VAXcluster and a software model generated for an IBM operating system.

Modeling of a distributed system.   The data used for the modeling was collected from a DEC VAXcluster system, consisting of seven machines, for 250 days (Tang, 1993a). For this system, an *error* was defined as an abnormality in any component of the system. If an error led to a termination of service on a machine, it was defined as a *failure*. A failure was identified by a reboot following one or multiple error reports.

Model Construction.   Since the measured VAXcluster has seven machines, an eight-state Markov error model is constructed. The eight states, $E_0, E_1 \ldots$, and E_7, are defined such that E_i represents the state wherein i machines observe errors at the same time (the time granularity is chosen to be 1 second). For example, state E_0 represents that none of the machines experiences errors, that is, the VAXcluster is in the normal (error-free) state; state E_7 represents that all the machines experience errors. At any measured time, the VAXcluster is in one of these states.

The transition probabilities for the eight-state model are estimated from the error event data. Given that the system is in state i, the probability that it will go to state j, p_{ij}, is calculated as follows:

$$p_{ij} = \frac{observed\ number\ of\ transitions\ from\ E_i\ to\ E_j}{observed\ number\ of\ transitions\ out\ of\ E_i} \tag{5.40}$$

Table 5.14 shows the transition probabilities calculated from the VAXcluster error data. Based on the table, an error propagation model can be obtained by calculating the probability that the system goes from state E_i ($i = 1, \ldots, 6$) to any of the lower states ($E_{i-1}, \ldots, E_0$) and the probability that it goes from Ei to any of the higher states ($E_{i+1} \ldots, E_7$). These probabilities are easily determined by summing all the row elements to the left of element (i, i), and all the row elements to the right of element (i, i), in the table. The error propagation model is shown in Figure 5.28. An interesting error propagation characteristic is uncovered with this model. Notice that the transition probabilities to higher states (numbers in the upper line) tend to increase as the state increases. That is, once an error domain encompasses more than one machine, the probability of the domain involving more machines increases. In such situations, error containment can become increasingly difficult.

Table 5.14: Transition Probability for the VAXcluster Error Model

State	E_0	E_1	E_2	E_3	E_4	E_5	E_6	E_7
E_0	.000	.891	.084	.014	.004	.002	.002	.003
E_1	.824	.000	.145	.023	.004	.003	.001	.000
E_2	.239	.594	.000	.118	.035	.009	.004	.001
E_3	.126	.211	.401	.000	.227	.024	.009	.003
E_4	.079	.147	.102	.422	.000	.205	.034	.011
E_5	.058	.115	.054	.073	.367	.000	.315	.018
E_6	.070	.081	.024	.016	.073	.406	.000	.331
E_7	.125	.104	.000	.021	.036	.161	.552	.000

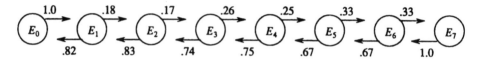

Figure 5.28: An error propagation model for the VAXcluster.

Reward Analysis. Markov models can be used to conduct reward analysis (Trivedi, 1992) to quantify the loss of service due to errors and failures. The key step is to define a reward function that characterizes the performance loss in each degraded state. For a multicomputer system, a generic reward function can be defined for both a single machine and the whole system. Given a time interval ΔT (random variable), a *reward rate* for the system in ΔT is determined by

$$r(\Delta T) = W(\Delta T) \,/\, \Delta T \tag{5.41}$$

where $W(\Delta T)$ denotes the useful work done by the system in ΔT and is calculated by

$$W(\Delta T) = \begin{cases} \Delta T & \text{in normal state} \\ \Delta T - n\tau & \text{in error state} \\ 0 & \text{in failure state} \end{cases} \tag{5.42}$$

where n is the number of raw errors (error entries in the log; see Section 5.5.2) in ΔT and τ is the mean recovery time for a single error. Thus, one unit of reward is given for each unit of time when the system is in the normal state. In an error state, the penalty paid depends on the recovery time the system spends in that state, which is determined by the linear function $\Delta T - n\tau$ (normally, $\Delta T > n\tau$; if $\Delta T < n\tau$, $W(\Delta T)$ is set to 0). In a failure state, $W(\Delta T)$ is by definition zero.

Applying Eq. (5.41) to the VAXcluster, the reward rate formula has the following form:

$$r(\Delta T) = \sum_{k=1}^{7} W_k(\Delta T) /(7 \times \Delta T) \tag{5.43}$$

where $W_k(\Delta T)$ denotes the useful work done by machine k in time ΔT. Here all machines are assumed to contribute an equal amount of reward to the system. For example, if three machines fail when the system is in E_3, the reward rate is $4/7$.

The expected steady-state reward rate, Y, can be estimated by

$$Y = \frac{1}{T} \sum_{\Delta t_j \in T} r(\Delta t_j)\Delta t_j \tag{5.44}$$

where T is the summation of all Δt_j's (particular values of ΔT) in consideration. If we substitute r from Eq. (5.43) and let ΔT represent the holding time of each state

Table 5.15: Steady-State Reward Rate for the VAXcluster

τ	0.1 ms	1 ms	10 ms	100 ms
Y	0.995078	0.995077	0.995067	0.994971

in the error model, Y becomes the steady-state reward rate of the VAXcluster, which is also an estimate of system availability (performance-related availability). If we substitute r from Eq. (5.43) and let ΔT represent the time span of the error event for a particular type of error, Y becomes the steady-state reward rate of the system during the event intervals of the specified error. Thus, $(1 - Y)$ measures the loss in performance during the specified error event. Note that it is possible that there are failed machines when the system is in an error state. Since the model is an empirical model based on the error event data (of which the failure event data is a subset), the information about errors and failures of all machines for each particular Δt_j can be obtained from the data.

The steady-state reward rate for the VAXcluster was computed with τ being 0.1, 1, 10, and 100 ms. The results are given in Table 5.15. The table shows that the reward rate is not sensitive to τ. This is because the overall recovery time is dominated by the failure recovery time, that is, the major contributors to the performance loss are failures, not nonfailure errors. In the range of these τ values, the VAXcluster availability is estimated to be 0.995. Table 5.16 shows the steady-state reward rate for each error type ($\tau = 1$ ms) for the VAXcluster. These numbers quantify the loss of performance due to the recovery from each type of error. For example, during the recovery from CPU errors, the system can be expected to deliver approximately 15 percent of its full performance. During the disk error recovery, the average system performance degrades to nearly 61 percent of its capacity. Since software errors have the lowest reward rate (0.00008), the loss of work during the recovery from software errors is the most significant.

Modeling of an operating system.   The modeled operating system is the IBM MVS system running on an IBM 3081 mainframe (Hsueh, 1987). The measurement period is one year. A Markov model is developed using data collected from the system to describe error detection and recovery inside an operating system. The MVS is a widely used IBM operating system. Primary features of the system are reported to be efficient storage management and automatic software error recovery. The MVS system attempts to correct software errors using recovery routines. The philosophy in the MVS is that for major system functions, the programmer envisages possible failure scenarios and writes a recovery routine

Table 5.16: Steady-State Reward Rate for Each Error Type in the VAXcluster

CPU	Memory	Disk	Tape	Network	Software
0.14950	0.99994	0.61314	0.89845	0.56841	0.00008

for each. It is, however, the responsibility of the installation (or the user) to write recovery routines for applications.

Recovery routines in the MVS operating system provide a means by which the operating system prevents a total loss on the occurrence of software errors. When a program is abnormally interrupted due to an error, the supervisor routine gets control. If the problem is such that further processing can degrade the system or destroy data, the supervisor routine gives control to the recovery termination manager (RTM), an operating system module responsible for error and recovery management. If a recovery routine is available for the interrupted program, the RTM gives control to this routine before it terminates the program. The purpose of a recovery routine is to free the resources kept by the failing program, to locate the error, and to request either a retry or the termination of the program.

More than one recovery routine can be specified for the same program. If the current recovery routine is unable to restore a valid state, the RTM can give control to another recovery routine, if available. This process is called *percolation*. The percolation process ends if either a routine issues a valid retry request or no more recovery routines are available. In the latter case, the program and its related subtasks are terminated. If a valid retry is requested, a retry is attempted to restore a valid state using the information supplied by the recovery routine and then give control to the program. For a retry to be valid, there should be no risk of error recurrence and the retry address should be properly specified. An error recovery can result in any of the following four situations:

1. Resume op (resume operation)—The system successfully recovers from the error and returns control to the interrupted program.

2. Task term (task termination)—The program and its related subtasks are terminated, but the system does not fail.

3. Job term (job termination)—The job in control at the time of the error is aborted.

4. System failure—The job or task, which was terminated, is critical for system operation. As a result of the termination, a system failure occurs.

Model Construction.   The model consists of a normal state, eight types of error states (listed in Table 5.17) and four states (corresponding to the above four situations: resume op, task term, job term, and system failure) resulting from error recoveries. The normal state represents the operating system running error-free. The transition probabilities from states to states were estimated from the measured data using Eq. (5.40).

Table 5.17 shows the mean waiting time characteristics of the normal and error states in the model. Note that the waiting time distribution of the normal state is the TTE distribution. It has been shown in Section 5.5.3 that this distribution is not simply exponential (a multistage gamma distribution), so the model is a semi-Markov model. In the table, a *multiple software error* is defined as an error burst consisting of more than one type of software error. The average duration of

Table 5.17: Mean Waiting Time

State	# Observations	Mean waiting Time (Sec.)	Standard Deviation
Normal (Error-Free)	2,757	10,461.33	32,735.04
CTRL (Control Error)	213	21.92	84.21
DLCK (Deadlock)	23	4.72	22.61
I/O (I/O & Data Management Error)	1,448	25.05	77.62
PE (Program Exception)	65	42.23	92.98
SE (Storage or Address Exception)	149	36.82	79.59
SM (Storage Management Error)	313	33.40	95.01
OTHR (Other Type)	66	1.86	12.98
MULT (Multiple Software Error)	481	175.59	252.79

a multiple error is at least four times longer than that of any type of single error, which is typically in the range of 20 to 40 seconds, except for DLCK (deadlock) and OTHR (others). The average recovery time from a program exception is twice as long as that from a control error (21 seconds versus 42 seconds). This is probably due to the extensive software involvement in recovering from program exceptions.

Model Evaluation. The steady-state measures evaluated from the model are listed in Table 5.18. The definitions of these measures are given in Howard (1971).

1. Transition probability (π_j)—probability that the transition is to state j, given a transition to occur

Table 5.18: Error/Recovery Model Characteristics

Measure	Normal State	Error State CTRL	DLCK	I/O	PE	SE	SM	OTHR	MULT
π	0.2474	0.0191	0.0020	0.1299	0.0060	0.0134	0.0281	0.0057	0.0431
Φ	0.9950	0.00016	—	0.00125	0.000098	0.000189	0.00036	—	0.002913

(a)

Measure	Recovery State Retry	Percolation	No Percolation	Resultant State Resume Op.	Task Term.	Job Term.
π	0.1704	0.0845	0.0030	0.1414	0.0712	0.0348
Θ (*hr.*)	4.25	8.55	241.43	5.11	10.16	20.74

(b)

2. Occupancy probability (Φ_j)—probability that the system occupies state j at any time point

3. Mean recurrence time ($\overline{\Theta}_j$)—mean recurrence time of state j

The occupancy probability of the normal state can be viewed as the operating system availability without degradation. The state transition probability, on the other hand, characterizes error detection and recovery processes in the operating system. Table 5.18a lists the state transition probabilities and occupancy probabilities for the normal and error states.

Table 5.18b lists the state transition probabilities and the mean recurrent times of the recovery and result states. A dash (—) in the table indicates a negligible value (less than 0.00001). Table 5.18a shows that the occupancy probability of the normal state in the model is 0.995. This indicates that in 99.5 percent of the time the operating system is running error-free. In the other 0.5 percent of the time, the operating system is in an error or recovery state. In more than half of the error and recovery time (i.e., 0.29 percent out of 0.5 percent) the operating system is in the multiple error state. The average reward rate for all software error and recovery states is estimated from data to be 0.2736. Based on this reward rate and the occupancy probability for all error and recovery states shown in the table (0.005), the steady-state reward loss in the modeled MVS can be evaluated to be 0.00363.

By solving the model, it is found that the operating system makes a transition every 43.37 minutes. Table 5.18a shows that 24.74 percent of all transitions made in the model are to the normal state, 24.73 percent to error states (obtained by summing the π's for all error states), 25.79 percent to recovery states, and 24.74 percent to result states. Since a transition occurs every 43 minutes, it can be estimated that, on the average, a software error is detected every three hours and a successful recovery (i.e., reaching the "resume op" state) occurs every five hours. Table 5.18b also shows that more than 40 percent of software errors lead to job or task terminations, which cause the loss of service to users. However, a few of these terminations lead to system failures. This result indicates that recovery routines in MVS are effective in avoiding system failures but are not so effective in avoiding user job terminations.

5.5.6 Software Dependability

As will be seen in Chapter 7 a great deal of research has been performed in the area of software reliability during the development phase. Different models have been proposed (reviewed in Musa, (1987)) to characterize the reliability growth of the candidate software through this phase. In general, these models can be divided into two classes. The first assumes that the failure rate is a function of the number of remaining defects in the software. Imperfect debugging and uncertainty in the projected number of initial defects have also been modeled (Goel, 1985). The second class of models does not depend on knowing the number of the remaining defects (Littlewood, 1980). The failure rate is assumed to be a random variable, and the software reliability model involves two stochastic processes. Although most models perform well within their own contexts, their performance varies significantly from one data set to another.

The operational phase of mature software is much different from the development phase. In the operational phase, a typical situation involves frequent changes and updates installed either by system managers or by vendors. Often, without notification to the installation management, the vendor will install a change (patch) to fix a fault found at some other installation. In a sense, the system being measured represents an aggregate of all such systems being maintained by the vendor. In addition, software reliability in the operational phase is attributed to workload effects, hardware problems, and environmental factors. Thus, software reliability in the operational phase cannot be characterized by simply applying analytical models proposed for the development phase.

Studies dealing with software dependability issues for the operational phase have also evolved over the past 15 years. Software TTE distributions (Section 5.5.3), dependency between software failure and workload (Section 5.5.4), and modeling of software error/recovery processes (Section 5.5.5) have been discussed. In this section, several other issues, including error interactions (i.e., hardware-related and correlated software errors), software fault tolerance, and software defect classification are discussed.

Error interactions.   When software is running in a complex system, interactions between hardware and software, and interactions among multiple processors can cause software error scenarios that cannot be seen during testing. Investigation of such error scenarios is helpful for understanding characteristics of software errors in operational systems. In the following sections, two kinds of such error scenarios are discussed: *hardware-related software errors*, which are a result of interactions between hardware and software, and *correlated software errors*, which are a result of interactions among processors through software protocols.

Hardware-Related Software Errors.   In Iyer (1985a), software errors related to hardware errors were described as hardware-related software errors. More precisely, if a software error (failure) occurs in close proximity (within a minute) to a hardware error, it is called a hardware-related software (HW/SW) error (failure). There are several causes of hardware-related software errors. For instance, a hardware error, such as a flipped memory bit, may change the software conditions, resulting in a software error. Therefore, even though the error is reported as a software error, it is actually caused by faulty hardware. Another possibility is that the software may fail to handle an unexpected hardware problem, such as an abnormal condition in the network communication. This can be attributed to a software design flaw. Sometimes, both the hardware error and the software error are symptoms of another unidentified problem.

Table 5.19 shows the frequency and percentage of hardware-related soft-

Table 5.19: Hardware-Related Software Errors/Failures

Category	HW/SW Errors		HW/SW Failure	
Measures	Frequency	Percent	Frequency	Percent
IBM/MVS	177	11.4	94	32.8
VAX/VMS	32	18.9	28	21.4

ware errors/failures (among all software errors/failures) measured from an IBM 3081 system running MVS (Iyer, 1985b) and two VAXclusters (Tang, 1992b). In the IBM system, approximately 33 percent of all observed software failures are hardware-related. HW/SW errors are found to have large error-handling times (high recovery overhead). The system failure probability for HW/SW errors is close to three times that for software errors in general. The VAXcluster data shows that most hardware errors involved in HW/SW errors are network errors (75 percent). This indicates that the major sources of hardware-related software problems in the measured VAXclusters are network-related hardware or software components. This is a unique feature in the multicomputer system, where processes rely heavily on intercommunications through the network.

Correlated Software Errors. When multiple instances of a software system interact with each other in a multicomputer environment, the issue of correlated failures should be addressed. Several studies (Tang, 1990; Wein, 1990; Lee, 1991) found that significant correlated processor failures exist in the measured multicomputer systems. Correlated software failures are also found in the VAX VMS and the Tandem GUARDIAN operating systems (Lee, 1993a) as already discussed in Chapter 2. The data showed that about 10 percent of software failures in the measured VAXcluster and 20 percent of software halts in the measured Tandem system occurred concurrently on multiple machines. To understand how correlated software failures occur, it is instructive to examine a real case in detail.

Figure 5.29 shows a scenario of correlated software failures. In the figure, Europa, Jupiter, and Mercury are machine names in the VAXcluster. A dashed line represents that the corresponding machine is in a failure state. At one time, a network error (net1) was reported from the CI (computer interconnect) port on Europa. This resulted in a software failure (soft1) 13 seconds later. Twenty-four seconds after the first network error (net1), additional network errors (net2,net3) were reported on the second machine (Jupiter), which were followed by a software failure (soft2). The error sequence on Jupiter was repeated (net4,net5,soft3) on the third machine (Mercury). The three machines experienced software failures concurrently for 45.5 minutes. All three software failures occurred shortly after network errors occurred, so they were network error related.

The higher percentage of correlated software failures in the Tandem system can be attributed to its architectural characteristics. In the Tandem system, a single software fault can cause halts of two processors on which the primary and backup processes (discussed below) of the faulty software are executing. If the

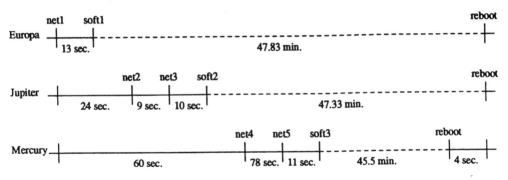

Note: soft1, soft2, soft3 — Exception while above asynchronous system traps delivery or on interrupt stack.
netl, net3, net5 — Port will be restarted.   net2, net4 — Virtual circuit timeout.

Figure 5.29: A scenario of correlated software failures.

two halted processors control a disk that includes files needed by other processors on the system, additional software halts can occur on these processors. (In the Tandem system, a disk can typically be accessed by two processors via dual-port disk controllers.) This explains why there is a higher percentage of correlated software failures in the Tandem system.

Note that the above scenario is a multiple-component failure situation not expected in general system design which assumes failure independence. Even the Tandem fault-tolerant system is not designed explicitly to guard against this situation. Generally, correlated failures can stress recovery and break the protection provided by the fault tolerance.

Software fault tolerance.   An in-depth discussion of software fault-tolerance is given in Chapter 7. The following briefly overviews certain basic concepts and how to evaluate their effectiveness. While hardware fault tolerance techniques have been used successfully, the issue of software fault tolerance is still not well addressed. Major approaches for software fault tolerance rely on design diversity (Avizienis, 1984; Randell, 1975). But these approaches are usually not applied to large operating systems because of the cost they would add to developing and maintaining the software. However, some fault tolerance techniques not explicitly designed for tolerating software faults can provide a certain amount of software fault tolerance. Understanding such techniques is important for designing good approaches to improving software dependability. The Tandem GUARDIAN system, running on the single-failure-tolerant multicomputer system, is a good target for such evaluations.

The Tandem GUARDIAN operating system is a message-based distributed system built for online transaction processing (Bartlett, 1978). High availability is achieved via single-failure tolerance techniques including the *process-pair* approach. For each user program, there are two processes—a *primary process* and a *backup process*—executing the same program on two processors. During normal operation, the primary process performs all operations for the user, while the

backup process passively watches message flows. The primary process periodically sends checkpoint messages to its backup. When the primary process detects
an inconsistency in its state, it fails fast and the backup process takes over the responsibility of the primary process. This approach can tolerate transient software
errors which will usually not be repeated by reexecuting the process.

A study of operating system fault tolerance achieved by the single-failure tolerance techniques implemented in a Tandem multiprocessor system was reported
in Lee (1992). The measured system had 16 processors and was working in a high-
stress environment. The data source was the processor halt log maintained by the
GUARDIAN system for a period of 23 months. The effect of the built-in fault tolerance mechanisms on software availability was evaluated by reward analysis. Two
reward functions were defined in the analysis. In the definition, i represents the
system state in which there are i failed processors, and n represents the total number of processors in the system. The first function (SFT) reflects the fault tolerance
of the Tandem system. In this function, the first processor halt does not cause any
degradation. For additional processor halts, the loss of service is proportional to
the number of processors halted. The second function (NSFT) assumes no fault tolerance. The difference between the two functions allows evaluation of the improvement in service due to the built-in fault tolerance mechanisms.

SFT (single-failure tolerance):

$$r_i = \begin{cases} 1 & \text{if } i = 0 \\ 1 - \dfrac{i-1}{n} & \text{if } 0 < i < n \\ 0 & \text{if } i = n \end{cases} \tag{5.45}$$

NSFT (no single-failure tolerance):

$$r_i = 1 - \frac{i}{n} \qquad \text{if } 0 \le i \le n \tag{5.46}$$

Based on the above reward functions, the expected steady-state reward rate, that
is, the Y in Eq. (5.44), was evaluated for software, nonsoftware, and all halts. The
results are given in Table 5.20. The bottom row shows the improvement in service

Table 5.20: Loss of Service Caused by Halts in the Tandem System

Measure		Software	Nonsoftware	All
NSFT	$1 - Y$	.00062	.00205	.00267
	Percent	23.2	76.8	100
SFT	$1 - Y$	.00007	.00016	.00023
	Percent	30.4	69.6	100
Improvement		89%	92%	91%

time (i.e., reduction in reward loss) due to the fault tolerance. It is seen that the single-failure tolerance in the measured system reduces the service loss due to software halts by 89 percent and that due to nonsoftware halts by 92 percent. This clearly demonstrates the effectiveness of the implemented fault tolerance mechanisms against software failures as well as nonsoftware failures. The table also shows that software problems account for 30 percent of the service loss in the measured system (with SFT). Although the system was working in a high-stress environment, the overall reward loss is small (10^{-4} with SFT). This reflects the high availability of the measured system.

Software defect classification.   Recent studies of software defects reported from the IBM MVS operating system (Sullivan, 1991) and two large IBM database management systems, DB2 and IMS (Sullivan, 1992), propose a software defect classification scheme. The scheme uses three concepts—error type, defect type, and error trigger—to classify software faults and errors. The *error type* classifies the low-level programming mistakes that lead to software failures. The *defect type* is a higher-level classification that distinguishes design mistakes, coding mistakes, and administrative mistakes. The *error trigger* is related to the running environment; it distinguishes several ways that defective code that was not executed during testing could be executed at the customer site. Tables 5.21 to 5.23 list major categories of error types, defect types, and error triggers.

The studies compared the error type, defect type, and error trigger distributions of the three products (DB2, IMS, and MVS) and found that the three products' distributions differ significantly. However, they have some common characteristics, such as the mode "undefined state." The studies also investigated the impact of software defects on system availability for the MVS operating system.

Table 5.21: Major Categories of Error Types

Error Type	Description
Allocation Management	A module uses a memory region after deallocating it.
Copying Overrun	The program copies data past the end of a buffer.
Data Error	The program produces or reads wrong data.
Interface Error	A module's interface is defined or used incorrectly.
Memory Leak	The program never deallocates memory it obtained from the system.
Pointer Management	A variable containing the address of data is corrupted.
Statement Logic	Statements are executed in the wrong order or are omitted.
Synchronization	An error occurs in locking or synchronization code.
Uninitialized Variable	A variable is used before it is initialized.
Undefined State	The system goes into a state the designers did not anticipate.
Wrong Algorithm	The program works but uses a wrong algorithm.

Table 5.22: Major Categories of Defect Types

Defect Type	Description
Function	A program's functionality is missing, incomplete, or incorrect
Data Struct/Algorithm	A data structure or algorithm has a design flaw.
Assignment/Checking	A coding mistake involves variable assignment or validation.
Interface	Errors are discovered in the interaction between components.
Timing/Synchronization	Errors occur in the management of shared or real-time resources.
Build/Package/Merge	Errors occur in version control or rollup of fixes.

A comparison between overlay defects (defects that corrupt a program's memory) and nonoverlay defects demonstrated that the impact of an overlay defect is much greater. Boundary conditions and allocation management were found to be the major causes of overlay defects.

5.5.7 Failure Prediction

Fault diagnosis and failure prediction are significant for maintaining highly reliable systems. Measurement-based studies have shown that it is possible to predict future failures based on the current and historical online error information. Several heuristic and statistical approaches have been proposed. The heuristic approach extracts characteristics of anomalous events and relates them to failures or faults by heuristic rules (Lin, 1990). The statistical approach uses statistical techniques to quantify relationships among system error states (defined on the basis of error rates) and recognizes failure patterns using the quantified relationships (Iyer, 1990). Recently, the fault injection method has been used on networks to diagnose faults based on the information of performance anomaly caused by the faults (Maxion, 1993). In the following sections we discuss these three approaches in detail.

Table 5.23: Major Categories of Error Triggers

Error Trigger	Description
Workload	Unusual workload conditions such as a user request with unexpected parameters.
Bug Fixes	A bug introduced when an earlier bug was fixed.
Client Code	Errors caused by propagation from application code running in protected mode.
Recovery/Exception	Problems in error recovery and exception handling.
Timing	Errors caused by an unanticipated sequence of events.

Prediction based on heuristic trend analysis.   This approach is based on the observation that a system usually experiences a period of intermittent errors before a hard failure occurs. The symptoms of intermittent errors can be used to predict impending failures. The early study of this approach showed qualitatively that the frequency of error tuples was correlated to system failures, based on measurements from a DEC disk subsystem (Tsao, 1983). Later, a heuristic trend analysis method, the *dispersion frame technique* (DFT), was developed (Lin, 1990), which determines the relationship among errors by examining their closeness in time and space.

Two concepts are used in the DFT: *dispersion frame* (DF), defined as the interval between two successive errors of the same type, and *error dispersion index* (EDI), defined as the number of error occurrences following the previous DF during the interval of one half of the previous DF or the DF before the previous DF. Each DF is applied to the following two errors. A high EDI implicates that the errors following the DF used to measure the EDI are highly correlated. DFT consists of five heuristic rules developed from the field experience:

- *3.3 rule*—The two consecutive EDIs obtained by applying the same frame are at least 3.
- *2.2 rule*—The two consecutive EDIs obtained by applying two successive frames are at least 2.
- *2 in 1 rule*—A frame is less than 1 hour.
- *4 in 1 rule*—Four errors occur within a 24-hour frame.
- *4 decreasing rule*—There are four monotonically decreasing frames, and at least one frame is half the size of its previous frame.

Figure 5.30 demonstrates an example, including some activated heuristics, of the DFT. In the figure, the top line represents the time sequence of five error occurrences (1, . . . , 5) in a particular device. DFT is activated when a frame size less than 168 hours (1 week) is encountered. Assume that all the frames in the figure fall into this threshold. Each frame is applied to the following two errors by

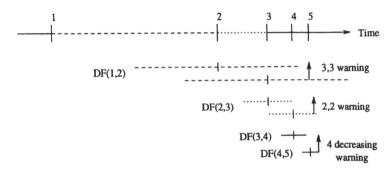

Figure 5.30: Dispersion techniques.

putting its center to the time points of the two error occurrences. For example, DF (1,2) is applied to errors 2 and 3, DF(2,3) is applied to errors 3 and 4, and so on. An upward arrow represents a failure warning issued under the above heuristic rules.

DFT was applied to the data collected from 13 public-domain file servers in Carnegie-Mellon University over a 22-month period. Among 16 hard failures examined, DFT predicated 15, with 5 false alarms. That is, the successful prediction rate is 93.7 percent. This result shows that DFT is very effective when coupled with good system instrumentation.

Prediction based on statistical analysis.   The objective of this approach is to recognize intermittent failures through statistical analysis and testing on recorded error data (Iyer, 1990). The approach starts by identifying key error patterns potentially symptomatic of failure occurrences and then refines these patterns by scanning the rest of the data in stages for similar error patterns. The approach is divided into three stages: (1) identification and validation of error groups, (2) identification and validation of error events, and (3) identification and validation of superevents. At each stage, validation is done by statistical testing.

In the first stage, data coalescing is performed on the raw data to eliminate redundant reports. The output of this stage are *error records* (tuples) characterized by *error states* (error type, machine condition, etc.). Next, all error records occurring within a small time interval (15 minutes) are identified together and identified as *error groups*. Error groups represent periods of high error activity (error bursts). Experience has shown that when system errors occur in bursts of a relatively high error rate, the errors are often related. Statistical analysis and hypothesis testing are performed on each error group to determine whether a valid correlation exists among its members (error records). Randomly formed groups in which members are statistically independent are rejected. Thus, the original error groups consisting of records among which relationships can exist are refined to the validated error groups consisting of records among which relationships do exist.

Relationships can exist across error groups, that is, a single cause can give rise to a persistent error and thus foster multiple-error groups within a short time. In the second stage, the output groups from the first stage are examined to recognize related error groups and to eliminate stray error records. Several concepts are introduced for the analysis in this state. An *error event* is defined as the collection of error groups occurring within a given period (e.g., 24 hours) and having at least two error states in common. A *symptom* is defined as a collection of statistically related error states that are common to at least half of the groups in an event. A *symptom set* is defined as the collection of all symptoms in an event. Figure 5.31 illustrates an event and its symptom set. The event is composed of three groups: G_1, G_2, and G_3. The error states in these groups are represented by

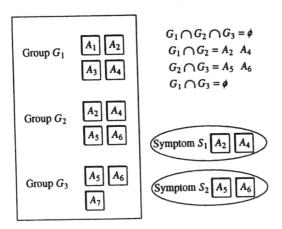

Figure 5.31: Derivation of an event's symptom set.

$A_1, \ldots, A_7$. Two symptoms are extracted from these error states: S_1, which consists of A_2 and A_4, and S_2, which consists of A_5 and A_6. Thus, S_1 and S_2 constitute the symptom set for this group.

In the third stage, three simple rules are used to recognize related events and to group them together into sets called *superevents*. The rules ensure that the events so grouped will have sufficiently common structure to permit testing for correlation. Two events are grouped into a superevent if they satisfy any one of the following criteria: (1) They have at least one symptom in common, (2) a symptom of one event is a proper subset of at least one symptom of another event, or (3) if they are single-group events, then they have at least two error states in common.

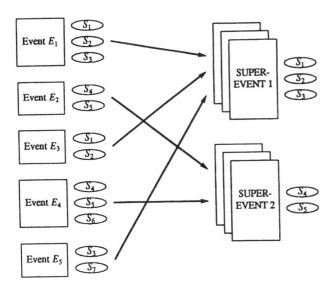

Figure 5.32: Construction of super-events.

Figure 5.32 illustrates how superevents are constructed. There is no time restriction when these rules are applied to the event data. When a superevent is created, a corresponding *supersymptom set* is also created, which starts with just the symptoms of the first event of that superevent. As another event is added, set intersection is performed between its symptom set and each of the symptom sets already in the superevent. All intersections are then added to the superevent set.

In each of the above states, statistical analysis and hypothesis testing are performed to validate the correlations among members in the formed groups or sets. The superevents derived in the final stage can be used by service engineers to judge potential failures. This methodology was applied to the online error log files from two CYBER systems and the results were compared to the log of failures and repair maintained by the system staff. In nearly 85 percent of the cases, the engineers confirmed that the validated superevents corresponded to real system problems. The evaluation was made both on the basis of their experience and from their field maintenance logs. For the remaining 15 percent of the cases, the engineers agreed that a problem had existed, but that its manifestation was not severe enough to be noticed by their analysis.

Prediction based on performance anomaly.   When faults occur in a fault-tolerant system, although the system may recover from the faults, the performance of the system may deviate from its normal conditions. Thus, the performance anomaly can be used to diagnose faults. This idea has been explored in (Maxion, 1990a, 1990b, 1993) by using fault injection to local computer networks and generating a set of diagnostic decision rules based on the information of network traffic anomaly caused by the injected faults.

The study was performed on five Ethernet networks at Carnegie-Mellon University (Maxion, 1993). There were in total 419 client machines and 20 server machines included in the five networks. These networks were representative of a diversity of network traffic characteristics. Five types of faults were selected for this study. They were considered to be typical network faults that could impair or disable network performance. The five fault types are

1. Pseudorunt flood—resource contention caused by runt flood. A runt packet is smaller than the 60-byte minimum size required by the Ethernet standard.

2. Networking paging—memory swaps of a client over the network to a file server, causing significant network transmission latency.

3. Bad memory sequence—wrong frame check sequence on a packet due to corruption or incorrect computation by the receiver, which requires a retransmission.

4. Jabber—excessive transmission of oversized packets, that is, packets longer than the protocol-specified 1,518-byte limit.

5. **Broadcast storm**—overuse of the Ethernet broadcast caused by flawed protocols or configurations and software errors.

The experimental instrumentation consisted of a software/hardware combined fault injection system and two out-of-band hardware monitoring systems. A dedicated machine is used to generate traffic patterns and faults and to inject them into the active network. Of the two hardware monitoring systems, one is used to collect statistics for packet traffic, collisions, percent utilization, and so on, and the other is used to collect data about packet types, lengths, sources and destinations, and so on. Because the monitoring instruments do not share the same data path, or band, as the measured devices, they do not influence the traffic in the measured network.

More than 500 faults were injected into the five networks. For each injected fault, 14 network performance parameters were measured, as described in Table 5.24. The 14 parameters, together with some information about the fault injection, are called a feature vector (or signature). Each feature vector was assigned a fault number from 1 to 5, according to the associated fault. Based on the feature vectors, a set of decision rules was determined. The technique used to generate decision rules is called recursive partitioning regression which forms homogeneous groups of vectors by recursively partitioning the dataset. The decision rule can be used to discriminate one fault from another on the basis of the features and values contained in the associated vectors.

By applying the decision rule to the feature vectors of new injected faults, fault detection and diagnostic classification accuracy can be determined. The results showed that the fault detection accuracy is 90.6 percent and the overall diagnostic classification accuracy is 86.8 percent. The identification errors can be at-

Table 5.24: Measured Network Performance Parameters

Sequence	Description
1	Destination Address, Unusual Activity
2	Destination Address, Increased Activity
3	Destination Address, Ceased Activity
4	Destination Address, Sudden Appearance
5	Source Address, Unusual Activity
6	Source Address, Increased Activity
7	Source Address, Ceased Activity
8	Source Address, Sudden Appearance
9	Percent Utilization
10	Packet Count
11	Collision Count
12	Packet Length ≤ 63
13	Packet Length in 64–127
14	Packet Length ≥ 1024

tributed to noises in the network environments. Since the generation of decision rules and the identification of faults can be done online and automatically, the approach is robust under a variety of environmental conditions.

5.6 CONCLUSION

In this chapter, we discussed methodologies and advances in the area of the experimental analysis of computer system dependability. The discussion covered three fields: simulated fault injection, physical fault injection, and measurement-based analysis of operational systems. The approaches used in the three fields are suited, respectively, to the dependability evaluation in the three phases of a system's life: design phase, prototype phase, and operational phase. Before discussing these fields, we introduced several statistical techniques used in all fields. For each field, we proposed a classification of research approaches or topics. Then we presented detailed methodologies and representative studies for each of these approaches or topics.

The statistical techniques introduced included the estimation of parameters and confidence intervals, probability distribution characterization, several multivariate analysis methods, and importance sampling. For simulated fault injection, we covered electrical-level, logic-level, and function-level simulation approaches as well as representative simulation environments, including FOCUS, NEST, REACT, and DEPEND. For physical fault injection, we discussed hardware, software, and radiation fault injection methods as well as several software and hybrid tools, including FIAT, FERRARI, HYBRID, and DEFINE. For measurement-based analysis of operational systems, after an introduction to measurement and data processing techniques, we presented methods used and representative studies in basic error characterization, dependency analysis, Markov reward modeling, software dependability, and fault diagnosis. The discussion covered several important issues previously studied, including workload/failure dependency, correlated failures, and software fault tolerance.

Fault injection simulation can be used to investigate the effectiveness of key design features of fault-tolerant systems and to provide timely feedback to system designers. Generally, most dependability measures (except input parameters such as failure and recovery rates) can be obtained from simulation. However, simulation requires accurate input parameters and the validation of output results which come from physical fault injection and measurement-based analysis. Fault injection on real systems can produce information about error latency, error detection, error propagation, error recovery, and system reconfiguration, but it can study only artificial faults and cannot produce system-level dependability measures, such as MTBF and availability. Measurement-based analysis of operational systems under real workloads can provide valuable information on actual failure characteristics and insight into analytical models. This type of analysis provides a means to study naturally occurring errors and all measurable dependability metrics, such as failure and recovery rates, reliability, and availability. However, the analysis is limited to detected errors. Further, conditions in the field can vary widely from one system to another, casting doubt on the statistical validity of the results. Thus, all three approaches are complementary and essential for accurate dependability analysis.

Significant progress has been made in all the three fields over the past 15 years, especially the past 5 years during which many dependability analysis tools have been developed. Increasing attention is being paid to (1) combining analytical modeling and experimental analysis and (2) combining system design and evaluation. In the first aspect, state-of-the-art analytical modeling techniques are being applied to real systems to evaluate various dependability and performance characteristics. Results from experimental analysis are being used to validate analytical models and to reveal practical issues that analytical modeling must address to develop more representative models. In the second aspect, dependability analysis tools are being combined with each other and with other CAD tools to provide an automatic design environment that incorporates multiple levels of joint evaluation of functionality, performance, dependability, and cost. Software failure data from testing and operational phases are also providing feedback to the software design for improving software reliability. Further interesting studies and advances in this area can be expected in the near future.

Analytical modeling can be very useful in guiding a designer especially at the early stages of the design. The following chapter provides an overview of basic theory and techniques used in reliability modeling.

REFERENCES

[Arlat90a] Arlat, J., M. Aguera, L. Amat, Y. Crouzet, J. C. Fabre, J. C. Laprie, E. Martins, and D. Powell, "Fault Injection for Dependability Validation: A Methodology and Some Applications," *IEEE Trans. Software Engineering*, vol. 16, no. 2 (February 1990) pp. 166–182.

[Arlat90b] Arlat, J. K. Kanoun, and J. C. Laprie, "Dependability Modeling and Evaluation of Software Fault-Tolerant Systems," *IEEE Trans. Computers*, vol. 39, no. 4 (April 1990), pp. 504–513.

[Artis86] Artis, H. P. "Workload Characterization Using SAS PROC FASTCLUS," *Workload Characterization of Computer Systems and Computer Networks*, G. Serazzi (ed.), Elsevier Science Publishers, 1986.

[Aupperle89] Aupperle, B. E., J. F. Meyer and L. Wei, "Evaluation of Fault-Tolerant Systems with Nonhomogeneous Workloads," *Proc. 19th Int. Symp. Fault-Tolerant Computing*, (June 1989), pp. 159–166.

[Avizienis84] Avizienis, A., and J. P. J. Kelly, "Fault Tolerance by Design Diversity: Concepts and Experiments," *IEEE Computer*, vol. 17, no. 8 (August 1984), pp. 67–80.

[Banerjee82] Banerjee, P. and J. A. Abraham, "Fault Characterization of MOS VLSI Circuits," *Proc. Int. Conf. Circuits and Computers*, 1982, pp. 564–568.

[Bartlett78] Bartlett, J. F. "A 'Nonstop' Operating System," *Proc. Int. Hawaii Conf. System Science*, 1978, pp. 103–117.

[Barton90] Barton, J. H., E. W. Czeck, Z. Z. Segall, and D. P. Siewiorek, "Fault Injection Experiments Using FIAT," *IEEE Trans. Computers*, vol. 39, no. 4 (April 1990), pp. 575–582.

[Bavuso87] Bavuso, S. J., J. B. Dugan, K. S. Trivedi, E. M. Rothman, and W. E. Smith, "Analysis of Typical Fault-Tolerant Architectures using HARP," *IEEE Trans. Reliability*, vol. 36, no. 2 (June 1987), pp. 176–185.

[Beh82] Beh, C. C., K. H. Arya, C. E. Radke, and K. E. Torku, "Do Stuck Fault Models Reflect Manufacturing Defects?" *Proc. Int. Test Conf.*, 1982, pp. 35–42.

[Bishop88] Bishop, P. G., and F. D. Pullen, "PODS Revisited—A Study of Software Failure Behavior," *Proc. 18th Int. Symp. Fault-Tolerant Computing*, Tokyo, Japan, (June 27–30, 1988), pp. 2–8.

[Bryant84] Bryant, R. E. "A Switch-Level Model and Simulator for MOS Digital Systems," *IEEE Trans. Computers*, vol. 33, no. 2 (February 1984), pp. 160–177.

[Butner80] Butner, S. E., and R. K. Iyer, "A Statistical Study of Reliability and System Load at SLAC," *Proc. 10th Int. Symp. Fault-Tolerant Computing*, (October 1980), pp. 207–209.

[Castillo81] Castillo, X. and D. P. Siewiorek, "Workload, Performance, and Reliability of Digital Computer Systems," *Proc. 11th Int. Symp. Fault-Tolerant Computing*, Portland, Maine, (June 24–26, 1981), pp. 84–89.

[Castillo82] Castillo, X., and D. P. Siewiorek, "A Workload Dependent Software Reliability Prediction Model," *Proc. 12th Int. Symp. Fault-Tolerant Computing*, Santa Monica, CA, (June 1982), pp. 279–286.

[Chillarege87] Chillarege, R., and R. K. Iyer, "Measurement-Based Analysis of Error Latency," *IEEE Trans. Computers*, vol. C-36, no. 5 (May 1987), pp. 529–537.

[Chillarege89] Chillarege, R., and N. S. Bowen, "Understanding Large System Failures—A Fault Injection Experiment," *Proc. 19th Int. Symp. Fault-Tolerant Computing*, (June 1989), pp. 356–363.

[Choi89] Choi, G. S., R. K. Iyer and V. Carreno, "FOCUS: An Experimental Environment for Validation of Fault Tolerant Systems: A Case Study of a Jet Engine Controller," *Int. Conf. Computer Design (ICCD)*, (October 1989), pp. 561–564.

[Choi90] Choi, G., R. Iyer, V. Carreno, "Simulated Fault Injection: A Methodology to Evaluate Fault Tolerant Microprocessor Architectures," *IEEE Trans. on Reliability, Special Issue on Experimental Evaluation*, vol. 39, no. 4 (October 1990), pp. 486–491.

[Choi92] Choi, G. S., and R. K. Iyer, "FOCUS: An Experimental Environment for Fault Sensitivity Analysis," *IEEE Trans. Computers*, vol. 41, no. 12 (December 1992), pp. 1515–1526.

[Choi93] Choi, G., R. Iyer, and D. Saab, "Fault Behavior Dictionary for Simulation of Device-Level Transients," *Proc. Int. Conf. Computer Aided Design*, November 1993.

[Choi93b] Choi, G., and R. Iyer, "Wear-Out Simulation Environment for VLSI Designs," *Proc. 23rd Int. Symp. Fault-Tolerant Computing*, Toulouse, France (June 1993).

[Clark92] Clark, J. A., and D. K. Pradhan, "Reliability Analysis of Unidirectional Voting

TMR Systems through Simulated Fault-Injection," *Proc. 1992 IEEE Workshop Fault-Tolerant Parallel and Distributed Systems,* (July 1992), pp. 72–81.

[Clark93a] Clark, J. A., and D. K. Pradhan, "REACT: A Synthesis and Evaluation Tool for Fault-Tolerant Multiprocessor Architectures," *Proc. Annual Reliability and Maintainability Symposium,* (January 26–28, 1993), Atlanta, Georgia, USA pp. 428–435.

[Clark93b] Clark, J. A., "Dependability Analysis of Fault-Tolerant Multiprocessor Architectures through Simulated Fault-Injection," Ph.D. diss., University of Massachusetts at Amherst, September 1993.

[Courtois79] Courtois, B., "Some Results about the Efficiency of Simple Mechanisms for the Detection of Microcomputer Malfunctions," *Proc. 9th Int. Symp. Fault-Tolerant Computing,* Madison, Wisconsin, (June 20–22, 1979), pp. 71–74.

[Cusick85] Cusick, J., R. Koga, W. Kolasinski, and C. King, "SEU vulnerability of the Zilog Z-80 and NSC-800 microprocessors," *IEEE Trans. Nuclear Science,* vol. NS-32 (December 1985), pp. 4206–4211.

[Czeck91] Czeck, E. W., "On The Prediction of Fault Behavior Based on Workload," Ph.D. diss., Dept. of Electrical and Computer Engineering, Carnegie-Mellon University, April 19, 1991.

[Czeck92] Czeck, E. W., and D. P. Siewiorek, "Observations on the Effects of Fault Manifestation as a Function of Workload," *IEEE Trans. Computers,* vol. 41, no. 5 (May 1992), pp. 559–566.

[Dewey92] Dewey, A., and A. J. de Geus, "VHDL: Toward a Unified View of Design," *IEEE Design and Test of Computers* (June 1992), pp. 8–17.

[Dillon84] Dillon, W. R., and M. Goldstein, *Multivariate Analysis,* John Wiley & Sons, New York, 1984.

[Duba88] Duba, P., and R. K. Iyer, "Transient Fault Behavior in a Microprocessor: A Case Study," *Proc. 1988 IEEE Int. Conf. Computer Design: VLSI in Computers & Processors,* (October 1988), pp. 272–276.

[Dugan91] Dugan, J. B., "Correlated Hardware Failures in Redundant Systems," *Proc. 2nd IFIP Working Conf. Dependable Computing for Critical Applications,* Tucson, Ariz., (February 1991), pp. 157–174.

[Dunkel90] Dunkel, J., "On the Modeling of Workload-Dependent Memory Faults," *Proc. 20th Int. Symp. Fault-Tolerant Computing,* Newcastle Upon Tyne, UK (June 1990), pp. 348–355.

[Dupuy90] Dupuy, A., J. Schwartz, Y. Yemini, and D. Bacon, "NEST: A Network Simulation and Prototyping Testbed," *Communications of the ACM,* vol. 33, no. 10 (October 1990), pp. 64–74.

[Finelli87] Finelli, G. B. "Characterization of Fault Recovery through Fault Injection on FTMP," *IEEE Trans. Reliability,* vol. R-36, no. 2 (June 1987), pp. 164–170.

[Goel85] Goel, A. L., "Software Reliability Models: Assumptions, Limitations, and Applicability," *IEEE Trans. Software Engineering,* vol. SE-11, no. 12 (December 1985), pp. 1411–1423.

[Goswami90] Goswami, K. K., and R. K. Iyer, "DEPEND: A Design Environment for Prediction and Evaluation of System Dependability," *Proc. 9th Digital Avionics Systems Conference,* October 1990.

[Goswami91] Goswami, K. K., and R. K. Iyer, "A Simulation-Based Study of a Triple Modular Redundant System using DEPEND," *Proc. 5th Int. Tests, Diagnosis, Fault Treatment Conf.*, (September 1991), pp. 300–311.

[Goswami92] Goswami, K. K., and R. K. Iyer, *DEPEND: A Simulation-Based Environment for System Level Dependability Analysis*, Technical Report, CRHC 92-11, University of Illinois at Urbana-Champaign, June 1992.

[Goswami93a] Goswami, K. K., R. K. Iyer, "Use of Hybrid and Hierarchical Simulation to Reduce Computation Costs," *Int. Workshop Modeling Analysis & Simulation of Computer & Telecomm. Sys.*, San Diego, Calif. (January 1993), pp.197–202.

[Goswami93b] Goswami, K. K., R. K. Iyer, and M. Devarakonda, "Prediction-Based Dynamic Load-Sharing Heuristics," *IEEE Trans. Parallel and Distributed Computing*, vol. 4, no. 6 (June 1993), pp. 638–648.

[Goswami93c] Goswami, K. K., and R. K. Iyer, "Simulation of Software Behavior Under Hardware Faults," *Proc. 23rd Int. Symp. Fault-tolerant Computing*, Toulouse, France (June 1993), pp. 218–227.

[Goyal87] Goyal, A., S. S. Lavenberg, and K. S. Trivedi, "Probabilistic Modeling of Computer System Availability," *Annals of Operations Research*, no. 8 (March 1987), pp. 285–306.

[Goyal92] Goyal, A., P. Shahabuddin, P. Heidelberger, V. F. Nicola, and P. W. Glynn, "A Unified Framework for Simulating Markovian Models of Highly Dependable Systems," *IEEE Trans. Computers*, vol. 41, no. 1 (January 1992), pp.36–51.

[Gray90] Gray, J., "A Census of Tandem System Availability Between 1985 and 1990," *IEEE Trans. Reliability*, vol. 39, no. 4 (October 1990), pp. 409–418.

[Gray91] Gray, J., and D. P. Siewiorek, "High-Availability Computer Systems," *IEEE Computers* vol. 24, no. 9 (September 1991), pp. 39–48.

[Gunneflo89] Gunneflo, U., J. Karlsson, and J. Torin, "Evaluation of Error Detection Schemes Using Fault Injection by Heavy-ion Radiation," *Proc. 19th Int. Symp. Fault-Tolerant Computing*, (June 1989), pp. 340–347.

[Han93] Han, S., H. Rosenberg, and K. G. Shin, "DOCTOR: An Integrated Software Fault Injection Environment," CSE Technical Report, CSE-TR-192-93, Department of Electrical Engineering and Computer Science, University of Michigan, Ann Arbor, Mich., December 1993.

[Hansen92] Hansen, J. P., and D. P. Siewiorek, "Models for Time Coalescence in Event Logs," *Proc. 22nd Int. Symp. Fault-Tolerant Computing*, Boston, MA. (July 1992), pp. 221–227.

[Heimann90] Heimann, D. I., N. Mittal, and K. S. Trivedi, "Availability and Reliability Modeling for Computer Systems," *Advances in Computers*, vol. 31 (1990), pp. 175–233.

[Hogg83] Hogg, R. V., and E. A. Tanis, *Probability and Statistical Inference*, 2nd ed. Macmillan, New York, 1983.

[Howard71] Howard, R. A., *Dynamic Probabilistic Systems*, John Wiley & Sons, New York, 1971.

[Hseuh87] Hsueh, M. C., and R. K. Iyer, "A Measurement-Based Model of Software Reliability in a Production Environment," *Proc. 11th Annual Int. Computer Software & Applications Conf.*, (October 1987), pp. 354–360.

[Hsueh88] Hsueh, M. C., R. K. Iyer, and K. S. Trivedi, "Performability Modeling Based on Real Data: A Case Study," *IEEE Trans. Computers*, vol. 37, no. 4 (April 1988), pp. 478–484.

[Iyer82a] Iyer, R. K., and D. J. Rossetti, "A Statistical Load Dependency Model for CPU Errors at SLAC," *Proc. 12th Int. Symp. Fault-tolerant Computing*, Santa Monica, CA, (June 1982), pp. 363–372.

[Iyer82b] Iyer, R. K., S. E. Butner, and E. J. McCluskey, "A Statistical Failure/Load Relationship: Results of a Multicomputer Study," *IEEE Trans. Computers*, vol. C-31, no. 7 (July 1982), pp. 697–705.

[Iyer85a] Iyer, R. K., and P. Velardi, "Hardware-Related Software Errors: Measurement and Analysis," *IEEE Trans. Software Engineering*, vol. SE-11, no. 2 (February 1985), pp. 223–231.

[Iyer85b] Iyer, R. K., and D. J. Rossetti, "Effect of System Workload on Operating System Reliability: A Study on IBM 3081," *IEEE Trans. Software Engineering*, vol. SE-11, no. 12 (December 1985), pp. 1438–1448.

[Iyer86] Iyer, R. K., D. J. Rossetti, and M. C. Hsueh, "Measurement and Modeling of Computer Reliability as Affected by System Activity," *ACM Trans. Computer Systems*, vol. 4, no. 3 (August 1986), pp. 214–237.

[Iyer90] Iyer, R. K., L. T. Young, and P. V. K. Iyer, "Automatic Recognition of Intermittent Failures: An Experimental Study of Field Data," *IEEE Trans. Computers*, vol. 39, no. 4 (April 1990), pp. 525–537.

[Jenn94] Jenn, E., J. Arlat, M. Rimen, J. Ohlsson, and J. Karlsson, "Fault Injection into VHDL Models: The MEFISTO Tool," *Proc. 24th Int. Symp. Fault-Tolerant Computing*, 1994.

[Jewett91] Jewett, D., "Integrity S2: A Fault-Tolerant Unix Platform," *Proc. 21st Int. Symp. Fault-Tolerant Computing*, Montreal, Canada, (June 1991), pp. 512–519.

[Kahn53] Kahn, H., and A. W. Warshall, "Methods of Reducing Sample in Monte Carlo Computations," *Journal of the Operations Research Society of America*, vol. 1, no. 5 (1953), pp. 263–278.

[Kanawati92] Kanawati, G. A., N. A. Kanawati, and J. A. Abraham, "FERRARI: A Tool for the Validation of System Dependability Properties," *Proc. 22nd Int. Symp. Fault-Tolerant Computing*, Boston, MA, (July 1992), pp. 336–344.

[Kanawati93] Kanawati, G. A., N. A. Kanawati, and J. A. Abraham, "EMAX: An Automatic Extractor of High-Level Error Models," *Proc. American Institute of Aeronautics and Astronautics*, 1993, pp. 1297–1306.

[Kao93] Kao, W., R. K. Iyer, and D. Tang, "FINE: A Fault Injection and Monitor Environment for Tracing the UNIX System Behavior under Faults," *IEEE Transactions on Software Engineering* (November 1993), vol. 19, no. 11, pp. 1105–1118.

[Kao94] Kao, W., and R. K. Iyer, "DEFINE: A Distributed Fault Injection and Monitor Environment," *The 1994 IEEE Workshop on Fault-Tolerant Parallel and Distributed Systems*, June 1994.

[Karlsson89] Karlsson, J., U. Gunneflo, and J. Torin, "The Effects of Heavy-ion Induced Single Event Upsets in the MC6809E Microprocessor," *Proc. 4th Int. Conf. Fault-Tolerant Computing Systems*, GI/ITG/GMA, Baden, Germany, 1989.

[Katzman78] Katzman, J. A., "A Fault-Tolerant Computing System," *Proc. Int. Hawaii Conference on System Science*, (1978), pp. 85–102.

[Kendall77] Kendall, M. G., *The Advanced Theory of Statistics*, Oxford University Press, 1977.

[Kim88] Kim, S., and R. K. Iyer, "Impact of Device Level Faults in a Digital Avionic Processor," *Proc. AIAA/IEEE 8th Digital Avionics Systems Conference (DASC)*, (October 1988), pp. 428–436.

[Kobayashi78] Kobayashi, H., *Modeling and Analysis: An Introduction to System Performance Evaluation Methodology*, Addison-Wesley Publishing Co., Reading, MA, 1978.

[Kronenberg86] Kronenberg, N. P., H. M. Levy, and W. D. Strecker, "VAXcluster: A Closely-Coupled Distributed System," *ACM Trans. Computer Systems*, vol. 4, no. 2 (May 1986), pp. 130–146.

[Lala83] Lala, J., "Fault Detection, Isolation, and Reconfiguration in FTMP: Methods and Experimental Results," *Proc. 5th AIAA/IEEE Digital Avionics Systems Conference (DASC)*, 1983.

[Laprie84] Laprie, J. C., "Dependable Evaluation of Software Systems in Operation," *IEEE Trans. Software Engineering*, vol. SE-10, no. 6 (November 1984), pp. 701–714.

[Laprie85] Laprie, J. C., "Dependable Computing and Fault Tolerance: Concepts and Terminology," *Proc. 15th Int. Symp. Fault-Tolerant Computing*, (June 1985), pp. 2–11.

[Law82] Law, A. M., and W. D. Kelton, *Simulation Modeling and Analysis*, McGraw-Hill, 1982.

[Lee91] Lee, I., R. K. Iyer, and D. Tang, "Error/Failure Analysis Using Event Logs from Fault Tolerant Systems," *Proc. 21st Int. Symp. Fault-Tolerant Computing*, Montreal, Canada, (June 1991), pp. 10–17.

[Lee92] Lee, I., and R. K. Iyer, "Analysis of Software Halts in Tandem System," *Proc. 3rd Int. Symp. Software Reliability Engineering*, Research Triangle Park, NC, (October 1992), pp. 227–236.

[Lee93a] Lee, I., D. Tang, R. K. Iyer, and M. C. Hsueh, "Measurement-Based Evaluation of Operating System Fault Tolerance," *IEEE Transactions on Reliability*, vol. 42, no. 2 (June 1993), pp. 238–249.

[Lee93b] Lee, I., and R. K. Iyer, "Faults, Symptoms, and Software Fault Tolerance in the Tandem GUARDIAN90 Operating System," *Proc. 23rd Int. Symp. Fault-Tolerant Computing*, Toulouse, France, (June 1993), pp. 29–29.

[Lewis84] Lewis, E. E., and F. Bohm, "Monte Carlo Simulation of Markov Unreliability Models," *Nuclear Eng. and Design*, vol. 77 (1984), pp. 49–62.

[Lin90] Lin, T. T., and D. P. Siewiorek, "Error Log Analysis: Statistical Modeling and Heuristic Trend Analysis," *IEEE Trans. Reliability*, vol. 39, no. 4 (October 1990), pp. 419–432.

[Littlewood80] Littlewood, B. "Theories of Software Reliability: How Good Are They and How Can They Be Improved?" *IEEE Trans. Software Engineering*, vol. SE-6, no. 5 (September 1980), pp. 489–500.

[Lomelino86] Lomelino, D., and R. Iyer, "Error Propagation in a Digital Avionic Processor: A Simulation-Based Study," *Proc. Real Time Systems Symposium*, (December 1986), pp. 218–225.

[Maxion90a] Maxion, R. A., "Anomaly Detection for Diagnosis," *Proc. 20th Int. Symp. Fault-Tolerant Computing*, Newcastle Upon Tyne, UK (June 1990), pp. 20–27.

[Maxion90b] Maxion, R. A., and F. E. Feather, "A Case Study of Ethernet Anomalies in a Distributed Computing Environment," *IEEE Trans. Reliability*, vol. 39, no. 4 (October 1990), pp. 433–443.

[Maxion93] Maxion, R. A., and R. T. Olszewski, "Detection and Discrimination of Injected Network Faults," *Proc. 23rd Int. Symp. Fault-Tolerant Computing*, Toulouse, France, (June 1993), pp. 198–207.

[McConnel79] McConnel, S. R., D. P. Siewiorek, and M. M. Tsao, "The Measurement and Analysis of Transient Errors in Digital Compute Systems," *Proc. 9th Int. Symp. Fault-Tolerant Computing*, Madison, Wisconsin, (June 20–22, 1979), pp. 67–70.

[McGough81] McGough, J. G. and F. L. Swern, *Measurement of Fault Latency in a Digital Avionic Mini Processor*, NASA Contract Report 3462, NASA, Washington, D.C., 1981.

[Myer88] Meyer, B. *Object-oriented Software Construction*, Prentice Hall International Series in Computer Science, 1988.

[MeyerJ80] Meyer, J. F. "On Evaluating the Performability of Degradable Computing Systems," *IEEE Trans. Computers*, vol. C-29, no. 8 (August 1980), pp. 720–731.

[MeyerJ88] Meyer, J. F., and L. Wei, "Analysis of Workload Influence on Dependability," *Proc. 18th Int. Symp. Fault-Tolerant Computing*, Tokyo, Japan, (June 1988), pp. 84–89.

[MeyerJ92] Meyer, J. F., "Performability: A Retrospective and Some Pointers to the Future," *Performance Evaluation*, vol. 14, (February 1992), pp. 139–156.

[Migneault85] Migneault, "The Diagnostic Emulation Technique in the Airlab," Internal Report, NASA-Langley Research Center, 1985.

[Mourad87] Mourad, S., and D. Andrews, "On the Reliability of the IBM MVS/XA Operating System," *IEEE Trans. Software Engineering*, vol. SE-13, no. 10 (October 1987), pp. 1135–1139.

[Musa87] Musa, J. D., A. Iannino, and K. Okumoto, *Software Reliability: Measurement, Prediction, Application*, New York, McGraw-Hill, 1987.

[Randell75] Randell, B. "System Structure for Software Fault Tolerance," *IEEE Trans. Software Engineering*, vol. SE-1, no. 2 (June 1975).

[Reibman89] Reibman, A., R. Smith, and K. Trivedi, "Markov and Markov Reward Model Transient Analysis: An Overview of Numerical Approaches," *European Journal of Operational Research*, vol. 40 (1989), pp. 257–267.

[Rogers85] Rogers, W., and J. Abraham, "CHIEFS: A Concurrent Hierarchical and Extensible Fault Simulator," *Proc. IEEE Int. Test Conference*, 1985, pp. 710–716.

[Rosenberg93] Rosenberg, H. A. and K. G. Shin, "Software Fault Injection and its Application in Distributed Systems," *Proc. 23rd Int. Symp. Fault-Tolerant Computing*, Toulouse, France, (June 1993), pp. 208–127.

[Ross85] Ross, S. M., *Introduction to Probability Models*, 3rd ed. Academic Press, San Diego, CA, 1985.

[Ruehli83] Ruehli, A. W., and G. S. Ditlow, "Circuit Analysis, Logic Simulation, and Design Verification for VLSI," *Proc. of the IEEE*, vol. 71, no. 1 (January 1983), pp. 34–48.

[Sahner87] Sahner, R. A., and K. S. Trivedi, "Reliability Modeling Using SHARPE," *IEEE Trans. Reliability*, vol. R-36, no. 2 (June 1987), pp. 186–193.

[Saleh84] Saleh, R. A., "Integrated Timing Analysis and SPLICE1," Mem. UCB/ERL M84/2, Elec. Res. Lab., University of California at Berkeley, 1984.

[Saleh90] Saleh, R. A., and A. R. Newton, *Mixed-Mode Simulation*, Kluwer Academic Publishers, 1990.

[SAS85] *SAS User's Guide: Basics*, SAS Institute, 1985.

[Segall88] Segall, Z., D. Vrsalovic, D. Siewiorek, D. Yaskin, J. Kownacki, J. Barton, R. Dancey, A. Robinson, and T. Lin, "FIAT—Fault Injection Based Automated Testing Environment," *Proc. 18th Int. Symp. Fault-Tolerant Computing*, Tokyo, Japan, (June 1988), pp. 102–107.

[Schwetman86] Schwetman, H., "CSIM: A C-Based Process-Oriented Simulation Language," *Proc. Winter Simulation Conf.*, 1986.

[Shin84] Shin, K., and Y. Lee, "Error Detection Process—Model, Design, and Its Impact on Computer Performance," *IEEE Trans. Computers*, vol. C-33, no. 6 (June 1984), pp. 529–540.

[Shin86] Shin, K. G., and Y. H. Lee, "Measurement and Application of Fault Latency," *IEEE Trans. Computers*, vol. C-35, no. 4 (April 1986), pp. 370–375.

[Siewiorek78] Siewiorek, D. P., V. Kini, H. Mashburn, S. R. McConnel, and M. Tsao, "A Case Study of C.mmp, Cm*, and C.vmp: Part I—Experience with Fault Tolerance in Multiprocessor Systems," *Proc. of the IEEE*, vol. 66, no. 10 (October 1978), pp. 1178–1199.

[Siewiorek92] Siewiorek, D. P. and R. W. Swarz, *Reliable Computer Systems: Design and Evaluation* , Digital Press, Bedford, Mass., 1992.

[Sullivan91] Sullivan, M. S., and R. Chillarege, "Software Defects and Their Impact on System Availability—A Study of Field Failures in Operating Systems," *Proc. 21st Int. Symp. Fault-Tolerant Computing*, Montreal, Canada (June 1991), pp. 2–9.

[Sullivan92] Sullivan, M. S., and R. Chillarege, "A Comparison of Software Defects in Database Management Systems and Operating Systems," *Proc. 22nd Int. Symp. Fault-Tolerant Computing*, Boston, MA (July 1992), pp. 475–484.

[Tang90] Tang, D., R. K. Iyer, and Sujatha Subramani, "Failure Analysis and Modeling of a VAXcluster System," *Proc. 20th Int. Symp. Fault-Tolerant Computing*, Newcastle Upon Tyne, UK (June 1990), pp. 244–251.

[Tang91] Tang, D., and R. K. Iyer, "Impact of Correlated Failures on Dependability in a VAXcluster System," *Proc. 2nd IFIP Working Conf. Dependable Computing for Critical Applications*, Tucson, Ariz., (February 1991), pp. 175–194.

[Tang92a] Tang, D., and R. K. Iyer, "Analysis and Modeling of Correlated Failures in Multicomputer Systems," *IEEE Trans. Computers*, vol. 41, no. 5 (May 1992), pp. 567–577.

[Tang92b] Tang, D., and R. K. Iyer, "Analysis of the VAX/VMS Error Logs in Multicomputer Environments—A Case Study of Software Dependability," *Proc. Third Int. Symp. Software Reliability Engineering*, Research Triangle Park, N.C., (October 1992), pp. 216–226.

[Tang93a] Tang, D., and R. K. Iyer, "Dependability Measurement and Modeling of a Multicomputer Systems," *IEEE Trans. Computers*, vol. 42, no. 1 (January 1993), pp. 62–75.

[Tang93b] Tang, D., and R. K. Iyer, "MEASURE+—A Measurement-Based Dependability Analysis Package," *Proc. ACM SIGMETRICS Conf. Measurement and Modeling of Computer Systems*, Santa Clara, Calif., (May 1993), pp. 110–121.

[Trivedi82] Trivedi, K. S., *Probability and Statistics with Reliability, Queuing, and Computer Science Applications*, Prentice Hall, Englewood Cliffs, N.J., 1982.

[Trivedi92] Trivedi, K. S., J. K. Muppala, S. P. Woolet, and B. R. Haverkort, "Composite Performance and Dependability Analysis," *Performance Evaluation*, vol. 14 (February 1992), pp. 197–215.

[Tsao83] Tsao, M. M., and D. P. Siewiorek, "Trend Analysis on System Error files," *Proc. 13th Int. Symp. Fault-Tolerant Computing*, Milano, Italy, (June 1983), pp. 116–119.

[Velardi84] Velardi, P., and R. K. Iyer, "A Study of Software Failures and Recovery in the MVS Operating System," *IEEE Trans. Computers*, vol. C-33, no. 6 (June 1984), pp. 564–568.

[Wein90] Wein, A. S., and A. Sathaye, "Validating Complex Computer System Availability Models," *IEEE Trans. Reliability*, vol. 39, no. 4 (October 1990), pp. 468–479.

[Yang92] Yang, F. L., "Simulation of Faults Causing Analog Behavior in Digital Circuits," Ph.D. diss., Dept. of Electrical and Computer Engineering, University of Illinois at Urbana-Champaign, May 1992.

[Young92] Young, L., R. K. Iyer, K. Goswami, and C. Alonso, "Hybrid Monitor Assisted Fault Injection Environment," *Proc. Third IFIP Working Conf. Dependable Computing for Critical Applications*, Mondello, Sicily, (September 1992), pp. 163–174.

PROBLEMS

5.1. Table 5.25 shows software time to failure (TTF) data measured on a multicomputer system. Table 5.26 shows the completion time (CT) of a benchmark running on a multiprocessor under different workload conditions. Do the following work using the data:

(a) Construct an empirical distribution for each set of data.

(b) Fit both empirical distributions to an exponential function, the TTF distribution to a two-phase hyperexponential function, and the CT distribution to a two-phase hypoexponential function, respectively.

(c) Do the chi-square and Kolmogorov-Smirnov significance tests for each fitting.

(d) Give the 95% confidence intervals for the mean and variance of each distribution.

5.2. Table 5.27 gives processor failure data collected from a distributed system consisting of five processors connected by a local network. Each record in the table has the following format:

processor ID	failure time	recovery time	error type

Table 5.25: Software TTF Data from a Multicomputer

TTF (days)	1	2	3	4	5	6	7	8	9	10	11	12	13
Frequency	29	8	6	5	3	3	1	3	1	1	1	2	1
TTF (days)	14	15	15	17	18	19	20	21	22	23	24	25	26
Frequency	0	2	0	1	0	0	0	0	0	0	0	0	1

Table 5.26: Completion Time of a Benchmark

Time* (min.)	1	3	5	7	9	11	13	15	17	19	21	23
Frequency	2	10	12	18	16	13	15	7	6	4	2	6
Time* (min.)	25	27	29	31	33	35	37	39	41	43	45	47
Frequency	4	1	0	1	4	0	0	1	1	0	0	0

*Each number represents the midpoint of a time interval of 2 minutes.

Table 5.27: Processor Failure Data from a Five-Processor Multicomputer System

Pr. ID	Start Time	End Time	Error Type
1	29604556	29605120	Software
1	29704893	29706486	I/O
1	29770774	29772334	Software
1	29779466	29779946	I/O
1	29918361	29919001	I/O
1	29938155	29938995	Unknown
1	29968514	29969314	I/O
1	30204850	30206947	I/O
1	30300136	30300482	I/O
1	30315829	30316496	I/O
1	30552159	30555408	Unknown
1	30571134	30571529	I/O
1	31762359	31762897	I/O
1	31830453	31831347	I/O
1	31837833	31838304	I/O
1	31839160	31839628	I/O
1	31951476	31952241	I/O
1	32123531	32124925	I/O
1	32126834	32127160	I/O
1	32177392	32178646	I/O
1	32963455	32964054	Software
1	33014870	33015438	I/O
1	33152933	33153737	Software
1	34616577	34617326	Software
1	34770846	34771459	I/O
1	37813703	37814561	Unknown
1	38007128	38049817	I/O
1	38955976	38956597	Unknown
1	38961843	38962658	Unknown
1	39465650	39467247	I/O
1	39809295	39810575	Unknown
1	40069978	40071607	I/O
1	41000249	41001273	Software
1	41366807	41387784	Software
1	41391480	41392113	Software
1	42272616	42273174	Software
1	42831896	42833058	Software
1	43309767	43313204	Software
1	43348292	43350322	Software
1	43952410	43953022	Software
1	44877091	44877998	Software
1	45841909	45842888	Software
1	46961851	46962724	Software
1	48878979	48880349	Unknown
1	48888392	48890586	Software
2	29570604	29570904	I/O
2	29577262	29577562	I/O
2	29767256	29767556	I/O
2	29782058	29782358	I/O
2	29788920	29789718	I/O
2	29886930	29887230	I/O

Table 5.27: Processor Failure Data from a Five-Processor Multicomputer System (cont.)

Pr. ID	Start Time	End Time	Error Type
2	29909506	29909806	I/O
2	29910884	29911926	I/O
2	29913095	29913465	I/O
2	29914121	29915273	I/O
2	29916032	29916705	I/O
2	29917194	2991784	I/O
2	29918236	29919428	I/O
2	29939825	29940125	Unknown
2	29946828	29947128	Unknown
2	29949602	29950199	I/O
2	29953804	29954104	I/O
2	29957176	29957476	I/O
2	29963079	29963379	I/O
2	29964579	29966271	I/O
2	29967435	29968115	I/O
2	30550260	30550560	Unknown
2	30550946	30553816	Software
2	30660369	30660669	Unknown
2	31774557	31774857	I/O
2	31775859	31776450	I/O
2	31781002	31781783	I/O
2	31832367	31832781	I/O
2	31839101	31841182	I/O
2	32122929	32129036	I/O
2	32176731	32177250	Software
2	32178134	32180594	I/O
2	32178134	32180594	I/O
2	32449592	32450399	Unknown
2	32962291	32962591	Unknown
2	32975370	32975670	I/O
2	32976674	32976974	I/O
2	32983427	32983727	I/O
2	33049654	33050104	I/O
2	33052795	33053095	I/O
2	33057253	33057553	I/O
2	33059795	33060095	I/O
2	33087233	33087533	I/O
2	33089396	33089696	I/O
2	33120965	33121265	Unknown
2	33148035	33148430	I/O
2	34011900	34012200	Unknown
2	34770845	34771810	I/O
2	34774453	34774753	Unknown
2	34775145	34776270	I/O
2	34777013	34777313	I/O
2	34777969	34778269	I/O
2	34780806	34781106	I/O
2	35659389	35662510	Unknown
2	35668585	35668885	I/O
2	35725413	35725713	I/O
2	35726840	35727669	I/O

Table 5.27: Processor Failure Data from a Five-Processor Multicomputer System (cont.)

Pr. ID	Start Time	End Time	Error Type
2	35730910	35731210	I/O
2	35744817	35745117	I/O
2	35753244	35753544	I/O
2	36785044	36785772	Unknown
2	36789532	36789988	Software
2	36796257	36847121	I/O
2	38249305	38249785	Software
2	38251655	38252099	Unknown
2	38744311	38744777	Software
2	38745674	38746341	CPU
2	38955454	38956597	Unknown
2	39805355	39808038	I/O
2	43064089	43065444	Unknown
2	44732995	44733453	Software
2	45221452	45221917	I/O
2	46375146	46375583	Unknown
2	49391794	49392273	Software
2	50068269	50069049	I/O
3	30550976	30554633	Software
3	31760114	31760624	Software
3	32806356	32806844	Software
3	33152933	33153558	Software
3	34370843	34385770	I/O
3	34779280	34779754	Unknown
3	36783938	36786522	I/O
3	36787771	36788262	Software
3	37800626	37811789	I/O
3	37812929	37813548	Software
3	43175442	43175990	Software
3	43326842	43327797	Unknown
3	43330318	4330785	CPU
3	43331708	43332312	CPU
3	43334898	43338477	CPU
3	43338720	43340663	I/O
3	43342983	43345110	CPU
3	43691509	43692018	Software
3	43693033	43693689	Unknown
3	43693580	43694622	I/O
3	43695584	43696455	Unknown
3	43697283	43698493	I/O
3	47651456	47651969	Software
3	49057997	49058626	Software
3	49568366	49568810	Unknown
3	50043031	50043500	Software
3	50697666	50698119	Unknown
3	50930312	50930764	Unknown
3	29939050	29940425	I/O
3	29943202	29948396	I/O
3	30550948	30554287	I/O
3	30762674	30762976	I/O
3	34777878	34778529	I/O

Table 5.27: Processor Failure Data from a Five-Processor
Multicomputer System (cont.)

Pr. ID	Start Time	End Time	Error Type
4	37563700	37567137	I/O
4	37811277	37811786	I/O
4	38956002	38963057	I/O
4	39204773	39205074	I/O
4	43175015	43175315	Unknown
4	47239532	47243366	I/O
4	47641698	47642345	I/O
4	48939418	48940072	Unknown
4	49144906	49145430	I/O
4	50662627	50663276	Unknown
4	50668168	50672456	I/O
4	50758111	50758751	I/O
4	50941271	50943381	I/O
5	30545108	30545606	Software
5	30551262	30553813	Unknown
5	31769662	31770215	Software
5	31953896	3194395	Unknown
5	33152335`	33153779	Unknown
5	33153616	33156417	Software
5	34774852	34780711	I/O
5	37813181	37813664	Unknown
5	38955806	38962854	Unknown
5	40928410	40934268	Software
5	40936013	40936767	Unknown
5	43189066	43193507	Software
5	43252583	43254201	Unknown
5	43256847	43257890	Unknown
5	43328379	43333113	Software
5	44903066	44903945	Unknown
5	47064423	47069097	I/O
5	49125607	49126676	Software
5	49478273	49478888	Unknown
5	50618397	50623146	Software

The time unit is second and time 0 is 12am, 10/1/1987. The measurement started
from 12am, 12/9/1987 (29,548,800) and ended at 12am, 8/15/1988 (51,148,800), covering 250 days. The error type means the type of error that causes a processor failure.
Possible error types are CPU, I/O (network or disk problems), software, and unknown. Do the following work using the data:

(a) Obtain failure rate and recovery rate for each processor.

(b) Assuming failures on different processors are independent, build a Markov
model, where S_i represents there are i failed processors, based on the failure and
recovery rates obtained in step (a).

(c) Assuming the modeled system is a 3-out-of-5 system, solve the model (using
SHARPE or similar tools) to obtain the reliability of the system.

(d) Build a measurement-based Markov model using the data.

(e) Solve the measurement-based model (using SHARPE or similar tools) to obtain the reliability of the (3-out-of-5) system, and compare the result with that obtained in step (c).

(f) Construct a data matrix and then use the matrix to calculate correlation coefficient for each pair.

5.3. Build a simulation model for the system described in the above question. Assume that (1) the modeled system is a 3-out-of-5 system and (2) the TBF (time between failures) and TTR (time to recovery) for each processor are exponentially distributed. Investigate the following dependability issues through simulation.

(a) Assume that failures on different processors are independent and that all processors have the same failure (recovery) rate which is the average of the five-processor failure (recovery) rates obtained in Problem 5.2. Construct the system TBF and TTR distributions and evaluate MTBF and unavailability.

(b) Assume that failures on different processors are related by shared resources and coordinated software. Specifically, the joint failure probability is 0.1 for any two processors, 0.03 for any three processors, 0.01 for any four processors, and 0.005 for all five processors (these numbers are close to the measured correlation parameters from the data in Problem 5.2). Evaluate MTBF and unavailability and compare them with those obtained in step (a).

(c) Assume that each processor failure is caused by an error and there is a latency between the error arrival and the failure occurrence. The latency follows an exponential distribution with a mean equaling the average processor recovery time. The error arrival rate and failure recovery rate for each processor are the same as the failure and recovery rates in step (a), respectively. Assume that each error causes a failure. Further, errors on different processors are related with the correlation parameters used in step (b). Evaluate MTBF and unavailability and compare them with the results from step (b).

6

Reliability Estimation

J. J. Stiffler

6.1 INTRODUCTION

As discussed earlier since the reliability of fault-tolerant systems frequently cannot be determined adequately by conventional testing and simulation methods, various reliability modeling techniques have been developed to help assess the reliability levels actually achieved. Several of these techniques are discussed in the literature [Conn, Merryman and Whilelaw (1977); Landrault and Laprie (1978); Ng and Avizienis (1977); Bjurman, Jenkins, Masreliez, McClellan, and Templeman (1976); Mathur (1972); Stiffler (1975); Butler (1985); Sahner and Trivedi (1987); Geist and Trivedi (1990)]. This chapter describes a class of reliability models based on a technique called *behavioral decomposition*.

Since, by definition, a fault-tolerant system must function correctly even after some of its elements have failed, it necessarily contains redundant elements.[1] Redundancy is therefore a necessary aspect of fault-tolerant systems. It is, however, far from sufficient. It is usually relatively easy to design enough redundancy into a

[1]This does not mean that the redundant elements are not able to contribute to the overall performance of the system; it does mean that the system can achieve an acceptable level of performance without them.

system to reduce to acceptably small levels the probability that it fails due to inadequate element resources. The dominant cause of failure in highly reliable systems thus tends to be due not to the exhaustion of resources but rather to the failure to detect and isolate a malfunctioning element before it has caused the system to malfunction. Such failures are called *coverage* failures [Bouricious, Carter, and Schneider, (1969)]. The reliability models to be discussed here differ from their predecessors in, among other things, the attention given to coverage failure mechanisms.

6.2 BACKGROUND

6.2.1 Element Reliability

All reliability models begin with certain assumptions about the rate at which the various elements that make up the system being modeled fail. If $P(t)$ is the probability that an element is still functioning properly at time t (i.e., the element's reliability), then the failure rate $\lambda(t)$ is defined by the equation

$$\lambda(t) = \lim_{\Delta t \to 0} \frac{P(t) - P(t + \Delta t)}{P(t)\Delta t} = -\frac{P'(t)}{P(t)} \tag{6.1}$$

It then follows that

$$P(t) = e^{-\int_0^t \lambda(\tau)d\tau} \tag{6.2}$$

For a large class of elements, $\lambda(t)$ is often characterized as a "bathtub function" of t; that is, it looks like a cross section of a bathtub, decreasing rapidly with t for small t until it reaches some level λ_0, staying at that value for an extended period and then gradually increasing again. The decreasing part is called the "infant mortality phase" during which inherent element defects and manufacturing flaws are exposed; the increasing portion is often called the "wear-out phase" and is typically due to the wearing down of the mechanical parts (e.g., bearings) of the element. For electronic elements that are well screened during the manufacturing process (during which those elements that would fail in infancy are identified and replaced) and which have few wear-out mechanisms, the constant value $\lambda(t) = \lambda$ seems to be an accurate model for a very large range of t. In this case,

$$P(t) = e^{-\lambda t} \tag{6.3}$$

and the reliability of the element in question is defined by an exponential distribution.

Some reliability models allow failure rates of somewhat greater generality by defining $\lambda(t) = \omega \lambda t^{\omega - 1}$. Then

$$P(t) = e^{-\lambda t^{\omega}} \tag{6.4}$$

and the reliability is defined by a Weibull distribution. If $\omega = 1$, the Weibull distribution degenerates to the exponential distribution. If $\omega < 1$, the failure rate is initially a rapidly, and subsequently a slowly, decreasing function of t, thereby approximating the infant mortality phenomenon. Similarly, if $\omega > 1$, the failure rate increases with time, a more appropriate model when wear-out mechanisms are significant.

The mean time between failures (MTBF) of an element is often used as a measure of its reliability. It is defined as the expected time before the element fails.[2] The MTBF of an element is easily derived from its reliability function:

$$MTBF = \int_0^{\infty} tP'(t)dt = \int_0^{\infty} P(t)dt \tag{6.5}$$

this last expression valid under the assumption that $\lim_{t \to \infty} tP(t) = 0$ and hence that the MTBF is finite. When $P(t)$ is defined by the Weibull distribution,

$$MTBF = \frac{\Gamma(\frac{1}{\omega})}{\omega \lambda^{\frac{1}{\omega}}} \tag{6.6}$$

where $\Gamma(x)$ is the gamma function

$$\Gamma(x + 1) = x\Gamma(x)$$

and

$$\Gamma(n) = (n - 1)!$$

when n is an integer. If $\omega = 1$, then the MTBF of an element is simply the reciprocal of its failure rate

$$MTBF = \frac{1}{\lambda} \tag{6.7}$$

[2]The literal definition of the term, mean time *between* failures, is appropriate when the element is replaced with a new, identical element following each failure. It should be noted, however, that unless the element failure rates are independent of time, the expected time for a *system*, composed of several elements, to fail is equal to its mean time between failures only if failed elements are replaced with elements of the same effective age whenever any one of them fails. In this chapter, the term MTBF is used to denote the expected time to failure starting at time $t = 0$. The term MTBF is sometimes defined as mean time *before* failure when used in this sense.

It is sometimes important to recognize in modeling the reliability of an element that its failure rate may be different depending upon whether or not it is being actively used. In the case of an electronic element, this tends to translate into whether or not it is under power. This distinction is often accommodated by defining a *dormancy factor* f_d which equals the (usually assumed constant) ratio of the failure rate of an active element to that of an inactive or dormant one. If the failure rate of the (active) element is a constant λ, the reliability of an element at time $t = t_a + t_d$, with t_a denoting the time the element has been in the active state and t_d the time it has been in the dormant state, is

$$P(t) = e^{-\lambda(t_a + t_d / f_d)} \tag{6.8}$$

The effect of dormancy can therefore be accounted for by replacing the time t with $t_{eff} = t_a + t_d/f_d$. This same time substitution can be used to account for dormancy in elements that do not have constant failure rates, but the justification for doing so is less apparent in this more general situation.

6.2.2 System Reliability

The reliability $R(t)$ of a system consisting of several elements is readily determined from the reliabilities of the individual elements if all elements must function properly for the system as a whole to function properly and if the reliabilities of the individual elements are statistically independent. In this case,

$$R(t) = \prod_i P_i(t) \tag{6.9}$$

where $P_i(t)$ is the reliability of the ith element and the index i ranges over all elements in the system. If the failure rate of the ith element is a constant λ_i for all i, then

$$R(t) = e^{-\lambda t} \tag{6.10}$$

where

$$\lambda = \sum_i \lambda_i$$

and the system MTBF is simply equal to the reciprocal of the sum of the reciprocals of the MTBFs of the individual elements:

$$MTBF = \frac{1}{\sum_i \lambda_i} \tag{6.11}$$

If the system is fault-tolerant, however, the above equations no longer apply and more complex reliability models are needed to predict overall system reliability. These models tend to fall into one of two classes: combinatorial or Markov. *Combinatorial models* attempt to categorize the set of operational states (or, conversely, the number of nonoperational states) of a system in terms of the functional states of its components in such a way that the probabilities of each of these states can be determined by combinatorial means. *Markov models* concentrate on the rate at which transitions take place between different system states and then use this information to determine the probabilities that the system is in each of these states at any given time. These two approaches are best illustrated by an example.

Consider a simple, redundant structure consisting of four identical elements, the (binary) outputs of which are passed through a majority voter. If the outputs of at least three of these units are correct, the voter output is likewise correct. Further, if any one unit is determined to be faulty, its outputs are subsequently ignored by the voter, so that a second failure can also be tolerated without producing an incorrect output. First, assume that the voter is perfect both in its ability to produce an output determined by the majority of its inputs and in its ability to identify and to ignore without further delay the outputs of the first faulty element.

The combinatorial method for assessing the reliability of such a structure is entirely straightforward: The probability that the output is correct is simply the probability that at most two of the four elements have failed. If any single element has a probability $P(t)$ of surviving until time t, the probability $R(t)$ that the voter outputs are still correct at time t is therefore

$$R(t) = \sum_{i=0}^{2} \binom{4}{i} [P(t)]^{4-i} [1 - P(t)]^i$$

(6.12)

$$= 6P^2(t) - 8P^3(t) + 3P^4(t)$$

The Markov model of the structure in question is equally straightforward. In general, a structure can be represented by a Markov model if it is possible to characterize it in terms of states (the various states defined, for example, by the number of component failures and other relevant parameters) and transition rates between states, with the proviso that the transition rate $r_{ij}(t)$ between state S_i and state S_j is, for all i and j, a function only of i and j and, possibly, the time t measured from the entry into some known initial state (see Figure 6.1). Thus, if the system is known to be in state S_i at time τ, the probability $S_i(t)$ that it has not left that state by time $t \geq \tau$ is given by the solution to the differential equation

$$-S_i'(t) = \sum_j r_{ij}(t) S_i(t) \qquad t > \tau$$

with the initial condition $S_i(\tau) = 1$.

If the transition rates $r_{ij}(t)$ are all independent of t, the Markov model is said to be (time) homogeneous. In this case, the differential equation is readily solved, yielding

From other states

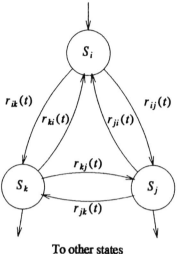

To other states

Figure 6.1: Segment of a Markov model.

$$S_i(t) = e^{-\lambda(t-\tau)} \qquad t \geq \tau$$

with $\lambda = \Sigma_j r_{ij}$. The *holding time* in each state, in this case, is exponentially distributed.

Consequently, if in the structure of concern here the probability $P(t)$ that any single element survives until time t is exponentially distributed [$P(t) = e^{-\lambda t}$], and if state S_i refers to the state of the system characterized by i component failures, then the distribution of the holding time in state i is just $e^{-(4-i)\lambda t}$, with 4 the number of initially operational elements and λ the hazard rate of each element. The transition rate $r_{ij}(t)$ is then simply

$$r_{ij} = -\frac{P_i'(t)}{P_i(t)} = \begin{cases}(4-i)\lambda & j = i+1 \\ 0 & j \neq i+1\end{cases}$$

and the Markov model is as shown as Figure 6.2. The three states, labeled 0, 1, and 2, correspond to the number of failed elements; the state labeled F denotes the failed state (more than two failed elements).

The reliability of the structure is also easy to determine from its Markov model: Let $P_i(t)$ be the probability that the system is in state i at time t. Then

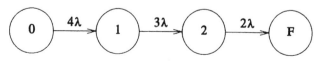

Figure 6.2: Markov model of a two-out-of-four structure.

$$P_0'(t) = -4\lambda P_0(t)$$

$$P_1'(t) = 4\lambda P_0(t) - 3\lambda P_1(t)$$

$$P_2'(t) = 3\lambda P_1(t) - 2\lambda P_2(t)$$ (6.13)

$$P_F'(t) = 2\lambda P_2(t)$$

This set of linear, first-order differential equations can be solved by conventional methods to yield

$$P_0(t) = e^{-4\lambda t}$$

$$P_1(t) = 4e^{-3\lambda t}(1 - e^{-\lambda t})$$

$$P_2(t) = 6e^{-2\lambda t}(1 - e^{-\lambda t})^2$$ (6.14)

$$P_F(t) = 1 - P_0(t) - P_1(t) - P_2(t)$$

so that

$$R(t) = 1 - P_F(t) = 6e^{-2\lambda t} - 8e^{-3\lambda t} + 3e^{-4\lambda t}$$ (6.15)

as before.

The analysis so far has assumed perfect coverage. In particular, it has been assumed that the first faulty element is correctly identified with probability 1. Suppose instead, that it is correctly identified with probability C; that is, with probability $1 - C$ the outputs of the first failed element are not ignored by the voter. Then with probability $1 - C$, a second failure will cause the voter to accept two erroneous inputs and hence to produce an unreliable output. The system reliability can be determined combinatorially by observing that the system will function properly if at time t it has sustained no more than one element failure or, with probability C, if it has sustained exactly two element failures. Thus

$$R(t) = \sum_{i=0}^{1} \binom{4}{i}[P(t)]^{(4-i)}[1-P(t)]^i + \binom{4}{2}C[P(t)]^2[1-P(t)]^2$$ (6.16)

$$= R^*(t) - 6(1-C)[P(t)]^2[1-P(t)]^2$$

with $R^*(t)$ the perfect-coverage reliability as given in Eq. (6.12).

The Markov model of Figure 6.2 needs only to be modified as shown in Figure 6.3 to account for this imperfect coverage effect. An analysis virtually identical to that of the previous Markov model establishes that

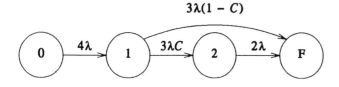

Figure 6.3: Markov model of a two-out-of-four structure with imperfect coverage.

$$P_0(t) = e^{-4\lambda t}$$

$$P_1(t) = 4e^{-3\lambda t}(1 - e^{-\lambda t})$$

$$P_2(t) = 6Ce^{-2\lambda t}(1 - e^{-\lambda t})^2 \qquad (6.17)$$

$$P_F(t) = 1 - P_0(t) - P_1(t) - P_2(t)$$

so that, again, the combinatorial model and the Markov model yield identical results.

The procedures for extending both the combinatorial and the Markov methodologies to more complex structures are generally straightforward. One of the major limitations to both approaches, however, is already evident in the simple example just considered. This limitation stems from the fact that it is rarely satisfactory to treat the coverage probability as a constant parameter. And since, as already observed, coverage failures are typically the dominant source of system failure in highly reliable systems, it is particularly important that coverage be accurately modeled.

Suppose, for example, that in the structure just considered, the reason coverage failures can occur is that a certain amount of time, say τ seconds, is needed to detect that an element has failed and to take the appropriate action to eliminate its output from subsequent voter inputs. Should a second failure occur during that interval, the voter is again presented with two potentially erroneous inputs and its output is consequently unreliable. The probability of a coverage failure, then, is the probability that two element failures occur within a τ-second interval. Unfortunately, this is not a constant probability.

To handle this case combinatorially, observe that the probability that the system has failed by time t is equal to the probability that it has sustained either more than two failures, or exactly two failures within τ seconds of each other. Thus

$$1 - R(t) = \sum_{i=3}^{4} \binom{4}{i} [P(t)]^{4-i}[1 - P(t)]^i$$

$$+ 12P^2(t) \int_0^t \int_{\eta_1}^{\min(\eta_1 + \tau, t)} P'(\eta_1)P'(\eta_2)d\eta_2 d\eta_1 \qquad (6.18)$$

If, as assumed earlier, $P(t) = e^{-\lambda t}$, this expression is easily evaluated, yielding

$$R(t) = \begin{cases} 4P^3(t) - 3P^4(t) & t < \tau \\ R^*(t) - 6P^2(t)[(1 - e^{-\lambda \tau}) - P^2(t)(e^{\lambda \tau} - 1)] & t \geq \tau \end{cases} \qquad (6.19)$$

with $R^*(t)$ as defined previously. The actual coverage probability [see Eqs. (6.5) and (6.8)] in this case is

$$C = C(t) = \begin{cases} 0 & t < \tau \\ 1 - \dfrac{(1 - e^{-\lambda \tau}) - P^2(t)(e^{\lambda \tau} - 1)}{[1 - P(t)]^2} & t \geq \tau \end{cases} \qquad (6.20)$$

and is indeed a function of time.

The Markov method of modeling redundant structures can also be extended to include more complex coverage situations by using the *method of stages* [cf. Cox and Miller (1968)]. The state diagram shown in Figure 6.4a illustrates the principle. This diagram is characterized by the differential equation.

$$P'_{A_1}(t) = -(\eta / \tau) P_{A_1}(t)$$

$$P'_{A_i}(t) = (\eta / \tau)(P_{A_{i-1}}(t) - P_{A_i}(t)) \qquad 1 < i \leq n$$

These are easily solved to yield, when $P_{A_1}(0) = 1$,

$$P_{A_1}(t) = \frac{(nt / \tau)^{i-1}}{(i-1)!} e^{-nt/\tau} \qquad 1 \leq i \leq n$$

Thus the expected delay $E(t)$ from entry into state A_1 to exit from state A_n is

$$E(t) = \int_0^\infty \sum_{i=1}^n P_{A_1}(t) dt = \tau$$

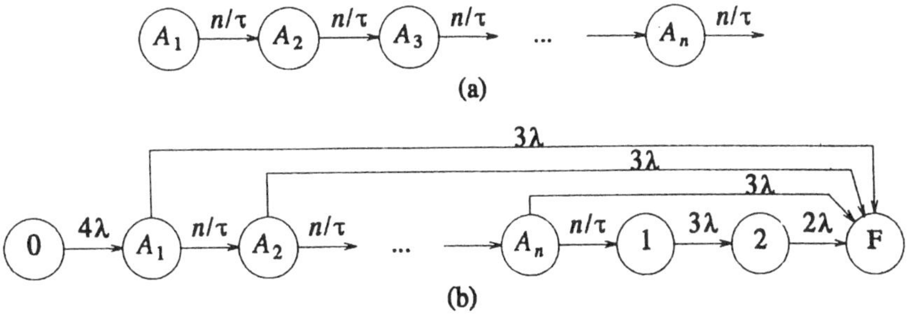

(a)

(b)

Figure 6.4: (a) Constant-delay model; (b) Incorporated into a 2-out-of-4 structure.

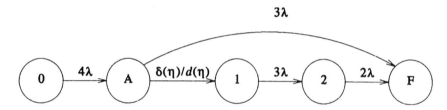

Figure 6.5: Semi-Markov model with imperfect coverage.

and the variance of that delay is

$$\mathrm{Var}(t) = 2 \int_0^\infty \sum_{i=1}^n t P_{A_i}(t) dt - E^2(t) = \tau^2 / n$$

For large n, then, the series of states shown in Figure 6.4a provides a good approximation to a constant τ-second delay. The same series of states embedded in the Markov model of a two-out-of-four structure (Figure 6.4b) represents, approximately, the constant-coverage-delay model under consideration here.

This method of stages can be generalized by introducing other combinations of pseudostates and selecting appropriate interstage transition rates. The advantage of this technique is that it provides an approximate method for handling nonexponentially distributed holding times without abandoning homogeneous Markov models. The disadvantage is that good approximations often entail a substantial increase in the number of required states, a number that can be enormous for the reliability models of interest here even without the addition of pseudostates.

It is possible to avoid adding pseudostates and still retain some advantages of the Markov method by generalizing the notion of a Markov process. Consider the state diagram shown in Figure 6.5. This diagram is similar to that of Figure 6.4b except that the n pseudostates in the latter diagram have been collapsed into a single state here. The cost of doing this is to introduce a transition rate $\delta(\eta)/d(\eta)$ which is now a function of the time η from the entry into state A. If η were a measure of the time from entry into the initial state of the model, the model would describe an inhomogeneous Markov process. As it is, however, the process is not even Markov; the probability of a transition from state A to state 1 is a function not only of the two states but of the time spent in state A as well. Such processes are called *semi-Markov* [Feller (1964)].[3]

Semi-Markov processes, although less analytically tractable than Markov

---

[3]The function $\delta(\eta)$ here represents the probability density of a transition from state A to state 1 exactly η time units after a transition into state A, under the condition that no other transitions were possible, and $d(\eta)$ is the probability that no such transition has yet taken place by time η. Thus the rate of such transitions, under the condition just described, is given by the ratio $\delta(\eta)/d(\eta)$.

processes, can nevertheless be represented in terms of linear integral equations and the state-occupation probabilities can often be obtained without undue difficulty. The state-occupation probabilities $P_i(t)$ of the process of Figure 6.5, in particular, satisfy the following set of equations:

$$P_0(t) = e^{-4\lambda t}$$

$$P_A(t) = 4\lambda \int_0^t e^{-\lambda(t-\eta)} d(\eta) d\eta \, e^{-3\lambda t}$$

$$P_1(t) = 4 \int_0^t (1 - e^{-\lambda(t-\eta)}) \delta(\eta) d\eta \, e^{-3\lambda t} \tag{6.21}$$

$$P_2(t) = 3\lambda \int_0^t P_1(\eta) e^{-2\lambda(t-\eta)} d\eta$$

[The probability $P_A(t)$, for example is just the product of the probability density of a failure at time $t - \eta$, the probability $d(\eta)$ that a transition from state A to state 1 has not taken place in the intervening time η, and the probability $e^{-3\lambda t}$ that no other failure has occurred by time t. Entirely similar arguments can be used to establish the other equations.] In the present example, $\delta(\eta) = \delta_d(\eta - \tau)$ with $\delta_d(t)$ the Dirac delta function and τ the (fixed) coverage delay. Consequently,

$$d(\eta) = 1 - \int_0^\eta \delta(\eta') d\eta' = \begin{cases} 1 & \eta < \tau \\ 0 & \eta \geq \tau \end{cases}$$

and

$$P_A(t) = \begin{cases} 4e^{-3\lambda t}(1 - e^{-\lambda t}) & t < \tau \\ 4e^{-3\lambda t}(e^{-\lambda(t-\tau)} - e^{-\lambda t}) & t \geq \tau \end{cases}$$

$$P_1(t) = \begin{cases} 0 & t < \tau \\ 4e^{-3\lambda t}(1 - e^{-\lambda(t-\tau)}) & t \geq \tau \end{cases} \tag{6.22}$$

$$P_2(t) = \begin{cases} 0 & t < \tau \\ 6e^{-\lambda(2t+\tau)}(1 - e^{-\lambda(t-\tau)})^2 & t \geq \tau \end{cases}$$

Since

$$R(t) = P_0(t) + P_A(t) + P_1(t) + P_2(t)$$

this analysis yields results identical to the previous combinatorial analysis of the same example [see Eqs. (6.19) and (6.22)].

6.2.3 System Availability

The discussion up to now has assumed that the system under investigation is allowed to run until it fails and that the measure of interest is its reliability, that is, the probability that it is still running at time t. If the system can be repaired, another useful measure is its *availability*, the probability that it is operational at any specified time t. Consider the non-redundant system represented by the Markov model shown in Figure 6.6.

The system consists of a single element and exists in one of two states, operational (state O) and failed (state F). If the failure rate is $\lambda(t)$ and the repair rate is $\mu(t)$, and if the probability that the system is in state i at time t is $P_i(t)$, then the system is described by the equations

$$P_O'(t) = -\lambda(t)P_O(t) + \mu(t)P_F(t)$$
$$P_F'(t) = \lambda(t)P_O(t) - \mu(t)P_F(t)$$

(6.23)

subject to the condition that $P_O(t) + P_F(t) = 1$ and that $P_O(0) = 1$.

These equations are easily solved for $P_O(t)$ and $P_F(t)$. When $\lambda(t)$ and $\mu(t)$ are both independent of t the solutions are simply

$$P_O(t) = \frac{\mu}{\mu + \lambda} + \frac{\lambda}{\mu + \lambda} e^{-(\mu + \lambda)t}$$

(6.24a)

and

$$P_F(t) = \frac{\lambda}{\mu + \lambda}(1 - e^{-(\mu + \lambda)t})$$

(6.24b)

The system availability is just $P_O(t)$.

Often the measure of interest is the steady-state availability, that is, the availability as $t \to \infty$, which in this case is $\mu/(\mu + \lambda)$. This can also be written

$$\text{Availability} = \frac{MTBF}{MTBF + MTTR}$$

where $MTBF$ is as previously defined and $MTTR$ is the mean time to repair a failed element, in this case $1/\mu$ time units. This expression is generally used as the

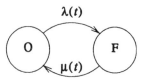

Figure 6.6: Nonredundant system with repair.

definition of availability for arbitrary systems, even when the element failure and repair rates are not constant.

If the system represented by the Markov model in Figure 6.3 is modified by allowing elements to be repaired, and if it is assumed that failed elements are repaired at the constant rate μ, then the model takes the form shown in Figure 6.7.

The relevant equations for this model are

$$P_0'(t) = -4\lambda P_0(t) + \mu P_1(t)$$

$$P_1'(t) = 4\lambda P_0(t) - (3\lambda + \mu)P_1(t) + \mu P_2(t)$$

$$P_2'(t) = 3\lambda C P_1(t) - (2\lambda + \mu)P_2(t) + \mu P_F(t)$$ (6.25)

$$P_F'(t) = 3\lambda(1 - C)P_1(t) + 2\lambda P_2(t) - \mu P_F(t)$$

(This model assumes, incidentally, that elements do not fail when the system is in state F and is hence not operational; that is, it assumes an infinite dormancy factor.)

While the solution to this system of linear differential equations can be obtained by conventional means, it involves the roots of a cubic equation and in any event is not particularly informative. The steady-state solution is easily obtained, however, since in the steady state, all of the derivatives $P_i'(t)$ vanish, yielding

$$P_0 = \frac{1}{1 + 4\rho + 12(2 - C)\rho^2 + 24\rho^3}$$

$$P_1 = 4\rho P_0$$ (6.26)

$$P_2 = 12\rho^2 P_0$$

$$P_F = [12(1 - C)\rho^2 + 24\rho^3]P_0$$

where $\rho = \lambda/\mu$. The system steady-state availability is $P_0 + P_1 + P_2 = 1 - P_F$.

A more realistic model would allow the repair rate to be a function both of the system state and of the time the system has been in that state. This latter capability implies a semi-Markov model, but, as previously discussed, adequate representation of coverage may require semi-Markov models to be used in any case.

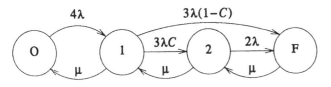

Figure 6.7: Markov model of a two-out-of-four structure with repair.

6.3 BEHAVIORAL DECOMPOSITION

As noted earlier, an overwhelming disadvantage of the Markov method of modeling and analyzing the reliability of redundant structures under the conditions of interest here (with the consequent heavy emphasis on coverage) is the extremely large number of states needed to describe the system. This, of course, is exacerbated if the method of stages is used to approximate nonexponential holding-time distributions, but it remains a decisive limitation even if semi-Markov modeling techniques are used.

To gauge the magnitude of the problem, consider a system consisting of n stages.[4] If the ith of these stages can sustain as many as m_i, faults and still be operational, and if the number of distinguishable states (e.g., active, benign, detected, repaired, etc.)[5] that can be occupied by a stage i fault is l_i, the number of possible operational system states is

$$N = \prod_{i=1}^{n} \sum_{j=0}^{m_i} \binom{l_i + j - 1}{j} \tag{6.27}$$

This number can be large even for relatively small parameters l_i, m_i, and n. When $n = 4$ and $l_i = 6$, $m_i = 2$ for all i, for example, $N = 614,656$. Since these parameters may actually have to be much larger than those used in this example to allow real systems to be modeled, it is clear that conventional Markov-like techniques are not appropriate to the problem at hand.

Unfortunately, the combinatorial approach to reliability analysis suffers from a similar computational explosion. A combinatorial analysis, in effect, entails an itemization of the (mutually exclusive) sequences of events that can lead to a failure and then a determination of the probability of each of these event sequences. Thus the emphasis is on the paths connecting the various possible system states rather than on the states themselves. Obviously, however, the number of such paths increases at least as rapidly as the number of states they interconnect, so a purely combinatorial approach to problems of the complexity of those of concern here does not appear to be very attractive either.

The motivation for the use of *behavioral decomposition* [Geist and Trivedi (1983)] in reliability and availability analyses is evident from an examination of Eq. (6.12). It will be noted, in particular, that the magnitude of N in Eq. (6.12) is a very rapidly increasing function of the parameter l_i. (If all l_i were equal to 1 rather than the 6 selected in the earlier example, N would be reduced from 614,656

---

[4]The term "stage" here refers to an ensemble of identical, interchangeable units [i.e., to any of the (presumably, but not necessarily) redundant entities which, in combination, comprise a fault-tolerant system]. This term should not be confused with the "method of stages" described earlier.

[5]The probability of recovering from a fault is in general a function of the amount of time it spends in each of several possible states; see Section 6.3.

to 81.) The reason these parameters l_i must, in general, be greater than unity is that the coverage associated with a fault depends on the states of other faulty elements in the system. That is, the probability that the system recovers from a fault in element A may well depend on whether or not element B has previously experienced a fault, whether its fault has been detected, whether an erroneous output has been produced as a result of that fault, and whether element B is in a failed-active state (capable of producing erroneous outputs) or in a failed-benign state (incapable, at least temporarily, of producing further errors).

The key to reducing l_i without decreasing the ability to include all relevant coverage factors in the reliability model is suggested by the previous analysis of the two-out-of-four structure. Figure 6.3 shows a Markov model of that structure with the entire effect of coverage reflected in the state-transition rates. While the coverage probability is shown as a constant in Figure 6.3, it was demonstrated that the effect of more complex coverage situations could be handled by allowing this probability to be a suitable defined function of time [see Eq. (6.20)].

The behavioral decomposition method, then, is to represent the system of interest by a state diagram, with different states distinguished only by the number of faulty elements in each of the system's various stages. The state transitions rates are separately determined using a coverage model to account for fault state effects.

The coverage model itself can assume several forms. Combinatorial techniques could be used [as they were, for example, to derive the results of Eq. (6.20)], but the analytical model found to be generally most appropriate is one based on semi-Markov techniques similar to those used in analyzing the model of Figure 6.5. An interesting alternative to analytical models is to use simulation to determine the coverage parameters [see section 6.3.2.2].

The potential advantage of this approach is apparent. The number of states that have to be accounted for in the reliability model is reduced from that given in Eq. (6.27) to a number more manageable:

$$N' = \prod_{i=1}^{n}(m_i + 1)$$

The cost of doing this, of course, is (1) to force the reliability model to be inhomogeneous,[6] and (2) to necessitate a separate analysis to determine the needed coverage parameters. For reliability assessment problems of the complexity of concern here, however, the advantages of this approach, in terms of computational effort, far outweigh its disadvantages. In effect, the model has been reduced from one having $N = n_1 \times n_2 \times \cdots \times n_l$ states to one having $n_1 + n_2 + \cdots + n_l$ states, with

---

[6]This increased flexibility does have ancillary advantages, however; the hazard rates associated with the various system elements are no longer restricted to be time independent. There are situations in which this added degree of freedom is needed to reflect accurately the physical events actually being modeled.

n_i denoting the number of relevant states given that i faults have already taken place. (The reduction is in fact more dramatic than this since much of the computational effort needed to determine the transition functions given i faults can also be used to determine these functions given $j \neq i$ faults.)

Behavioral decomposition offers another major advantage over alternative reliability and availability estimation procedures. This is a consequence of the fact that the fault and coverage parameters normally encountered in such analyses have vastly different time scales. Element failure rates are usually measured in hours and are typically on the order of thousands or even millions of hours. Coverage parameters, in contrast, are generally measured in seconds or milliseconds. The set of differential equations resulting from an analysis of a unified model that includes time parameters of such diversity in scale is called *numerically stiff* [Gear (1969)] and solving it numerically is subject to serious roundoff errors. Behavioral decomposition eliminates this problem by segregating the model into different submodels, with all of the parameters associated with any one submodel having similar time dependencies.

6.3.1 The Reliability Model

The resulting reliability model is a generalization of the model shown in Figure 6.3. The system, as represented by the model, passes through a sequence of states defined by the sequence of faults it sustains and by its success in recovering from them. Such a model is not of much value unless it is possible to determine, as a function of time, the probability that the system is in any particular state, given the transition rates between states. The following paragraphs describe how this can be accomplished.

Let $P_{j|i}(t|\tau)$ denote the conditional probability that a system is in state j at time t given that it was in state i at time τ. Similarly, let $P_{l|j,i}(t|\eta,\tau)$ denote the conditional probability that a system is in state l at time t given that it was in state j at time η and in state i at time τ. Then, clearly, for any $\tau < \eta < t$,

$$P_{l|i}(t|\tau) = \sum_j P_{j|i}(\eta|\tau) P_{l|j,i}(t|\eta,\tau) \tag{6.28}$$

with the sum taken over all the (assumed finite number of) possible intermediate states j. (If, for all $\tau < \eta < t$, $P_{l|j,i}(t|\eta,\tau) = P_{l|j}(t|\eta)$, then Eq. (6.28) reduces to the Chapman-Kolmogorov equation for continuous-time, discrete-state systems.)

It follows from Eq. (6.28) that

$$P_{l|i}(t + \Delta t|\tau) = P_{l|i}(t|\tau) P_{l|l,i}(t + \Delta t|t,\tau)$$

$$+ \sum_{j \neq l} P_{j|i}(t|\tau) P_{l|j,i}(t + \Delta t|t,\tau) \tag{6.29}$$

Let

$$\lambda_{\bar{l}|i}(t|\tau) = \lim_{\Delta \to 0} \frac{1 - P_{\bar{l}|l,i}(t + \Delta t|t, \tau)}{\Delta t}$$

and

$$\lambda_{ji|i}(t|\tau) = \lim_{\Delta \to 0} \frac{1 - P_{\bar{l}|j,i}(t + \Delta t|t, \tau)}{\Delta t}$$

Then, rearranging terms in Eq. (6.28), dividing by Δt, and taking the limit as $\Delta t \to 0$ yields

$$\frac{\partial P_{l|i}(t|\tau)}{\partial t} = -P_{l|i}(t|\tau)\lambda_{l|i}(t|\tau) + \sum_{j \neq l} P_{j|i}(t|\tau)\lambda_{jl|i}(t|\tau) \tag{6.30}$$

This set of equations is a form of the *Kolmogorov forward equations*. If the notation indicating the condition that the system be in state i at time τ is suppressed, Eq. (6.29) can be expressed in the more convenient form

$$\frac{dP_l(t)}{dt} = -P_l(t)\lambda_l(t) + \sum_{j \neq l} P_j(t)\lambda_{jl}(t) \tag{6.31}$$

It must be remembered in the ensuing discussion, however, that the transition parameters may also be functions of the initial conditions.

For reliability modeling purposes, it is necessary to distinguish states both in terms of the number of faults that have been sustained in each stage of the system but also, of course, with regard to whether or not the system is still operational. A general structure is shown in Figure 6.8. Here P_l denotes an operational state with l faults and Q_l a failed state with l faults. (Since distinction is made as to where the faults are located the index l is actually an n-component vector with n the number of system stages.) The term $\lambda_l^{(0)}(t)$ represents the rate of occurrence, in a system which is still operational after l failures, of events that cause the system to fail even though no new faults have taken place.[7] The terms $\lambda_{jl}^{(1)}(t)$ and $\lambda_{jl}^{(2)}(t)$ represent the rates of occurrence of faults that take the system from operational state j to, respectively, operational state l and failed state l.

If $P_l(t)$ and $Q_l(t)$ are the probabilities of being in states P_l and Q_l, respectively, at time t, Kolmogorov's equations take the form

$$\frac{dP_l(t)}{dt} = -P_l(t)\lambda_l(t) + \sum_{j \neq l} P_j(t)\lambda_{jl}^{(1)}(t) \tag{6.32a}$$

---

[7]Such events can be caused, for example, by latent faults becoming active and producing erroneous outputs; this will be elaborated upon shortly.

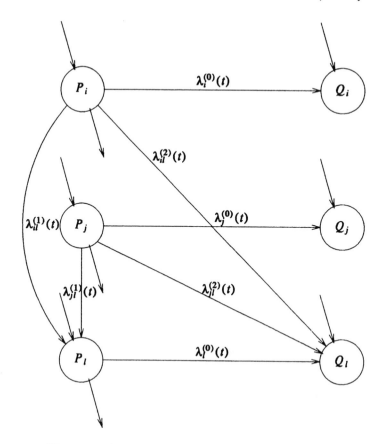

Figure 6.8: Segment of a reliability model state diagram.

$$\frac{dQ_l(t)}{dt} = -P_l(t)\lambda_l^{(0)}(t) + \sum_{j \neq l} P_j(t)\lambda_{jl}^{(2)}(t) \tag{6.32b}$$

with

$$\lambda_l(t) = \lambda_l^{(0)} + \sum_{j \neq l}\left[\lambda_{lj}^{(1)}(t) + \lambda_{lj}^{(2)}(t)\right]$$

The state diagram in Figure 6.8 does not include any state transitions due to repaired elements.[8] While it would be easy to include such transitions in the model, doing so is at variance with the concept of behavioral decomposition since

[8]Repairs in systems having time-varying failure rates pose an additional modeling complication. Since different elements in the system may have different time origins, the system can no longer be represented by a Markov model that assumes that all transition rates are dependent upon the same time variable.

repair rates are generally orders of magnitude greater than failure rates. More-over, as noted previously, constant repair rates are not generally reflective of real situations; more realistic repair rate models allow the rate at which repairs are completed to be a function of the amount of time the element is under repair. This requires a semi-Markov model to be used. Both of these observations suggest that, if availability rather than unattended reliability is the measure of interest, the repair model should be incorporated into the coverage model.[9]

The state transition rates needed by the reliability model are determined from the coverage model as follows: Let f_1 represent a fault that is present when the system enters state P_j and let f_2 represent a fault that can take the system from state P_j into either state P_l or state Q_l. Further, let $p_f(\tau \mid i,t)$ be the probability density of a type f fault at time τ, given that the system is in state P_i at time t and let $P_{CF}(\tau \mid f,t)$ be the probability, as determined by the associated coverage model, of a coverage failure by time t due to a type f fault at time $t - \tau$. Then,

$$\lambda_j^{(0)}(t) = \sum_{\text{all } f_1} \int p_{f_1}(t - \tau \mid j,t)dP_{CF}(\tau \mid f_1,t) \tag{6.33a}$$

$$\lambda_{jl}^{(1)}(t) = \sum_{\text{all } f_2} p_{f_2}(t \mid j,t)[1 - P_{CF}(0 \mid f_2,t)] \tag{6.33b}$$

and

$$\lambda_{jl}^{(2)}(t) = \sum_{\text{all } f_2} p_{f_2}(t \mid j,t)P_{CF}(0 \mid f_2,t) \tag{6.33c}$$

Applying Bayes' rule yields

$$p_{f_1}(\tau \mid j,t) = \frac{P_j(t \mid f_1,\tau)p_{f_1}(\tau)}{P_j(t)}$$

with $p_{f_1}(\tau)$ the unconditional probability density of a type f_1 fault and $P_j(t \mid f_1,\tau)$ the probability that the system is in state P_j at time t conditioned on the event of a type f_1 fault at time τ. But, for $\tau \leq t$, this is just the probability that all the other faults needed to take the system into state P_j have taken place by time t. That is, since element faults are assumed mutually independent,

$$P_j(t \mid f_1,\tau) = \frac{P_j(t)}{P_{f_1}(t)}$$

[9]The fact that repair rates are usually small compared to fault coverage rates sug-gests a further extension of the behavioral decomposition concept; viz: a third level in the decomposition hierarchy devoted to repair only. This idea of decomposing a reliability model into more than two hierarchical levels has been exploited in a reliability modeling program called SHARPE (symbolic hierarchical automated reliability and performance evaluator) [Sahner and Trivedi (1987)].

so that

$$p_{f_1}(t-\tau \mid j,t) = \frac{p_{f_1}(t-\tau)}{P_{f_1}(t)} \tag{6.34}$$

with $P_{f_1}(\tau)$ the unconditional probability that a type of f_1 fault has occurred by time τ. Similarly, the term $p_{f_2}(t \mid j,t)$ is just the probability density of a type f_2 fault given that one has not yet occurred, that is, the rate of occurrence of such faults at time t,

$$p_{f_2}(t \mid j,t) = \lambda_{f_2}(t) \tag{6.35}$$

Note, that $\lambda_j^{(0)}(t)$ is, and that $\lambda_{jl}^{(1)}(t)$ and $\lambda_{jl}^{(2)}(t)$ may be, functions of t even when all the element failure rates are constant, so the reliability model is unavoidably inhomogeneous.

Since the reliability models associated with real fault-tolerant systems may still involve a large number of states, even after behavioral decomposition, they are usually solved by computer. To this end, it can be useful to introduce approximations that simplify the resulting numerical analysis and reduce the potential for large accumulated round-off errors. If the system being modeled is highly reliable, $\lambda_{jl}^{(1)}(t)$ must in general be much larger than $\lambda_{jl}^{(2)}(t)$ and $\lambda_l(t)$ must be large compared to $\lambda_l^{(0)}(t)$. Thus, to a good approximation, Eq. (6.32a) can be rewritten in the form

$$\frac{dP_l(t)}{dt} = -P_l(t)\lambda_l^*(t) + \sum_{j \neq l} P_j(t)\lambda_{jl}^*(t) \tag{6.36a}$$

with $\lambda_{jl}^*(t) = \lambda_{jl}^{(1)} + \lambda_{jl}^{(2)}$ and $\lambda_l^*(t) = \Sigma_{j \neq l} \lambda_{lj}^*(t)$. And, if the solutions to these equations are denoted by $P_l^*(t)$, Eq. (6.32b) assumes the approximate form

$$\frac{dQ_{l(t)}}{dt} = P_l^*(t)\lambda_l^{(0)}(t) + \sum_{j \neq l} P_j^*(t)\lambda_{jl}^{(2)}(t) \tag{6.36b}$$

Although the differential equations (6.32) could be solved directly, the approximations introduced in replacing $P_l(t)$ by $P_l^*(t)$ are indeed negligible for many cases of interest. It will be observed, in fact, that $P_l^*(t)$ is just the probability that the system would be operating with l failures were the coverage perfect. Thus, replacing $P_l(t)$ in Eq. (6.32b) by $P_l^*(t)$ is equivalent to allowing systems that have already suffered from a coverage failure to be counted among those still susceptible to coverage failures. Such approximations introduce an error of the order of p^2, with p the presumably very small probability of any one of these events. The advantage of introducing this approximation is that the probabilities $P_l^*(t)$ can be readily evaluated using straightforward combinatorial techniques, thereby avoiding the need for the more time consuming, and more roundoff-error prone, calculation of the probabilities $P_l(t)$ as defined by Eq. (6.32a).

6.3.2 Coverage Models

Several computer programs have been developed for evaluating the reliability of systems using models based on behavioral decomposition. The reliability models used in these programs are all basically the generic model just described (although different numerical techniques may be used to obtain solutions). The coverage models, however, differ considerably from one model to the next. This section discusses coverage models associated with two reliability estimation computer programs, CARE III and HARP.

6.3.2.1 The CARE III coverage model.

The first reliability model to use the technique that later became known as behavioral decomposition was CARE III (Computer-Aided Reliability Estimation, version 3) [Stiffler and Bryant (1982)]. The CARE III coverage model recognizes three basic causes of coverage failure: (1) An existing latent fault causes the system to take some unacceptable action (an error is propagated); (2) a new fault occurs which, in combination with an existing latent fault, prevents the system from functioning properly; and (3) a pair of existing latent faults for the first time reach a system-disabling state. The transition rates associated with the first and third of these events are collectively represented by the term $\lambda_l^{(0)}(t)$ in Eq. (6.36b); the rate of occurrence of the second type of event is represented by the term $\lambda_{jl}^{(2)}$. A fault is said to be latent from the time it first occurs until it is either detected and isolated from the system or, in the case of a transient fault, reaches a benign state. The function of the coverage model is to represent the behavior of each fault during its latency period.

Note that the second and third causes of coverage failure both depend on the existence of a pair of latent faults. It often happens that a fault, while entirely benign itself, can become lethal in combination with some other fault. (A triple-modular-redundant configuration consisting of three identical elements feeding a majority voter is an obvious example of this. If any one element malfunctions, its output is ignored by the voter. If a second element fails before the first failure is detected, however, the combination of the two could well produce an erroneous output.) In many reliability analyses, such second-order effects are negligible compared to other causes of failure and consequently are simply ignored. In the highly reliable systems for which CARE III was designed, however, such effects are frequently the dominant cause of system failure.

Obviously, not all pairs of latent faults pose any threat to the system. Two modules, separately protected by independent voters, for example, should create no difficulty even if both are simultaneously in the active, error-producing, state. It is therefore necessary for the user to specify all *critical pairs* of faults, that is, to specify those pairs of modules that could cause the system to fail should the second module malfunction before the first one has been identified as faulty.

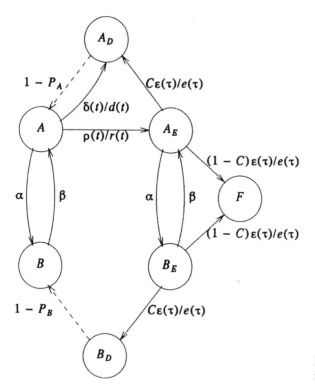

Figure 6.9: CARE III single-fault model.

The coverage model thus actually consists of two coverage models: a single-fault model to trace the various states of a single fault, and a double-fault model to track fault pairs. The single-fault model is shown in Figure 6.9. When a fault first occurs, it is said to be in the active state (state A in Figure 6.9). If the fault is transient or intermittent,[10] it may jump from the active to the benign state (state B). These transitions take place at an assumed constant rate α; for permanent, nonintermittent faults, of course, $\alpha = 0$. If the fault is intermittent, the reverse, benign-to-active, transition takes place at some assumed constant rate β; for transient faults, $\alpha \neq 0$ and $\beta = 0$.

In the benign state, the fault is incapable of causing any discernible malfunction. Thus it can neither be detected nor can it produce erroneous output. In the active state, however, the fault is both detectable and capable of producing incorrect output. The respective rates $\delta(t)/d(t)$ and $\rho(t)/r(t)$ at which these events take place depends on the operating environment and, in particular, on how frequently and how often the faulty element is exercised in a way that causes the de-

[10]A fault is said to be *transient* if it remains in the active state (and is thus capable of causing the element to malfunction) for some finite time t and then permanently returns to the benign state (in which it can no longer cause the element to malfunction). It is said to be *intermittent* if it randomly oscillates between the active and benign states.

fect to manifest itself. Once an erroneous output is produced, the system is said to be in the active-error state (A_E). Again, if the fault is either intermittent or transient, it may jump to the benign state, although now the error is still present so the state is designated the benign-error state (state B_E; the reason for distinguishing between states A_E and B_E will shortly become apparent). When the faulty element is in either of the two error states, the error propagates at some rate $\varepsilon(\tau)/e(\tau)$, with the time τ measured from the first entry into state A_E to that instant at which the error is either detected (e.g., through a decoder or a voter) or else escapes undetected and results in a system failure (state F). The probabilities of these two alternatives are equated to C and $1 - C$, respectively. If the fault is detected, either through testing or through the detection of an erroneous output, the faulty element enters the active-detected state A_D or benign-detected state B_D, depending on the state of the fault when it was detected. At that time a decision is made as to whether the faulty element is to be retired from the system or whether it can continue to be used. The latter decision might be made, for example, if the fault recovery procedure included a diagnostic routine designed to distinguish between permanent and transient faults. If the fault is detected in the active state, the decision is made with probability P_A that the element must be retired from service; if it is detected in the benign state, the same decision is made with probability P_B. Thus, with probabilities $1 - P_A$ and $1 - P_B$, respectively, the faulty element is returned to service following the detection of the fault. (The dashed lines in Figure 6.9 indicate that the transition takes place immediately with the probability indicated.)

Note that as long as the option is available to diagnose a detected fault as transient, it is possible that this decision is made erroneously. Thus P_B and even P_A may be less than unity even when the fault is, in fact, permanent or intermittent. Similarly, P_B and especially P_A may be greater than zero when the fault is indeed transient. The model assumes that the effect of a decision that the fault is transient is to eliminate the error if an error had already been produced, and to return the faulty element to the error-free active or benign state, depending on its state when the fault was detected. If the fault was transient and detected in the benign state, it either remains in the benign-detected state or returns to the error-free benign state. In either case, since $\beta = 0$, it can never again become active, so it ceases to pose any further threat to the system. If the fault is transient and detected in the active state, or if it is permanent or intermittent and detected in either state, and if it is diagnosed as transient, it remains latent and may have another chance to cause the system to fail.

Even more detailed single-fault models could, of course, be defined. Nonconstant active-to-benign and benign-to-active transition rates could be allowed, for example, and distinctions could be made between single and multiple errors. Moreover, such models could easily be incorporated into the CARE III structure. The model selected, however, was felt to be an effective compromise between the desire to allow the user as much flexibility as possible in defining the behavior of a faulty element, and the need to keep the model from becoming so baroque that the user despairs of ever defining all the parameters.

The fault detection rate $\delta(t)/d(t)$, the fault generation rate $\rho(t)/r(t)$, and the error propagation rate $\varepsilon(t)/e(t)$ are all restricted to assume the form

$$\frac{\phi(t)}{1 - \int_0^t \phi(\eta)d\eta} \tag{6.37}$$

with

$$\phi(t) = \phi e^{-\phi t} \qquad 0 < t$$

or

$$\phi(t) = \begin{cases} \phi & 0 < t < 1/\phi \\ 0 & \text{otherwise} \end{cases}$$

That is, either the transition rates or the transition density functions are assumed to be constant over some range; the function and, of course, the constant can be independently selected by the user for each of the three transition rates. In addition, the user can define up to five fault types, each with its own set of specifiers $[\alpha, \beta, \delta(t), \rho(t), \varepsilon(t), C, P_A, P_B]$, and designate that any or all of these types can afflict each of the system stages, with arbitrary rates of occurrence for each type at each stage.

It might be supposed that the double faults could be modeled by simply combining two single-fault models and then determining if, and when, the two independent fault states form some lethal combination. The problem with this approach is that the two-fault states may independently form a lethal combination repeatedly and the same system failure thereby counted multiply. (Since a second entry into a state is not necessarily a small probability event given that the first entrance took place, the argument used previously—that the probability of both events is of the order of the square of the probability of either of them—is not applicable here.) It is therefore necessary to introduce a separate double-fault model. The model selected is shown in Figure 6.10. This model is applicable if a second fault occurs when the first fault is in the benign (error-free) state. (If this is not the case, the combination of the two faults is treated as lethal upon the occurrence of the second fault; events in this category define $\lambda_{ji}^{(2)}$.) Thus the occurrence of the second fault places the fault pair in the A_2B_1 state (first fault benign, second fault active). From there, the fault pair can go to the B_1B_2 state (both faults benign) if the second fault becomes benign before the first fault becomes active, to the detected state D if the active fault is detected and diagnosed as permanent, or to the failed state F if the first fault becomes active with the second fault still also in the active state or if the second fault causes an error to be produced or is diagnosed as transient while still active. Since both faults are benign in the B_1B_2 state,

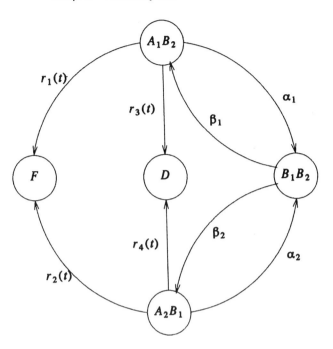

Figure 6.10: Double-fault model

the only possible transitions from that state are back to the A_2B_1 state or to the A_1B_2 state (one fault active, the other benign).

The transition rates $r_i(t)$ are defined in terms of the single-fault transition parameters as follows:

$$r_1(t) = \beta_2 + \rho_1(t)/r_1(t) + (1 - P_{A_1})\delta_1(t)/d_1(t)$$
$$r_2(t) = \beta_1 + \rho_2(t)/r_2(t) + (1 - P_{A_2})\delta_2(t)/d_2(t)$$
$$r_3(t) = P_{A_1}\delta_1(t)/d_1(t)$$
$$r_4(t) = P_{A_2}\delta_2(t)/d_2(t)$$

The subscripts on the single-fault transition rates distinguish between the two faults in the critical pair.

It will be noted that the double-fault model is conservative relative to the single-fault model in its definition of a failed state. If both faults are ever simultaneously active, the system fails regardless of whether or not either fault has resulted in an error. Moreover, a system failure results if either fault produces an error even though that error could potentially be detected before it causes any system damage. Obviously, a more elaborate model could have been postulated, one containing additional states to distinguish, among other things, the various possible error conditions. As in the case of the single-fault model, however, a compromise is required between the need to model accurately the important contributors to coverage failures and the desire not to overburden the user with overly fine distinctions. If both faults in a critical pair are active, for example, and one of them produces an error, the probability that that error is detected before it causes system damage is presumably altered, possibly significantly, by the presence of the second fault. Similarly, the coverage parameters may well be affected if both faults produce errors before either error propagates. A more elaborate double-fault model would force the user to examine these issues for every critical-fault pair.

The compromise represented by the double-fault model seems to be a reasonable one for two reasons:

1. The most significant event in determining the probability of a lethal double fault is the existence of the latent first fault at the time of the second. The probability of this event, however, is determined using the single-fault model and hence does not depend on the details of the double-fault model.

2. The conservatism of the double-fault model causes the probability of a double-fault coverage failure to be overbounded.

Thus the double-fault model is consistent with the other CARE III approximations in that it overbounds the system unreliability.

The probability $P_{CF}(\tau|f,t)$ used in Eq. 6.33 is determined from these coverage models as follows: Let $P_X(\tau,f_1)$ and $P_X(\tau,f_1,f_2)$ be the probabilities that state X in the single-fault and double-fault coverage models, respectively, is occupied τ time units after the occurrence of fault f_1 and let f' represent a fault that forms a critical pair with f and that occurred sometime prior to it. Then, in Eq. (6.33a),

$$P_{CF}(\tau|f_1,t) = P_F(\tau,f_1)$$

$$+ \sum_{\text{all } f_1'} P_F(\tau,f_1,f_1') \int_0^{t-\tau} P_B(\eta,f_1') p_{f_1'}(t-\tau-\eta|j,t)d\eta \qquad (6.38a)$$

with $p_f(\tau|j,t)$ as previously defined and with j denoting the system state P_j occupied after the second fault. Similarly, in Eqs. (6.33b) and (6.33c).

$$P_{CF}(0|f_2,t) = \sum_{\text{all } f_2'} \int_0^t P_A(\tau,f_2') p_{f_1'}(t-\tau|j,t)d\tau \qquad (6.38b)$$

6.3.2.2 The HARP coverage model. As previously noted, it is not practical to attempt to determine the reliability of complex fault-tolerant systems by simulating their behavior. This is because the failure probabilities of interest are typically extremely small (in some cases 10^{-9} or less). The simulation time needed to get even rough estimates of failure probabilities of this magnitude can be extreme. (For example, if the system is to have a failure probability of less than 10^{-9} after 10 hours of operation, over 100,000 *years* of operation would have to be simulated, on average, for each observed system failure.)

This same argument does not hold for simulation as a means for obtaining coverage probabilities, however, since the time scales and probabilities of interest may be considerably different and, most importantly, coverage models are concerned only with very small subsets of the overall system reliability model. If meaningful simulation can be accomplished in a reasonable period of time, it may be easier for a designer to determine the coverage associated with various element faults by this method than by attempting to estimate the different parameters required by the previously described semi-Markov models. This is the premise that motivated the designers of HARP (Hybrid Automated Reliability Predictor) [Dugan, et al. (1986), Bavuso and Martensen (1988)].

The simulation tool used in HARP is based on extended stochastic Petri nets [Dugan, Nicola, Geist and Trivedi (1985)]. A Petri net is a graph containing two types of vertices. One type, generally represented by a circle, is called a *place;* the other, usually represented by a bar or line segment, is called a *transition.* The arcs interconnecting these places and transitions are also of two types, *standard* and *inhibitor,* the first represented by arrows, the second by lines with small circles on one end. At any given time, some of the places in the Petri net may contain one or more *tokens,* usually represented by small solid circles.

The rules governing the dynamics of a Petri net are as follows. If each place connected directly to a transition through a standard arc contains at least one token and if none of the places connected to it through an inhibitor arc contains any tokens, the transition *fires;* that is, one token is removed from each standard input place and one token is added to each output place. An *extended stochastic* Petri net adds to this structure by associating with each transition a firing time distribution. When the above conditions for a transition to fire obtain, the actual firing is delayed for a time determined by a sample taken from the associated distribution. If the conditions still obtain at the end of that time, the firing then takes place as before. Further, arcs from transitions to places are allowed to be probabilistic, with the likelihood that a token takes a specific arc determined by an assigned probability.

An example of the use of an extended stochastic Petri net to model fault coverage is shown in Figure 6.11. The place labels here have the same meaning as those used in Figure 6.9 with the following exceptions: The place D is a precursor to the two places A_D and B_D and corresponds to the states in Figure 6.9 before the active or benign status has been resolved. The states A_E and B_E in Figure 6.9 have been replaced by the place E representing the error state, again before the active or benign status has been resolved. The place I (isolated) corresponds to the destination state, implicit in Figure 6.9, when the transitions indicated there by the dashed arrows are not taken. The place S is a starting point for a token following an element failure.

Single-fault coverage can be simulated with this Petri net by placing a token on place A and a second token on place S and determining whether the latter ends up on place F or on place I. The first of these tokens will transfer back and forth between places A and B. The second will remain on place S until one of its output transitions fires and the token moves to either place D or place E. From

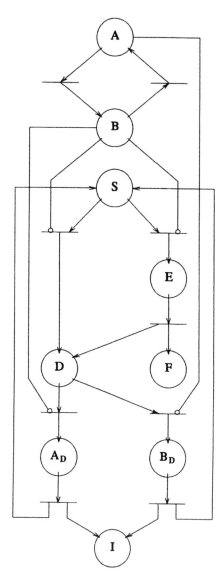

Figure 6.11: Petri Net Model of a Single Fault.

place E it moves either to place F or D in accordance with the probabilities assigned to the two arcs. From place D it moves to A_D or to B_D depending upon whether the other token is on place A or place B at the time.

Different element failures can be modeled by assigning the appropriate distributions to these various transitions. The single fault model used in CARE III (Figure 6.9) can be duplicated here by assigning the following distributions and probabilities:

$1 - e^{-\alpha t}$	distribution of the transition from place A to place B
$1 - e^{-\beta t}$	distribution of the transition from place B to place A
$1 - d(t)$	distribution of the transition from place S to place D
$1 - r(t)$	distribution of the transition from place S to place E
C	probability of the left branch of the transition between place E and places D and F
$1 - C$	probability of the right branch of the transition between place E and places D and F
$1 - P_A$	probability of the left branch of the transition between place A_D and places I and S
P_A	probability of the right branch of the transition between place A_D and places I and S
P_B	probability of the left branch of the transition between place B_D and places I and S
$1 - P_B$	probability of the right branch of the transition between place B_D and places I and S

Those transitions not having an associated distribution fire immediately when the requisite conditions are met.

The benefit of the HARP program, however, is not that it can be used to obtain the same results through simulation that could be more easily obtained using semi-Markov analysis, but that it can be used to obtain results in cases in which it is difficult to specify an appropriate analytic model. By using Petri net structures, it is possible to simulate a wide variety of fault coverage scenarios that might otherwise be impossible to model accurately.

6.4 AN EXAMPLE

Consider again the four-element, single-stage system described in Section 6.2. As before, the system is assumed to be operational unless either at least three of the four elements have failed or it has experienced a coverage failure. Each of the four elements is subject to faults belonging to a single category characterized by the parameters λ, ω, α, β, $\rho(t)$, $\varepsilon(t)\delta(t)$, C, P_A, P_B (see Section 6.3.2.1).

This system is an extremely simple example of the class of systems the reliability estimation programs described here were designed to model. Nevertheless, because it is so simple, it provides a useful vehicle for analyzing the relative effects of the different reliability and coverage parameters.

The CARE III program was used to estimate the reliability of this system for various sets of reliability and coverage parameters. In all cases each element is subject to faults at the rate $\lambda = 10^{-5}$ faults per hour, and the reliability is that predicted for time $t = 1$ hour. Further, it is assumed that all faults detected while still in the active state are always diagnosed as permanent and that all faults detected in the benign state are always diagnosed as transient ($P_A = 1$, $P_B = 1$).

Thus, if all faults are permanent, then in the absence of a coverage failure, the probability that the system fails to survive until time $t = 1$ hour is [See Eq. (6.12)]

$$1 - R^*(t) = 1 - [6e^{-2\lambda t^\omega} - 8e^{-3\lambda t^\omega} + 3e^{-4\lambda t^\omega}] = 4.000 \times 10^{-15}$$

The parameters C and ω (the Weibull distribution parameter introduced in Eq. 6.4) in Table 6.1 are both equal to 1 except where indicated and the functions $\delta(t)$, $\rho(t)$ and $\varepsilon(t)$ are all constant-rate functions (see Eq. 6.37) except for the specifically designated constant-density-function cases; the specified parameter is either the rate or the density, as appropriate. The failure probabilities are listed as multiples of the failure probability ($1 - R^*(t) = 4 \times 10^{-15}$) realized when the faults are all permanent and the coverage is perfect. (Note that the imperfect-coverage, transient-fault failure probabilities can be less than the perfect-coverage permanent-fault failure probabilities.)

Several observations can be made concerning the results tabulated in Table 6.1:

1. The probability of a system failure can actually decrease as the error generation rate increases (e.g., compare cases 1a and 1b). This is evidently due to the fact that the longer a fault remains hidden, the longer the system is vulnerable to a subsequent fault.

2. The preceding statement holds as well for relatively long-term transients (cases 2a and 2c), but the reverse holds for short-term transients (cases 2b and 2d) since the cost of erroneously identifying a transient failure as permanent offsets the effects of longer latency.

3. Nonconstant hazard rates can exacerbate coverage failure problems by concentrating failure events in time (compare cases 1e and 1f with 1a). (Note that the probability of a noncoverage failure is identical in all three cases.)

4. A nonzero probability ($1 - C$) that the system fails to recover from a propagated error can be significant, even when this probability is as small as one chance in a billion (compare cases 1c and 1g).

5. The distributions of the various coverage events can also affect the failure probability. Compare the failure probabilities in cases 1h and 1i. The only difference in the two cases is in the detection distribution $\delta(t)$; even the mean time to detection is the same in the two cases.

6. The failure probability decreases as the detection rate increases, but an improved detection rate is not very valuable when it is small relative to the error generation rate and the coverage of propagated errors is certain (compare cases 1b and 1c).

7. The shorter the transient, the less likely it is to cause a system failure. This is

Table 6.1: Example Parameters

Case	alpha (1/sec)	beta (1/sec)	delta (1/sec)	rho (1/sec)	epsilon (1/sec)	Failure Probability x (1 − R*(t))
Permanent failures						
1a	0	0	0	1	10	46.57
1b	0	0	0	10	100	5.56
1c	0	0	1	10	100	5.14
1d	0	0	100	10	100	1.22
1e(1)	0	0	0	1	10	57.75
1f(2)	0	0	0	1	10	62.05
1g(3)	0	0	1	10	100	14.05
1h	0	0	2	1	10	16.20
1i(4)	0	0	1	1	10	17.78
Transient failures						
2a	0.1	0	0	1	10	0.38
2b	1	0	0	1	10	0.05
2c	0.1	0	0	10	100	0.24
2d	1	0	0	10	100	0.18
2e	10	0	0	10	100	0.02
Intermittent failures						
3a	1	1	0	1	10	99.71
3b	1	1	10	1	10	13.12
3c(4)	1	1	10	1	10	12.33
3d	1000	1000	0	1	10	115.69
3e	1000	1000	10	1	10	9.06
3f(4)	1000	1000	10	1	10	8.99
3g	1	1000	0	1	10	46.68
3h	1	1000	10	1	10	5.15
3i(4)	1	1000	10	1	10	3.24

Notes: (1) $\omega = 1/2$ (2) $\omega = 2$ (3) $C = 1 - 10^{-9}$ (4) constant-density functions

presumably due to two factors: a detected transient fault is less likely to be diagnosed as permanent if it is detected after it reaches the benign state; and, the shorter the time spent in the active state, the less likely the effect of the fault will be present at the time of a subsequent fault.

8. The effect of an intermittent fault depends both on the fraction of time it spends in the active state (compare cases 3b and 3h, for example) and on the rate at which it jumps between the active and benign states (compare cases 3b and 3e).

It is apparent that even in the context of this simple example, both the absolute and the relative magnitudes of the coverage and reliability parameters can significantly affect the system unreliability. Often, the increase in unreliability caused by a change in a single coverage parameter exceeds the total contribution to that unreliability due to all noncoverage failures. Although in this simple example the unreliability is always extremely small, this relationship between the magnitudes of coverage and non-coverage failures is typical of much more complex and, hence, much less reliable systems as well.

6.5 SUMMARY

It is, of course, obvious that the more reliable a system becomes, the more improbable are the events that cause it to fail. Accordingly, reliability models designed to estimate the reliability of such systems must necessarily take into account effects that could be ignored or only roughly approximated in models designed for less reliable structures. These effects are generally referred to as coverage effects, that is, effects that result in system failure due, not to an exhaustion of resources, but rather to faults that, while circumventable, are not detected and isolated before they have caused the system as a whole to malfunction.

The reliability modeling techniques discussed here were designed to allow the user to model coverage effects to a detail heretofore impossible. To take full advantage of this capability, the user must attempt to specify more completely just how the effects of a fault make themselves manifest to the system. For example, to estimate or to simulate the distribution of the time from the occurrence of a fault to its detection, consideration must be given to the frequency and thoroughness with which the faulty module is tested. If the module is tested every τ seconds, for example, and if the probability is unity that the fault is detected if it is present when the test is conducted, the distribution of the time to detection is well modeled as $d(t) = 1 - t/\tau$, $0 \le t < \tau$. If, on the other hand, the module is tested at random intervals with a less than certain outcome even if the fault is present, a distribution of the form $d(t) = e^{-\delta t}$ might be more appropriate. Similar considerations are needed to select the other relevant functions and parameters used to model coverage.

In many cases, coverage may be difficult to model or even to simulate. Even in these cases, the inclusion of coverage effects in reliability models can still play a valuable role for two reasons: (1) it forces the user to examine aspects of a system that might otherwise have been ignored; and (2) more importantly, it provides a means for determining the sensitivity of a system's reliability to assumptions made both about the behavior of faults and about the mechanisms provided to recover from them. One of the major threats to reliability is software errors. The following chapter enumerates various techniques for designing robust software.

REFERENCES

[Bavuso88] Bavuso, S., and M. Martenson, "A Fourth-Generation Reliability Predictor," *Proceedings of the Annual Reliability and Maintainability Society*, 1988.

[Bjurman76] Bjurman, B. E., G. M. Jenkins, C. J. Masreliez, K. L. McClellan, and J. E. Templeman, "Airborne Advanced Reconfigurable Computer System (ARCS)," Final Report, NASA Contract NASI-13654, (August 1976).

[Bouricius69] Bouricius, W. G., W. C. Carter, and P. R. Schneider, "Reliability Modeling Techniques for Self-Repairing Computer Systems," *Proc. 24th Natl. Conf. ACM*, 1969.

[Bryant82] Bryant, L. A. and J. J. Stiffler, *CARE III User's Manual*, NASA Contract NAS1-15072, (March 1982).

[Butler85] Butler, R. W., "The SURE 2 Reliability Analysis Program", NASA Langley Research Center Technical Report, (January 1985).

[Conn77] Conn, R., P. Merryman, and K. Whitelaw, "CAST—A Complementary Analytic-Simulative Technique for Modeling Complex, Fault-Tolerant Computing Systems," *Proc. AIAA Comput. Aerosp. Conf.*, (November 1977).

[Cox68] Cox, D. R., and H. D. Miller, *The Theory of Stochastic Processes*, Methuen, London, 1968.

[Dugan85] Dugan, J., V. Nicola, R. Geist, and K. Trivedi, "Extended Stochastic Petri Nets: Applications and Analysis," *Performance '84*, North-Holland, Amsterdam, 1985.

[Dugan86] Dugan, J., K. S. Trivedi, E. M. Rothman, and W. E. Smith, "The Hybrid Automated Reliability Predictor," *AIAA Journal Guidance, Control and Dynamics*, vol. 9, no. 3 (May–June 1986).

[Feller64] Feller, W., "On Semi-Markov Processes," *Proc. Natl. Acad. Sci.*, vol. 51, 1964.

[Gear69] Gear, C., "The Automatic Integration of Stiff Ordinary Differential Equations," *Information Processing '68*, North-Holland, Amsterdam, 1969.

[Geist83] Geist, R., and K. Trivedi, "Ultra-High Reliability Prediction for Fault-Tolerant Computer Systems," *IEEE Transactions on Computers*, vol. C-32, no. 12 (December 1983).

[Geist90] Geist R., and K. Trivedi, "Reliability Estimation of Fault-Tolerant Systems: Tools and Techniques," *Computer* (July 1990).

[Landrault78] Landrault, C., and J. C. Laprie, "SURF—A Program for Modeling and Reliability Prediction for Fault-Tolerant Computing Systems," *Informative Technology*, J. Moneta ed., North-Holland, Amsterdam, 1978.

[Mathur72] Mathur, F. P., "Automation of Reliability Evaluation Procedures through CARE—The Computer-Aided Reliability Estimation Program," *AFIPS Conf. Proc.*, vol. 41, 1972.

[Ng77] Ng, Y. W., and A. Avizienis, "ARIES—An Automated Reliability Estimation System," *Proc. 1977 Annu. Reliab. Maintainability Symp.*, (January 1977).

[Sahner87] Sahner, R., and K. Trivedi, "Reliability Modeling Using SHARPE," *IEEE Transactions on Reliability*, vol. R-36, no. 2 (June, 1987).

[Stiffler75] Stiffler, J. J., "An Engineering Treatise on the CARE II Dual Mode Reliability and Coverage Models," Final Report, NASA Contract L-I8084A, 1975.

[Stiffler80] Stiffler, J. J., "Robust Detection of Intermittent Faults," *Dig., 10th Annu. Int. Symp. Fault-Tolerant Comput.*, Kyoto, Japan, (October 1980).

[Stiffler82] Stiffler, J., and L. Bryant, "The CARE III Phase II Report—Mathematical Description," NASA Contractor Report 3566, 1982. Fault-Tolerant Comput., Kyoto, Japan, (Oct. 1–3 1980).

[Trivedi82] Trivedi, K. S., *Probability and Statistics with Reliability, Queuing, and Computer Science Applications*, Prentice Hall, Englewood Cliffs, N.J., 1982.

PROBLEMS

6.1 [Trivedi (1982)]

    (a) Consider a structure consisting of two identical elements, each having a constant failure rate λ. Their outputs are compared; a miscompare invokes a self-diagnostic routine which, with probability C, correctly identifies the faulty element. The diagnostic routine requires τ seconds of running time, with τ an exponentially distributed random variable with mean $1/\delta$. Thus, if $\delta \ll \lambda$ and if the structure is considered operational as long as at least one element is operational and has not been misdiagnosed as faulty, the structure can be modeled as a four-state Markov chain, as shown in Figure 6.12. Find the structure's reliability $R(t)$ using both the differential equation and the combinatorial techniques discussed in Section 6.2.

    (b) Show that this same structure can be modeled as a three-state semi-Markov process of the form shown in Figure 6.12. Find expressions for $\lambda_1(t)$ and $\lambda_2(t)$. (*Note:* Since t here is a measure of the elapsed time since entry into the initial state, all transition parameters in this case are functions only of the structure's age; such restricted semi-Markov processes are called nonhomogeneous Markov processes.)

6.2 Consider a two-out-of-four structure designed to operate as follows. If at most one element has been identified as faulty, the structure's outputs are obtained by passing all remaining element outputs through a majority voter (assumed to be fault-free). If two elements have been identified as faulty, one of the two remaining elements is discarded and the outputs obtained directly from the other. Since a majority voter cannot produce reliable outputs unless more than half its inputs are correct, and since an element's outputs are not ignored until it is found to be defective, show that this structure can be modeled by adding one more state to the semi-Markov model shown in Figure 6.5. Use the technique described in Section 6.2 to derive the structure's reliability when the time between the failure of an element and the detection of that event is a constant τ-seconds. Show that this structure is more reliable than the one modeled by Figure 6.5 by the amount $2e^{-\lambda t}(e^{-\lambda \tau} - e^{-\lambda(t-\tau)})^3$ with λ the element failure rate, for all times $t > 2\tau$.

6.3 [Stiffler (1980)] Consider a generalized version of the single-fault model shown in Figure 6.9 in which the transition rates α and β are allowed to assume the more general forms $\alpha(t)/a(t)$ and $\beta(t)/b(t)$. Assume that $P_A = P_B = 1$ and show that the probability that a fault leads to a system failure is maximized for

$$a(t) = \begin{cases} 1 & t < \tau \\ 0 & t \geq \tau \end{cases}$$

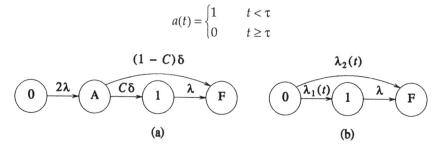

              (a)   (b)

Figure 6.12: Markov models of a one-out-of-two structure.

for some τ which depends only on the fault detection rate $\delta(t)/d(t)$. (It is useful to note that, when $P_A = P_B = 1$, the states A_E and B_E in the model of Figure 6.9 can be combined, as can the states A_D and B_D.)

6.4 Consider the double-fault model of Figure 6.10 when the transition rates are all independent of time and of the subscripts (1,2) and when $P_{A_1} = P_{A_2} = P$.

(a) Show that, in accordance with this model, the probability of a failure due to a double fault t seconds after the occurrence of the second fault, given that the first fault was initially benign and that $\beta \neq 0$, can be expressed in the form

$$P_F(t) = \frac{\beta + \rho + (1 - P)\delta}{\beta + \rho + \delta}\left[1 - ae^{-\lambda_a t} - be^{-\lambda_b t}\right]$$

Find a, b, λ_a, and λ_b. (*Hint:* Under the conditions specified, states $A_1 B_2$ and $A_2 B_1$ can be collapsed into a single state.)

(b) Show that the conditional probability of an eventual failure due to the double fault under consideration is a function of α if and only if $\beta = 0$ (i.e., if and only if the two faults are transient).

7

Fault-Tolerance in Software

Herbert Hecht & Myron Hecht

7.1 MOTIVATION FOR FAULT-TOLERANCE IN SOFTWARE

Thus far, our attention has focused primarily on architectural and design issues of fault-tolerant systems. As discussed earlier in Chapter 5, one of the weakest links in system reliability is software reliability. Even for control applications which usually have less complex software, it is already well established that many failures are, in fact, results of software bugs.

Because software does not degrade physically as a function of time or environmental stresses, it was long assumed that concepts such as reliability or failure rate were not applicable to computer programs. It is true that a program that has once performed a given task as specified will continue to do so provided that none of the following change: the input, the computing environment, or user requirements. However, because it is not reasonable to expect a program to be constantly operating on the same input data and because changes in the computing environment and user requirements must be accommodated in most applications, past and current failure-free operation cannot be taken as a dependable indication that there will be no failures in the future. Failure rates and error densities of existing programs are discussed in the following paragraphs. Later topics in this chapter deal with the consequences of failure and with current approaches to increased software reliability.

7.1.1 Failure Experience of Current Software

Every computer professional has experienced software failures, and even the general public is coming to understand that when "the computer is down," it is not always due to a hardware failure. The initial reaction is that the latest software failure is caused by stupidity or worse on the part of a particular programmer, and that it is the "natural" state for software to be perfect and to operate without failure. Unfortunately, there is hard data to indicate that this is not the case and that existing software products exhibit a fairly constant failure frequency in operation. The key to this finding is that the number of failures must be correlated with the execution time that the program has experienced over a given calendar interval. The theoretical basis for using execution time as the denominator for software reliability measurements has been established by John D. Musa (1987).

From a practical point of view, execution-time-based measurements are suitable for assessing software reliability because they (1) show consistency in time for a given program, and (2) show consistency among different programs that are of approximately the same magnitude and at the same life-cycle phase. Consistency in time is illustrated in Figure 7.1 which is based on the experience of a Federal Reserve Funds Transfer program that is active approximately 12 hours per day, five days each week. The solid curve in the figure shows the monthly failures due to software while the dashed curve shows equivalent hardware data. The descriptive statistics for each curve are very similar. The last entry in the statistics, the *index of variability* (the ratio of the standard deviation to the mean), is

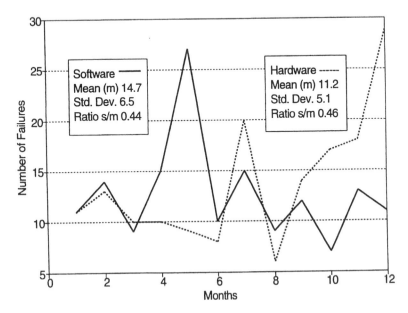

Figure 7.1: Consistency of failure rates in time.

Table 7.1: Failure Rates of Command and Control Systems

Project	Execution Time (hrs)	No. of Failures	Failure Rate
T1	24.6	136	5.53
T2	30.2	54	1.79
T3	18.7	38	2.03
T4	14.6	53	3.63
Mean			3.24
Std. Dev.			1.4900

very nearly the same for the software failures as for the hardware failure data. A small value for this ratio indicates consistency of the data over the interval for which it was evaluated, and the data shown in the table therefore indicates that the software failure rate is at least as consistent over this interval as the hardware failure rate.

Consistency among programs is indicated by the data of Table 7.1, abstracted from a database compiled by Musa (DACS, 1980). Another indication that software faults will always be with us is found in the fault density (the number of faults per 1,000 lines of code), which ranges from 10 to 50 for "good" software and from 1 to 5 after intensive testing using automated tools (Miller, 1981).

7.1.2 Consequences of Software Failure

Most readers will have personal experience with incorrect billing, lost airline or hotel reservations, and similar mishaps attributed to faulty programs. Most of these will on closer examination be found to be due to a data entry error, but the software cannot be completely exonerated. To cope with the propensity of data entry personnel for making such errors, checking routines or other protection mechanisms should have been provided. In these cases the consequences of lack of software reliability is inconvenience to a third party and possibly some loss of business or goodwill to the software user. More serious errors are occasionally reported in the media, such as the disruption of phone service to over 20 million customers during the summer of 1991 which was traced to a coding error in a new generation digital switch [IEEE, 1992].

The most serious consequences of faulty software occur in real-time control systems, where either human life can be endangered or large economic losses can be incurred due to a failure. In spite of the employment of the best available software development techniques and the participation of highly motivated personnel in spacecraft control applications, there have been spectacular failures due to software errors. These errors span almost the entire history of embedded computing, including the launch failure of Mariner I in 1962, the destruction of a French meteorological satellite in 1968, and several problems during the Apollo missions in the early 1970s. The increasing complexity and proliferation of real-time software systems have led to a resultant increase in software failures including the

NASA Space Shuttle and fly-by-wire aircraft such as the Airbus A320 and the NASA Magellan spacecraft while orbiting Venus in 1991. While techniques are being perfected to cope with known sources of errors in these programs, the growth of software complexity continues with a resultant increase in its vulnerability to errors. Of particular concern in terms of consequences of software failures are applications in the control of passenger aircraft (either on-board flight control or the air traffic control on the ground), in safety systems of nuclear power plants, and in the launch control of strategic missiles. The fault tolerance techniques described in this chapter have been developed primarily for use in critical real-time control applications.

7.1.3 Difficulties in Test and Verification

Although improvements in software development technology can undoubtedly reduce the incidence of software faults, the final line of defense rests on test and verification. The latter term is used here in the sense of a formal verification technique for computer programs, sometimes referred to as formal methods or proof of correctness (Gerhart, 1990; Zave, 1991). Still, proof of correctness ultimately rests on mathematical induction and is therefore subject to the shortcomings of that process (Dijkstra, 1972; Reynolds, 1976; Fetzer, 1988). Other major limitations are the expense in handling large programs, difficulties in verifying adherence to timing constraints (important for real-time programs), and uncertainty about how well requirements stated in a natural language can be translated into a formal specification that is suitable as the starting point for verification.

The latter problem, the potential for faulty translation of user requirements into the document which forms the basis for fault avoidance or fault tolerance efforts, is common to most of the techniques discussed in this chapter. It is a particularly critical issue with regard to formal methods because the specifications written for this purpose are usually constrained to a rigid syntax and terminology.

Conventional software testing consists largely of functional and performance requirements verification. However, conventional testing generally does not include robustness tests (input data outside specifications), limit tests (input data at boundary regions), or tests of all branches and loops. Conventional testing will find some errors, but it is true that "program testing can be used to show the presence of bugs, but never to show their absence" (Dijkstra, 1972). Complete testing of any practical programs is impossible because of the vast number of possible input combinations (Goodenough, 1980). Considerable research and development effort has therefore been expended to define equivalence classes of inputs, that is, data sets which will be handled in an exactly equivalent manner by the program such that running a single test case for that set will demonstrate the action of the program for the entire set. The techniques that have been proposed include (Howden, 1978):

Path testing: Each possible path from input to output is traversed once.

Branch testing: Each exit from each node is traversed at least once.

Functional testing: Each functional decomposition is tested at least once.

Special values testing: Testing for all values assumed to cause problems.

Anomaly analysis: Testing for program constructs that can cause problems.

Interface analysis: Testing for problems at interfaces of modules.

These techniques were evaluated on six practical programs that contained 28 known errors. Path testing, the most intensive form of testing, found 64 percent of the coding errors; interface analysis found 61 percent. There was at least one error that could not be found by any technique or combinations of these techniques. A more recent study conducted by Basili and Selby (1987) found that functional and structural testing found only 20 percent of the coding defects in software units. These results further confirm the statement by Dijkstra quoted above. Indeed, the implications of data reported by Miller (noted in the previous section) for very extensive testing which showed a factor of 10 reduction in fault density may be optimistic when applied more generally.

Symbolic execution is a technique that combines elements of formal verification with those of methodical testing (King, 1975). By executing a test case with symbolic rather than actual values, it is assumed that the test results will then be valid for all values of the symbolic variables. Various forms of symbolic execution are also evaluated in (Howden, 1978) and are found to discover 14 to 17 of the 28 faults (50 percent to 61 percent).

Hence, neither formal verification techniques nor extensive testing are sufficient to provide the degree of reliability that is required for software in critical applications, particularly in real-time control systems. However, one or both are *necessary* for dependable software-based systems. Moreover, as will be discussed below, because software-based fault-tolerant systems frequently rely on system or executive level routines which in themselves have only limited fault tolerance, testing is an integral part of the system development process for fault-tolerant software.

7.1.4 A Framework for Further Discussion

Over the two decades since the term "software fault tolerance" was first introduced, a number of different uses have emerged:

1. *Management of faults originating from the design or implementation of software components.* This is the classic definition of software fault tolerance (Randell, 1975; Avizienis, 1977) in which robustness, software diversity, or temporal redundancy are used to detect and recover from faults whose origin is related to software.

2. *Management of hardware failures.* Some researchers (Robinson, 1978; Wensley, 1978; Siewiorek, 1982) have used "software fault tolerance" to describe a

software-implemented hardware fault detection and recovery mechanism, that is, software which detects and recovers from *hardware* failures, typically through the management of hardware redundancy. This usage differs from the previous category because it handles failures arising in hardware; it does not handle failures arising from the design or implementation of the software itself unless it includes attributes of software fault tolerance.

3. *Management of network failures.* Yet a third usage of the term "software fault tolerance" refers to software which can detect and recover from a restricted class of failures (generally timing or "fail-stop") in a distributed system (Tripathi, 1986; Knight, 1987; Cristian, 1990). Because this usage encompasses provisions within both the operating system of an individual processor (i.e., network node) and communications services, it can be considered fault tolerance on the distributed operating system level. This usage encompasses some (but not all) elements of the previous two usages in that (a) some hardware failures which can be detected by means of a late or absent heartbeat can be recovered from using redundant elements, and (b) some classes of software failures that manifest themselves by overloading or crashing the processor can be detected and recovered from by means of initiating execution on a redundant element. In its design and implementation, software relating to this use of the term is distinguished by the presence of protocols for replicated interprocessor communication, time synchronization, replicated data consistency management, and rollback management.

Each of these usages is associated with a significant body of research and some commercial products, and this "overloading" makes it difficult to distinguish the intent of the speaker or author. The priority in this chapter is the classical definition of software fault tolerance, definition 1. Because the second kind of software fault tolerance is simply a software implementation of the fault detection and recovery logic that has been designed into the hardware of other fault tolerant systems, we direct the reader to other appropriate sections in this text. Distributed systems fault tolerance is discussed in the context of the distributed recovery block and extended distributed block in Sections 7.3.4, 7.3.5, and 7.7.

7.2 DEALING WITH FAULTY PROGRAMS

It was shown in the preceding discussion that any practical program can be presumed to contain faults, and that designers must deal with these faults if a program failure has serious consequences. Techniques for accomplishing this are introduced next under the following headings: robustness (Section 7.2.1); temporal redundancy (Section 7.2.2); and software diversity (Section 7.2.3). The latter includes static software fault tolerance, such as N-version programming, and dynamic software fault tolerance, such as the recovery block. Design considerations for these important approaches are discussed in Section 7.3. Practical fault-tolerant systems frequently employ combinations of these techniques.

7.2.1 Robustness

Robustness has been defined as "the extent to which software can continue to operate correctly despite the introduction of invalid inputs" (IEEE, 1982). Taken literally, this includes all fault tolerance techniques. In the current context, robustness is restricted to those techniques that do not involve redundancy. The minimum requirement is that the program will properly handle inputs out of range, or in a different type or format than defined, without degrading its performance of functions not dependent on the nonstandard input. As the examples suggest, robustness techniques are frequently used in checking input data. When these are found not to comply with the program specification, a new input may be requested (particularly where this can be supplied by a human operator), the last acceptable value of a variable can continue to be used, or a predefined default value can be assigned. In all cases a flag is usually raised to notify operators of an exceptional program state and to facilitate the handling of the exception condition by other program elements.

Most of the techniques described as self-checking software are covered by the definition of robustness above. Self-checking (Yau, 1975) features can include testing of

The function of a process (e.g., by checks on the output)

The control sequence (e.g., by setting an upper limit on loop iterations)

Input data (e.g., by use of error-detecting code and type checks)

A distinctive feature of the robustness technique is that it provides protection against predefined causes of software problems. In this respect it can be regarded as an implementation of anomaly analysis and interface analysis (see Section 7.1.3) within the program itself. An advantage of this specificity is that errors are usually detected early, before they can contaminate related programs or data sets. On the other hand, robustness cannot usually be depended on to provide complete protection against faulty software because of the possibility of faults for which no checks have been incorporated.

7.2.2 Temporal Redundancy

Temporal redundancy consists of the reexecution of a program when an error is encountered. The error may involve faulty data, faulty execution (such as accessing protected memory), or incorrect output as detected by an acceptance test (see Section 7.5). Reexecution will clear errors that arose from temporary circumstances that are no longer present when a new pass through the program is taken.

Examples of such circumstances are busy or noisy communication channels, full buffers, power supply transients, and others that are discussed in Section 7.4.1. If repeated executions fail to clear the error, the program can enter an exception state which at the very least prevents propagation of incorrect output to other portions of the program or of the controlled system. This capability is referred to as *fault containment*.

Where there are no or only loose time constraints, temporal redundancy is probably the most efficient software fault tolerance technique. This is particularly true for interactive programs (e.g., decision support programs, expert systems) where a human observer can initiate other recovery techniques if the automated reexecution fails.

7.2.3 Software Diversity

Software diversity is a programming methodology which provides for (1) explicit or implicit error detection for all fault conditions and (2) backup routines for continued service to critical functions in case errors arise during operation of the primary software. Software diversity permits uninterrupted operation in the presence of program faults through multiple implementations of a given functional process and it is therefore particularly applicable to real-time control systems and other applications that operate under tight time constraints. When the term "fault-tolerant software" is used in the context of real-time systems, it implies software diversity, and it is sometimes used in this narrower sense in the following paragraphs.

The major divisions of the technique are static fault tolerance as exemplified by N-version programming and dynamic fault tolerance as exemplified by the recovery block. In static fault tolerance, a given task is executed by several programs and the result accepted only if a specified number of programs agree within specified limits. In principle these programs can run consecutively on a single computer that then also performs the comparison and selects the result to be propagated to the external system or to be used in subsequent computation. But in practice the programs are executed concurrently and therefore multiple computers are required to implement this technique. The term "static" is used because the selection of the acceptable result does not affect the subsequent execution of the programs. In dynamic fault tolerance, a single program is executed and the result (including intermediate results) is subjected to an *acceptance test*. Alternate versions are invoked only if the acceptance test fails. The term "dynamic" is used because the selection of the original or alternate program is made during execution based on the outcome of the acceptance test.

Early implementations of the dynamic fault tolerance were described by Randell (1975) and one of the authors of this chapter (Hecht, 1981). Static software fault tolerance techniques were pioneered by Avizienis (1977). Further developments with each of these implementations are described in the following sections.

7.3 DESIGN OF FAULT-TOLERANT SOFTWARE USING DIVERSITY

The design of static fault-tolerant software in the following sections is described with reference to N-version programming, and examples of dynamic fault tolerance are described with reference to the recovery block.

7.3.1 N-Version Programming

N-version programming is defined as the independent generation of $N \geq 2$ functionally equivalent programs, called *versions*, from the same initial specification. When $N = 2$, N-version programming can be expected to provide good coverage for error detection but may be found wanting in assuring continued operation of the software. Upon disagreement among the versions, three alternatives are available: (1) retry or restart (in which case fault containment rather than fault tolerance is provided, (2) transition to a predefined "safe state," possibly followed by later retries, or (3) reliance on one of the versions, either designated in advance as more reliable or selected by a diagnostic program (in the latter case the technique takes on some aspects of dynamic redundancy). The second alternative may be acceptable for some process control or transportation applications where an infrequently occurring "halt" can be tolerated. However, for the broad class of critical applications none of these options is desirable; hence, more than two independent versions must be provided.

For $N > 2$, a majority voting logic can be implemented. Most of the recent publications in the field utilize $N = 3$ (Avizienis, 1984; Kelly, 1983; Tso, 1986). Further discussion is therefore primarily directed at three-version programming, which requires

1. Three independent programs, each furnishing identical output formats
2. An acceptance program that evaluates the output of requirement 1 and selects the result to be furnished as N-version output
3. A driver (or executive segment) that invokes requirements 1 and 2 and furnishes the N-version output to other programs or the physical system

An important design decision is the frequency with which comparisons and voting are to be carried out (the scope of the fault tolerance provisions). Fault tolerance of large scope (infrequent comparisons) minimizes the performance penalties caused by the fault tolerance procedures and permits a large measure of independence in the program design. On the other hand, it must accommodate a wide divergence of numerical variables because of the large number of independent program steps between comparisons and may require long wait states for synchronization of results (execution time can vary over a range of 5:1 between versions (Kelly, 1988)). Fault tolerance of small scope requires commonality of program structures at a detailed level and thus reduces the degree of independence of the individual versions. Also, the overhead required for frequent comparisons may interfere with the throughput objectives. For most applications it will be desirable to aim for the largest scope possible without violating desired tolerances on comparison of variables or incurring excessive wait times.

Voting, selection of the result to be output, and finally furnishing the output should also be conducted in a fault-tolerant manner. Where the three versions are running on three computers this can be accomplished by

1. Furnishing results to each computer and comparing locally.
2. Communicating the comparison to the other computers (e.g., in the form 1,0,1 meaning that computers 1 and 3 agree but that computer 2 has a different result).
3. Comparing the comparisons (the 1,0,1 forms), and if in agreement, furnishing the majority result as output of the program.
4. If there is no agreement in step (3), repeating all of the preceding steps or invoke an exception handling program.

These operations require a significant amount of intercomputer communication, and because this usually proceeds at a much lower rate than the information transfer over the internal computer channels, voting can have serious negative impact on the throughput of a computer system. If the intercomputer communication utilizes a bus, each of the voting messages will have to be encapsulated in a protocol that will add to the delay. The design of an effective and efficient voting algorithm is therefore a very important part of the overall N-version software design.

An early evaluation of the fault tolerance capabilities of three-version programming at UCLA (Chen, 1978) is synopsized in Table 7.2. These results were obtained on the RATE program, a partial differential equation algorithm for estimating temperatures over a two-dimensional region. Each individual version of the program consisted of over 600 PL/I statements, and seven separate versions were available. From these, 12 three-version sets were constructed, and each set was subjected to 32 test cases, yielding the 384 total tests indicated in the table.

Table 7.2: Results of an Early N-version Programming Experiment

Number of Faulty Versions	Number of Cases	Number of Faulty Executions	Fraction of Faulty Executions
0	290	0	0
1	71	12	0.031
2	18	18	0.047
3	5	5	0.013
Total	384	35	0.091

An important finding of that experiment relevant to design was that in cases where a single faulty version resulted in incorrect execution, the standard operating system of the computer intervened before the program reached the voting stage. Most later N-version experiments overcame this problem by incorporating acceptance tests for abort conditions and precluding the intervention of the operating system under these conditions.

Because of the promising outcome of the early UCLA experiments, a follow-up of much larger scope was conducted (Kelly, 1983). Because ambiguities of the specification were considered to be a major cause of correlated version failures, three different types of program specifications were developed: in a formal specification language (OBJ), in a program design language, and in plain English. Also, the specifications underwent special review prior to start of the programming (which was in PL/I). In this experiment only 3 percent of the executions failed due to undetected errors, but on the other hand only 45 percent resulted in full and valid agreement among all three versions. For the remainder either the fault was masked or the execution was aborted. The experiment did not show a clear advantage for programs developed from the formal specification language (OBJ). The fraction of completely successful computations was higher for the OBJ programs (at 0.49) than the overall number, but so was the fraction of undetected errors (at 0.05).

An even larger-scale experiment was carried out in the mid-1980s under sponsorship of the NASA Langley Research Center at four universities, involving 10 programmers from each and producing a total of 20 independent versions (Kelly, 1988). The software handled redundancy management in a redundant strap-down inertial measurement unit (RSDIMU) and the specification was derived from a commercial product and underwent extensive review for correctness and avoidance of ambiguity. The individual program versions ranged between 2,000 and 5,000 lines of Pascal. Great care was taken to keep individual programming teams independent and at the same time to give them equal access to information. All questions about the specification were handled by computer mail and questions as well as answers were available to all participants. Under conditions which stressed the redundancy management, again about 3 percent of the three-version combinations had correlated faults that permitted output of wrong results (Eckhardt, 1985). A significant finding was that diverse errors might lead to identical wrong results.

Because N-version programming will in most cases cause each of the participating computers to be in a different state sequence during the execution of a program, it is not easily used in tightly coupled computer configurations (that depend on synchronized comparisons for hardware fault tolerance) such as the Fault Tolerant Multi-Processor (FTMP) (Hopkins, 1978). This difficulty does not arise when it is applied in loosely synchronized fault-tolerant computers (such as Software Implemented Fault Tolerance (SIFT) (Wensley, 1978), but these usually involve additional performance penalties.

The software design effort required to generate truly independent versions and the hardware resources required to overcome the inherent performance penalties associated with this approach need to be investigated further. Inherent limitations on the ability to avoid correlated failures in two or more versions have been cited as an obstacle to acceptance of this technique for the most demanding applications in terms of safety (Knight, 1986; Eckhardt, 1985). Finally, N-version programming does not overcome the problems of a common statement of requirements and omissions or ambiguities in this that result in common failures. However, this shortcoming is shared, at least in principle, by all fault tolerance and fault avoidance techniques.

7.3.2 Recovery Block

The recovery block structure was originated by a group of researchers at the University of Newcastle-on-Tyne (Randell, 1975) and represents the dynamic redundancy approach to software fault tolerance. In its simplest form it consists of three software elements: (1) a *primary routine*, which executes critical software functions; (2) an *acceptance test*, which tests the output of the primary routine after each execution; and (3) at least one *alternate routine* which performs the same function as the primary routine (but may be less capable or slower) and is invoked by the acceptance test upon detection of a failure.

The basic structure of the recovery block is

```
Ensure T
  By P
  Else by Q
Else Error
```

where T is the acceptance test condition that is expected to be met by successful execution of either the primary routine P or the alternate routine Q. The structure is easily expanded to accommodate several alternates Q1, Q2, . . . , Qn.

The significant differences from *N*-version Programming are that (1) only a single implementation of the program is run at a time (in the case above either P or Q), and (2) the acceptability of the results is decided by a test rather than by comparison with functionally equivalent alternate versions. A more subtle difference between the recovery block and *N*-version programming is that P and T (and frequently also P and Q) are deliberately designed to be as uncorrelated (orthogonal) as possible, whereas the independence of the N versions depends usually on the more random differences in programming style among programmers. Real-time control applications require that the results furnished by a program be both correct and timely. For this reason the recovery block for a real-time program should incorporate a watchdog timer which initiates execution by Q if P does not produce an acceptable result within the allocated time (Hecht, 1976). A flow diagram of the resulting software structure is shown in Figure 7.2. Program flow under direction of the application module is shown in solid lines; timer-triggered interrupts are shown in dashed lines.

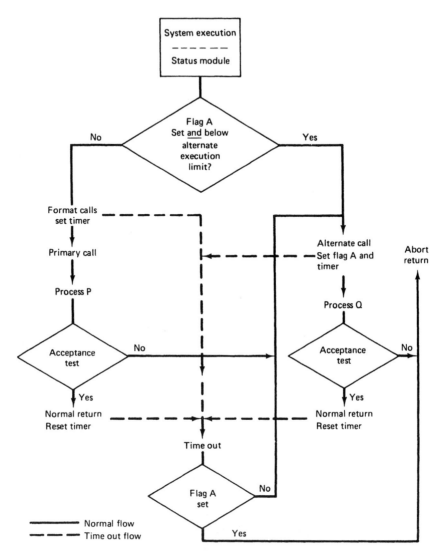

Figure 7.2: Recovery block for real-time application.

The system executive in this example has a status module, a primary routine failure flag A, and an alternate routine execution counter. Prior to entering the recovery block, the status module checks flag A. If A has not been set (i.e., the primary routine has not failed), the status module formats a call to the primary routine and the recovery block proceeds normally. On entering this block, the executive formats calls to both P and Q and sets the timer for the expected maximum run time of P. Control passes to the primary call and process P is executed. After P is complete, the acceptance test is run, and if the results are acceptable and on time, control returns to the executive. The timer is reset (loaded with an appropriate interval for the next operation) and another recovery block is called (or the previous one is repeated with new data). If the acceptance test rejects the results of P or if the results are not furnished within the allocated time, a transfer is made to the alternate call. The flag A is set, the timer is reset for the expected maximum duration of Q, and process Q is executed. At the (timely) conclusion of Q, the acceptance test is once again run, and if passed, a normal return to the executive occurs and the timer is reset as described above.

When flag A has been set, a different entry to the recovery block occurs. The status module of the system executive examines the alternate routine execution counter. If this counter is below an execution limit (which may be either a systemwide fixed value or routine-specific), the status module increments the counter and formats a call to the alternate routine. If, however, the alternate execution limit has been exceeded, the status module resets flag A, resets the alternate execution counter, and formats a call to the primary routine. The advantages of this reversion scheme are discussed in Section 7.4.2.

An essential feature of the recovery block structure is that the primary and alternate processes furnish results which can be treated interchangeably by other software elements. The fact that an alternate process was executed may be made known to the executive (e.g., from the state of flag A) but should be transparent to other application programs. If this transparency is not achieved, the execution of subsequent recovery blocks will be affected by the path taken within a prior recovery block. This results in a complex control structure which is difficult to validate and should be avoided for critical applications.

If the acceptance test rejects the results of Q, an abort condition exists and the program exits differently. The abort exit will also be taken if the timer runs out before a result is furnished by Q. The setting of flag A prevents repeated execution of Q when this program does not furnish suitable results within the expected time.

This basic recovery block structure can be augmented in detail as shown in Figure 7.3. The acceptance test is divided into several separate tests which are invoked both before and after execution of the primary routine. The first acceptance test checks on the call format and parameters. If these are not proper, an immediate exit to the alternate routine is taken. The second test, also executed before the primary routine, checks on the validity of the input data. The data test is particularly important because circumstances over which the software designer has no control can so corrupt the data that normal execution of the program is impossible. Where data errors are common, provision of an alternate data source may be considered, and the program can then be structured as shown within the dashed box of Figure 7.3. The final acceptance test is executed after the primary routine (as shown in Figure 7.2) and examines the output data. Failure of any of these tests causes control to pass to the alternate routine as indicated in the figure. Further details on design techniques for these acceptance tests are given in Section 7.5.

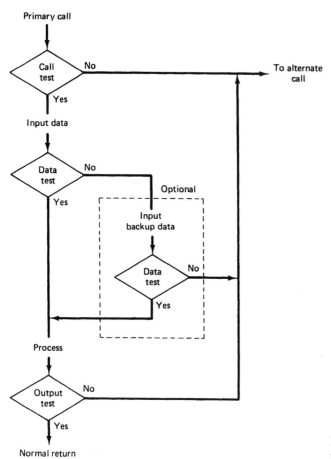

Figure 7.3: Internal structure for primary application module.

The integration of application modules structured as recovery blocks into a fault-tolerant software system is shown in Figure 7.4. The box labeled "Application Modules" and the decision diamond labeled "Return" together represent the structure shown in Figure 7.2. When a normal return is taken, the task select function will access the next application module from a task list that has been generated as part of the initialization. In the absence of failures of the recovery blocks, the process will always remain within the inner loop. If an abort exit is taken, the failure is recorded and some diagnostics may be performed. In case of a first failure in a recovery block, a retry may be initiated. If the failure persists, further execution of the task represented by the recovery block is suspended. A new task list is then generated and this replaces the one with which the system had been initialized. If the system has any higher level standby provisions, such as an emergency control system, these may be activated when an abort condition is encountered.

It is sometimes believed that real-time control situations do not permit the

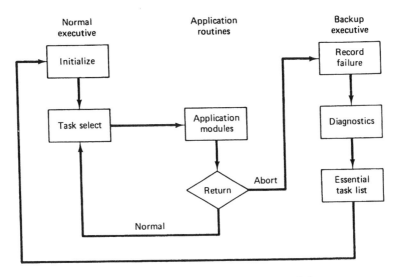

Figure 7.4: Executive and application modules.

invocation of alternate routines, accessing alternate data sources, or retries because timing constraints inherent in the application will be violated. Actually, the iteration rates are selected to provide a desired stability margin under the most demanding operating conditions. If a single delay equivalent to an iteration period is encountered, or if a single control output is skipped for several iteration periods, this will at worst result in a transient disturbance from which the system will recover as soon as the normal iteration frequency is restored and in most cases it will not result in any unacceptable degradation of system performance.

In the recovery block approach, a single program is executed at any given time, and therefore no special demands on computer redundancy or computer architecture are made. The performance penalty in normal operation is small (the execution of the acceptance test). Storage requirements are expanded because in addition to the primary application program, the acceptance test and the backup program must also be available in memory. Software development cost will be increased due to the need to generate two programs and the associated acceptance test.

An experiment on the effectiveness of the recovery block in improving operational software reliability was conducted by the University of Newcastle-on-Tyne in 1983–1985 (Anderson, 1985). This involved a medium-scale naval command and control system, comprising for the primary version approximately 8,000 statements in the Coral language. The evaluation showed increasing effectiveness of the fault tolerance provisions in the three phases of the project. During the final phase, 91 out of 117 abnormal events were correctly recovered (78 percent) and recovery failed in 4 (3 percent). The other events included some recoveries that were not correct but did not result in program failure (15 percent), and some unnecessary recoveries that did not result in failure (3 percent).

7.3.3 Composite Designs

It will be recognized that the data test in Figure 7.3 fits the definition of a robustness technique and its incorporation into the recovery block is therefore an example of composite design. Data tests and other means of detecting abort conditions in programs were incorporated in the individual versions used in the later N-version programming experiments. The motivation for this is to initiate corrective action as soon as possible, usually to prevent propagation of invalid data and specifically to prevent interference of the operating system with the fault tolerance provisions.

Similarly, N-version constructs may find their way into a recovery block program, such as consecutive execution of two or more versions of a short routine because it is the most efficient way of constructing an acceptance test. There is little room for strict adherence to any one technique in current practice. The cooperating diverse experts (CDE) methodology [Pradhan, 1995] draws upon techniques used in N-version programming and in distributed recovery clocks. Acceptance tests are conducted in a distributed fashion and the methodology relies on a reusable implementation of a parameterizable arbitrator module. It is discussed in [Pradhan, 1995] why the CDE methodology is most suitable to the development of expert systems and decision support systems.

7.3.4 The Distributed Recovery Block

The distributed recovery block (DRB) was formulated by Kim (1984, 1989) as a means of integrating hardware and software fault tolerance in a single structure. As the name suggests, it is a modification of the recovery block construct described earlier in that it consists of a primary routine, one or more alternate routines, and acceptance tests for both logic and time. The difference between the DRB and the standard recovery block is that the primary and alternate routines are *both* replicated and are resident on two or more nodes interconnected by a network.

Figure 7.5 is a top-level diagram representing a DRB. There are two replicated network nodes designated as *primary* and *backup*. Each of these has the primary and alternate versions of the program resident as well as an acceptance test. In Kim's terminology, the primary routine is referred to as the primary *try block*; the alternate routine is referred to as the *alternate try block*. Under normal (fault-free) circumstances, the primary node runs the primary try block whereas the backup node runs the alternate try block concurrently. Both will pass the acceptance test and update their local database. Upon success of the primary node, it informs the backup which updates its own database with its own result. Only the primary outputs the result to successor nodes.

In the event of a failure of the primary try block (i.e., routine) as detected by the acceptance test, the primary node attempts to inform the backup of the failure. When the backup receives notice, it assumes the role of the primary node.

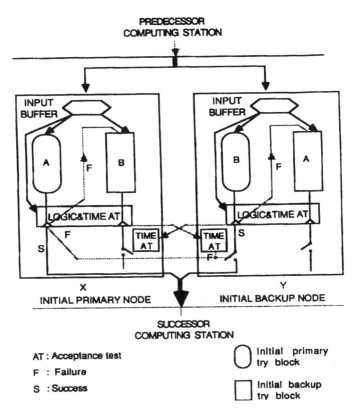

Figure 7.5: Distributed recovery block as described in Kim (1989).

Because it has been processing the alternate routine concurrently, a result will generally be immediately available for output. Thus, the recovery time for this type of failure is much shorter than if both try blocks were running on the same node. If the primary node stops processing entirely (due to a hang in the application or a crash of the operating system), no update message will be passed to the backup node which detects the crash by means of the expiration of a local timer which constitutes the time acceptance test. Notice that under these circumstances, the time acceptance test, which determines that a try block on the primary node has exceeded its execution deadline, can also be used to determine that the node has experienced an operating system or hardware failure. This is the key to the integration of hardware and software fault tolerance.

   The course of processing after a failure depends on the failure. If the primary node failed due to an error in the try block, then the node attempts to become the backup. It will then be ready to recover from a failure when the newly promoted primary node fails. In order to effect this transition, the node first attempts a rollback and retry with the alternate try block to process the data that the node failed to process when it was the primary. Processing of this data is necessary to keep the state data consistent with the companion node. When the retry is successful, the failed node can then transition to become a backup node. The data arrival rate and processor capacity must be such that it is possible to perform this rollback without falling behind for an excessive period of time.

It is desirable that the two nodes execute different try blocks whenever possible. As a result of recovery from a failure, it is possible that the same try block is executing in both, and then one of the nodes should attempt to change to the other try block. The decision criteria for when and how this should occur is left open to the designer, but should be defined as a *recovery block reconfiguration strategy*. An example of such a reconfiguration strategy is the current primary node always uses routine A as the current try block and routine B as the backup try block whereas the current backup node always uses the try blocks in the reverse order.

Kim (1989) demonstrated the feasibility of the DRB using a radar tracking application. Salient results included an increase in the average response time from 1.8 to 2.6 milliseconds (small relative to the 40 millisecond maximum response time), an average of 8 percent processor utilization for the acceptance test, and that backup processing was not a significant portion of the total workload.

7.3.5 The Extended Distributed Recovery Block

The DRB was developed for applications such as command and control in which data was collected by interface processors and distributed over a network, and in which data from one pair of processors was output to another pair of processors. However, when the authors attempted to apply these constructs of the DRB to real-time process control, a significant number of changes were necessary. These changes included:

a. Network nodes were interfaced directly with process equipment rather than passing data to successor nodes. This configuration change meant that the successor nodes could not be relied on to resolve ambiguous or inconsistent situations such as both nodes being primary or both nodes being backup. As will be discussed below, the problem was solved by adding a new kind of node called the *supervisor* to the network which would verify failure indications and arbitrate inconsistencies.

b. A recovery block reconfiguration strategy was defined.

c. A means of *restoring* nodes after a failure was added through reset hardware. This capability is dictated by practical rather than design considerations. Specifically, because most computer failures are transient, rebooting the processor will clear the problem.

d. A network architecture was defined to provide redundancy and fault isolation.

Because these changes resulted in a sufficiently different structure from the original DRB, it was designated as the *Extended* DRB, or EDRB.

Figure 7.6 is a top-level diagram of a typical EDRB configuration which con-

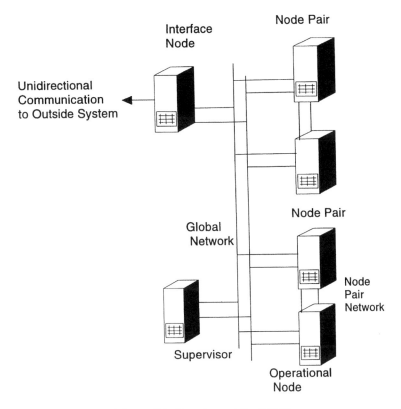

Figure 7.6: Structure of the EDRB.

sists of dual redundant and nonredundant processors which are interconnected by dual redundant networks. Nodes responsible for control of the process and related systems are called *operational nodes*. Operational nodes are critical because they perform real-time control (either directly or through lower-level programmable logic controllers) and store nonrecoverable state information (e.g., system modes, or status of control sequences). Hence, they are redundant; a set of dual redundant operational nodes is called a *node pair*. Members of the node pair exchange periodic status messages called *heartbeats*. A member in a node pair is capable of recovering from failures in its companion if the malfunction has been declared as part of the heartbeat message. Such failures do *not* include immediately fatal hardware or system software failures which result in the absence of a heartbeat. If an operational node *does* sense the absence of its companion's heartbeat, it requests confirmation of the failure from a second kind of node called the *supervisor*. The supervisor is a nonredundant processor which confirms the absence of a heartbeat, arbitrates inconsistent states in operational node pairs, and logs all status changes and failures. Although the supervisor is important to EDRB operation, the node is not critical because its failure only impacts the ability of the system to recover from failures requiring its confirmation or arbitration. The EDRB system can continue to operate without a supervisor if no other failures occur.

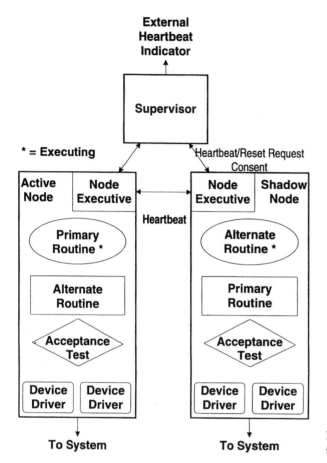

Figure 7.7: Software structure of the EDRB.

A simplified view of the software structure in a node pair and its interaction with the supervisor is shown in Figure 7.7. Operational nodes employ active redundancy. One node pair member is always *active* (i.e., controlling); the other is *shadow* (i.e., standby) if it is functional. Under normal circumstances and in steady state, the active node executes a *primary* version of a control task in parallel with an *alternate* version executed on the shadow node. Both nodes check the correctness of the results of the control task outputs with an *acceptance test*. The subsequent actions are determined by a *node manager* whose operation will be described in detail below. If·the primary routine acceptance test is passed (the usual case), the node manager permits a control signal to be passed to the actuators under its control. If the acceptance test is not passed, the active node manager might request the shadow node manager to promote itself to active and immediately send out its result to minimize recovery time.

When an operational node fails to issue a heartbeat, an EDRB software component called the *monitor* task requests permission from the supervisor to assume control if not in the active role. If the supervisor concurs that a heartbeat is absent, consent is transmitted and the shadow promotes itself as if the failure were announced by the companion node. It is possible for an inconsistent state to occur, for example, the active node spuriously decides to become a shadow node or a shadow node makes an incorrect decision to assume control. In the event of such a state, the supervisor node will detect the problem from periodic status reports. It will then send an arbitration message to the operational nodes in order to restore consistency.

The recovery block strategy is implemented as a set of tasks representing operating system extensions called the *executive layer*. Within an operational node, a set of tasks communicates with the companion and supervisor to control fault detection and recovery. The two tasks responsible for node-level fault decision making are called the *node manager*, which is associated primarily with the node on which it resides, and the *monitor* which is concerned primarily with generating a heartbeat and determining the state of the companion node. The node manager task determines which *version* of the application software to run (i.e., the primary or alternate routine), and the *role* of the local node (i.e., active or shadow). The monitor task generates a periodic status message called a *heartbeat* and monitors the heartbeat of its companion operational node. The time interval between heartbeats is called a *frame* and is typically set at 0.020 seconds (on a 33 MHz Intel 80486-based PC/AT compatible computer). The heartbeat contains the node's role, version and a 32-bit *frame number* which is incremented at the beginning of each new frame. When the companion computer heartbeat message is not received, the monitor task (after receiving concurrence from the supervisor) initiates a hardware reset of the node from which a heartbeat message had not been received.

The design and implementation issues encountered by developers of the EDRB are typical of many software fault-tolerant systems and are therefore further discussed in Section 7.7. Additional design detail on the EDRB has also been published (Hecht, 1991a, 1991b).

7.4 RELIABILITY MODELS FOR FAULT-TOLERANT SOFTWARE

The preceding sections have provided an overview of the concepts and methods of software fault tolerance, and later sections are devoted to a more detailed discussion of several key areas in the analysis and design of fault-tolerant software. The subject of the present section is reliability modeling. The benefits of fault tolerance techniques, and particularly of the recovery block approach, can be demonstrated very clearly by modeling. The fact that this benefit can be shown by modeling gives recovery blocks a substantial advantage over other approaches to reliability improvement. Section 7.4.1 introduces the terminology used for modeling and the basic software failure model, which is subsequently developed into a practical and realistic model for the reliability of fault-tolerant software structures.

7.4.1 Terminology and Software Failure Models

When the output of a computer program produces results that do not meet user requirements (or place the computer into a state that does not support user needs), it has produced an error. The execution of the program has resulted in a failure or more specifically a software failure. To produce this failure, a fault must have been present in the software, but software faults result in a failure only when suitable input data or computer states exist. These conditions external to the program which are necessary to activate the fault are called triggers or, more generically, external events.

The basic software failure model of Figure 7.8 illustrates the relations discussed above. The figure also indicates that the error becomes evident only through observation. Some errors may not be observed at all, while others may be manifested in a way that makes determination of the actual failure a difficult matter.

The application of this model at the system level is shown in Figure 7.9. The fault in this example is assumed to be the lack of zero-divide protection in the attitude calculation program of an aircraft flight control system. The external event that activates the fault is the occurrence of a data set that causes a zero denominator to be generated. The immediate error produced is an incorrect altitude value observable only under exceptional conditions (e.g., when extensive data recording is provided as part of a flight test program). The error results in a faulty input to the autopilot, which in turn causes an incorrect control surface deflection. This condition may be observed by an alert pilot, who can prevent propagation of the failure by disengaging the autopilot and taking over manual control. If the pilot is distracted, the surface deflection error will not be observed until the aircraft executes a violent maneuver, possibly causing injury to passengers.

As this example suggests, fault tolerance provisions might be incorporated at several levels in the system. In this case the first level is in the attitude calculation.

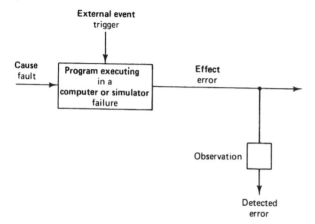

Figure 7.8: Basic failure model.

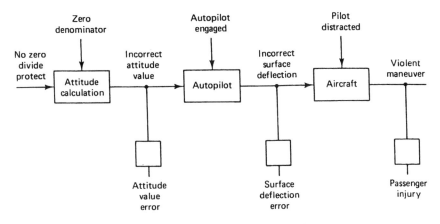

Figure 7.9: System failure model.

Had this module been structured as a recovery block, the incorrect attitude value would have been detected internally and would have triggered the invocation of a backup attitude calculation routine. Fault tolerance provisions in the autopilot might have prevented acceptance of the faulty attitude input, or they might have detected that the surface deflection command issued was incorrect.

7.4.2 Reliability Models

Reliability models are intended to illustrate the effect of failures of elements on the overall system, particularly where some elements are redundant or incorporate fault tolerance provisions. In the conventional (hardware) reliability model, shown in Figure 7.10, redundant elements are placed in parallel and all essential functions required for a system are placed in series. The failure probability of a function that consists of two redundant elements, such as C in the figure, is the product of the failure probabilities of the individual elements, here C_1 and C_2. If

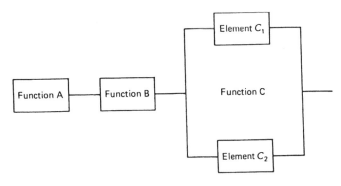

Figure 7.10: Conventional reliability model.

both elements have the same failure probability, the function failure probability, $F[C]$, is given by

$$F[C] = F[C_1] = F[C_2] \qquad (7.1)$$

The reliability of a system is the product of the reliability of all its functions. In the case of Figure 7.10, the system reliability $R[S]$, is given by

$$R[S] = R[A] \cdot R[B] \cdot R[C] \qquad \text{where} \qquad R[x] = 1 - F[x] \qquad (7.2)$$

While this modeling technique can be used to depict the structure of fault-tolerant software, it is not suitable for quantitative evaluation because it does not account for the two most significant factors that contribute to system failure after fault tolerance is implemented in a software package: undetected failures and correlated faults. In N-version programming the undetected failures include those that never reach the voter (see Section 7.3.1), while in the recovery block approach they arise from inadequate coverage of the acceptance test. Correlated faults are those present in two or more versions of a program (in the recovery block case failures will result only if the primary and all alternates are faulty).

Figure 7.11 is a representation of these potential causes of system failure for a recovery block with a single alternate. A given recovery block can be in one of the following four states:

1. Primary routine operates satisfactorily.
2. A failure in the primary software has been detected.
3. Alternate routine operates satisfactorily.
4. Recovery block fails (abort condition).

The possible transitions between these states are shown by the arcs in Figure 7.11. Of particular interest is the arc 3,1, which models reversion to the primary routine after satisfactory operation in the backup mode. This arc represents the capability (not usually present in hardware failure models) of permitting an element that has caused a failure to be returned to service. In software the failure is not due to a physical deterioration. It is due to the inability of the primary routine to process correctly a particular data set in a particular machine state. Because the primary routine is presumed to be more efficient or to possess other capabilities superior to those of the backup, it is desirable to return it to service as soon as the data and machine states have changed. This can be done by initially limiting the operation of the alternate to a fixed number of iterations, say 10. If there are repeated failures of the primary after it is returned to service, a longer interval for operation in the backup mode will be allowed.

The system failure probability is represented by the probability of all paths that originate at state 1 and terminate at state 4. These paths are

| 1,4: | undetected failure of the primary routine |
| 1,2 and 2,4: | detected failure of the primary routine and a correlated |

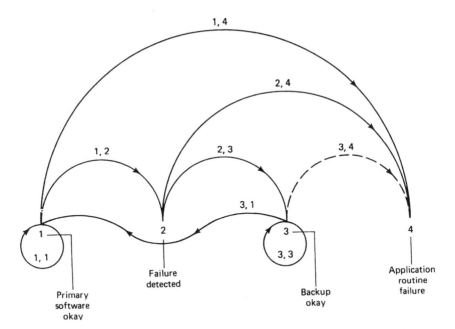

Figure 7.11: State transition model.

	fault in the alternate that prevents state 3 from being achieved
1,2 and 2,3 and 3,4:	detected failure of the primary routine followed by satisfactory operation of the alternate and then followed by an uncorrelated fault in the alternate before reversion to the primary

This latter arc is shown dashed because it represents an extremely small contribution to the probability of failure, as will be seen in the numerical example below. However, this is the only uncorrelated failure of the primary and backup routines modeled in Figure 7.10. The transition probabilities associated with this model are shown in Table 7.3, where the following symbols are used:

Table 7.3: Transition Probabilities for the Model of Figure 7.11

		To			
		1	2	3	4
	1	$1-f$	cf	0	$f(1-c)$
From	2	0	0	u	$1-u$
	3	0^a	0	s	$1-s$
	4	0	0	0	1

[a]The reversion to state 1 is a deterministic process which is outside the scope of this analysis.

c = coverage (error detection capability) of the acceptance test
f = failure probability of the primary routine
s = success probability of the alternate routine
u = probability that no correlated faults exist in the primary and alternate

The probability of failure of the recovery block, $P[F]$, is the sum of the probabilities leading to state 4, or

$$P[F] = P[1,4] + P[1,2]P[2,4] + P[1,2]P[2,3]P[3,4]$$
$$= f(1 - c) + cf(1 - u) + cfu(1 - s)$$
$$= f(1 - cus) = f(1 - E)$$

where the notation E has been introduced to represent the effectiveness of the fault tolerance provisions. When there is no fault tolerance (when any factor contributing to the product cus is 0), the failure probability of the recovery block is identical with the failure probability of the primary routine.

As a means of enabling the reader to gain some experience with this model and to illustrate the reliability improvement possible with the recovery block approach, we consider a software system composed of ten tasks of approximately equal size and complexity. The software operates 24 hours a day and it uses 50 percent of the CPU time. The execution time is therefore 12 hours per day. We assume that the software maintenance cycle for critical programs is 15 calendar days. Thus, between the first detection of a fault and its correction, the software will be executed a total of 180 hours, and each individual task will be executed 18 hours. From Table 7.1 it is seen that the best operational software has a failure rate of 0.01 per hour, so that the expected number of failures during the maintenance interval is almost 2 for the entire software and 0.18 for the specific task in which the fault was found.

We now assume that each task is structured as a recovery block with a single alternate. Two implementations of fault tolerance are considered: a standard implementation in which the probability of undetected failures for each acceptance test is 10 percent ($c = 0.9$) and the probability of correlated failures between the primary and the alternate is also 10 percent ($u = 0.9$), and a very carefully validated implementation which reduces each of these probabilities to 5 percent ($c = u = 0.95$). The success probability of the alternate software in both cases is assumed to be 0.998. This value is based on the alternate executing only 1 percent of the time that the primary module is invoked. The resulting failure probabilities are shown in Table 7.4.

The standard implementation reduces the failure probability of the recovery block to slightly less than 20 percent of the original value, while the validated approach reduces it to 10 percent. If additional recovery provisions are incorporated at the system level (such as the ones shown in Figure 7.4), it is quite reasonable to expect that one-half of the remaining failures can be avoided. Under the most favorable assumptions used here, fault tolerance techniques can thus reduce the failure probability to about 5 percent of the level that prevails without their use.

Table 7.4: Failure Probabilities for a Single Recovery Block

Condition	Symbol	Probability	
		Standard Implementation	Validated Implementation
Primary failure	f	0.180	0.180
Coverage	c	0.900	0.950
Uncorrelatedness	u	0.900	0.950
Success of alternate	s	0.998	0.998
Fault tolerance effectiveness	cus	0.808	0.901
Failure of block	$P[F]$	0.034	0.018

7.5 CONSTRUCTION OF ACCEPTANCE TESTS

This section describes types and selection criteria for acceptance tests, the key element of the recovery block approach described in Section 7.3. There are two levels on which the acceptance tests can be performed. The higher-level acceptance test (i.e., one which tests that the outputs of the program are consistent with the functional requirements) is called a functional acceptance test. The lower-level test is called the structural acceptance test and tests sections of code to ensure that key variables and functions have been properly executed. Functional-level tests are always required. However, for programs under development, the addition of structural tests provides the following benefits:

1. Unexpected behavior of the primary system will be noted even in cases where only a mild degradation is encountered. This aids in program evaluation.
2. Switching to the alternate program is exercised more often under realistic (unplanned) conditions. Realistic testing of the fault tolerance mechanism is a difficult undertaking.
3. As a program matures, it is usually easier to relax acceptance conditions than to make them more restrictive.

7.5.1 Program Characteristics Useful for Acceptance Tests

Most acceptance tests currently used fall into one of the following categories: (1) satisfaction of requirements, (2) accounting tests, (3) reasonableness tests, and (4) computer run-time checks. Although the distinctions between these categories is sometimes blurred, the classifications do serve a useful starting point for the designer confronting a section of critical code.

Acceptance tests may be devised such that they test for what a program should do or for what a program should not do. For example, acceptance tests in software controlling an automated rail transit system can be written to test for conformance to specified velocities at each location on the route or for violation of safety rules (e.g., the train should not exceed a certain velocity around curves or in the vicinity of a station). Testing for a violation of safety conditions (i.e., testing for what the program should not do) may be simpler and provide a higher degree of independence of the acceptance test from the primary routine than testing for conformance to the preplanned velocity profile (i.e., what the program should do).

Unfortunately, there is no methodology for deciding on the most appropriate type of test for a given situation. Thus the primary problem facing the software designer is what kind of acceptance test should be used, a choice that is often dictated by run-time, storage, and error detection requirements. Ultimately, one would like to see a classification of acceptance tests that characterize them by these parameters to allow a rational selection for each application. The fact that this stage has not been realized, however, need not deter advancing with practical applications; there is little methodology for the routine testing of software, yet it sometimes yields satisfactory results.

Satisfaction of requirements.   In many cases the problem statement or the specifications of the software impose conditions that must be met at the completion of program execution. These conditions may be used to construct the acceptance tests. The simplest example is inversion of mathematical operations (e.g., squaring the result of a square-root operation to see if it equals the original operand). Another simple illustration of this concept is the sort operation acceptance test described by Randell (1975). At the completion of a sort, the acceptance test checks that the elements are in uniformly descending order and that the number of elements in the sorted set is equal to the number of elements in the original set. This test is not complete; changes in an element during execution would not be detected. An additional component of the test, ensuring that every element in the sorted set appeared in the unsorted set, would make the test exhaustive. However, this component was rejected because of run-time requirements.

As noted previously, independence is a crucial consideration in the design of acceptance tests. Devising independent satisfaction of requirements tests may be a difficult and subtle problem. For example, the famous "eight queens" problem requires that eight queens be located on a chess board such that no two queens threaten each other. An acceptance test based on satisfaction of requirements might check that the horizontal, vertical, and two diagonals associated with each queen do not contain the location of any other queen. If the primary routine involves the same check as part of the solution algorithm, this acceptance test is not suitable.

As will be shown in Section 7.5.2, testing for satisfaction of requirements is usually most effective when carried out on small segments of code. Accounting tests and reasonableness tests discussed below can handle larger sections of code, a consideration that may be desirable if capacity or timing constraints prove to be limiting. However, for text editing systems, compilers, and similar programs, tests for satisfaction of requirements constitute the most promising approach at present.

Accounting checks.   Accounting checks are suitable for transaction-oriented applications with simple mathematical operations such as airline reservation systems, library records, and the control of hazardous materials. The simplest form of accounting checks is the checksum. Whenever a large number of records is transmitted or reordered, a tally for both the total number of records and the sum over all records of a particular data field can be compared between source and destination.

The double-entry bookkeeping system has evolved over the last 500 years as an effective means of detecting errors due to incorrect transcriptions or information losses in the noncomputerized commercial environment. Such accounting practices have been instituted in financial computing and are applicable in other high-volume transaction applications. A complete description of this procedure may be found in most elementary accounting texts.

When the software involves control of physically measurable inventories such as nuclear material, dangerous drugs, or precious metals, the reconciliation of authorized transactions with the physical inventory can be used as an acceptance test. In many cases, determination of the physical quantity can be automated so that the entire process can be handled without operator intervention.

In the examples described above, discrepancies detected by the acceptance test may be due to a software failure, deliberate alteration of input or internal data, or actual theft. Thus the dividing line between software reliability and security becomes blurred. Although intellectually distressing, this lack of distinction opens the way for software reliability techniques to be used in computerized security applications, and vice versa.

Reasonableness tests.   Reasonableness tests detect software failures by use of precomputed ranges, expected sequences of program states, or other relationships that are expected to prevail. The difference between satisfaction of requirements tests and reasonableness tests is that the latter are based on physical constraints while the former type are based on logical or mathematical relationships.

Reasonableness tests are suitable in control or switching systems where physical constraints can determine the range of possible outcomes. An illustration of the principle of the reasonableness test is the determination of the true airspeed, a computed quantity, from the indicated airspeed, a sensed quantity, in a flight control system. The first level of acceptance test based on a precomputed range arrived at from physical constraints is that the speed must be within the structural capabilities of the airframe (e.g., 140 to 1,100 km/h for a commercial subsonic aircraft). Thus, if the true airspeed is outside this range, there is something wrong with either the sensor or the computer (an additional possibility is that the aircraft is out of control).

Further refinements on this test would use a reasonable range of changes to true airspeed. Thus, if changes between the current airspeed and the previous value indicate accelerations beyond the design limit of the aircraft, an abnormal condition exists. This test is actually considerably more powerful in that much smaller deviations can be detected. For example, if the previous true airspeed is 1,000 km/h and the subsequent calculation, which may occur in the next tenth of a second, results in an airspeed of 1,020 km/h, the acceptance test will detect an error because the implied acceleration is almost 6g!

A second type of reasonableness test is based on progression between subsequent states. For example, in an electronic telephone switching system, it is not reasonable to proceed from a connected state to a ringing state or line-busy state. However, such a test is not exhaustive; it would not detect the premature termination of a connection.

Tests for reasonableness of numerical or state variables are quite flexible and effective for constructing fault-tolerant process control software. They permit acceptance criteria to be modified as a program matures.

Run-time checks.   Run-time checks consist of those provided by most current computers as continuous execution sequences which are often hardware implemented. Such tests detect anomalous states such as divide by zero, overflow, underflow, undefined operation code, end of file, or write-protection violations. Although not specifically designed as such, these run-time tests can serve as additional acceptance tests that cover a much wider area and detect more subtle discrepancies. Upon detection of a run-time condition error, a bit in a status register is set and transfer to an alternate routine can be effected.

Run-time checks can also incorporate data structure and procedure-oriented tests that are embedded in special support software or in the operating system. Such examples include array value checking or unauthorized entries to subroutines. Stucki (1975) and Yau (1975, 1976) describe a number of interesting run-time monitoring techniques, many of which are now incorporated in commercial software products.

7.5.2 Fault Trees as a Design Aid

The overall design goal of fault-tolerant software can be briefly stated as preparing for the unexpected. A key step in reaching this goal is the identification of conditions that should trigger invocation of the alternate routine.

Unfortunately, even in principle, there is no way to anticipate all the problems that will be encountered. However, in designing fault-tolerant software, one can have a conception of the general classes of failures that can occur. Fault trees can be used as a means of identifying these classes of faults in a top-down manner, and if used as part of a formal design process, can serve as documentation of potential software failures which are covered in the fault-tolerant design. In addition, review of the fault-tolerant aspects of the software is facilitated by the use of the trees: Failures that are covered are explicitly listed; uncovered failures do not appear.

Traditionally, fault trees have been used for the evaluation of hardware reliability. The basic notion in this application is that a top event (i.e., failure of the system) is broken down into simpler events (e.g., failures of subsystems or individual circuits) that are characterized as "yes/no" occurrences. These simpler events are linked together by AND or OR gates.

This process of breaking down complex events into simpler events is continued until the failures of individual components or other events with known probabilities are identified. One then determines the probability of successively higher-level events by combining probabilities of the immediately lower events in the ways dictated by the gates linking them together: addition in the case of an OR gate; multiplication in the case of an AND gate. The final result of this process is an estimation of the probability of the top event as the probabilities of the lower events are combined. Detailed descriptions on the applications of fault trees to hardware systems reliability can be found in the Fault Tree Handbook (NRC, 1981).

The application of this technique for software reliability proceeds along similar lines as for hardware. The top event is the failure of a software system, and successive levels describe various types of failures that can occur in the system. The bottom-level events, also known as primal events, consist of specific modules or sections of code.

Unlike hardware fault trees, however, these primal events do not have specific failure probabilities. Instead, they represent events whose success or failure can be tested relatively simply and in real time. If it can be shown that all events leading into an OR gate can be tested in such a way, the higher-level event in question is said to be covered by the set of acceptance tests. On the other hand, if any single event leading into an AND gate can be simply tested, the higher-level event is covered (i.e., all inputs to an AND gate must be uncovered in order for the output to be uncovered). If all higher-level events can be covered by acceptance tests on the primal events that have been identified, one can characterize the system as having 100 percent coverage. Techniques for demonstration of complete coverage in complex trees are available (e.g., complementary cut sets discussed in the U.S. Atomic Energy Commission study (1976)). However, even for the relatively complex software systems, the trees may be sufficiently understandable that demonstration of coverage can be shown by means of inspection.

Although fault trees do not guarantee comprehensive coverage, they are an improvement over existing techniques for the placement of acceptance tests, which are basically intuitive and which depend on "reasonable" assumptions and undocumented "truths" about the system as perceived by its designers. Advantages of the fault tree approach include:

A more pictorial method for deriving and placing acceptance tests which is easy to understand.

Documentation of all assumptions on anticipated inputs, outputs, and operations.

Easier design reviews for verification of completeness, correct reasoning, and proper assumptions.

Documentation of deliberate omissions (perhaps on the basis of being "extremely unlikely" or because of a design decision).

Together with these advantages, there are some problems inherent in the use of this methodology. As noted above, the method does not ensure coverage, nor does it guarantee that all flaws will be spotted. Like any graphical method, fault trees tend to take up a lot of space.

The drawing of fault trees is more an art than a science. A useful, comprehensible fault tree, like a flowchart, is an aesthetically pleasing work which can greatly facilitate the comprehension of a complex computer program. Some research has been done on the automated drawing of fault trees for hardware (Lapp, 1977) and software systems (Leveson, 1983). However, fault tree usefulness in providing engineering insight into the system under consideration is limited. A thorough understanding of the system and a goal of explicitness are prerequisites for the drawing of coherent, logical, and comprehensive fault trees.

7.5.3 Placement of Acceptance Tests within the Program

The exact form of the fault trees depends on the system requirements. However, one can develop a framework for their general form as shown in Figure 7.12. The module under consideration will perform several operations associated with its overall function. The top event in this case will be failure of the module to meet its overall functional requirements, and beneath that will be failure of the module to fulfill its functional specifications (there may be several levels of OR gates if the functional specifications for the module are subdivided). Development continues until either

1. A sufficiently detailed and explicit failure is identified which can be tested for and bypassed with an alternate routine, or
2. A predetermined level is reached (perhaps by a separate set of design specifications).

In many cases it may be possible to devise recovery blocks that can both detect and correct errors on the functional requirements level. However, in other cases, development of an acceptance test or a parallel alternate routine may be too complicated, and development of the fault trees below the functional level will provide a simpler alternative.

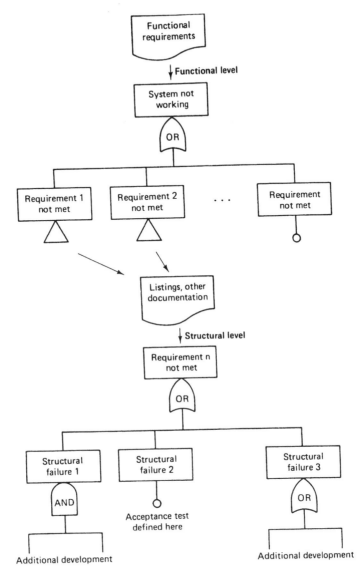

Figure 7.12: Development of fault trees for the placement of acceptance tests.

As shown in Figure 7.12, development of the trees below the functional re-quirements level involves a description of the structural aspects of subroutines, procedures, or data structures contained within the module. This description will generally involve more detailed documentation than the requirements listings for the functional-level recovery blocks. The documentation may involve some textual material, but for the most part, it will involve the source listings. Structural acceptance tests and alternate routines are developed by examining the input, transformation processes, and output of the component procedures or subroutines. Additional considerations are where particular sections of code sit in the hierarchy of routines, or the execution order.

To illustrate the approach, an example is taken from a module from the operating system of the fault-tolerant multiprocessor computer (FTMP) developed by the C. S. Draper Laboratories (Hopkins, 1978). The FTMP architecture consists of ten processors configured as three triads and a single spare. The component processors of each triad are tightly coupled (i.e., execute each instruction cycle together), but the triads are more loosely coupled to each other (i.e., synchronization occurs only after a number of tasks have been performed). The software module under consideration is called the dispatcher and is responsible for assigning tasks to each of the triads. The dispatcher also designates one of the triads to restart the task list at periodic intervals and interfaces with a hardware timer to handle interrupts. The following are briefly stated functional requirements for the dispatcher. The dispatcher must

1. Initialize certain variables upon power-up and at the beginning of a new task iteration cycle.
2. Execute tasks at one of three predetermined iteration rates.
3. Recognize the timer interrupt for the start of a new iteration cycle.
4. Provide for retirement of faulty processors and reconfiguration of the system if a hardware fault is detected.
5. Execute a set of data transfer operations at predetermined iteration rates.

A top-level fault tree for the dispatcher based on these requirements is shown in Figure 7.13. The OR gate indicates that failure to meet any of the five require-

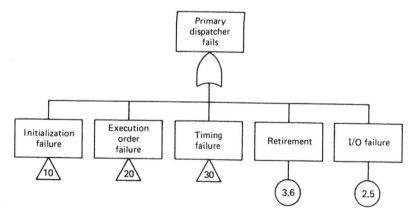

Figure 7.13: Top-level fault tree for the FTMP dispatcher.

ments listed above is a failure of the system. The term "primary" is used to distinguish this dispatcher from alternate versions which are called in the event of a failure in the primary. The triangles under the first three failures are transfers to subsequent development; the circles under the last two indicate that this level of detail is sufficient for development of the acceptance tests.

Figure 7.14 shows a further development of transfer 30 of Figure 7.13. The development moves beyond the terminology of the functional specifications into the vocabulary of variable names, procedure failures, and other specific coding implementation details. The tree is terminated once the failure can be detected with a specific acceptance test or is out of the scope of software reliability. Thus the failure "interval timer not loaded" can be detected with acceptance test 1.4, and "clock failure," which is considered to be a hardware failure, is not checked by any acceptance test.

The Boolean properties of the AND and OR gates are employed in the placement of acceptance tests. When an OR gate links the failures, all must be tested, but when an AND gate joins the failure, it is necessary that only one event be tested. Thus, for the "Stuck in R4 Rate Group" failure, the three possible causes—"Stuck in R4 Applications Task," "Stuck in Task Selection," or "Stuck in Uninterruptible ASM Routine"—must each be tested for. However, the "Stuck in Applications Routine" failure can occur only when two conditions prevail simultaneously: (1) The interval timer is not set and (2) a design flaw in the applications routine causes a failure to terminate. In this case, only one of these potential failures needs to be covered with an acceptance test. Checking the status of the interval timer is easier than proving the correctness of every applications task for all possible data states and configurations.

As is evident from this example, considerable insight into the operation of the software system is required for the drawing of fault trees. This understanding can be difficult to achieve because of the following three factors:

1. The system is under development. Thus design specifications, coding, and even requirements are subject to change. It is possible that assumptions used in the derivation of earlier acceptance tests are no longer valid, or that the recovery block itself is no longer appropriate because of changes in design.

2. As a result of the system being under development, documentation is often insufficient (if available at all). The definitive information is the source code. In a disciplined environment, supporting information will be current, complete, and organized. Unfortunately, it is often the case that informal communications are used: excerpts from articles, progress reports, and hastily drawn diagrams produced on lunch napkins.

3. From the organizational point of view, it is desirable that the primary design and fault tolerance groups communicate only formally to ensure a truly independent assessment of the software vulnerabilities. However,

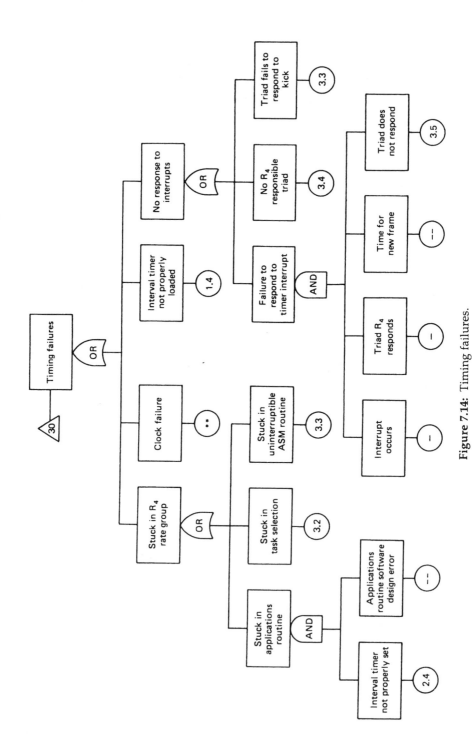

Figure 7.14: Timing failures.

during development, this assessment can be extremely difficult because of frequent and informal interaction between the two groups.

It is thus necessary to balance a variety of concerns (design stability versus ability to adjust to unforeseen developments, resources devoted to documentation versus coding, independence of the design and fault-tolerant groups versus the need for one to explain to the other what it is doing) in the management of the design process.

7.6 EXCEPTION HANDLING

Exception handling is the interruption of the normal execution flow of a program upon detection of a predefined anomalous condition and the branching to a predefined section of code. It is well suited for implementation of the robustness and temporal redundancy techniques described above. Exception handling was first implemented as a formal construct within the PL/I programming language and has since been implemented in the Ada programming language. Rudimentary forms of exception handling are also found in other languages such as C and FORTRAN. Because Ada is intended for use in real-time critical systems and is mandated for use by the U.S. Department of Defense and many other governmental agencies throughout the world, exception handling has assumed greater importance as a technique for implementing software fault tolerance. A discussion of the structure and syntax of exception handling in Ada can be found in the Ada language reference manual (DOD, 1983). A few particularly pertinent issues are discussed in the following sections.

7.6.1 Design Issues

Effective use of exception handlers requires that anticipated triggering effects, detection of their manifestations within the executing system, and the appropriate means of mitigating undesired effects must be well understood. This understanding can best be arrived at through the following process:

1. Identification of appropriate levels for handling exceptions within the software architecture (i.e., overall program level, task level, module level)
2. Development of a classification of anticipated triggering events for each level of the software (e.g., invalid input, no file, device failure, database inconsistency, late response, early response, queue overflow, arithmetic overflow, constraint error)
3. Enumeration of potential effects and desired mitigating actions for each of these triggering event classes at each appropriate level (e.g., substitute de-

fault value, retry, terminate this iteration and return, terminate the task, terminate the program)

Definition of the desired mitigating actions is a nontrivial activity—particularly in a large software project. For example, if a module is expected to terminate without potentially disastrous effects on the remainder of the system, it must do so in an orderly fashion. It may be necessary to issue "death notices" to communicating tasks (which must then take their own recovery actions) and to release locks on system resources. This in turn results in derived requirements in the software to monitor these activities so that the exception handler can take the appropriate action. When rollback is involved, the "cleanup" required to coordinate the orderly reversion to a previous state among multiple processes may be even more involved.

In order to manage the potential complexity of the design of exception handlers, general exception handling philosophies may be defined at each level. For example, at the lowest level, the intent may be to mask the failure through robustness or rollback/retry where the scope of the rollback is limited to the module or programming unit. At higher levels, the intent may be to perform an orderly abort and termination of the thread, task, or process. At the highest level, an orderly shutdown of the node and notification of interfacing systems should be the primary goal of the exception handlers.

7.6.2 Implementation Issues

The control flow during exception handling is much harder to visualize than that of normal execution because exception handling may be dispersed throughout the code. Thus, development of a detailed design and means of verification that the design has been conformed to are both necessary. Within Ada this can be facilitated by using the scope and visibility rules to control which exceptions will be used at a given level of the exception handling hierarchy. Naming conventions and predefined exceptions can be used to further simplify this process. The objective is to ensure that

- exceptions are not propagated out of scope so that the caller won't handle the exception explicitly.
- exceptions are not mapped to the incorrect handlers because the same name has been inadvertently used.
- exceptions to be handled by the calling program are not raised prior to the "begin" statement; the most likely way for this undesirable event to happen is if a subprogram is called in the declaration.

A part of the exception handling verification process in Ada should be to map every "raise" clause to its handler. In other languages, it should be an explicit evaluation of the ON statement.

7.7 CASE STUDY: IMPLEMENTATION OF THE EXTENDED DISTRIBUTED RECOVERY BLOCK

The objective of this discussion is to acquaint the reader with implementation issues that must be faced in the development of a fault-tolerant software architecture—particularly in a distributed system.

7.7.1 Notes on the System Architecture

The EDRB computing platform consists of commercially available hardware and real-time operating systems. The advantages of conventional hardware and operating systems are maturity, reliability, functionality, and low cost.

The executive layer transforms the basic platform into a fault-tolerant system. However, the executive layer software itself does *not* have any of the robustness, time redundancy, or software diversity characteristics described in the previous section. The reasons are: (a) this software is subjected to a relatively limited input domain and can therefore be tested thoroughly to establish its behavior in the presence of normal and anomalous situations; (b) the consequences of a failure in the executive layer are similar to the failure of an operating system or hardware component *if the failures can be contained within the node* so that to the companion and other nodes in the system the failure is a "fail-stop" event.

The details of the hardware and software commercial products used in the prototype installation are described below. The component selection aimed at low cost and this objective was readily achieved. Indeed, the hardware complement chosen for the implementation is a graphic demonstration of the primary attractions of distributed system fault tolerance: low cost, standardization, and modularity. The net benefit is extensibility which is crucial for any longlived system.

7.7.2 EDRB Networks

Figure 7.6 shows the connectivity scheme within the EDRB. There are two types of networks in the EDRB: the *node pair* network and the *global* network. Both the node pair and global networks are dual redundant. This two-level configuration minimizes delays for time-critical functions between operational nodes in large networks and contains faults that might propagate across a single network. The node pair network is used for local communication between the operational nodes. The global network connects all operational nodes with the supervisor and display nodes. The global network can be configured such that all nodes are connected to both networks (dual redundancy) or so that an arbitrary set of nodes (e.g., even numbered nodes) is connected on one network and the remaining nodes (e.g., odd numbered nodes) are connected on the second. For systems with a small number of nodes, connection of all nodes to the global network provides the benefit of dual redundancy without a significant message delay penalty. In systems with a larger number of nodes, segregation provides the benefit of fault containment and reduction of network delays. Appropriate partitioning of nodes can reduce the impact of loss of a single supervisor network.

Messages are passed as datagrams, that is, connectionless messages, rather than using virtual circuits. The rationale for this implementation is that messages contain repetitive data and are sent across multiple physical paths so that loss of individual datagrams is tolerable. Application-level integrity of received messages is checked by means of a task-specific test such as an alternate representation of the sender identification. For messages requesting or confirming a change in state, protocols for acknowledgement are implemented within the communicating tasks; in many cases acknowledgement is implicit in the announcement of a periodic message indicating the new state.

Virtual circuits provide end-to-end acknowledgement of messages and additional services for multipacket transmission which allow greater flexibility in interprocessor communication. Such communication is well supported on the operating system used in this design. However, many messages are repetitive and time-critical. Thus, delays due to the retries which are a feature of virtual circuits can create significant problems—particularly if the destination node has failed. In some cases, the excessive delays brought on by retries together with the operating system responses to delayed communications disable the network for periods of minutes.

7.7.3 Response Time, Recovery Time, and Throughput

One of the key characteristics of a real-time system is that an output signal is required to be generated within a certain interval of when the input is received. This is called the *response time requirement*. The recovery time requirement can usually be set somewhat longer (see discussion at the end of Section 7.3). The consequences of excessive recovery time depend on the operating mode and response times of the system. Computer-assisted landing of an aircraft in bad weather is an example of very restrictive requirements for recovery time.

Although a very fast response time (1 ms or less) is possible today using inexpensive processors, fault tolerance requirements impose significantly greater limitations. For example, the maximum EDRB recovery time for a fail-silent event is five frames. The highest heartbeat interval that has thus far been used is 20 ms. Thus, the EDRB as currently implemented can be used for systems whose response time requirements are 100 ms or greater. This capability is adequate for most process control applications (including nuclear reactor control). To put this capability into perspective, the reaction time for a star 100-meter sprinter leaving the starting block was reported at 125 ms.

Recovery time and processor throughput must usually be traded off. Specifically, in a distributed system, the most common form of detecting a "fail-silent" or "fail-stop" event is the absence of a heartbeat. As the heartbeat frequency is increased, the recovery time will be decreased because of a decrease in detection latency. On the other hand, the greater the heartbeat frequency, the more process-ing capacity is required. Efficient heartbeat monitoring and recovery logic (allo-cated to the monitor and node manager tasks described in the following section) are important for minimizing the throughput penalties. In addition, the increas-ing availability of high-performance processing reduces the importance of this factor.

The two basic strategies for real-time data acquisition are polling and inter-rupt handling. In polling, the application task is run at a fixed interval, and the data which happens to be present in the input buffer at the time the process is run is the data that will be used in the calculation. In interrupt handling, the presence of input data causes the application to be run immediately. If the control system is based on polling, it is convenient to use heartbeat intervals as a time basis. Specifically, fast "rate group" tasks (i.e., those required to maintain system stabil-ity) would be run every interval; medium rate group tasks would be run every two intervals; and so forth. However, in asynchronous systems, the heartbeat in-terval must be maintained independently of the data input intervals.

For distributed fault-tolerant systems to be useful in real-time control appli-cations preemptive task dispatching in the operating system is necessary so that high priority tasks are guaranteed to be invoked at the next timer interrupt (this is not the case in standard UNIX). This dispatcher should also minimize the amount of time spent in switching tasks and in processing interrupts. This im-plies a small and efficient operating system kernel with very limited functionality in areas other than task switching (file system management, networking, etc.). Using this design philosophy, other system services would be implemented as processes which are executed under the control of the kernel.

7.7.4 Key Executive Layer Tasks

This subsection describes the node manager, monitor, and supervisor software in further detail.

Node manager task. The node manager determines the node's role and version and responds to requests or confirmations of companion node role switches. This determination is made during each of the following events:

- Start of a new frame.
- Application completion.
- Expiration of the application timer (i.e., application has not completed in al-lowed time).
- Expiration of the data timer (i.e., no data has arrived within the anticipated interval).
- Receipt of a message that the companion has started a new frame.
- Companion application completion.

- Expiration of the companion application timer.
- Expiration of the companion data timer.

Whenever the node manager task determines that a role switch is necessary because of an application failure or timeout, it immediately sends a *switch request* to the companion. When a node manager receives a switch request, it immediately sends a *switch confirm* to the companion. Switch requests and confirms are sent to the supervisor node only at the beginning of each heartbeat frame in order to limit message processing workload during recovery actions.

In most cases application failures and data timeouts (that is, timeouts on the application waiting for new system data) will result in the transition from active primary to shadow. The single exception is if the active node runs the primary application version and there is a temporary loss of system data to that node. It is desirable that the node should not immediately revert to running the alternate application (although it should still request to switch roles with its companion node).

The node manager considers the previous failure history before deciding which version of the software to run and on which node. For example, when there have been failures in the previous cycle using the primary routine and there is a failure in the current cycle, the alternate routine will be used and there will not be a hardware switchover. The alternate routine will be used for three subsequent iterations and then the primary routine will be tried once again. Some special cases must also be considered in the recovery logic. For example, if there is a primary failure on one node and an alternate failure on the shadow, then control is retained at the active node, and the supervisor is notified. If this simultaneous failure happens multiple times, then the supervisor sounds an alarm. This algorithm results in additional processing before a recovery action is attempted. However, the benefit is stability in the roles of the nodes during a complex failure. This stability increases reliability of the system.

Generally, any run of the application which completes within its allotted time frame and which passes all of its acceptance test criteria will result in control output if the node is in the active role at the time of application completion. Additionally, the node manager will force output to the controlled device any time a node transitions from shadow to active and has successful data to output from the previous application run. If this transition occurs due to a supervisor approved companion restart, the node may or may not have acceptable results to output. On the other hand, if the transition is due to a confirmed companion role switch request, the node must have acceptable results from the previous run in order to satisfy the transition criteria.

The action taken by repeated failures of the shadow node also can not be depicted in the state diagram. When such a failure occurs, the affected node ceases to generate heartbeats. This action causes its companion node (after receiving supervisor approval) to trigger a hardware reset, perhaps curing the sustained failure. In order to avoid repeated restarts of this type, the node manager will only take this action if it has a record of at least one successful application run since the node was booted (and only after eight consecutive failures or timeouts while in the shadow role).

Monitor task. The monitor task is responsible for detecting and recovering from failures on the companion node manifested by a sustained loss of heartbeat (i.e., power failure, operating system crash). Any time the monitor determines that the most recently received companion frame number is three or more frames behind its own, it begins transmitting companion restart requests to the supervisor. These requests continue, one per frame, until one of two events occurs: (1) the companion node's heartbeat falls back into the range of acceptability, or (2) the monitor receives a companion restart approval message from the supervisor. In the latter case, the monitor would then signal the node manager task to take over the active role and run the primary version of the application, irrespective of its previous state.

Other than handling companion restart requests, the only time the monitor task determines a node's role or version is during system startup (or restart). Simply stated, the logic used by the monitor in determining the node's initial state is as follows: If the companion node has already communicated that it is running in the active role, begin by running shadow/alternate; otherwise run active/primary. This information is then passed to the node manager, which takes over control of the node's role and version for the duration.

Supervisor node. The supervisor node provides system configuration, node role (i.e., active or shadow), and application specific parameters needed by the operational computers for initialization and recovery after restart. The supervisor must also consent to a restart request before any operational node performs a restart on its companion. Because issuing a restart command results in the disabling of an operational node for a period of tens of seconds, spurious restarts can cause system failures. For example, if the shadow node fails to detect a heartbeat from the active computer, the problem may exist in its own communication interface or in the operating system rather than a problem in the primary. Issue of a restart command under these circumstances could result in the system being left without any functional computer—a situation far worse than if there were only a single computer in charge of control. This is the primary reason for requiring consent of a third computer, that is, the supervisor, before a restart is allowed. This strategy ensures that no single failure results in loss of system control. However, it does so at the cost of additional computing resources and a longer response time than would be necessary if no concurrence were needed before issuing a restart.

The supervisor is not a single point of failure and operates in strictly a passive role. It cannot cause an operational node to change its state through a command or a restart request. Thus, a supervisor failure only impacts the ability of the system to recover from unannounced failures involving the monitor task but does not affect system operation in the absence of such failures. The supervisor log is recorded to nonvolatile storage, and the actions of the supervisor require three or fewer frames of operational history. Thus, the supervisor can fail and be manually restored. The EDRB tolerance of an extended supervisor outage allows greater flexibility in the design of the supervisor, assurance of an unambiguous single point of higher level system control, greater functionality, and a more so-phisticated user interface. The greater functionality and enhanced user interface benefit maintainability and support operator resolution of anomalies. Paradoxi-cally, the result is a greater contribution to system availability relative to a less functional but more available fault-tolerant high-level system manager.

In addition to well-behaved supervisor faults such as a "fail-silent" state, the EDRB can tolerate Byzantine supervisor faults (active, false results). For example, if the supervisor fails "active," that is, starts outputting invalid data, there will be no effect unless a second failure occurs, that is, a faulty shadow node believes it has is-sued a restart request. A "babbling" supervisor will be disregarded because opera-tional nodes limit the amount of messages that they will process in a frame. All analyses thus far have shown that in the event of such a failure, data restoration could be achieved within a matter of minutes, and that loss of a recovery capability during this time does not significantly affect overall system availability.

7.7.5 Implementation Details

The EDRB has been implemented using ISA bus and Std-32 bus-based PC/AT compatible computers running under the QNX 4 operating systems (QNX, 1992) and on a VME bus-based 68040 system using the VxWorks 5 real-time kernel (Wind, 1993). The EDRB architecture allows for operational nodes to be inter-faced directly to the plant systems which they control. The benefits of such inter-facing are (1) enhanced fault containment because only a limited portion of the control system and a limited portion of the plant are interconnected and (2) faster response times relative to the use of plantwide networks of "data highways" be-cause of the elimination of intermediate network interface delays. However, be-cause operational nodes are connected only to specific plant functions, allocation of redundant resources is static.

Each operational node also has a circuit which generates a hardware reset based on the receipt of an appropriate coding sequence from the companion op-erational node. This mechanism is effective for maintenance-free restoration of re-sources, disabled operating system failures (e.g., deadlock or nonavailability of a critical resource) or transient hardware faults (e.g., a power surge or a memory read/write error). Reset signals are generated under software control of the com-panion operational node working with the consent of the supervisor under a pro-tocol that was described above.

For PC/AT systems, EDRB networks are implemented using ARCNET (SMS, 1987). Advantages of the ARCNET are low cost, wide use in industrial con-trol applications, deterministic response time, extensibility, versatility (from 2.5

to 100 Mbits/sec. on coaxial, twisted pair, or fiber optic cable), and MAC-level error-handling features implemented in hardware. This configuration allows worst case single failure recovery times of less than 100 ms. with a background load of approximately 30 percent using Intel 80486 33 MHz microprocessors. For the VME systems now under development, the global network is implemented using point to point fiber optic links with memory mapping. The advantages of this configuration are fast response times which are needed for very high-speed applications such as fault-tolerant robotics control.

REFERENCES

[Anderson85] Anderson, T., P. A. Barrett, et al., "Software Fault Tolerance: An Evaluation," *IEEE Trans. on Software Engineering*, vol. SE-11 no. 12 (December 1985), pp. 1502–1510.

[Avizienis77] Avizienis, A., and L. Chen, "On the Implementation of N-version Programming for Software Fault Tolerance during Execution," *Proc, COMPSAC'77*, (November 1977), IEEE Cat. 77CH1291-4C, pp. 149–155.

[Avizienis84] Avizienis, A., and J. P. J. Kelly, "Fault Tolerance by Design Diversity: Concepts and Experiments," *Computer*, vol. 17 no. 8 (August 1984), pp. 67–80.

[Basili87] Basili, V., and R. Selby, "Comparing the Effectiveness of Software Testing Strategies," *IEEE Trans. Softw. Engr.*, vol. SE-13, no. 12 (December 1987).

[Chen78] Chen, L., and A. Avizienis, "N-version Programming: A Fault Tolerance Approach to Reliability of Software Operation," *Dig. 8th Ann. Int. Symp. Fault-Tolerant Comput.*, Madison, Wis., (June 21–23, 1978), IEEE Cat. 78CH1286-4C, pp. 3–9.

[Cristian90] Cristian, F., B. Dancey, and J. Dehn, "Fault Tolerance in the Advanced Automation System", *Proc. 20th Annual Fault Tolerant Computing Symposium*, (June, 1990), pp. 6–17, IEEE Cat. No. CH2877-9/90.

[DACS80] Data and Analysis Center for Software (DACS), "Software Reliability Data Submitted to the DACS by John D. Musa," (January 1980).

[Dijkstra72] Dijkstra, E. W., "Notes on Structured Programming," in *Structured Programming*, Academic Press, New York, 1972.

[DOD83] Department of Defense, *Military Standard, Ada Programming Language*, ANSI/MIL-STD-1815A, (February 1983).

[Eckhardt85] Eckhardt, D. E., and L. D. Lee, "A Theoretical Basis for the Analysis of Multi-Version Software Subject to Coincident Errors," *IEEE Trans. on Software Engineering*, vol. SE-11, no. 12, (December 1985), pp. 1511–1516.

[Eckhardt91] Eckhardt, D. E., A. K. Caglayan et al., "An Experimental Evaluation of Software Redundancy as a Strategy for Improving Reliability," *IEEE Trans. on Software Engineering*, vol. 17 no. 7, (July 1991), pp. 692–701.

[Elspas73] Elspas, B., J. C. Knight, C. D. Lee, D. F. McAllister, M. A. Vorck, and J. P. Kelly, "An Interactive System for the Verification of Computer Programs," SRI Project 1891, Stanford Research Institute (now SRI International), (September 1973).

[Fetzer88] Fetzer, James H., "Program Verification: The Very Idea," *Communications of the ACM,* vol. 31 no. 9 (September 1988), pp. 1048–1063.

[Gerhart90] Gerhart, Susan L., "Applications of Formal Methods: Developing Virtuoso Software," *IEEE Software,* vol. 7 no. 9 (September 1990), pp. 7–10.

[Goodenough80] Goodenough, J. B., and C. L. McGowan, "Software Quality Assurance: Testing and Validation," *Proc. IEEE,* vol. 68 no. 9 (September 1980), pp. 1093–1098.

[Hecht76] Hecht, H., "Fault Tolerant Software for Real-Time Applications," *Comput. Surv.,* vol. 8 no. 4 (December 1976), p. 462.

[Hecht81] Hecht, M., and H. Hecht, "Fault Tolerant Software Modules for SIFT," SoHaR, Inc. Rep. TR-81-04, (April 1981).

[Hecht91a] Hecht, M., J. Agron, H. Hecht, and K. H. Kim, "A Distributed Fault Tolerant Architecture for Nuclear Reactor and Other Critical Process Control Applications," *Proc. Fault Tolerant Computing Symposium (FTCS-21),* Montreal, Canada, (June 1991), p. 469.

[Hecht91b] Hecht, M., J. Agron, and H. Hecht, "A New Lost Cost Distributed Fault Tolerant Architecture for Process Control Applications," *Proc. Southeastcon* (March 1991), vol. 1 p. 253, IEEE Cat. No., 91CH2998-3.

[Hopkins78] Hopkins, A. L., et al., "FTMP-A Highly Reliable Fault Tolerant Multiprocessor for Aircraft," *Proc. IEEE,* vol. 66, no. 10 (October 1978), pp. 1221–1239.

[Howden78] W. E. Howden, "Methodology for the Generation of Program Test Data," *IEEE Trans. on Computers,* C-24, (1979), pp. 554–559.

[IEEE82] IEEE Std. 729-1982, "IEEE Glossary of Software Engineering Terminology," The Institute of Electrical and Electronics Engineers, Inc., 1982.

[IEEE92] "Faults and Failures," *IEEE Spectrum,* vol. 29 no. 5 (May 1992), p. 52.

[Kelly83] Kelly, J. P. J., and A. Avizienis, "A Specification-Oriented Multi-Version Fault-Tolerant Software Experiment," *Digest 13th Ann. Int'l. Symp. on Fault Tolerant Computing,* Milano, Italy, (June 1983), pp. 120–126.

[Kelly88] Kelly, J. P. J., D. Eckhardt et al., "A Large Scale Second Generation Experiment in Multi-Version Software: Description and Early Results," *Digest of Papers, FTCS-18,* Tokyo, Japan, (June 1988), pp. 9–14.

[Kim84] K. H. Kim, "Distributed Execution of Recovery Blocks: An Approach to Uniform Treatment of Hardware and Software Faults," *Proc. 4th International Conference on Distributed Computing Systems,* (May 1984), pp. 526–532.

[Kim89] Kim, K. H., and H. O. Welch, "The Distributed Execution of Recovery Blocks: An Approach for Uniform Treatment of Hardware and Software Faults in Real-Time Applications," *IEEE Trans. on Computers,* vol. 38 no. 5 (May 1989), pp. 626–636.

[King75] King, J. C., "A New Approach to Program Testing," *Proc. 1975 Int. Conf. Reliable Softw.,* (April 1975), IEEE Cat. 75 CHO940-7CSR, pp. 228–233.

[Knight86] Knight, J. C., and N. G. Leveson, "An Experimental Evaluation of the Assumption of Independence in Multiversion Programming," *IEEE Trans. on Software Enginering,* vol. SE-12 no. 1 (January 1986), pp. 96–109.

[Knight87] Knight, J. C., and J. Urquart, "On the Implementation and Use of Ada on Fault Tolerant Distributed Systems," *IEEE Trans. Softw. Engr.,* vol. SE-13 no. 5 (May 1987).

[Lapp77] Lapp, S. A., and G. J. Powers, "Computer Aided Synthesis of Fault Trees," *IEEE Trans. Reliab.* (April 1977).

[Leveson83] Leveson, N. G., and J. L. Stolzy, "Safety Analysis of Ada Programs," *IEEE Trans. Reliability*, vol. R-32 no. 5 (December 1983), pp. 496–484.

[Miller81] Miller, E. F., Jr., et al., "Application of Structural Quality Standards to Software," *Softw. Eng. Stand. Appl. Workshop*, (July 1981), IEEE Cat. 81CH1633-7, pp. 51–57.

[Musa87] Musa, John, Iannino, and Okumoto, *Software Reliability Measurement Prediction, Application*, McGraw-Hill, 1987.

[NRC81] Vesely, W. E., F. F. Goldberg, N. H. Roberts, and D. F. Haasl, *Fault Tree Handbook*, Office of Nuclear Regulatory Research, U.S. Nuclear Regulatory Commission, Washington D. C., January 1981.

[Pradhan95] Pradhan, D., H. Hecht, M. Hecht, F. Meyer, and N. Vaidya, "Cooperating Diverse Experts: A Methodology to Develop Quality Software for Critical Decision Support Systems," IEEE Aerospace Applications Conference, Aspen, CO, Feb. 1995.

[QNX92] Quantum Software Sytems, Ltd. *QNX Reference Guide, Version 4.1*, QNX Software Systems, Ltd., Kanata, Ottawa, Canada, 1992.

[Randell75] Randell, B., "System Structure for Software Fault Tolerance," *IEEE Trans. Softw. Eng.*, vol. SE-1 no. 1 (June 1975), pp. 220–232.

[Reynolds76] Reynolds, C., and R. T. Yeh, "Introduction as the Basis for Program Verification," *IEEE Trans. Softw. Eng.*, vol. SE-2 no. 4 (December 1976), pp. 244–252.

[Robinson78] Robinson, J. G., and E. S. Roberts, "Software Fault Tolerance in the Pluribus," *AFIPS Conference Preceedings*, vol. 47, pp. 563–569, AFIPS Press, Montvale, N.J., 1978.

[Siewiorek82] Siewiorek, D. P., and S. Swarz, *The Theory and Practice of Reliable System Design*, Digital Press, Bedford, Mass., 1982.

[SMS87] Standard Microsystems Corporation, *ARCNET Local Area Network Controller Designer's Guide*, Standard Microsystems Corporation, Hauppage, N.Y., (January 1987).

[Stucki75] Stucki, L. G., and G. L. Foshee, "New Assertion Concepts for Self-Metric Software Validation," *Proc. 1975 Int. Conf. Reliab. Softw.*, (April 1975), IEEE Cat. 75CHO940-7CSR, pp. 59–71.

[Tripathi86] Tripathi, A., and J. Silverman, "System Level Primitives for Fault Tolerant Distributed Computing," *Proc. 16th Annual Fault Tolerant Computing Symposium*, 1986, pp. 56–61, IEEE Press, Catalog No. 0731-3071.

[Tso86] Tso, K. S., A. Avizienis, and J. P. J. Kelly, "Error Recovery in Multi-Version Software," *Proc. IFAC Workshop SAFECOMP'86*, Sarlat, France, (October 1986).

[US76] U.S. Atomic Energy Commission, Reactor Safety Study, WASH1400, vol. 1, 1976.

[Wensley78] Wensley, J. H., et al., "SIFT: The Design and Analysis of a Fault Tolerant Computer for Aircraft Control," *Proc. IEEE*, vol. 66 no. 10 (October 1978), pp. 1040–1054.

[Wind93] Wind River Systems, *VxWorks Programmer's Guide*, Release 5.1, Wind River Systems, Alameda, Calif., 1993.

[Yau75] Yau, S. S. and R. C. Cheung, "Design on Self-Checking Software," *Proc. 1975 Int. Conf. Reliab.*, April 1975, IEEE Cat. 75CHO940-7CSR, pp. 450–457.

[Yau76] Yau, S. S., R. C. Cheung, and D. C. Cochrane, "An Approach to Error-Resistant

Software Design," *Proc. 2nd Int. Conf. Softw. Eng.*, October 1976, IEEE Cat. 76CH11245-4C, pp. 429–436.

[Zave91] Zave, Pamela, "An Insider's Evaluation of PAISLey," *IEEE Transactions on Software Engineering*, vol. SE-17 no. 3 (March 1991), pp. 212–225.

PROBLEMS

7.1 Classify each of the following practices as (A) fault avoidance, (B) robustness, (C) fault containment, or (D) fault tolerance.
  (a) Structured programming.
  (b) Invocation of alternate routine when primary exceeds time limit.
  (c) Use of checksums on transmittal of data.
  (d) Automatic restart on divide by zero.
  (e) Indication to data entry personnel when data is out of range.
  (f) Proof of correctness for all data manipulation routines.
  (g) Use of default data when data entered is out of range.
  (h) Stopping a program when loop iterations exceed a limit.

7.2 A program consists of ten independent routines. The probability that a routine is faulty is 0.01 (for each of the routines). It is intended to use three-version programming, with voting to be conducted after execution of each routine. The effectiveness of the voting in eliminating faults is 0.85 when one out of three routines is faulty and 0 when more than one routine is faulty (compare these assumptions with Table 7.2). What is the probability of a fault-free program:
  (a) When only a single version is produced and routine testing is conducted?
  (b) When only a single routine is used but extensive testing is conducted that reduces the fault content to 10 percent of the original level?
  (c) When three-version programming is used?

7.3 Devise acceptance tests for each of the following programs:
  (a) A routine that sorts all orders received in a given day by ZIP code of the originator.
  (b) A program that computes sales tax on the same orders.
  (c) A program that computes rate of climb increment for aircraft from data supplied by inertial instruments. The basic algorithm is

$$RC = 0.1 \sum_i VA[i]$$

where VA is vertical acceleration in ft/s/s and the summation is conducted over the last 10 samples. Assume that a barometric rate of climb transducer is available and that the accuracy of the data obtained from it is 10 percent $\pm$ 30 ft/s. The data obtained from a correctly operating inertial acceleration algorithm has only negligible error.

7.4 Why are conventional reliability models (e.g., that shown in Figure 7.10) not suitable for software?

7.5 A fault-tolerant software system has been operating satisfactorily for a number of years (i.e., no failures that are significant at the overall system level have occurred). It is now proposed to install a logging routine which will record every failure of the primary software and the number of attempted reversions to the primary program after the backup software has been invoked. The logging routine will impose a 0.5 percent performance penalty on the system. Do you favor installation of the logging routine? What are the reasons for your decision?

7.6 The operating system for a spacecraft computer is to be implemented in read-only memory (ROM) which cannot be modified after the spacecraft is launched. The expected life of the spacecraft is seven years, and on the basis of prior experience, it is expected that five failures of the operating system will occur during that interval. In case of previous failures, recovery has been possible by shutdown of the computer and restart, but this involves data loss and there is no certainty that it will always be successful. It has therefore been decided to make the operating system fault-tolerant. Assume that all failures of the primary operating software will be detected. What is the largest value for correlated failure probability of the backup software that will permit the expected number of failures during the mission to be reduced to one?

7.7 Construct a fault tree for a program that assigns students to classes. Each class has an attendance limit.

7.8 A fault-tolerant software system that controls fuel flow into a boiler will fail if the primary software fails and the backup software is not invoked and a special routine fails which shuts off fuel flow when the steam pressure exceeds a certain limit. How many software failures can be sustained before the system fails?

8

System Diagnosis

Gerald M. Masson, Douglas M. Blough, Gregory F. Sullivan

8.1 INTRODUCTION

As seen in Chapter 3, one of the important issues in effecting quick recovery is fast diagnosis. In this Chapter we have briefly reviewed the basic concepts defining the field of system diagnosis. As discussed there, this field of system diagnosis is concerned with what can be done to cope with failure conditions in the processor units of multiprocessor systems. Three developments make the system diagnosis area increasingly relevant.

First, multiprocessor computer systems with thousands of processors are being built and systems with millions of processors are being envisioned. It must certainly be expected that at least some of these processors will fail during operation. Second, computer systems are being embedded in machinery and vehicles such as robot welders and aircraft. Failure of these systems can, at a minimum, be problematic and, in the worst case, catastrophic. Third, computer systems are being placed in nearly inaccessible areas, such as underground, underwater, or in space. Failure of these systems may incapacitate them for lengthy periods and necessitate expensive repairs or even abandonment.

Hence, there is a need for underlying theories associated with faulty processor identification that incorporate aspects of intelligent units testing each other such that, on the basis of the results of this testing, the fault situation can be diagnosed with varying degrees of accuracy and efficiency. The area of system diagnosis addresses the fundamental issues associated with doing this in an enormously broad spectrum of contexts. Indeed, the range of deep, elegant results that have been achieved by researchers in this field span such a wide variety of issues that only a voluminous document could even begin to cover them all. Furthermore, there have previously been a number of surveys, comparisons, and generalizations of system level diagnosis results that each deal with some focused set of topics in the field, i.e., Friedman and Simoncini (1980), Kime (1986), Somani, Agarwal and Avis (1987), Dahbura (1988), Kavianpour and Kim (1992), Barborak, Malek, and Dahbura (1993), and Lee and Shin (1994). Collectively these provide a window to some generic cross-section of contributions. It is not our intention to significantly replicate these surveys. Rather, we will attempt to provide the reader with a tour of the field concentrating on system diagnosis results that are admittedly influenced by our personal opinions regarding those contributions which currently represent significant advancements as well as hold considerable promise for future applications.

8.2 SYSTEM DIAGNOSIS UNDER BOUNDED MODELS

The now classical system diagnosis fault model studied by Preparata, Metze, and Chien (1967) assumes an upper bound on the number of processors in a system that can simultaneously be faulty. Additionally, it is assumed that tests administered by non-faulty processors to either faulty processors or non-faulty processors are sufficiently comprehensive so that the outcomes of those tests are always correct. Finally, it is assumed that the tests administered by faulty processors are unreliable thereby opening the possibility that faulty processors might act as deceptively as possible in order to elude detection. These assumptions on the fault model are now broadly referred to as the *PMC model* in the system diagnosis literature. The assumptions associated with the PMC model demand that the underlying failure mechanisms constituting the source of the faulty operation of any processor in the system are permanent in nature and that all tests given by non-faulty processors are certain to detect these faults. This renders the applicability of the theory of system diagnosis based on the PMC model questionable. However, while it may be unlikely that general processors and testing capabilities in a system will adhere precisely to this collection of assumptions in practice, the broad spectrum of results associated with system diagnosis analysis on the basis of the PMC model are nevertheless quite useful in assessing the diagnostic attributes of a distributed or multiprocessor system. Indeed, some of the current research activity centered around applications of system diagnosis results utilizes the PMC model, for example, work by Bianchini, Goodwin, and Nydick (1990) and Bianchini and Buskens (1992).

8.2.1 *t*-Diagnosis under the PMC Model

In the seminal paper in the field of system diagnosis by Preparata, Metze, and Chien (1967), a directed graph model $G = (U, E)$ of the *testing assignment* in a system was introduced wherein each processor was represented by a node $u \in U$ and the capability of one processor, say, u_i, to test another processor, say, u_j, was represented by a directed edge, $(u_i \rightarrow u_j) = t_{i,j} \in E$, from the testing processor to the tested processor. An outcome $a_{i,j} \in \{0, 1\}$ was associated with the result of each test, $t_{i,j} \in E$, depending on whether the test was passed ($a_{i,j} = 0$) or the test was failed ($a_{i,j} = 1$). As mentioned above, it is assumed that the outcome associated with a test given by a nonfaulty processor is always accurate, but that the outcome of a test given by faulty processor, regardless of whether the tested processor is faulty or nonfaulty, is unreliable. This model is broadly referred to as the PMC model for system diagnosis. Figure 8.1 is an example of a directed graph representation of the PMC model. In the figure, the outcome of a test given by a faulty processor is denoted by ϕ to indicate that, in general, such an outcome could be either a 0 or a 1 and cannot be predicted.

t-Fault diagnosability.   Hakimi and Amin (1974) utilized the representation and the assumptions of the PMC model to establish necessary and sufficient conditions on the testing assignment such that a collection of test results, referred to as a *syndrome*, would always contain sufficient information to correctly diagnose the existing set of faulty processors. If t denotes the maximum number of faulty processors, then a system with such a testing assignment is referred to as a *t-fault diagnosable*, or more simply a *t-diagnosable*, system. An alternative way of

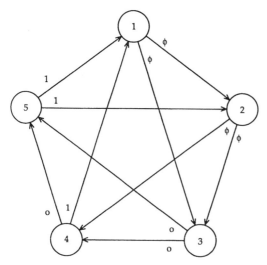

Figure 8.1: A graph representation of a five-processor system with a syndrome resulting from processors 1 and 2 being faulty.

defining a t-diagnosable system is one in which, for each possible syndrome that can be produced by at most t faulty processors, there is a unique set of at most t faulty processors that could have produced the syndrome.

In Example 8.1 which is shown in Figure 8.1, a digraph representation of a five-processor system is illustrated in which a syndrome is indicated. Given that the assumptions associated with the PMC model hold, and that no more than two processors (that is, fewer than half of the processors) can be faulty at any given time, Hakimi and Amin's characterization of system diagnosability can be used to show that any of the resulting 16 syndromes permits identification of the faulty processors (note total number of syndromes $16 = \binom{5}{2} + \binom{5}{1} + \binom{5}{0}$).

It should be noted that in Figure 8.1 no two processors test each other. For this special case, Hakimi and Amin (1974) have shown that a system is t-diagnosable if and only if each processor is tested by at least t other processors. This means that in Figure 8.1, each of the 16 possible indicated syndromes can be produced only by the processors represented by nodes 1 and 2 being faulty.

For the more general case where units can test each other, the characterization for t-diagnosability is somewhat more complex. There are a number of equivalent versions of this characterization including, of course, that originally put forth by Hakimi and Amin (1974). Possibly, the simplest version of the characterization of t-diagnosability states that given $G = (U, E)$, for all $Z \subseteq U$ where $Z \neq \emptyset$, we must have that the sum of the number of processors not in Z that test processors in Z plus the number of processors in Z divided by 2 must be greater than t. That is, defining

$$\Gamma^{-1}(Z) = \{u : u \in U \text{ and } \exists z \in Z \text{ and } (u \to z) \in E\} - Z$$

Theorem 8.1.   A system is t-diagnosable if and only if for all $Z \subseteq U$ where $Z \neq \emptyset$,

$$\left| \Gamma^{-1}(Z) \right| + \frac{|Z|}{2} > t$$

Proof.   Part I: Let $G = (U, E)$ be the directed graph of a system which is not t-diagnosable. We will show there exists $Z \subseteq U$ with $Z \neq \emptyset$ and $\left| \Gamma^{-1}(Z) \right| + |Z|/2 \leq t$. Note, since the system is not t-diagnosable, there must exist a syndrome, S, which does not allow the faulty processors to be correctly and completely identified. Thus, there are at least two distinct explanations for the syndrome test results, for example, either F_1 might be the faulty processors or F_2 might be the faulty processors according to S. Let $Z = (F_1 \cup F_2 - (F_1 \cap F_2)$. Since $F_1 \neq F_2$ we know $Z \neq \emptyset$. We claim there is no edge from a node $u \in U - (F_1 \cup F_2)$ to a node $z \in Z$. Suppose there is such an edge. Since u is nonfaulty with respect to both F_1 and F_2, the test performed by u on z is accurate according to these two possible sets of faulty processors. However, z is in exactly one of the two sets. Thus, the test result must be both zero and one—a contradiction. We can now conclude that $\Gamma^{-1}(Z) \subseteq F_1 \cap F_2$ since $U - Z = (U - (F_1 \cup F_2)) \cup (F_1 \cap F_2)$. Further;

$$|F_1| \leq t, |F_2| \leq t$$
$$|F_1| + |F_2| \leq 2t$$
$$|F_1 \cap F_2| + - |F_1 \cup F_2| \leq 2t$$
$$2|F_1 \cap F_2| + |Z| \leq 2t$$
$$|F_1 \cap F_2| + |Z|/2 \leq t$$
$$|\Gamma^{-1}(Z)| + |Z|/2 \leq t$$

This completes part I.

Part II: Let Z be a nonnull subset of nodes in G with $|\Gamma^{-1}(Z)| + |Z|/2 \leq t$. Note, since $|\Gamma^{-1}(Z)|$ and t are integers, we may also state $|\Gamma^{-1}(Z)| + \lceil |Z|/2 \rceil \leq t$. We will show G is not t-diagnosable. Partition Z into two sets Z_1 and Z_2 with $|Z_1| \leq \lceil |Z|/2 \rceil$ and $|Z_2| \leq \lceil |Z|/2 \rceil$. Now consider $F_1 = Z_1 \cup \Gamma^{-1}(Z)$ and $F_2 = Z_2 \cup \Gamma^{-1}(Z)$. Note, $F_1 \neq F_2$ and also note

$$|F_1| = |Z_1| + |\Gamma^{-1}(Z)|$$
$$|F_1| \leq \lceil |Z|/2 \rceil + |\Gamma^{-1}(Z)|$$
$$|F_1| \leq t \text{ similarly } |F_2| \leq t$$

We shall now construct a syndrome S such that F_1 might be the faulty processors or F_2 might be the faulty processors. All tests of the form $(u \rightarrow v)$ where u or v are in $\Gamma^{-1}(Z)$ have outcome 1. All tests $(u \rightarrow v)$ with $u \in Z_1$ and $v \in Z_2$ have outcome 1. All tests $(u \rightarrow v)$ with $u \in Z_2$ and $v \in Z_1$ have outcome 1. All other tests have outcome 0. To see that F_1 might be the set of faulty processors according to S observe that all the tests from $U - F_1$ to F_1 have outcome 1, and all tests between elements of $U - F_1$ have outcome 0. A similar argument shows F_2 might be the set of faulty processors. We conclude G is not t-diagnosable which completes part II of the proof. Together, parts I and II complete the theorem.

The characterization theorem above allows us to easily prove the special case result for t-diagnosability discussed earlier.

Lemma 8.1.   Let $G = (U, E)$ be a system with the property that no two nodes test each other. Then the system is t-diagnosable if and only if each node is tested by at least t other nodes.

Proof. Suppose there is a node, u, which is tested by fewer than t other nodes. If we let $Z = \{u\}$, then the characterization theorem above tells us that the system is not t-diagnosable. Now suppose that no two nodes test each other and each node is tested by at least t other nodes. Let Z be an arbitrary subset of nodes. At least $|Z|t$ tests must be performed on the nodes in Z. Further, at least $|Z|t - ((|Z| - 1)|Z|)/2)$ of these tests must be performed by nodes which are not in Z. Since a node can perform at most $|Z|$ tests on nodes in Z it follows that $|\Gamma^{-1}(Z)| \geq t - ((|Z| - 1)/2)$. We can now conclude $|\Gamma^{-1}(Z)| + (|Z|/2) > t$ and thus the system is t-diagnosable.

Diagnosability evaluation.   The above characterization for t-diagnosability was the basis for determining the diagnosability of a system. Given a digraph model, $G = (U, E)$, of a multiprocessor or distributed system, it is of interest to determine the maximum value of t for which the system is t-diagnosable. Obviously, a brute-force application of one of the characterizations of t-diagnosability would accomplish this. However, it would be hoped that some more efficient algorithm could result in this determination of t. Sullivan (1984) was able to relate the evaluation of the maximum value of t for $G = (U, E)$ based on the above characterization of t-diagnosability with the solution of a set of network flow problems in a related graph. We now define a digraph and capacity function which show the basic relationship between network flow and t-diagnosability. The network used has capacities on vertices and edges.

Given a digraph $G = (U, E)$ and $s_1 \notin U$, we define the digraph $G' = (U', E')$ as follows:

$$U' = U \cup \{s_1\}$$
$$E' = E \cup \{(s_1 \rightarrow u) : \in U\}$$

We also define a capacity function c' on $E' \cup U'$:

For all $e \in \{(s_1 \rightarrow u) : u \in U\}, c'(e) = 1/2$.
For all $e \in E, c'(e) = \infty$
For all $u \in U', c'(u) = 1$.

See Example 8.2 shown in Figure 8.2. The algorithm to quickly determine t-diagnosability is based on the following theorem.

Theorem 8.2.   System $G = (U, E)$ is t-diagnosable if and only if, for all $u \in U$, the value of the max-flow in the flow network with digraph $G' = (U', E')$ with source s_1 with sink u and with capacity function c' is greater than t.

Proof. This proof uses some elementary facts from network flow theory, for example, the max-flow equals the min-cut. Also note, since there are capacities assigned to both edges and nodes in our flow graph, a cut contains both edges and nodes.

Part I: Suppose there exists $s_2 \in U$ such that the max-flow in $G' = (U', E')$ with source s_1 with sink s_2 and with capacity c' is less than or equal to t. We will show G is not t-diagnosable. Let C_1 and C_2 be the edges and nodes, respectively, in a min-cut. There are two types of edges in G', those with capacity $1/2$ and those with infinite capacity. Since C_1 and C_2 form a cut of finite capacity, we can conclude each edge in C_2 has capacity $1/2$. All nodes in G' have capacity one so

$G = (U, E)$

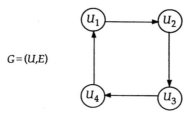

$G' = (U', E')$

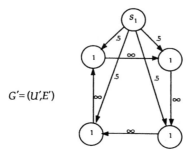

Figure 8.2: Example of network flow graph used for determining diagnosability.

each node in C_2 has capacity one, thus $|C_1|/2 + |C_2| \le t$. Let $Z = \{u : (s_1 \to u) \in C_1\}$, and note $Z \ne \emptyset$ because $(s_1 \to s_2)$ must be in C_1, thus $s_2 \in Z$. Also note, trivially, $Z \subseteq U$. We claim $\Gamma^{-1}(Z) \subseteq C_2$ (this is $\Gamma^{-1}(Z)$ in $G = (U, E)$). Assume not. There exists $y \in \Gamma^{-1}(Z)$ with $y \notin C_2$. Thus , there exists $u \in Z$ with $(y \to u) \in E$. Since $(s_1 \to u) \in C_1$, there is a path from u to s_2 which is not cut by any member of C_1 or C_2. This follows because if all paths from u to s_2 were cut, then $C_1 - \{(s_1 \to u)\}$ and C_2 would be a smaller cut than the min-cut.

Now, consider the path from s_1 to y (an edge), from y to u (also an edge), and from u to s_2. Below, we will show this path is not cut by any members of C_1 or C_2. s_1 is not in the cut by definition of a cut. $(s_1 \to y)$ is not in the cut; else y would be in Z and by definition y is in $\Gamma^{-1}(Z)$. y is not in the cut, because by definition above $y \notin C_2$. $(y \to u)$ is not in the cut because it has infinite capacity. u is not in the cut; else $C_1 - \{(s_1 \to u)\}$ and C_2 would be a smaller cut than the min-cut. Finally, the fact that the path from u to s_2 is not cut was shown above. This reasoning allows us to conclude by contradiction that $\Gamma^{-1}(Z) \subseteq C_2$. So,

$$|C_1|/2 + |C_2| \le t$$
$$|Z|/2 + |C_2| \le t$$
$$|Z|/2 + |\Gamma^{-1}(Z)| \le t$$

This shows G is not t-diagnosable by our earlier characterization, and thus completes part I of the proof.

Part II: Suppose G is not t-diagnosable. We will show that for some $s_2 \in U$, there is a cut in the flow network $G' = (U', E')$ with source s_1 with sink s_2 and with capacity function c' which has capacity less than or equal to t. Let Z be a nonnull set of nodes such that $|\Gamma^{-1}(Z)| + |Z|/2 \le t$. Let s_2 be an arbitrary member of Z. We claim the following sets form a cut in the flow network:

$$C_1 = \{(s_1 \to z) : (s_1 \to z) \in E', z \in Z\}$$
$$C_2 = \Gamma^{-1}(Z) \text{ where } \Gamma^{-1}(Z) \text{ is with respect to } G$$

Suppose $C_1 \cup C_2$ is not a cut. Consider some uncut path from s_1 to s_2. Since $s_1 \notin Z$ and $s_2 \in Z$, there is an edge $(q_1 \to q_2)$ in the path with $q_1 \notin Z$ and $q_2 \in Z$. If $q_1 = s_1$ then $(q_1 \to q_2) \in C_1$—a contradiction. If $q_1 \ne s_1$, then $q_1 \in \Gamma^{-1}(Z)$ and hence $q_1 \in C_2$—another contradiction. So $C_1 \cup C_2$ is a cut. Its capacity is less than or equal to t because $|Z|/2 + |\Gamma^{-1}(Z)| \le t$ and thus $|C_1|/2 + |C_2| \le t$. This finishes part II and our proof is complete.

To achieve a faster algorithm, Sullivan (1984) defined a new network which has capacity limitations only on vertices and is such that these capacities are all exactly one. By solving max-flow problems in this new network, a time complexity of $O(|E\|U|^{3/2})$ is obtained for finding the maximum t such that a digraph is t-diagnosable. Recently, Raghavan and Tripathi (1991a) have built upon this result to yield a new faster algorithm which has a time complexity of $O(|U| t^{2.5})$.

System diagnosis under adaptive models.   One stream of research that has seen renewed interest recently is based on *adaptive* models. The term adaptive refers to the fact that such models allow the choice of which test(s) to perform to depend on the results of tests which have been performed previously. This differs from most other models in the area of system-level diagnosis which may be viewed as *nonadaptive*. For example, in the original model due to Preparata, Metze, and Chien (1967), the digraph representing the set of tests conducted is selected before any test results are known. In a popular adaptive model, it is possible for any processor to test any other processor, and the digraph of tests which are actually performed is not determined in advance. One advantage of an adaptive model is the fact that sometimes fewer tests can be used to locate all faulty processors. To illustrate this, consider the original PMC model in which Preparata, Metze, and Chien were able to show that at least nt tests must be conducted in a t-diagnosable system of n processors. In this adaptive model, Hakimi and Nakajima (1982, 1984a) were able to identify a nonfaulty processor using only at most $2t - 1$ tests. They then used this processor to identify the status of the remaining $n - 1$ processors, thus using at most $n + 2t - 2$ tests to identify the status of all processors. Blecher (1983) improved this bound with a new algorithm which required only $n + t - 1$ tests to identify the status of all processors. He also proved a lower bound on the number of tests which matched the upper bound provided by his algorithm. To provide the reader with a flavor of these results, we present Blecher's algorithm and its analysis below. Note, that a strict majority of processors must be nonfaulty in order to make possible the identification of the faulty processors, that is, $t < n/2$.

- Base case: If n is 1 or 2, then all the processors are nonfaulty.
- Main case: Arbitrarily choose a processor and call it *candidate*. Now choose a sequence of other processors and have them each perform a test on *candidate* until one of the two subcases below becomes true.
- Subcase 1: t of the test results indicate that *candidate* is nonfaulty. In this subcase, we may conclude that *candidate* is nonfaulty since otherwise there would be more than t faulty processors. We may also conclude that all processors that tested *candidate* and obtained the result faulty are themselves faulty. Thus, the algorithm may be concluded by using *candidate* to test all the other processors and the total number of tests is $n + t - 1$.
- Subcase 2: The majority of test results say faulty. Note, this subcase is entered immediately when its condition is satisfied. Thus, if x test results say faulty, then $x - 1$ say nonfaulty. Note also that there are at least x faulty processors in the set containing *candidate* and its $2x - 1$ testers. (To see this, consider the cases in which *candidate* is faulty and nonfaulty.) Therefore the algorithm can be recursively applied to the processors which did not participate in tests. There are $n' = n - 2x$ such processors and at most $t' = t - x$ are faulty. When these processors are recursively identified, a nonfaulty processor is chosen from among them and is used to test *candidate*. Finally, all the processors whose test results for *candidate* were accurate are tested by the nonfaulty processor. Now, consider the total number of tests for this subcase. Initially, $2x - 1$ tests are performed on *candidate*. Next, $n' + t' - 1 = (n - 2x) + (t - x) - 1$ tests are performed by the recursion. Finally, $1 + x$ tests are performed to identify the remaining processors. These values sum to $2x - 1 + (n - 2x) + (t - x) - 1 + 1 + x = n + t - 1$.

After Blecher's work, a new direction for adaptive research was introduced by Hakimi and Schmeichel (1984b) who considered the possibility of conducting tests in parallel. In this new *parallel adaptive* model, tests are conducted in a series of *rounds* of testing. During a single round of testing it is possible to conduct multiple tests simultaneously; however, a single processor may participate in at most one test, as either a tester or a testing processor. Tests conducted during a round may be chosen based on results obtained from previous rounds of tests but may not be chosen based on results from tests conducted in the same round. Hakimi and Schmeichel noted that algorithms presented prior to their algorithm had been "highly serial," that is, during the execution of the algorithm the choice of which test to perform next depended on very many of the previous test results. These dependencies are a significant handicap if one wishes to perform many tests in parallel. Hakimi and Schmeichel presented a new algorithm and showed it is possible to identify a nonfaulty processor after at most $\lfloor \log_2 t \rfloor + 1$ rounds of testing. They also showed that the status of all processors may be determined after an additional $(t-1) + \lfloor \log_2(n - t + 1) \rfloor$ rounds of testing. This result was substantially improved by Schmeichel, Hakimi, Otsuka, and Sullivan (1990) who showed $O(1 + \log_{\lfloor n/t \rfloor} t)$ rounds of testing using $O(n)$ tests were adequate for identifying the fault status of all processors. Finally, Beigel, Kosaraju, and Sullivan (1989) showed that a constant number of rounds of testing were adequate for identifying the fault status of all processors.

Another direction in adaptive models has emerged recently which emphasizes distributed algorithms. We will discuss distributed algorithms and algorithms which are both distributed and adaptive in the next section.

System diagnosis in distributed models.   The algorithms discussed above all assume a central observer and coordinator whereas distributed algorithms do not make this assumption. There are many variations in the distributed models which have been analyzed in the area of system diagnosis; however, most models share the following central features. There are two types of links between processors: *testing* links and *communication* links. If there is a testing link from processor u to processor v, then processor u can perform a test on processor v. If there is a communication link from processor u to processor v, then processor u can send a message to processor v. In some models, a link is used to indicate a two-way interaction. For example, a communication link connecting processor u and v allows messages to be sent from u to v and from v to u. Also, in some models only one type of link is used which can be used for both testing and communication. In some models, faults may be present in the processors, the communication links, or the testing links. Usually, however, faults are restricted to occur only in the processors and are not allowed in the links. The goal of a diagnosis algorithm is to perform tests and exchange messages until the following property can be guaranteed: Every nonfaulty processor knows the fault status of every other processor in the system.

The initial work in distributed algorithms for system-level diagnosis was by Kuhl and Reddy (1980). Their initial basic model allows only processor faults and has two-way links which are used for testing and communication. Their algorithm requires $O(n^2)$ testing operations and $O(n^3)$ message transmissions to diagnose a system. Hosseini, Kuhl, and Reddy (1984), considered more general models including systems in which processors can fail during diagnosis and can later reenter a system. Recently, Bagchi and Hakimi (1994) took an adaptive distributed approach and presented an optimal algorithm for diagnosis which requires at most $3n \log p + O(n + pt)$ message transmissions by nonfaulty processors where p nonfaulty processors simultaneously start the algorithm. Their model differs from most others because it assumes that processors initially have no global knowledge of the system, that is, each processor knows only its own identifier number and the identifier numbers of processors that are directly linked to it.

Some of the most important work in distributed diagnosis from an applied point of view has been performed by Bianchini, Goodwin, and Nydick (1990) and by Bianchini and Buskens (1992). The second paper uses an adaptive distributed approach to the diagnosis problem. This work has culminated in a practical and valuable system which has been used in the Department of Electrical and Computer Engineering at Carnegie-Mellon University since November 1990. We will now present some of the major features of their basic model and algorithm which are oriented toward fault diagnosis in systems based on local area networks. Their model assumes any two processors can send messages to one another and any processor can test any other processor. It also assumes that faults are present only in processors and not in links. Some of these assumptions can be weakened or removed as shown in their papers; however, for simplicity in our discussion we will retain these assumptions. The processors in the system are given numbers ranging from 0 to $N - 1$. These numbers define a circular ordering on the processors based on modular arithmetic.

When the diagnosis algorithm starts, each processor tests the processor with an index which is one larger, that is, processor i tests processor $i + 1$ (arithmetic in this section is mod N). If a processor determines that the processor it is testing is faulty, then it tests the processor with the next larger index until it finds a nonfaulty processor. Hence, processor i would test $i + 1$, $i + 2$, $i + 3$, . . . until it finds its first nonfaulty processor. In addition to performing these tests, processors also must exchange messages. The contents of these messages are based on arrays called TESTED_UP. There are N versions of the array TESTED_UP (one version per processor) and each array contains N elements. For example, processor i maintains the array TESTED_UP$_i$ which contains values TESTED_UP$_i$[0], TESTED_UP$_i$[1], TESTED_UP$_i$[2], . . . , TESTED_UP$_i$[$N - 1$]. The contents of these array elements have the following intended meaning: TESTED_UP$_i$[x] = y if and only if processor i has received a message from a nonfaulty processor indicating that processor x has tested processor y and found y to be nonfaulty. Further, processor y is the first processor which was tested as nonfaulty by processor x with respect to the circular ordering.

It is beyond the scope of this chapter to detail the full algorithm which uses several rounds of testing and message exchanges; however, we can detail the final step in which each nonfaulty processor determines the fault status of all other processors. For concreteness, let us consider processor i. This processor considers itself to be nonfaulty and it can locate all the other nonfaulty processors by using a "pointer tracing" procedure on the array TESTED_UP$_i$. Suppose TESTED_UP$_i$[i] = j, then processor i concludes that processor j is nonfaulty. Next suppose TESTED_UP$_i$[j] = k, then processor i concludes that processor k is also nonfaulty. Similarly, if TESTED_UP$_i$[k] = l, then processor l is also nonfaulty. These processor numbers are traced in this manner until they lead back to processor i. Lastly, processor i concludes that all processors which were not identified as nonfaulty are faulty. The details of this algorithm and experimental results showing its utility are contained in Bianchini and Buskens (1992).

Finally, in general, testing may have to interrupt all the computations in the array. Since it is assumed that the testing is done periodically, it is desirable that the number of tests and the testing time should be minimized when there are no faults. The testing time should be proportionate to the number of faults; thus, a fault-free array would require a minimum number of tests, the number of tests increasing with the number of faults. In (Meyer and Pradhan, 1989), a possible diagnosis strategy was suggested that makes the testing very simple in the absence of any fault; the testing becomes progressively more time-consuming with the number of faults. Since there are usually no faults present, the performance penalty due to interruption for testing can be minimal. This is further illustrated below.

Diagnosis algorithms.   Given that a syndrome has been produced in a *t*-diagnosable system, the issue of determining the set of faulty processors on the basis of it must be confronted. This is sometimes referred to as syndrome processing or syndrome decoding. It would be possible, of course, in small systems to simply perform a table lookup whereby the syndrome could be used to address a table location at which the unique set of faulty processors associated with the syndrome would be stored. For larger systems, this is not feasible and so the notion of efficiently processing the syndrome so as to identify faulty processors has emerged as an area of considerable interest in the system diagnosis field. Due to the robust structures of systems that satisfy the characterizations for *t*-diagnosability, it follows that graph theoretic properties should be available which can be taken advantage of when processing a syndrome to assess a fault situation. Indeed, Dahbura and Masson (1984a) were able to relate results dealing with vertex cover sets and maximum matchings with syndrome processing so as to produce what is currently the most efficient technique available.

Example 8.3 appears initially in Figure 8.3 which depicts a graph representation with an associated syndrome. This example will serve throughout the dis-

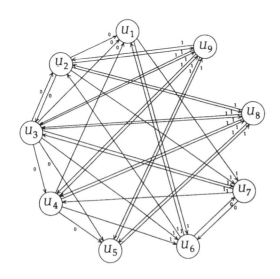

Figure 8.3: A digraph representation and an associated syndrome for a nine-processor system which is four-fault diagnosable.

cussions of syndrome processing. It can be shown that the system represented in Figure 8.3 is four-fault diagnosable. However, the faulty processors in this system (namely, u_6, u_7, u_8, and u_9) are not readily apparent from the syndrome.

To decode the syndrome of Figure 8.3, the notion of an implied fault set (see Meyer (1980) is useful. For each $u_i \in U$, $L(u_i)$ is the set of processors that can be deduced as faulty if it is assumed that u_i is fault-free. $L(u_i)$ is referred to as the implied fault set of u_i. Given the implied fault set of each processor represented in $G = (U, E)$, an undirected L-graph, $G_L = (U_L, E_L)$ can be defined where $U_L = U$ and

$$E_L = \{(u_i \rightarrow u_j): u_i \in L(u_j)\}$$

The L-graph $G_L = (U_L, E_L)$ of a syndrome for $G = (U, E)$ can be generated in $O(n^{2.495})$ operations. The L-graph of the system and associated syndrome for Example 8.3 is shown in Figure 8.4.

A *vertex cover set* of the graph $G_L = (U_L, E_L)$ is a subset $U^* \subseteq U_L$ where every edge of E_L has at least one end in U^*. A vertex cover set of minimal cardinality is called a minimum vertex cover set. Dahbura and Masson (1984a) have shown that given a syndrome for a t-diagnosable system, the set of faulty processors is the unique minimum vertex cover set of the undirected graph $G_L = (U_L, E_L)$ generated by the directed graph $G = (U, E)$. It can further be shown that while there is no known algorithm of polynomial time complexity that can determine the minimum vertex cover set of a general undirected graph, the class of L-graphs generated by t-diagnosable systems have a special property that permits their minimum vertex cover set to be generated in $O(n^{2.5})$ operations. Examination of Figure 8.4 reveals that processors u_6, u_7, u_8, and u_9 form the unique minimum vertex cover set.

To achieve this efficient generation of the minimum vertex covering set for the special case of $G_L = (U_L, E_L)$, the concept of a maximum matching must be utilized. A *matching* in the graph $G_L = (U_L, E_L)$ is a subset $M^* \subseteq E_L$ if no vertex in U_L

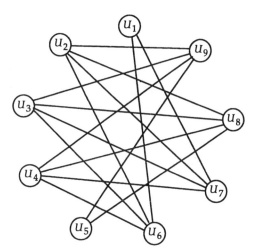

Figure 8.4: The L-graph of the system and associated syndrome for the Dahbura-Masson diagnosis algorithm example.

is incident to more than one edge in M^*. A matching of maximum cardinality in $G_L = (U_L, E_L)$ is called a maximum matching. A maximum matching M^* can be determined for $G_L = (U_L, E_L)$ in $O(n^{2.5})$ operations. Figure 8.5 shows the maximum matching of $G_L = (U_L, E_L)$ for our running Example 8.3.

Dahbura and Masson (1984a) have shown that given a syndrome for a t-diagnosable system, if M^* is a maximum matching for $G_L = (U_L, E_L)$, then each node corresponding to a faulty processor is incident to exactly one edge of M^* and each edge of M^* is incident to exactly one faulty processor node. If a node $u \in U_L$ is incident to an edge in M^*, then the matching M^* is said to saturate node u; similarly, u is said to be M^*-saturated; otherwise, u is said to be M^*-unsaturated.

Note that each edge of the maximum matching in Figure 8.5 is incident to exactly one of the faulty processors. Also note that there is a processor that is M^*-unsaturated. In general, such a node will always exist. It follows that this M^*-unsaturated node can be labeled as nonfaulty (for otherwise it would be M^*-saturated). Thus, by the definition of the L-graph, each node connected by an edge to a M^*-unsaturated node can be labeled as faulty. Then each of the nodes connected by edges of M^* to these faulty nodes must be labeled as nonfaulty (since each edge of M^* is incident to exactly one faulty node).

This labeling process can be continued until all the nodes are labeled as either faulty or nonfaulty. This labeling process requires $O(n^2)$ operations as shown in Dahbura and Masson (1984a). Figure 8.5 shows a completed labeling. Thus, the overall complexity of this syndrome processing procedure is $O(n^{2.5})$ operations and the result is the unique minimum vertex cover set of $G_L = (U_L, E_L)$ corresponding to the faulty set of processors.

A somewhat more practical variation of the diagnosis algorithm is also available in Dahbura and Masson (1984b). In this version, the use of the some-

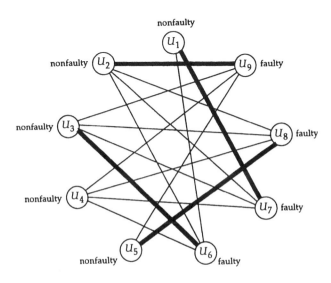

Figure 8.5: A maximum matching (indicated by the dark edges) and the L-graph labeling for the Dahbura-Masson diagnosis algorithm example.

what complicated best-known algorithms for computing a maximum matching of an undirected graph is avoided. The simplification results from the use of an undirected bipartite graph to represent test information. Such a representation permits the employment of the Hopcroft-Karp (1973) algorithm for finding a maximum matching in bipartite graphs.

Finally, other diagnosis algorithms for special cases of t-diagnosable systems have been developed by Dahbura, Masson and Yang (1985), Meyer and Masson (1978), and Meyer (1980). These diagnosis algorithms exploit additional properties of the systems to which they are applicable. These properties are not generally available in t-diagnosable systems. Another diagnosis algorithm which does work for the general case was developed by Sullivan (1988). This algorithm has a time complexity of $O(t^3 + |E|)$ which is efficient when t is small compared to $|U|$.

8.2.2 Other Models and Other Types of Diagnosabilities

There are numerous other types of deterministic system diagnosability measures; too many, in fact, to address in a chapter such as this. Fortunately, many of these diagnosability measures have been treated in previous surveys: Friedman and Simoncini (1980), Kime (1986), Dahbura (1988), and Barborak, Malek, and Dahbura (1993). Thus, our omissions are compensated for by others. In the following sections, a small subset of the host of interesting diagnosabilities treated in the literature are discussed to varying extents.

Comparison-based diagnosis.   One of the key issues in system diagnosis is how the processors should be tested. A practical mechanism for testing in multiprocessor systems is to compare the outputs of two processors that perform identical jobs. This approach is attractive, given that many fault-tolerant multiprocessor systems use redundant processing as a means of detecting or masking faults. For these systems, the comparison testing mechanism is already in place and, as a result, a comparison-based diagnosis algorithm incurs little or no overhead for testing.

Comparison-based models for diagnosis were proposed at approximately the same time in Malek (1980), and Chwa and Hakimi (1981b). These models use undirected graphs to represent the comparison tests and assume a centralized supervisor that is capable of doing comparisons and performing diagnosis reliably. In the model introduced by Malek (1980), the outputs of two processors performing the same job have the following behavior. If both processors are nonfaulty, then the processors' outputs always match, while if either processor is faulty, then their outputs always mismatch. In the Chwa and Hakimi (1981b) model, the assumptions are the same with the exception that the outputs of two faulty processors may either match or mismatch. Pelc (1991) performed a comprehensive study of the design of optimal diagnosable systems under these two models.

Shortly after the concept of comparison-based diagnosis was introduced,

Maeng and Malek (1981) proposed a new comparison model in which processors in the system compare the outputs of neighboring processors. This removes the need for a centralized supervisor to perform the comparisons. We refer to a processor that performs a comparison of neighboring processors as a comparator. In this model, a nonfaulty comparator behaves in the same manner as the centralized supervisor described above. However, the comparisons produced by a faulty comparator can not be trusted, that is, they can be either match or mismatch regardless of the statuses of the processors being compared.

Sengupta and Dahbura (1992) studied the problems of diagnosability and diagnosis under the Maeng and Malek model. They presented a characterization for t-diagnosable systems under a generalized version of this model. In addition, they provided a polynomial time diagnosis algorithm for the original model. Their algorithm proceeds in six steps described below. In this description, $N(i)$ denotes the neighbor set of a processor i.

Step 1. Let P be the set of processors that does not produce a single match. Let Q be equal to the set P but with any processors having more that $t + 1$ neighbors deleted.

Step 2. Partition Q into two sets, X_1 and X_2, such that the processors in X_1 have $t + 1$ neighbors and the processors in X_2 have t neighbors. (A necessary condition for t-diagnosability is that each processor have at least t neighbors.)

Step 3. For all pairs $i \in X_1$ and $k \in N(i)$, check whether $N(i) - \{k\}$ is consistent with the given syndrome. If so, then output $N(i) - \{k\}$ and stop.

Step 4. For all $i \in X_2$, check whether $N(i)$ is consistent with the given syndrome. If so, then output $N(i)$ and stop.

Step 5. Given a syndrome S in a graph $G = (U, E)$, let $Z = (U, H)$ be a hypergraph with H constructed as follows. First, let $L = \{(i, j, k) : k$ compares i and $j\}$ and let $G(i)$ represent the set of processors that has produced a match involving i. Now, initialize H to L and repeat the following until H does not change.

$$\text{If } (i, j, k) \in H, m \in G(k), \text{ and } (i, j, m) \notin H, \text{ then } H \leftarrow H \cup (i, j, m)$$

Now, for all pairs $i \in X_2$ and $k \in N(i)$ check whether $N(i) - \{k\}$ and one additional node form a vertex cover set of Z. If so, output this vertex cover set and stop.

Step 6. Given a syndrome S in a graph $G = (U, E)$, let $Y = (U, M)$ be a graph defined as follows.

1. For all $i \notin P$, if i produces a mismatch on j and k, $i \in G(j)$, and $i \in G(k)$, then $(i, i) \in M$.
2. For all $i \notin P$, if i produces a mismatch on j and k and $i \notin G(j)$, then $(i, j) \in M$.
3. For all $i \in P$, if $j \in N(i) \cap P$, then $(i, j) \in M$.

4. For all $i \in P$, if $j \in N(i) \cap (U - P)$, then if $j \in G(i)$, then $(j, p) \in M$, for all $p \in N(i) - \{j\}$; whereas, if $j \notin G(i)$, then $(i, j) \in M$.

5. For all $(p, q) \in M$, if $\alpha \in G(p)$ and $\beta \in G(q)$, then $(\alpha, q) \in M$ and $(\beta, p) \in M$.

Construct Y and delete all self-loops. Output the minimum vertex cover set of this graph.

Sengupta and Dahbura proved that, except for special cases which are checked for in steps 1–5, the fault set is given by the minimum vertex cover set of the graph Y defined in step 6. The special cases are checked exhaustively to determine if any of them produces a consistent fault set. If not, the minimum vertex cover set of Y is found in a manner similar to that used by Dahbura and Masson (1984a) in their t-diagnosis algorithm for the PMC model. The following example illustrates the operation of the Sengupta-Dahbura algorithm.

Example 8.4   Operation of Sengupta-Dahbura diagnosis algorithm

Assume a completely connected graph containing four processors and the syndrome shown in Table 8.1. In this table, the value 1 is used to represent a mismatch and the value 0 is used for a match.

In this syndrome, every processor produces at least one match and so the set P is empty. This means that the special cases in which the fault set is not the minimum vertex cover set of Y cannot occur and steps 2–5 can be skipped. Hence, we go immediately to step 6. The graph V constructed in step 6 is shown in Figure 8.6. The minimum vertex cover set of this graph, and therefore the fault set of the system, is $\{u_2\}$.

Recently, Wang, Blough, and Alkalaj (1994) studied a generalization of the Maeng and Malek model in which processors are allowed to compare themselves with one of their neighbors in addition to comparing two neighbors. This generalization was first proposed by Sengupta and Dahbura (1992). This model corresponds closely to the way redundant processing is done in many fault-tolerant

Table 8.1: Syndrome Used in Example 8.4

Comparator Processor	Compared Processors	Outcome
u_1	u_2, u_3	1
u_1	u_2, u_4	1
u_1	u_3, u_4	0
u_2	u_1, u_3	1
u_2	u_1, u_4	1
u_2	u_3, u_4	0
u_3	u_1, u_2	1
u_3	u_1, u_4	0
u_3	u_2, u_4	1
u_4	u_1, u_2	1
u_4	u_1, u_3	0
u_4	u_2, u_3	1

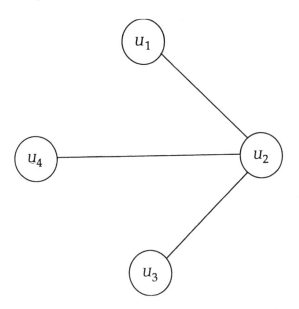

Figure 8.6: The graph V for
Example 8.4.

multiprocessor systems. Interestingly, the comparison outcomes that can be produced by a processor comparing itself with a neighbor are identical to the test outcomes in the PMC model. Hence, this model generalizes both the PMC model and the Maeng and Malek model. As a result, the model has many desirable properties such as being able to minimize the number of comparisons performed or the number of communication links required. Wang, Blough, and Alkalaj (1994) provided a new diagnosability characterization under this model that generalizes Sullivan's characterization for the PMC model. However, it is still unknown whether an efficient algorithm exists to determine the maximum diagnosability of a system under this model. Wang, Blough, and Alkalaj (1994) have also incorporated their diagnosis algorithm into the Common Space-Borne Multicomputer Operating System (COSMOS) developed at the Jet Propulsion Laboratory and have evaluated its performance on the JPL MAX multicomputer.

There has been a great deal of work on comparison-based diagnosis in probabilistic models. This work is discussed in detail in Section 8.3.

t/s-diagnosability.   Many other types of deterministic system diagnosability measures are quite fascinating in that the digraph model of a given system can have surprisingly different system diagnosis capabilities when viewed from the perspectives of these various types of diagnosability measures. For example, Friedman (1975) introduced the notion of t/s-*diagnosability*; others have refined and extended this work, for example, Kavianpour and Friedman (1978). Chwa and Hakimi (1981a), Yang, Masson, and Leonetti (1986b). In this model of t/s-diagnosability, the set of faulty processors can be localized to within a set of size s assuming that no more than t processors are faulty. A system that is t/s-diagnosable can employ fewer tests than a system that is t-diagnosable. Example 8.5 shown in Figure 8.7 depicts a particularly interesting special case of t/t-diagnosability. In a t/t-diagnosable system, the set of faulty processors need only be localized to within a set of t processors even when fewer than t processors are actually faulty. Figure 8.7 shows a system which is three-diagnosable, is not four-diagnosable, but is five/five-diagnosable. Sullivan (1986) showed that deciding if a system is t/s-diagnosable for given values of s and t is co-NP-complete; however, he also presented polynomial time algorithms for finding the largest integer t such that a system is t/t-diagnosable and $t/t + 1$-diagnosable. This work complements the polynomial time diagnosis algorithm of Yang, Masson, and Leonetti (1986b) for t/t-diagnosable systems and the recent work of Das, Thulasiraman, and Agarwal (1991, 1994).

Detection and diagnosis.   The notion of combining both fault detection and diagnosis in a system is addressed by Vaidya and Pradhan (1994). This idea bears a resemblance to error correction and detection codes. In cases where t-diagnosis is performed, fault sets of size greater than t can be misdiagnosed so as to incorrectly or incompletely indicate that a smaller set of faulty processors exists in the system where this smaller set satisfies the upper bound t. The results of Vaidya and Pradhan (1994) consider systems in which as many as t' faulty processors, $t' < t$, can always be correctly and completely diagnosed on the basis of the syndrome, but where additionally, fault situations involving as many as u faulty processors, $u > t$, can be detected. Hence, the diagnosis is safe in that if the

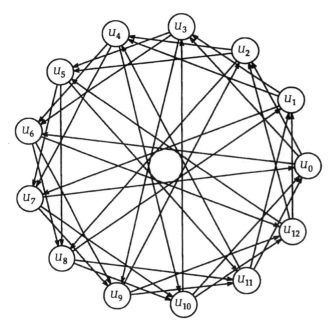

Figure 8.7: A system which is three-diagnosable is not four-diagnosable but is five/five-diagnosable.

diagnostic capacity of the system is exceeded (up to a certain point), this situation is detected. Vaidya and Pradhan (1994) characterize t'-diagnosable/u-detectable systems and provide diagnosis algorithms. Situations involving permanent faults, intermittent faults, adaptive diagnosis, distributed diagnosis, and user diagnosis are all considered.

Sequential diagnosability. In the original paper by Preparata, Metze and Chien (1967) two very different models for diagnosis were defined. So far we have concentrated on models in which the fault status of all processors must be determined during a diagnosis. It is possible to weaken this requirement and instead demand only that one faulty processor must be identified. Note, this assumes that one or more faulty processors are actually present. If this is not true, then a diagnosis simply indicates that all processors are nonfaulty. The motivation for this alternate form of diagnosis stems from systems in which diagnosis can be performed in a sequence of stages. For example, it may be possible to repair the processor which is identified as faulty and repeat the diagnosis. If a new processor is identified as faulty, then it can also be repaired and these actions of diagnosing and repairing can be repeated until all the faulty processors are repaired. This model is called *sequential diagnosis* or *diagnosis with repair* while the basic model we discussed earlier is sometimes called a *one-step diagnosis* model.

Example 8.6 in Figure 8.8 illustrates one of the major motivations for examining the sequential diagnosis model. It contains a small number of tests relative to the number of processors when compared to t-diagnosable systems in the one-step model. Preparata, Metze and Chien defined a simple class of sequentially t-diagnosable systems and also examined systems which consisted of single simple cycles. Later work also considered subclasses of systems which contain a relatively small number of tests relative to the number of processors, for example, Ciompi and Simoncini (1979), and Manber (1980). Despite this work no efficient

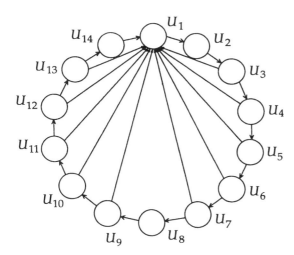

Figure 8.8: System which is six-diagnosable in the sequential model.

algorithms have been developed for diagnosis or diagnosability in the general case and no deeply insightful characterizations have yet been discovered. Indeed, we now know it is unlikely that an efficient algorithm will be discovered for diagnosability because of the recent fine result due to Raghavan and Tripathi (1991b). They show that determining if a digraph is t-diagnosable is co-NP-complete in the sequential model.

BGM diagnosability.   Another significant alternative to the PMC model is called the BGM model whose name is also a three-letter acronym based on the model's original proponents, Barsi, Grandoni, and Maestrini (1976). In this model, the constraints which test results must satisfy are more stringent than in the PMC model. If a unit is faulty, then its test result is unconstrained in the PMC model; however, in the BGM model if a test result says a processor is nonfaulty, then one may conclude that the processor is nonfaulty even if the tester is faulty. One rationale for this model is based on the method employed to accomplish processor testing. Consider systems which perform large numbers of comparisons between the responses of the testing processor and the tested processor to perform a test evaluation. If all these comparisons indicate that the two processors are generating the same responses, then the testing processor "passes" the tested processor, that is, the test result indicates that the testing processor considers the tested processor to be nonfaulty. Note, if the testing processor fails, then it is unlikely that its pattern of responses will be identical to the tested processor if it has also failed. Thus, if a processor is tested and found to be nonfaulty, then it really must be nonfaulty even if the testing processor is also faulty. This does assume that failures in distinct processors always express themselves with distinct observable manifestations, an assumption which is acceptable for some systems and unacceptable for others.

In summary, the only difference between the PMC model and the BGM model occurs when a faulty processor tests a faulty processor. In the PMC model the test may be passed or failed, while in the BGM model the test must be failed. The BGM model is called the *asymmetric invalidation* model to contrast it with the PMC model which is referred to as the *symmetric invalidation* model. An efficient diagnosis algorithm for the BGM model was developed by Meyer (1984). The first diagnosability algorithm for the BGM model was developed by Narasimhan and Nakajima (1986). This result was later improved by Raghavan and Tripathi (1991a). Their algorithm finds the maximum t for which a system is t-diagnosable under the BGM model in $O(nt^2/\log t)$ time.

Intermittent fault diagnosability.   In the above discussions, there has generally been an implicit assumption that the nature of the underlying fault mechanisms causing processor faults have been permanent in nature. A significant ramification of this assumption is that the outcomes of tests administered by nonfaulty processors are always correct. In other words, the fault conditions that can inflict a faulty processor are permanently active in the sense that a nonfaulty processor can always detect their presence. Alternatively—and perhaps more realistically—faults can instead be intermittent in nature such that tests administrated by nonfaulty processors cannot always detect their presence. Similarly, a particular test set employed by a nonfaulty processor could be incomplete relative to the particular fault condition existing in a faulty processor. This would also give rise to situations in which nonfaulty processors might not always detect fault conditions in faulty processors.

The inability of a nonfaulty processor to always detect a fault condition in a faulty processor, whether caused by the intermittent nature of the fault condition and/or the incompleteness of the test set being utilized, significantly complicates system diagnosis. For example, relative to the five-processor system and associated testing assignment represented by the digraph of Figure 8.1, suppose that instead of the illustrated fault condition and test outcomes, processors 1 and 2 were intermittently faulty. These intermittently faulty processors could elude detection by processors 4 and 5, and also (incorrectly) indicate that processor 3 is faulty. Diagnosis based on the resulting syndrome under the incorrect assumption that only permanently faulty processors must be handled would conclude that a fault situation existed in which processor 3 had a permanent fault condition.

Mallela and Masson (1978, 1979) were first to address the interesting issue of system diagnosis in the presence of intermittent faults. When dealing with intermittent faults, it is possible that the combinations of test failures and passes resulting after a system test set application could be such that the syndrome could not be interpreted. Thus, to handle intermittent faults, the approach proposed by Mallela and Masson was to repeat the application of the test set while accumulating test failures. At some point, sufficient test failures would hopefully accumulate to permit a diagnosis to take place. Mallela and Masson (1978) defined a type of diagnosis in which at least some intermittently faulty processors will be correctly diagnosed whenever the syndrome took on a form that was compatible with a permanent fault situation. Such diagnosability was called t_i-diagnosability, where t_i is the upper bound on the number of processors in the system that could be intermittently faulty. t_i-diagnosability also ensures that no nonfaulty processor will ever be diagnosed as faulty. Thus, the diagnosis is possibly incomplete, but always correct in the sense that no nonfaulty processor is ever diagnosed as faulty. To distinguish t_i-diagnosability from the type of diagnosability for permanent fault conditions characterized by Theorem 8.1, the latter type of permanent fault diagnosability was referred to as t_p-diagnosability. Clearly, Example 8.7 shown in Figure 8.1 indicates that a system which is $t_p = 2$-diagnosable for permanently faulty processors is not, in general, $t_i = 2$-diagnosable for intermittently faulty processors. Accordingly, Mallela and Masson (1978) were motivated to characterize t_i-diagnosability as follows.

Theorem 8.3. A system is t_i-diagnosable if and only if for all $Z \subseteq U$, where $|Z| \leq t_i$,

$$|\Gamma^{-1}(Z)| > t_i$$

Proof. The necessity part of the proof follows directly from the observation that if it is supposed there exists a $Z \subseteq U$ where $|Z| \le t_i$, and where also $|\Gamma^{-1}(Z)| \le t_i$, an incorrect diagnosis based on a permanent fault compatible syndrome is possible. This follows since the processors in $\Gamma^{-1}(Z)$ could all be intermittently faulty and, therefore, pass all tests applied to them. Moreover, the processors in $\Gamma^{-1}(Z)$ could also (incorrectly) fail all the processors they test in Z. Since no other processors in $U - Z - \Gamma^{-1}(Z)$ test processors in Z, this results in a permanent fault compatible syndrome that incorrectly indicates that the processors in Z are faulty.

The sufficiency of the theorem can be shown by demonstrating a contradiction arises if it is assumed that the conditions of the theorem are satisfied but the system is not t_i-diagnosable. Such an assumption would mean that for some intermittently faulty $Z \subseteq U$, where $|Z| \le t_i$, a syndrome can be produced which is permanent fault compatible for some $Z_j \subseteq U$, where $|Z_j| \le t_i$ and $Z_j \not\subseteq Z$. Observe that this would mean that there were no tests from the processors in $U - Z - Z_j$ to processors $Z_j' = Z_j - Z$. If there were such tests, these tests to processors Z_j' would always be passed, and no syndrome could be produced which is permanent fault compatible with Z_j being faulty. In other words, $\Gamma^{-1}(Z_j') \subseteq Z$. But $|Z| \le t_i$, so $|\Gamma^{-1}(Z_j')| \le t_i$, which contradicts the assumption.

Yang and Masson (1986a) provided an elegant $O(|E|)$ algorithm to perform t_i-diagnosability in systems satisfying Theorem 8.3.

This work was later extended by Mallela and Masson (1979) to include *hybrid fault situations*, where combinations of permanently and intermittently faulty processors can exist. In such a case, an upper bound t is given for the total number of faulty processors (intermittent and permanent) which exist in the system at any time, and a second upper bound, t_i, where $t_i \le t$, is also given for the total number of intermittently faulty units that can exist in the system at any time. For example, a system could have as many as t total faulty processors, but at most t_i of the faulty processors could be intermittently faulty. Mallela and Masson denoted the extension of correct, but possibly incomplete, t_i-diagnosability as described above to hybrid fault situations as t/t_i-diagnosability. They were able to characterize the necessary and sufficient conditions for t/t_i-diagnosability as follows:

Theorem 8.4. A system is t/t_i-diagnosable if and only if for all $Z_i \subseteq U$, where $|Z_i| \le t$, and for all $Z_j \subseteq U$, where $|Z_j| \le t$, where $Z_i \cap Z_j = \Phi$ either

$$\Gamma^{-1}(Z_i) \not\subseteq Z_j$$

and/or

$$|\Gamma^{-1}(U - Z_i - Z_j)| > t + t_i - |Z_i|$$

This theorem will not be formally proven here, but a number of interesting observations can be made regarding its relationship to previously discussed results. Note that t-diagnosability as characterized by Theorem 8.1 is a special case of t/t_i-diagnosability where $t_i = 0$. Similarly, t_i-diagnosability as characterized by Theorem 8.3 is also a special case of t/t_i-diagnosability where $t = t_i$. Illustrating that these characterizations are equivalent under these special conditions is left as an exercise.

Finally, hybrid fault diagnosis as represented by t/t_i-diagnosability permits intriguing trade-offs to be examined between the values of t and t_i for a given system test assignment. For example, for the test assignment corresponding to Figure 8.1, it has been seen that while the system is $t = 2$-diagnosable, the system is not $t/t_i = 2/1$-diagnosable. An interesting question is whether reducing the total number of faulty processors which are to be tolerated allows the number of intermittently faulty processors to be increased for t/t_i-diagnosability. In general, this is, indeed, the case. In fact, it can be shown that for t/t_i-diagnosability, when the t value is reduced by one, the t_i value can be increased at least by two. Different test assignments support vastly different combinations of t_i and t.

8.3 SYSTEM DIAGNOSIS UNDER PROBABILISTIC MODELS

8.3.1 Motivation

Although the work described in the previous section covers a wide variety of models and types of diagnosis, it shares one common element, namely, the use of a bounded fault model. This bounded fault model assumes worst-case behavior in an attempt to guarantee a certain level of diagnosis. Under this model, any combination of faulty processors up to a particular size must be diagnosable, even those with extremely low probability of occurrence. A consequence of this model is that the cost of diagnosis, in terms of the number of tests that must be performed, is very high.

Consider, for example, a system containing 10,000 processors in which it is assumed that there are at most ten faults. Under the PMC model, each processor must be tested by at least 10 other processors. This is done in order to guard against the possibility of a processor of unknown status being tested only by faulty processors. Now, assume that each processor fails with a probability of 0.0005, independently of other processors. Under this assumption, the expected number of faulty processors is five. If each processor is tested only by nine other processors rather than ten, the probability that some processor will be tested only by faulty processors is less than $10,000 \times (.0005)^9 \approx 1.95 \times 10^{-26}$. To put this into perspective, if diagnosis were performed once per second in this system, the PMC model would guard against a situation that occurs, on average, once every 10^{18} years!

One argument often put forward in favor of bounded fault models is that they can "guarantee" some level of diagnosis. This is true only if the assumptions of the model hold, namely that the assumed maximum number of faulty processors is not exceeded. Consider, once more, the example from the previous paragraph. In this situation, the probability that there are at least 11 faulty processors is about 0.014. Thus, the event that the assumptions of the bounded fault model are violated is about 10^{23} times more probable than the worst-case fault situation. The point to be emphasized is that no matter what type of model is utilized, diagnosis can never be guaranteed but only accomplished with a certain probability.

The above paragraphs motivate the consideration of probabilistic models for system diagnosis. The power of these models is that they reflect the true environment more accurately. Under these models, only fault sets that have a non-negligible probability of occurrence are considered and, as a result, diagnosis can be accomplished at a greatly reduced cost when compared with bounded fault models. This of one of the primary advantages in utilizing probabilistic models for system diagnosis. An added benefit of the use of these models is that the diagnosis algorithms produced are often simpler than their counterparts in bounded fault models. This is because algorithms in bounded fault models must be capable of diagnosing *all* fault sets up to a particular size while algorithms for probabilistic models need diagnose far fewer fault sets.

The second major advantage of probabilistic models is that they can naturally model the occurrence of intermittent faults or the use of incomplete tests. As described previously, either of these possibilities results in a situation where tests performed by nonfaulty processors on faulty processors can be passed. This differs from the classical PMC model in which it is assumed that such tests are always failed. These situations were addressed in nonprobabilistic settings in Russell and Kime (1975a, 1975b), Mallela and Masson (1978, 1979), Yang and Masson (1986a), and Gupta and Ramakrishnan (1987).

It has been shown that for intermittent faults, the standard approach was to repeat tests many times in the hope that the faults would be detected at some point in this process. The work of Mallela and Masson (1978, 1979) defined a type of diagnosis in which some intermittently faulty processors will be correctly diagnosed whenever the syndrome takes on a form that is compatible with a permanent fault situation. This diagnosis also ensures that no nonfaulty processor will ever be diagnosed as faulty. This work was later extended to include *hybrid fault situations*, where both permanently and intermittently faulty processors can exist. The difficulty with this approach is that there is no bound on the number of tests that must be performed before all faulty processors are diagnosed.

Several authors have considered incomplete testing. Russell and Kime (1975a, 1975b) introduced models that use multiple invalidation to model incomplete testing. Gupta and Ramakrishnan (1987) use a parameter called minimum test multiplicity which is the minimum number of tests that are guaranteed to be complete for any fault in a processor. Even though individual tests can be incomplete in these works, some combination of tests must be complete for diagnosis to be accomplished.

Intermittent faults and incomplete tests can be modeled naturally using probabilistic models by having nonfaulty processors randomly fail faulty processors. We will see that this approach yields a powerful result, namely that correct diagnosis of intermittently faulty processors can be accomplished with extremely high probability using a single round of testing and making no assumptions about the completeness of a group of tests.

8.3.2 Probabilistic Models

A probabilistic model for the system diagnosis problem consists of two parts: a processor failure distribution and a conditional test outcome distribution. The former specifies the probability of each possible fault set in the system while the latter specifies the distribution of syndromes given a particular fault set. In general, these two distributions are completely separate and arbitrary. Probabilistic models for system diagnosis typically specify both distributions. In the remainder of this section, the various models that have been proposed will be compared and contrasted. It should be noted that additional models can be generated by combining the processor failure distribution of one model with the conditional test outcome distribution of another. We prefer to discuss only those models that have been proposed and studied in the literature. It is left to the reader to consider the possible effects of utilizing the remaining model combinations.

Directed models.   We first examine probabilistic models that have been proposed using the classical assumption of processors testing other processors. This situation is modeled using a directed graph and so we refer to these as directed models.

Maheshwari, Hakimi Model.   Maheshwari and Hakimi (1976) proposed the first probabilistic model for system diagnosis. This model, referred to as the MH model, is characterized by having a distinct probability of failure for each processor in the system. Once the failure probabilities are known, the processor failure distribution is specified. As for the conditional test outcome distribution, Maheshwari and Hakimi followed the assumptions in the PMC model. Thus, in the MH model, nonfaulty processors always pass other nonfaulty processors and always fail faulty processors while outcomes of tests performed by faulty processors are arbitrary. Hence, the test outcomes are nonprobabilistic in the MH model. For this reason, we classify this model as a *partially probabilistic model*. For this reason, we classify this model as a *partially probabilistic model*.

The precise assumptions made in the MH model for a system represented by a digraph $G = (U, E)$ are as follows:

1. Processors fail independently, and
2. $\forall x \in U$, p_x represents the probability that processor x is faulty.

The a priori probability of a fault set $F \subseteq U$ for this processor failure distribution is

$$P(F) = \left(\prod_{x \in F} p_x \right) \cdot \left(\prod_{y \in U - F} (1 - p_y) \right).$$

An example system is shown in Figure 8.9. In this system, the a priori probability of $F = \{u_1, u_3, u_5\}$ is

$$p_{u_1} \cdot p_{u_3} \cdot p_{u_5} \cdot (1 - p_{u_2}) \cdot (1 - p_{u_4}) \cdot (1 - p_{u_6}) = 8.4645 \times 10^{-5}$$

Because processors have distinct probabilities of failure in this model, we refer to the types of systems to which the model applies as *heterogeneous* systems.

Blount Model. Shortly after Maheshwari and Hakimi, Blount (1977) proposed an alternative probabilistic model. Blount's model was the first *fully probabilistic model*, that is, it was the first containing both a processor failure distribution and a conditional test outcome distribution. Blount's model is extremely general in both of these distributions. For the processor failure distribution, any joint distribution on the processors in the system is allowed. The distribution is specified by assigning a probability to each possible fault set in the system. In this model, there is not even an assumption of independence between failures in different processors, which is a standard assumption in all other models.

Blount's conditional test outcome distribution is quite general also. For each pair of processors (u_i, u_j) such that u_i tests u_j in the system, there are four possible distributions of the test outcome. These distributions cover the four possible combinations of faulty and nonfaulty testing processor and tested processor. A complete list of the assumptions of Blount's model in a system represented by a digraph $G = (U, E)$ is as follows:

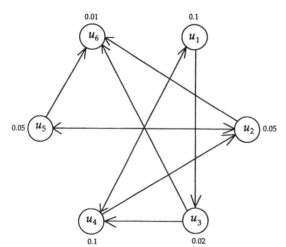

Figure 8.9: A system with distinct processor failure probabilities.

1. The processor failure distribution is an arbitrary distribution over the set of all possible fault sets;

2. $\forall (u_i \rightarrow u_j) \in E$, p_{ij} is the probability that u_i passes u_j given that both u_i and u_j are nonfaulty.

3. $\forall (u_i \rightarrow u_j) \in E$, r_{ij} is the probability that u_i fails u_j, given that u_i is nonfaulty and u_j is faulty,

4. $\forall (u_i \rightarrow u_j) \in E$, q_{ij} is the probability that u_i passes u_j given that u_i is faulty and u_j is nonfaulty,

5. $\forall (u_i \rightarrow u_j) \in E$, s_{ij} is the probability that u_i fails u_j given that both u_i and u_j are faulty, and

6. test outcomes are conditionally independent, given a fault set.

Blount's conditional test outcome distribution models the outcomes of all tests as random events regardless of the statuses of the processors involved in the test. This has some interesting consequences. For example, Blount's model allows the occurrence of *false alarms*, *i.e.* a non-faulty processor failing another non-faulty processor. To our knowledge, this is the only model with this property. A second consequence of the model is that the test outcomes of faulty processors are restricted. Whereas the PMC model and some probabilistic models (in particular, the Blough, Sullivan, Masson Model described later) allow the faulty processors' test outcomes to be arbitrary, the Blount model restricts them to be random and independent. This prevents certain test outcomes, *e.g.* those which involve collusion between faulty processors, that should be allowed if faulty processors can produce arbitrary outcomes.

Although Blount's model is quite general, it is enormously complex. Having an arbitrary processor failure distribution means that the probability of every possible fault set must be known. In addition, four separate distributions are needed for each test in the system. The complexity of this model makes it extremely hard to analyze. In practice, some assumptions must be made to simplify the models. This is precisely what has been done in the other models described in this section. Blount's model is interesting from a theoretical standpoint since it represents the most general possible model in many respects. As mentioned earlier, the only restricting part of the model is the assumption of random and independent behavior of faulty processors' test outcomes.

Let us examine a simplified version of Blount's model in order to illustrate some concepts related to the conditional test outcome distribution. Assume the processor failure distribution is the same as in the MH Model, namely a processor x fails with probability p_x, independently of other processors. Further assume that the conditional test outcome distribution is such that $\forall i, j$, $p_{ij} = p = 0.99$, $r_{ij} = r = 0.8$, $q_{ij} = q = 0.5$, and $s_{ij} = s = 0.5$. Hence, the outcome of a particular test depends only on the statuses of the processors involved in the test and not on the identities of the processors. Now, consider the system shown in Figure 8.10. The

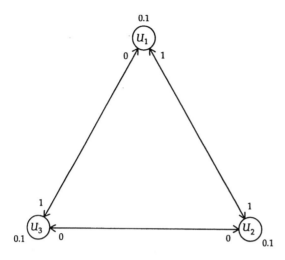

Figure 8.10: A syndrome in a system with given processor failure probabilities.

probability of a particular fault set in this system can be calculated as in the MH Model. For example, the probability of the fault set $F = \{u_2, u_3\}$ is $0.1 \times 0.1 \times 0.9 = 0.009$. The following example illustrates how to calculate both the conditional and a priori probabilities of a particular syndrome.

Example 8.8.   **Computing the probability of a syndrome**

The conditional probability that a single test outcome occurs can be calculated easily from p, q, r, or s, depending on the statuses of the processors involved in the test. Since different test outcomes are conditionally independent given a fault set, the individual test outcome probabilities can be multiplied to obtain the conditional probability of a particular syndrome. Consider, for example, the test performed by u_1 on u_2 given the fault set $F = \{u_2, u_3\}$. In this situation, u_1 is nonfaulty and u_2 is faulty so the probability that the test is failed is $r = 0.8$. Repeating this process for each test and multiplying yields a probability of $0.8 \times 0.5 \times 0.5 \times 0.5 \times 0.5 \times 0.8 = 0.04$ for the syndrome shown in Figure 8.10, given the fault set $F = \{u_2, u_3\}$.

It is sometimes necessary to calculate the a priori probability of a particular syndrome. This can be done from the conditional test outcome distribution using the Law of Total Probability. This implies that the a priori probability of a syndrome S in a system represented by a digraph $G = (U, E)$ is given by

$$P(S) = \sum_{F \subseteq U} P(S \mid F) \cdot P(F)$$

In the system of Figure 8.10, there are only eight possible fault sets so this expression can be evaluated fairly simply. Table 8.2 shows the values in this summation for the syndrome of Figure 8.10 and for each possible fault set. The a priori probability of the syndrome is equal to 0.00369676, which is the sum of the probabilities in the rightmost column of Table 8.2.

This example can also be used to illustrate the concept of optimal probabilistic diagnosis. A diagnosis algorithm takes a syndrome as input and outputs a

Table 8.2: Joint Probabilities of Syndrome from Figure 8.10 and All Fault Sets

Fault Set	$P(S \mid F)$	$P(F)$	$P(S \cap F)$
{}	0.00000097	0.729	0.00000071
$\{u_1\}$	0.039204	0.081	0.00317552
$\{u_2\}$	0.000396	0.081	0.00003208
$\{u_3\}$	0.000004	0.081	0.00000032
$\{u_1, u_2\}$	0.0025	0.009	0.0000225
$\{u_1, u_3\}$	0.01	0.009	0.00009
$\{u_2, u_3\}$	0.04	0.009	0.00036
$\{u_1, u_2, u_3\}$	0.015625	0.001	0.00001563

fault set. An optional diagnosis algorithm should output the fault set which is most likely to have produced the syndrome that is input. In other words, the algorithm should output a fault set F that maximizes $P(F \mid S)$ over all possible fault sets. Since $P(F \mid S) = (P(F \cap S)/P(S))$ and $P(S)$ is independent of F, this amounts to maximizing $P(F \cap S)$. In Table 8.2, the maximum value of $P(F \cap S)$ occurs for $F = \{u_1\}$ and hence, this is the most likely fault set given the syndrome of Figure 8.10. A limitation of optional diagnosis is that it usually requires calculation of $P(F \cap S)$ for every possible fault set and therefore uses exponential time.

Blough, Sullivan, Masson Model.   In 1988, Blough, Sullivan, and Masson (journal version 1992c) introduced a fully probabilistic model that allows for intermittent faults and/or incomplete tests. The assumptions of this model, referred to as the BSM Model, are as follows:

1. Processors fail with probability p, independently of other processors.
2. Nonfaulty processors always pass other nonfaulty processors.
3. Nonfaulty processors fail faulty processors with probability q, independently of other test outcomes.
4. Faulty processors' test outcomes are arbitrary.

In this model, q represents the probability of detection of an intermittent fault or the coverage of an incomplete test. Since processors have identical failure probabilities in this model, we refer to systems for which the model applies as *homogeneous* systems. A special case of the model, corresponding to the situation where faults are permanent and tests are complete, results when $q = 1$. This model, proposed by Scheinerman (1987), is also a special case of the MH Model where processor failure probabilities are identical. The a priori probability of a fault set $F \subseteq U$ for the homogeneous processor failure distribution is $P(F) = p^{|F|}(1 - p)^{|U - F|}$.

The strength of this model is in its simplicity and generality. There are only two parameters in the model, the failure probability and the fault detection probability. Despite this simplicity, the model is quite general and powerful, since it does not restrict the faulty processors' test outcomes in any way. This allows the faulty processors to produce test outcomes in an arbitrary fashion, including coordinating them so as to try to confuse the diagnosis algorithm. This generality is not without a price. Because faulty processors' test outcomes are arbitrary, there is no probability distribution defined on them. Hence, the conditional test outcome distribution is specified only over tests performed by nonfaulty processors, meaning that the probability of a particular syndrome cannot be computed. The system in Figure 8.11 will be used to illustrate this point.

Example 8.9 Computing the conditional probability of a collection of syndromes

Assume the fault set $F = \{u_3\}$. Under the BSM model, it is possible to calculate the probabilities of all outcomes of tests performed by nonfaulty processors. This leaves the outcomes of tests performed by u_3 without a specified probability distribution. Hence, the syndrome shown in Figure 8.11 cannot be assigned a conditional probability. In this model, only collections of syndromes can have probabilities assigned. Call the syndrome in Figure 8.11, S_1. Let S_2 be the same as S_1 except with $a_{3,4} = 1$, let S_3 be the same as S_1 except with $a_{3,5} = 0$, and let S_4 be the same as S_1 except with $a_{3,4} = 1$ and $a_{3,5} = 0$. Hence, (S_1, S_2, S_3, S_4) represents the collection of syndromes with the test outcomes shown in Figure 8.11 from the nonfaulty processors and all possible test outcomes from the faulty processor u_3. With the assumptions of the BSM model, the best that can be done is to assign a probability to this collection of syndromes. Since tests on nonfaulty processors by nonfaulty processors are always passed, the only random outcomes are the tests performed by nonfaulty processors on faulty processors. In Figure 8.11, the conditional probability of the collection of syndromes (S_1, S_2, S_3, S_4), given $F = \{u_3\}$, is q^2, since both tests on u_3 are failed. In general, the conditional probability of a collection of syndromes, where the collec-

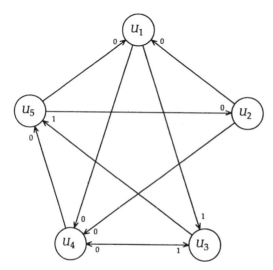

Figure 8.11: A syndrome in a system under the BSM Model.

tion ranges over all possible outcomes of tests performed by faulty processors, is $q^{|E_1|}(1 - q)^{|E_0|}$, where $|E_1|$ is the number of tests in which nonfaulty processors fail faulty processors and $|E_0|$ is the number of tests in which nonfaulty processors pass faulty processors.

The fact that the conditional probability of a single syndrome is not defined in the BSM model complicates its analysis. Fortunately, a method of dealing with this situation has been proposed and applied several times, for example, by Blough (1988) and Blough, Sullivan and Masson (1992b, 1992c). We will not present here the mathematical subtleties that are necessary to handle this situation but rather we refer the reader to one of the papers in which this issue is discussed in detail. This added complexity does not in any way prevent the model from being utilized to solve real problems as will be illustrated in the next section.

Undirected models.   Undirected models, also referred to as comparison models, for system diagnosis assume that tests are performed by having two processors execute the same job and then comparing their results. Since, in this situation, there is no notion of one processor testing another but rather just two processors participating in a test, this is modeled using an undirected graph. We will refer to a test in which the two processors produce identical results as an *agreement*. Similarly, *disagreement* will refer to a test in which the two processors produce different results.

Dahbura, Sabnani, King Model.   The first probabilistic comparison model was proposed by Dahbura, Sabnani, and King (1987). No processor failure distribution was proposed for this model, referred to as the DSK model. Instead, the authors computed probabilities conditioned only on the number of faulty processors. Hence, this model is a partially probabilistic model. For the conditional test outcome distribution, the DSK model makes the following assumptions:

1. Two nonfaulty processors always agree;
2. A nonfaulty processor and a faulty processor agree with probability r;
3. Two faulty processors agree with probability r^2; and
4. Test outcomes are conditionally independent, given a fault set.

Note that in this model, disagreements between two faulty processors are more likely than those between one nonfaulty processor and one faulty processor. This has the following important consequence. The status of a processor that is tested by l processors, all of which are faulty, can be determined with high probability in this model. In this situation, the processor will agree with about rl processors if it is nonfaulty but it will agree only with about r^2l processors if it is faulty. The authors give the following justification for this. Assume that a faulty processor produces a correct result of a job with probability r. Since nonfaulty processors always produce correct results, the probability that a nonfaulty processor and a faulty processor agree is r. Now, assume that when a faulty processor produces an incorrect result, all incorrect values are equally likely to be produced. Then, the probability that two faulty processors agree is the probability that they both produce the correct result plus the probability that they both produce the same incorrect result which is given by $r^2 + ((1 - r)^2/k)$, where k is the number of possible incorrect results. Reasoning that the number of possible incorrect results is large yields an agreement probability of approximately r^2 in this case.

Pelc Model.   More recently, Pelc (1991) proposed an alternative probabilistic comparison model. The model utilizes exactly the assumptions listed for the DSK model except that the probability that two faulty processors agree is the same as the probability that a faulty processor and a nonfaulty processor agree. Let us denote this probability by s so as not to confuse it with the parameter from the DSK model. Pelc reasons that a faulty processor should produce results uniformly and so the probability that any particular result, including the correct one, is produced is $1/m$, where m is the number of possible results. Hence, $s = 1/m$ and the probability that two faulty processors agree is $m \cdot (1/m^2) = 1/m = s$. Note that in this case, outcomes of tests between two faulty processors are indistinguishable from the outcomes of tests between one faulty processor and one nonfaulty processor. Hence, the status of a processor that is tested only by faulty processors *cannot* be determined with high probability in Pelc's model.

It is worth examining more closely the assumptions in these two probabilistic comparison models to determine in what situations they may be useful. With $r = s$ and $k = m - 1$, the probability of an agreement between two faulty processors in both models is given by $r^2 + ((1 - r)^2/k)$. In the DSK model, it is assumed that $r \gg 1/k$ so that the second term is neglected. In Pelc's model, it is assumed that $r = 1/m = 1/(k + 1)$ so that the second term is not neglected and, in fact, is exactly $r - r^2$. The basic assumption in the DSK model is that a faulty processor is much more likely to produce a correct result than it is to produce any single incorrect result. Pelc's model, on the other hand, assumes that the correct result from a faulty processor has the same likelihood as a single incorrect result.

From this analysis, the DSK model appears to be well suited for modeling intermittently faulty processors in which, at any point in time, there is a fixed probability that the fault is inactive. This would lead to a situation where, with fixed probability, faulty processors produce the correct result. Pelc's model appears well suited to modeling permanently faulty processors for which the correct result is no more likely than any single incorrect result.

Fussell, Rangarajan Model.   The assumptions of the model proposed by Fussell and Rangarajan (1989), referred to as the FR model, are

1. Processors fail with probability p, independently of other processors;
2. Two nonfaulty processors always agree;

3. Faulty processors perform a job correctly with probability r; and
4. Test outcomes are conditionally independent, given a fault set.

Assumption 3 is the same assumption used in the DSK model, although Fussell and Rangarajan do not approximate the probability of an agreement between two faulty processors by r^2 as is done in the DSK model. In the FR model, the probability that two faulty processors agree is exactly $r^2 + ((1 - r)^2/k)$, where k is the number of possible incorrect results. For this reason, the conditional test outcome distributions are slightly different in the two models. However, it is still true that disagreements between two faulty processors are more likely than those between one nonfaulty processor and one faulty processor.

It should be noted that Fussell and Rangarajan proposed this model for use in a multiple test situation. By multiple test situation, we mean a situation where the same two processors may be involved in multiple tests. The classical PMC model and all other models described in this section deal with the single test situation, that is, each testing link is exercised exactly once.

8.3.3 Results in Directed Models

Classical work on system diagnosis considered algorithms either for t-diagnosis (in various models) or optimal diagnosis (finding the minimum-size fault set consistent with a syndrome.) This line of research carried over into probabilistic domains, translating into algorithms for p-diagnosis (see Maheshwari and Hakimi (1976) or optimal probabilistic diagnosis (see Blount [1977]). All of this work shared the same basic diagnosis philosophy; given a system and a syndrome, choose the fault set which is most likely to have produced the syndrome. For t-diagnosis and optimal diagnosis, the chosen fault set is the most probable assuming that processors fail with identical probability $p < 1/2$. It should be noted that, in the cases of t-diagnosis and p-diagnosis, effort was also put into the design of systems amenable to diagnosis, resulting in diagnoses that were guaranteed to be unique among all fault sets of some minimum a priori probability.

While the maximum-likelihood diagnosis philosophy has merit, it also has one fundamental weakness. There is no guarantee that the diagnosis that is produced is correct with high probability. This is best illustrated by examining the p-diagnosis framework. In this framework, fault sets that are produced are guaranteed to be unique among fault sets with a priori probability of occurrence of p or greater. However, if the diagnosis results in choosing a fault set that has a priori probability only slightly greater than p and there are many consistent fault sets of a priori probability only slightly less than p, then the probability of incorrect diagnosis may be quite high. The same comment is true of all procedures that utilize the maximum-likelihood diagnosis philosophy.

Since 1987, there has been a dramatic shift in research focus away from the maximum-likelihood diagnosis philosophy. This new research has focused on ensuring that diagnosis is correct with high probability. This trend began with Scheinerman (1987), followed closely by Blough, Sullivan, and Masson (1992b, 1992c), and soon after by many others including Fussell and Rangarajan (1989), Berman and Pelc (1990), Lee and Shin (1990), Pelc (1991), Blough and Pelc (1993). The basic philosophy of this research, which was fueled by new probabilistic models and techniques, was to design diagnosis algorithms for classes of systems such that the diagnosis produced is almost certainly correct. Almost certain diagnosis is defined as diagnosis which is correct with a probability that approaches one as the size of the systems approaches infinity. Typically, proofs that a diagnosis algorithm is almost certain also yield concrete bounds on the probability of its correctness. Hence, this approach has the desirable property that for a particular system, diagnosis is known to be correct with some probability. Furthermore, this probability can be made arbitrarily close to one by increasing the size of the system. Typically, even for fairly small systems, the probability of correctness of the proposed algorithms turns out to be quite high.

In this section and the next, we will illustrate the use of this new design philosophy by considering results that have been obtained under several models.

Homogeneous case of the Maheshwari, Hakimi model.   The homogeneous case of the MH model, in a system represented by a digraph $G = (U, E)$, corresponds to the situation where, $\forall x \in U$, $p_x = p$. In other words, all processors have the same probability of failure. Note that this is also a special case of the BSM model, where $q = 1$. Recall that q is the probability that a nonfaulty processor fails a faulty processor. Hence, this special case corresponds to the situation where nonfaulty processors always fail faulty processors, that is, the situation where faults are permanent and tests are complete. To remove ambiguity, we refer to this special case as the MH homogeneous model.

Scheinerman (1987) was the first to prove that almost certain diagnosis was possible. Two classes of systems were considered in his paper: those with random connections between processors and $D_{1,k}$ systems, which are a special case of the $D_{\delta,t}$ systems introduced by Preparata, Metze, and Chien (1967). For both of these classes of systems, Scheinerman proved that $O(n \log n)$ tests are sufficient for almost certain diagnosis under the MH homogeneous model. Note that, under this model, the expected number of faulty processors is pn. To diagnose this many faulty processors under the bounded fault model requires pn^2 tests. Hence, the number of tests required for diagnosis was reduced from $\Theta(n^2)$ to $O(n \log n)$ by moving from the worst-case fault model to a probabilistic model.

To illustrate the type of analysis that is performed under probabilistic models, let us examine the proof of Scheinerman's result for $D_{1,k}$ systems. A $D_{1,k}$ system consists of n processors organized in a circle with each processor testing the next k processors around the circle in a clockwise direction. Figure 8.12 shows an example of a syndrome in a $D_{1,3}$ system with nine processors.

In order to prove that diagnosis is almost certain, one must first design a di-

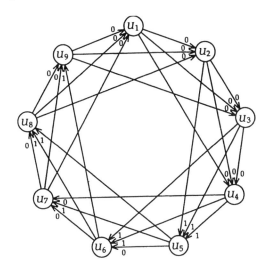

Figure 8.12: A $D_{1,3}$ system with nine processors.

agnosis algorithm. Scheinerman's diagnosis algorithm, referred to as Algorithm FindFault, works in the following way. The algorithm takes a syndrome (represented by a weighted directed graph as in Figure 8.12) and deletes all failed tests. The remaining digraph, referred to as the 0-digraph, contains only tests that were passed. It is straightforward to show that any strongly connected component of this digraph must contain only faulty processors or only nonfaulty processors but not both. Algorithm FindFault finds the largest strongly connected component in the 0-digraph. If this connected component contains at most $n/2$ processors, all processors in the system are considered faulty. This case is not important since it will be shown to occur with negligible probability. The more interesting case is when the connected component contains more than $n/2$ processors. In this case, the processors in the component are all assumed to be nonfaulty. These processors are then used to determine the statuses of the remaining processors. As an example, consider the operation of Algorithm FindFault in the system of Figure 8.12. The 0-digraph for this system is shown in Figure 8.13. The largest strongly connected component of this digraph contains the processors u_1, u_2, u_3, u_4, u_7, u_8, and u_9. Since $7 > n/2 = 4.5$, these seven processors are considered nonfaulty by Algorithm FindFault. Since u_5 and u_6 are both failed by u_4 which is assumed to be nonfaulty, these two processors are considered faulty. Hence, the fault set produced by Algorithm FindFault in this situation is $F = \{u_5, u_6\}$.

In a $D_{1,k}$ system, if no k consecutive processors are faulty, then the set of nonfaulty processors will be connected in a cycle. Since a test of a nonfaulty processor by another nonfaulty processor is always passed, this cycle will form a strongly connected component in the 0-digraph. Thus, as long as

1. there are more than $n/2$ nonfaulty processors in the system and

2. no k consecutive processors are faulty,

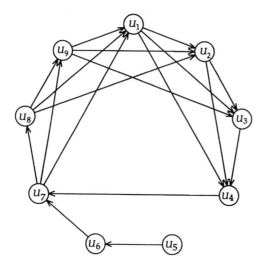

Figure 8.13: The 0-digraph for the system of Figure 8.12.

then all nonfaulty processors will be contained in a strongly connected component in the 0-digraph of size greater than $n/2$. Hence, all nonfaulty processors
will be considered nonfaulty by Algorithm FindFault in the first round and subsequent diagnoses are guaranteed to be correct. Therefore, if conditions 1 and 2
can be shown to hold almost certainly, then almost certain diagnosis can be accomplished.

Let X represent the number of faulty processors in an n-processor system. X
is a binomial random variable with parameters n and p. By Chebyshev's Inequality (see Feller [1968]), for any $\epsilon > 0$,

$$P(X > np + n^{(\epsilon+1)/2}) \le \frac{np(1-p)}{n^{1+\epsilon}} \to 0$$

as $n \to \infty$. Since $p < 1/2$, $P(X > n/2) \to 0$ and condition 1 holds almost certainly.
Now, let $k = c \log_2 n$, where c is a constant satisfying $c > (1/\log_2 1/p)$. The probability that k consecutive processors are faulty is p^k. Since there are n possible such
sequences, the probability that there exist k consecutive faulty processors is no
greater than

$$np^k = np^{c \log_2 n} = n \cdot n^{-c \log_2 1/p} = n^{1-c \log_2 1/p} \to 0$$

as $n \to \infty$, since $c > (1/\log_2 1/p)$. Thus, condition 2 holds almost certainly and almost certain diagnosis is accomplished by Algorithm FindFault. Note that the
condition $k = c \log_2 n$ is needed to ensure that no k consecutive processors are
faulty. Hence, the number of tests needed to ensure almost certain diagnosis in
$D_{1,k}$ systems is $cn \log_2 n$.

Scheinerman conjectured that almost certain diagnosis could not be accomplished in any systems with $o(n \log n)$ tests. However, Blough, Sullivan, and Mas-

son (1992b) showed this conjecture to be false. They showed that almost certain diagnosis is possible in systems with slightly more than a linear number of tests. Their result also implies that, for any desired probability of correct diagnosis less than one, there exists a class of systems with a linear number of tests in which this goal can be met. Hence, while $\Theta(n^2)$ tests are necessary in the bounded fault model to ensure correct diagnosis with high probability, the result of Blough, Sullivan, and Masson shows that this can be done using only $O(n)$ tests under the MH homogeneous model.

As stated earlier, another advantage of the use of probabilistic models is that the diagnosis algorithms produced are often far simpler than the ones produced under bounded fault models. The next diagnosis algorithm, referred to as Algorithm Majority, is a perfect example. This algorithm was proposed by Blough, Sullivan, and Masson (1992b). The algorithm declares as faulty any processor that is failed by more than one-half of the processors that test it. In this algorithm, fail (u) is used to denote the set of processors that fail a processor u and $\Gamma^{-1}(u)$ denotes the set of processors that test u.

Algorithm Majority

Input: A syndrome S in a digraph $G = (U, E)$

Output: A set $F \subseteq U$

```
F ← ∅
for each u ∈ U
    if |fail(u)| > (|Γ⁻¹(u)|/2) then F ← F ∪ {u}
```

Note than in diagnosing an individual processor using Algorithm Majority, only test outcomes that are local to the processor are utilized. This allows an efficient distributed implementation of the algorithm in which a majority voter is placed at each processor and receives input only from neighboring processors. This approach is made even more attractive by the fact that the 1-bit majority voting function executed by Algorithm Majority can be easily implemented in hardware.

The sparse systems for which Algorithm Majority produces correct diagnosis with high probability are represented by core digraphs. Core digraphs contain a small set of processors, known as the core set, that test all other processors. No processor outside the core set conducts any tests. An example of a core digraph with eight processors, three of which form the core set, is shown in Figure 8.14. Core digraphs were initially proposed by Blough (1988) for the system diagnosis problem but have subsequently been shown to be important for many fault-tolerant communication problems such as Byzantine agreement (see Pelc (1992a)) and fault-tolerant broadcasting (see Pelc (1992b)) as well. The favorable property of core digraphs is that if the majority of the processors in the core set are nonfaulty, then Algorithm Majority will produce correct diagnosis. Since $p < 1/2$, Chebyshev's inequality implies that, as long as the size of the core set approaches infinity

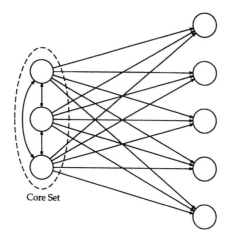

Core Set

Figure 8.14: A core digraph with five noncore processors and three core processors.

with n, this condition will be satisfied. Note that the number of tests performed in such a system is $|C| \cdot (n-1)$, where C is the core set. Since the size of the core set can grow arbitrarily slowly, the number of tests used is only slightly more than linear in n. The formalization of this argument results in the following theorem.

Theorem 8.5 (Blough, Sullivan, Masson, (1989, 1992b)).   Let $w(n)$ be any function such that $w(n) \to \infty$ as $n \to \infty$. If $p < 1/2$, then for any sequence of n-processor systems represented by core digraphs with $w(n)$ core processors, Algorithm Majority achieves almost certain diagnosis.

An important byproduct of the proof of this theorem is the following lower bound on the probability of correct diagnosis for Algorithm Majority in core digraphs. C again represents the core set in the digraph.

$$P(\text{Alg. Majority correct}) \geq \sum_{i=0}^{\left\lceil \frac{|C|}{2} \right\rceil - 1} \binom{|C|}{i} p^i (1-p)^{|C|-i}$$

Note that this lower bound depends on the size of the core set and on p but not on n. This has the important consequence that, for any desired probability of correct diagnosis less than one, a core set whose size is independent of n can be found that achieves it. Hence, the number of tests required in core digraphs to achieve any correct diagnosis probability arbitrarily close to one is $O(n)$. To illustrate this point more clearly, Table 8.3 shows the core set size required to achieve specified probabilities of correct diagnosis for various values of p. The number of core processors required to achieve a probability of correct diagnosis of 0.999999 is only seven, even when the failure probability is 0.01. Hence, only about $7n$ tests are needed to achieve this extremely high probability.

Table 8.3: Size of Core Set Required
to Achieve a Given Probability
of Correct Diagnosis

p	Correct Diagnosis Probability	$\lvert c \rvert$
0.001	0.9999	3
	0.99999	3
	0.999999	5
0.005	0.9999	3
	0.99999	5
	0.999999	7
0.010	0.9999	5
	0.99999	5
	0.999999	7
0.050	0.9999	9
	0.99999	11
	0.999999	15
0.100	0.9999	17
	0.99999	19
	0.999999	23

To put these results into perspective, Table 8.4 compares the number of tests required under the bounded fault model to the number required by Algorithm Majority. Both numbers of tests were chosen so as to achieve a correct diagnosis probability of 0.99999. The number of tests required under the bounded fault model was calculated in the following manner. For a given n and p, determine t such that the probability of more than t out of the n processors being faulty is no greater than 0.00001. Table 8.4 shows the results of this comparison for various values of n and p. For large n, the number of tests required under the probabilistic model is dramatically lower than the number required under the bounded fault model. For example, when $n = 100000$ and $p = 0.10$, the number of tests required

Table 8.4: Total Number of Tests Necessary for Correct
Diagnosis Probability of 0.99999

n	p	Bounded Fault	Probabilistic
100	0.001	300	297
100	0.010	700	495
100	0.100	2500	1881
1000	0.001	8000	2997
1000	0.010	26,000	4995
1000	0.100	143,000	18,981
10000	0.001	260,000	29,997
10000	0.010	1,450,000	49,995
10000	0.100	11,300,000	189,981

in the probabilistic model is reduced by a multiplicative factor of 60 over the bounded fault model.

So far, the work presented has been concerned solely with minimizing the number of tests that must be conducted in order to achieve almost certain diagnosis. However, one should also be concerned with the feasibility of implementing the systems of interest. While core digraphs utilize only a linear number of tests, they possess a maximum degree of $n - 1$. For systems that are implemented using direct interconnection networks, low degree and regularity are important issues for scalability.

Blough, Sullivan, and Masson (1992b) addressed these issues by considering the sparest possible regular systems in which almost certain diagnosis can be achieved using Algorithm Majority. This resulted in the following theorem.

Theorem 8.6 (Blough, Sullivan, Masson (1989, 1992b). Let c be any constant such that

$$c > \left\{ \frac{\log_2 e}{2} \left[\log_e \frac{1}{2(1-p)} + \log_e \frac{1}{2p} \right] \right\}^{-1}.$$

If $p < 1/2$, then for any class of systems of n processors having a tester set of size at least $c \log_2 n$ for every processor, Algorithm Majority achieves almost certain diagnosis.

This theorem generalizes Scheinerman's result in that it expands the class of systems containing $O(n \log n)$ tests for which almost certain diagnosis can be achieved. While Scheinerman's result was specific to $D_{1,k}$ systems, Theorem 8.6 requires only that each processor be tested by at least $c \log_2 n$ other processors. The classes of systems that satisfy this condition include, among others, regular systems of degree at least $c \log_2 n$. For binary hypercubes, the maximum number of testers of a processor is exactly $\log_2 n$ and so the theorem condition is satisfied when $p < 0.067$. Thus, for small failure probabilities, diagnosis of a linear number of faulty processors is possible in hypercubes under the MH homogeneous model, while only a logarithmic number of faults can be handled under bounded fault models.

One might wonder whether correct diagnosis can be achieved with high probability in sparser regular systems. The answer is, unfortunately, no. Blough, Sullivan, and Masson (1992c) proved that for regular systems of degree $o(n \log n)$, any diagnosis algorithm has a probability of correct diagnosis that approaches zero as n approaches infinity. This result is even stronger than saying that almost certain diagnosis is not possible. It says instead that all diagnosis algorithms are almost certainly incorrect, that is, no algorithm can achieve even a constant probability greater than zero of correct diagnosis.

Although almost certain diagnosis is not possible in constant-degree, regular systems under the MH homogeneous model, LaForge, Huang, and Agarwal (1994) showed that it is possible to diagnose "almost every" nonfaulty processor with high probability. Their results show that a large connected component of nonfaulty processors can be identified with high probability in these systems. While the statuses of the processors outside of this component remain unknown, identifying a large set of connected, nonfaulty processors is sufficient for some applications.

BSM model.   We now examine the general BSM model, that is, the case where $q < 1$. This case has been studied in Blough, Sullivan and Masson (1992). In this paper, a threshold-based diagnosis algorithm was proposed. We present here a slightly simplified version of this algorithm that has the same asymptotic performance. This version of the algorithm, referred to as Algorithm SimpleThresh, is intuitively pleasing since it is a natural extension of Algorithm Majority. Just as in Algorithm Majority, Algorithm SimpleThresh diagnoses as faulty any processor that is failed by at least some fraction of its testers. Whereas in Algorithm Majority, the fraction was $1/2$, for Algorithm SimpleThresh the fraction depends on the parameters p and q. The selection and optimization of this fraction, which is denoted by f in the following description, will be discussed later.

Algorithm SimpleThresh
Input: A syndrome S in a digraph $G = (U, E)$
Output: A set $F \subseteq U$

```
F ← ∅
for each u ∈ U
    if |fail(u)| > f · |Γ⁻¹(u)| then  F ← F ∪ {u}
```

The following theorem was proven in Blough, Sullivan and Masson (1992c).

Theorem 8.7 (Blough, Sullivan, Masson, (1992c)   Let $f = (p + q(1 - p))/2$ and let c be a sufficiently large constant. If $q < p/(1 - p)$, then for any class of systems of n processors having a tester set of size at least $c \log_2 n$ for every processor, Algorithm SimpleThresh achieves almost certain diagnosis.

The crux of Theorem 8.7 is that even in the presence of intermittently faulty processors, almost certain diagnosis can be achieved in systems with $cn \log_2 n$ tests. The exact value of c for which the theorem holds is quite complicated and is given by Blough (1988). For reasonable values of p and q, c is quite small. For example, it is shown in Blough, Sullivan and Masson (1992c) then when $q \geq 0.82$ and $p \leq 0.001$ almost certain diagnosis can be achieved in hypercubes, that is, when

$c = 1$. The important thing to note is that under the BSM model, $O(n \log n)$ tests are sufficient to diagnose a linear number of intermittently faulty processors while under the bounded fault model $\Theta(n^2)$ tests are needed just to diagnose a linear number of permanently faulty processors.

Note that the theorem requires $q > p/(1-p)$. Since q cannot exceed one, this implicitly enforces the restriction $p < 1/2$ which was the only restriction in the permanent fault case. Th closer p is to $1/2$, the closer q must be to one, that is, the better the fault coverage must be. An intuitive explanation of why q must exceed $p/(1-p)$ is as follows. Consider the situation where faulty processors fail all non-faulty processors and pass all faulty processors. It can be shown that this is the worst type of behavior as far as Algorithm SimpleThresh is concerned. Recall that we do not constrain the test outcomes of faulty processors in any way, so this behavior is perfectly allowable under the BSM model. If this situation occurs, then for a processor u, one would expect about $p \cdot \left| \Gamma^{-1}(u) \right|$ failures of u when u is nonfaulty and about $q(1-p) \left| \Gamma^{-1}(u) \right|$ failures of u when u is faulty. When $q > p \left| (1-p) \right|$, faulty processors are failed, on average, more often than nonfaulty processors. This allows Algorithm SimpleThresh to distinguish faulty and non-faulty processors. Note that the choice of f in Theorem 8.7 makes $f \cdot \left| \Gamma^{-1}(u) \right|$ fall exactly on the midpoint between these two values in this situation. Suppose however that $q = p/(1-p)$. Then the expected number of failures of a processor is the same whether it is faulty or nonfaulty. In this case, no diagnosis algorithm should be able to distinguish faulty and nonfaulty processors. Similarly, if $q < p/(1-p)$, then faulty processors can fail appropriate fractions of faulty and nonfaulty processors so as to make them indistinguishable to any diagnosis algorithm.

It should also be noted that in actual systems, the selection of f may have significant influence on the performance of Algorithm SimpleThresh. Analytical optimization of f can be achieved using Bayesian techniques. Lee and Shin (1993) used Bayesian analysis to derive a diagnosis algorithm that is optimal among all algorithms which use only local syndrome information. This optimal local algorithm was derived for a model in which faulty processors' test outcomes are constrained to be random and independent, as in Blount's model. A similar analysis can be performed under the BSM model to derive an optimal value for f under worst-case behavior of faulty processors. Both the value of f used for asymptotic analysis and the optimal value depend on p and q. This is somewhat undesirable since the values of these parameters may not be known exactly. The robustness of the algorithm to variations in f depends on how close q is to $p/(1-p)$. As described above, f must be chosen between these two values. Hence, if q and $p/(1-p)$ are close, the choice of f must be quite accurate but if q and $p/(1-p)$ are far apart, then there is a significant margin for error in the selection of f.

The proof of Theorem 8.7 yields the following bound on the probability of correct diagnosis for Algorithm SimpleThresh on a digraph $G = (U, E)$ with $n = |U|$, $N = \max_{u \in U} \left| \Gamma^{-1}(u) \right|$, common threshold value k, failure probability p, and detection probability q:

$P(\text{Alg. SimpleThresh Correct})$

$$\geq 1 - n(1-p) \sum_{j=k+1}^{N} \binom{N}{j} p^j (1-p)^{N-j}$$

$$-np \sum_{j=0}^{N} \left[\binom{N}{j} (1-p)^j p^{N-j} \sum_{l=0}^{\min(j,k)} \binom{j}{l} q^l (1-q)^{j-l} \right].$$

Figure 8.15 shows plots of this lower bound versus N for $p = 0.01$, $q = 0.8$, and three values of n. The threshold value used by Algorithm SimpleThresh for a given N was chosen to maximize the bound. It is clear from Figure 8.15 that Algorithm SimpleThresh works with extremely high probability on very sparse digraphs. For example, in a 1,000-processor system only approximately seven tests

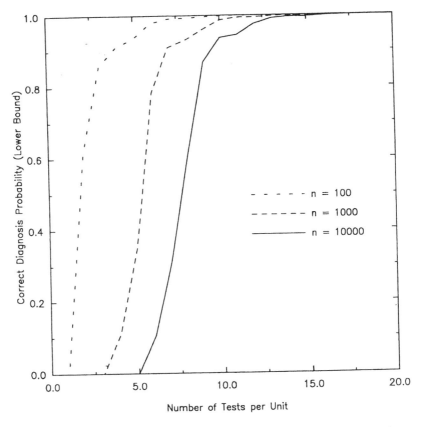

Figure 8.15: Lower bound on the probability of correct diagnosis for $p = 0.01$ and $q = 0.8$.

per processor are required to achieve a probability of correct diagnosis of greater than 0.95.

Table 8.5 shows the feasibility of using Algorithm SimpleThresh on binary hypercubes. This table compares the number of tests needed to achieve correct diagnosis with probability 0.99 for several values of n, p, and q with the number of tests available in a binary hypercube. The number of tests available per processor on a binary hypercube of n processors is $\log_2 n$. For all choices of p and q shown in the table, there are a sufficient number of connections available in the hypercube to achieve a probability of correct diagnosis of 0.99. Consider, for example, $n = 65536$ and $p = 0.004$. Note that the maximum number of *permanently* faulty processors that can be diagnosed under the bounded fault model in this situation is 16. Under the BSM model, the expected number of intermittently faulty processors is 328 and yet even when the detection probability is only 0.75, these faults can be correctly diagnosed with a probability of 0.99. So even for relatively large probabilities of failure and modest detection probabilities the proposed algorithm performs exceptionally well.

Since we have seen that a linear number of tests are sufficient to diagnose permanent faults, one could ask whether $o(n \log n)$ tests suffice for the intermittent fault situation. This question was answered by Berman and Pelc (1990) who showed that when $q < 1$, no diagnosis algorithm can achieve almost certain diagnosis for systems with $o(n \log n)$ tests. Hence, unlike the permanent fault situation, diagnosis of intermittent faults does not get easier when the regularity restriction is removed. Using the BSM model, Berman and Pelc (1990) were also able to show that diagnosis can be accomplished with high probability in a dis-

Table 8.5: Number of Tests per Processor Required for Correct Diagnosis Probability of 0.99

n	$\log_2 n$	p	q	$\| \Gamma^{-1}(u) \|$
128	7	0.001	0.9	3
128	7	0.001	0.75	4
128	7	0.004	0.9	4
128	7	0.004	0.75	7
512	9	0.001	0.9	4
512	9	0.001	0.75	5
512	9	0.004	0.9	6
512	9	0.004	0.75	8
2048	11	0.001	0.9	6
2048	11	0.001	0.75	8
2048	11	0.004	0.9	6
2048	11	0.004	0.75	11
65536	16	0.001	0.9	7
65336	16	0.001	0.75	13
65336	16	0.004	0.9	10
65336	16	0.004	0.75	16

tributed fashion on systems with $O(n \log n)$ communication links. This important work was the first to combine probabilistic modeling and distributed diagnosis.

Diagnosis and repair.   We have seen that, under both the MH homogeneous model and the BSM model, almost certain diagnosis is not possible in constant-degree systems. Unfortunately, this class includes many widely utilized systems such as meshes, rings, and grids. The reason for this lies in the fact that in such low-degree systems, there is a high probability that some processors will be tested only by faulty processors. Such a fault situation is shown in Figure 8.16. Note that processor a can be tested only by two processors, both of which are faulty. In this situation, there is no hope of diagnosing a as long as its two neighbors remain faulty. One possible method of handling this situation is to use sequential diagnosis, or diagnosis with repair, in which diagnosis is performed in stages that are alternated with repair or replacement of faulty processors. In Figure 8.16, the two neighbors of processor a could first be diagnosed and repaired, allowing the subsequent diagnosis of a.

This idea was investigated by Blough and Pelc (1993) who proposed a generalization of classical sequential diagnosis, referred to as diagnosis and repair. In diagnosis and repair, an arbitrary number of processors are diagnosed as faulty and repaired at each stage. The definition of correct diagnosis is then modified to be a sequence of partial diagnoses and repairs that leave the system without any faulty processors. A partial diagnosis is one that may correctly diagnose some of the faulty processors but does not incorrectly diagnose any nonfaulty processor. This prevents the trivial solution of diagnosing all processors as faulty and repairing them. In order to analyze this problem, Blough and Pelc used the BSM model and extended it to allow for the possibility of faulty spare processors. Hence, their model contains four cases: the permanent fault, perfect spare case;

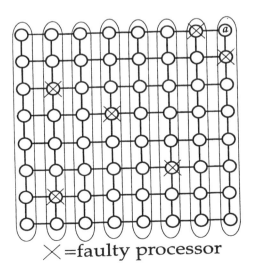

$\times$ =faulty processor

Figure 8.16: A fault situation in a grid together with test assignments for first round of diagnosis and repair.

the permanent fault, imperfect spare case; the intermittent fault, perfect spare case; and the intermittent fault, imperfect spare case.

Blough and Pelc focused on a class of systems referred to as log-divisible systems, which includes rings, grids, meshes, tori, and hypercubes. Their diagnosis algorithm, referred to as Algorithm Diag_and_Repair works by assigning initial groups of processors in which all possible tests are performed. One possible set of initial assignments is indicated in Figure 8.16 by the circles. Once these initial tests are executed, Algorithm Diag_and_Repair looks for groups in which all tests are passed. Three such groups are found in the example from Figure 8.16. These groups are considered to be nonfaulty. The subsequent stages of diagnosis and repair consist in using these core groups of nonfaulty processors to test unknown processors and repairing any processors found to be faulty. This process causes the core groups of faulty processors to expand at each stage, eventually including the entire system. In the system shown in Figure 8.16, the second stage of diagnosis would consist in having the processors in column 1 test their neighbors in column 2, those in column 3 test those in column 4, and those in column 5 test those in column 6. After this diagnosis stage, the four processors found to be faulty would be repaired. This allows the column 6 processors to test the column 7 processors in the next stage. Once the faulty processor in column 7 is repaired, the processors in column 8 can be diagnosed and repaired, completing the process.

This procedure will correctly diagnose and repair systems under the permanent fault, perfect spare assumption. However, Blough and Pelc proved that almost certain diagnosis and repair can be accomplished in the class of log-divisible systems under all four fault scenarios. Their main result is summarized in the following theorem. In this theorem, p_1 denotes the initial processor failure probability and p_2 represents the spare processor failure probability ($p_2 = 0$ in the perfect spare case).

Theorem 8.8 (Blough, Pelc, (1993)). Let S_n be any class of strongly connected, log-divisible systems of n processors with $p_1 < 1/2$, $p_2 < 1$, and $q > 0$. Almost certain diagnosis and repair can be achieved in S_n under all four fault scenarios using:

1. $O(n)$ tests when faults are permanent and spares are perfect;
2. $O(n \log n)$ tests when faults are permanent and spares are imperfect or when faults are intermittent and spares are perfect; and
3. $O(n^2)$ tests when faults are intermittent and spares are imperfect.

Heterogeneous case of the Maheshwari, Hakimi model.   The heterogeneous case of the MH model refers to the MH model as originally proposed by Maheshwari and Hakimi in which processors have distinct failure probabilities. To date, there have been no studies concerning almost certain diagnosis in this model. However, due to its historical importance, we discuss briefly some results that have been obtained in this model.

In their landmark paper, Maheshwari and Hakimi (1976) introduced the notion of p-diagnosability. This generalized the notion of t-diagnosability by requiring that diagnosis be unique among all fault sets having a priori probability greater than p. Maheshwari and Hakimi translated this problem of probabilistic diagnosability to one of weighted diagnosability in the following way. In a system represented by a digraph $G = (U, E)$, the unique fault set of probability greater than p, call it F, must satisfy

$$P(F) = \prod_{u_i \in F} p_i \prod_{u_i \in U - F} (1 - p_i) > p$$

Taking the logarithm of each side and multiplying by -1 yields

$$\sum_{u_i \in F} \log \frac{1}{p_i} + \sum_{u_i \in U - F} \log \frac{1}{1 - p_i} < -\log p$$

Simplifying the above expression gives

$$\sum_{u_i \in F} \log \frac{1 - p_i}{p_i} < -\log p + \sum_{u_i \in U} \log (1 - p_i)$$

If one associates with each processor u_i a weight $\log ((1 - p_i)/p_i)$, then this translates the problem of finding a fault set of sufficiently high probability to one of finding a fault set of sufficiently small weight. This follows because the right-hand side of the above inequality is independent of F. Note that for these problems to be exactly equivalent, the weight of each processor must be computable with arbitrary precision. Since this is not possible in practice, performing weighted diagnosis only provides an approximation to probabilistic diagnosis. However, this is sufficient in many cases.

Maheshwari and Hakimi also proved necessary and sufficient conditions for a system to be p-diagnosable. Sullivan (1987) proved that the problem of deciding whether a system is p-diagnosable is co-NP-complete. Finally, Dahbura (1986) provided an $O(n^3)$ diagnosis algorithm for the weighted diagnosis problem.

8.3.4 Results in Undirected Models

Fussell, Rangarajan model. Fussell and Rangarajan also considered the problem of diagnosis with high probability in constant-degree systems. Diagnosis in such systems is limited by two factors. The first of these factors, as explained previously, is that there are likely to be processors tested only by faulty processors in such systems. If faulty processors are allowed to produce test outcomes in any possible manner, then diagnosis is impossible unless these faulty processors are first removed as is done in Blough and Pelc (1993). Fussell and

Rangarajan chose instead to utilize what could be termed an optimistic fault model. As explained in Section 8.3.2, their comparison-based model assumes that the probability of two faulty processors disagreeing is different from the probability that a faulty and a nonfaulty processor disagree. This makes it possible to determine the status of a processor that is tested only by faulty processors. The second factor that limits constant-degree systems is the small number of tests performed on each processor. Fussell and Rangarajan overcome this by having each processor perform multiple tests on each of its neighbors. If these test outcomes are independent, then a large number of useful test outcomes are obtained for each processor.

Diagnosis in the FR model proceeds as follows. First, a set of m test jobs are run on all processors in the system. The results of these jobs are then compared for each pair of neighboring processors in the system. All comparison results in the system are then input to a diagnosis algorithm for analysis. The Fussell and Rangarajan diagnosis algorithm is threshold-based. Their algorithm used two thresholds per processor. The first threshold defines, for a particular test job, the minimum number of disagreements that result in the processor "failing" that job. The second threshold gives the minimum number of failed jobs that result in the processor being diagnosed as faulty. Lee and Shin (1990) showed how these thresholds can be chosen in an optimal fashion. The following example illustrates the operation of this diagnosis algorithm and also demonstrates how the approach makes use of faulty processors in the diagnosis.

Example 8.10 Diagnosis of a processor by the Fussell, Rangarajan algorithm

Consider the algorithm applied to a processor u with four neighbors v_1, v_2, v_3, and v_4. Assume that five test jobs are applied to all processors and that the thresholds are set as follows: If a processor disagrees with at least two neighbors on a particular job, then that job is failed; and, if a processor fails at least two jobs, then the processor is diagnosed as faulty. Let the outputs produced by the processors of interest on the five test jobs be as follows:

$$
\begin{aligned}
O(u) &= (1, 3, 7, 4, 2)\\
O(v_1) &= (5, 3, 7, 6, 9)\\
O(v_2) &= (1, 3, 7, 4, 2)\\
O(v_3) &= (1, 3, 7, 4, 2)\\
O(v_4) &= (1, 4, 8, 7, 2)
\end{aligned}
$$

In this example, test jobs 1, 2, 3, and 5, are all passed by processor u, while test job 4 is failed since it disagrees with both processor v_1 and processor v_4 on that job. Since u fails only a single test job, it is diagnosed as nonfaulty.

Note that, in this case, it appears that processors v_1 and v_4 are faulty since their outputs differ from those produced by the remaining three processors. Since two disagreements are enough to cause a test job to be failed, it would seem that having two faulty neighbors might cause a nonfaulty processor to be diagnosed as faulty. However, in this case, both v_1 and v_4 perform two of the five test jobs correctly which allows u to pass those test jobs and to be correctly diagnosed as nonfaulty.

The main result in Fussell and Rangarajan (1989) proved that, under the FR model, almost certain diagnosis can be achieved with their diagnosis algorithm in systems with a minimum degree of at least

$$\frac{\log \dfrac{1}{1-r}}{\log \dfrac{1}{1-r} + \log \left(1 - \dfrac{1-r}{k}\right)}$$

where $r > 0$ is the probability that a faulty processor performs a job correctly and k is the number of possible incorrect results. The number of test jobs that must be run to accomplish this is $\omega(n) \log n$, (where $\omega(n)$ is any function that approaches infinity with n). Thus, the total number of job comparisons (tests) that must be done is $O((n \log n) \cdot \omega(n))$.

Rangarajan and Fussell (1992) strengthened and generalized this result. In their paper, it was shown that as long as the product of the number of testers and the number of tests of any processor is $\Omega(\log n)$, then almost certain diagnosis can be achieved in their model. Thus, a trade-off exists between the number of testers and the number of tests. At one extreme, constant degree and $O(\log n)$ tests per processor are sufficient. At the other extreme, $O(\log n)$ testers and a constant number of tests will suffice. No matter how these two parameters are selected, the total number of tests is $O(n \log n)$ which was proven to be a lower bound for almost certain diagnosis in their model.

This model was also used to study the problem of wafer testing. In Rangarajan, Fussell, and Malek (1990), a similar threshold-based diagnosis approach was used to diagnose the status of dies on a wafer. In Huang, Agarwal, LaForge, and Thulasiraman (1992), the same problem was studied but with a diagnosis algorithm that attempts to find large factions of units which all produce exactly the same outcomes on the sequence of tests.

Pelc model.   Blount (1977) first defined the problem of optimal probabilistic diagnosis. As detailed in Section 8.3.2, this problem is defined as, given a system and a syndrome, choose the fault set that is most likely to have produced the syndrome. Unfortunately, Blount's diagnosis algorithm requires exponential time since it enumerates all possible fault sets to determine the most probable one.

Under Pelc's comparison-based model, Blough and Pelc (1992a) proved that the optimal probabilistic diagnosis problem is NP-complete. In fact, an even stronger result was proven in this paper. Define the performance of a diagnosis algorithm A in the following way:

$$\text{Perf}(A) = \frac{P(\text{Alg. } A \text{ is correct})}{P(\text{optimal alg. is correct})}$$

Blough and Pelc showed that, if $P \neq NP$, then for any polynomial-time diagnosis algorithm A in Pelc's model, there exists a system for which Perf $(A) < \epsilon$, for any $\epsilon > 0$. So, for any polynomial-time algorithm, there exists a system for which the algorithm's performance is arbitrarily bad when compared to the optimal. In Blough and Pelc (1992a), a polynomial-time algorithm was given for the optimal probabilistic diagnosis problem in rings. This is the only special case currently known for which optimal probabilistic diagnosis can be performed in polynomial time.

Finally, Pelc (1991) studied the problem of unique optimal probabilistic diagnosis, that is, to design systems in which, for any syndrome, there is a unique fault set of maximum conditional probability. Pelc was able to design such systems using a minimum number of tests for small probabilities of failure.

8.4 CONCLUDING DISCUSSION

The topics described and discussed in this chapter should be viewed as the tip of an iceberg: Beneath them sits a mountain of other deep, broad, and significant results more fully representing the field of system diagnosis. No single chapter can do justice to the breadth of the total system diagnosis area. The field of system diagnosis has expanded enormously since its inception with the publication of the first paper in this research area by Preparata, Metze, and Chien (1967) over 25 years ago. The range of topics that have since been treated by researchers has grown tremendously and still continues to do so.

Moreover, there is ample evidence that technology is increasingly catching up with system diagnosis theory. Distributed computing applications involving hundreds of highly intelligent processing units are not uncommon. While maintaining a high level of operational availability in such systems is always important, in some cases the need for fault-tolerant operation based on highly efficient detection and diagnosis methodologies is absolutely critical. Thus, while in its early formative stages of development system diagnosis theory could perhaps have been justifiably described as being of primarily academic interest, this is clearly no longer the case. Many interesting and challenging system fault diagnosis applications are now forthcoming that are based on variations of fundamental theoretical results. These applications not only provide a window through which the power of the theory can be observed and appreciated, but additionally the persuasive significance of these applications cannot be ignored by researchers in the system diagnosis area. As the field of system diagnosis moves into its second quarter century, its maturity and importance will be underscored by robust applications. Innovative applications will often be the driving force behind further development of the system diagnosis field. This will undoubtedly lead to the healthy situation where theory and applications will be continually engaged in a push-pull process, each driving and being driven by the other.

REFERENCES

[Bagchi94] Bagchi, A., and S. L. Hakimi, "Information Dissemination in Distributed Systems with Faulty Units," *IEEE Transactions on Computers*, vol. 43 (June 1994), pp. 698–710.

[Barborak93] Barborak, M., M. Malek, and A. Dahbura, "The Consensus Problem in Fault-Tolerant Computing," *ACM Computing Surveys*, vol. 25 (June 1993), pp. 171–220.

[Barsi76] Barsi, F., F. Grandoni, and P. Maestrini, "A Theory of Diagnosability of Digital Systems," *IEEE Transactions on Computers*, vol. C-25 (June 1976), pp. 585–593.

[Beigel89] Beigel, R., S. R. Kosaraju, and G. Sullivan, "Locating Faults in a Constant Number of Parallel Testing Rounds," *Proceedings of the 1989 ACM Symposium on Parallel Algorithms and Architectures*, Santa Fe, New Mexico (June 18–21, 1989), pp. 189–198.

[Berman90] Berman, P., and A. Pelc, "Distributed Probabilistic Diagnosis for Multiprocessor Systems," *Digest of the 20th International Symposium on Fault-Tolerant Computing*, Newcastle Upon Tyne UK (1990), pp. 340–346.

[Bianchini90] Bianchini, R., Jr., K. Goodwin, and D. S. Nydick, "Practical Application and Implementation of Distributed System-Level Diagnosis Theory," *Digest of the 20th International Symposium on Fault-Tolerant Computing*, (June 1990), pp. 332–339.

[Bianchini92] Bianchini, R., Jr., and R. Buskens, "Implementation of On-Line Distributed System-Level Diagnosis Theory," *IEEE Transactions on Computers*, vol. 41 (May 1992), pp. 616–626.

[Blecher83] Blecher, P. M., "On a Logical Problem," *Discrete Math*, vol. 43 (January 1983), pp. 107–110.

[Blough88] Blough, D. "Fault Detection and Diagnosis in Multiprocessor Systems," Ph.D. diss., Department of Computer Science, Johns Hopkins University, 1988.

[Blough92a] Blough, D., and A. Pelc, "Complexity of Fault Diagnosis in Comparison Models," *IEEE Transactions on Computers*, vol. 41 (March 1992), pp. 318–324.

[Blough92b] Blough, D., G. Sullivan, and G. Masson, "Efficient Diagnosis of Multiprocessor Systems under Probabilistic Models," *IEEE Transactions on Computers*, vol. 41 (September 1992), pp. 1126–1136. (Expanded version of "Fault Diagnosis for Sparsely Interconnected Multiprocessor Systems," *Digest of the 19th International Symposium on Fault-Tolerant Computing*, Chicago, Illinois (June 21–23, 1989), pp. 62–69.

[Blough92c] Blough, D., G. Sullivan, and G. Masson, "Intermittent Fault Diagnosis in Multiprocessor Systems," *IEEE Transactions on Computers*, vol. 41 (November 1992), pp. 1430–1441. (Expanded version of "Almost Certain Diagnosis for Intermittently Faulty Systems," *Digest of the 18th International Symposium on Fault-Tolerant Computing*, Tokyo, Japan (June 27–30, 1988), pp. 260–265.

[Blough93] Blough, D., and A. Pelc, "Diagnosis and Repair in Multiprocessor Systems," *IEEE Transactions on Computers*, vol. 42 (February 1993), pp. 205–217.

[Blount77] Blount, M., "Probabilistic Treatment of Diagnosis in Digital Systems," *Digest of the 7th International Symposium on Fault-Tolerant Computing*, IEEE Computer Society Press, Los Angeles, CA (June 1977), pp. 72–77.

[Chwa81a] Chwa, K.-Y., and S. Hakimi, "On Fault Identification in Diagnosable Systems," *IEEE Transactions on Computers*, vol. C-30 (June 1981), pp. 414–422.

[Chwa81b] Chwa, K.-Y., and S. L. Hakimi, "Schemes for Fault-Tolerant Computing: A Comparison of Modularly Redundant and t-diagnosable Systems," *Information and Control*, vol. 49 (June 1981), pp. 212–238.

[Ciompi79] Ciompi, P., and L. Simoncini, "Analysis and Optimal Design of Self-Diagnosable Systems with Repair," *IEEE Transactions on Computers*, vol. C-28 (May 1979), pp. 362–365.

[Dahbura84a] Dahbura, A., and G. Masson, "An $O(n^{2.5})$ Fault Identification Algorithm for Diagnosable Systems," *IEEE Transaction on Computers*, vol. C-33 (June 1984), pp. 486–492.

[Dahbura84b] Dahbura, A., and G. Masson, "A Practical Variation of the $O(n^{2.5})$ Fault Diagnosis Algorithm," *Digest of the 14th International Symposium on Fault-Tolerant Computing*, Kissimmee, Florida (June 1984), pp. 428–433.

[Dahbura85] Dahbura, A., G. Masson, and C. L. Yang, "Self-implicating Structures for Diagnosable Systems," *IEEE Transactions on Computers*, vol. C-34 (August 1985), pp. 718–725.

[Dahbura86] Dahbura, A. T., "An Efficient Algorithm for Identifying the Most Likely Fault Set in a Probabilistically Diagnosable System," *IEEE Transactions on Computers*, vol. C-35 (April 1986), pp. 354–356.

[Dahbura87] Dahbura, A. T., K. Sabnani, and L. King, "The Comparison Approach to Multiprocessor Fault Diagnosis," *IEEE Transactions on Computers*, vol. C-36 (March 1987), pp. 373–378.

[Dahbura88] Dahbura, A. T., "System-Level Diagnosis: A Perspective for the Third Decade," in *Concurrent Computation: Algorithms, Architectures, Technologies*, New York, Plenum, 1988.

[Das91] Das, A., K. Thulasiraman, and V. K. Agarwal, "Diagnosis of t/s-Diagnosable Systems," *Journal of Circuits, Systems and Computers*, vol. 1 (July 1991), pp. 353–371.

[Das91a] Das, A., K. Thulasiraman, and V. K. Agarwal, "Diagnosis of $t/(t + 1)$-Diagnosis Systems," *SIAM Journal on Computing*, vol. 23 (October 1994), pp. 895–905.

[Feller68] Feller, W., *An Introduction to Probability Theory and its Applications*, John Wiley, New York, 1968.

[Friedman75] Friedman, A., "A New Measure of Digital System Diagnosis," *Digest of the Fifth International Symposium on Fault-Tolerant Computing*, Paris France (June 18–20, 1975), pp. 167–169.

[Friedman80] Friedman, A., and L. Simoncini, "System-Level Fault Diagnosis," *Computer*, vol. 13 (March 1980), pp. 47–53.

[Fussell89] Fussell, D., and S. Rangarajan, "Probabilistic Diagnosis of Multiprocessor Systems with Arbitrary Connectivity," *Digest of the 19th International Symposium on Fault-Tolerant Computing*, Chicago, Illinois (June 21–23, 1989), pp. 560–565.

[Gupta87] Gupta, R., and I. V. Ramakrishnan, "System-Level Fault Diagnosis in Malicious Environments," *Digest of the 17th International Symposium on Fault-Tolerant Computing*, Pittsburgh, Penn. (July 6–8, 1987), pp. 184–189.

[Hakimi74] Hakimi, S., and A. Amin, "Characterization of Connection Assignment of Diagnosable Systems," *IEEE Transactions on Computer*, vol. C-23 (January 1974), pp. 86–88.

[Hakimi82] Hakimi, S. L., and K. Nakajima, "On Adaptive System Diagnosis (Preliminary

Version)," *Proceedings of the 20th Allerton Conference on Communications, Control and Computing*, Urbana, Illinois (October 1982), pp. 231–240.

[Hakimi84a] Hakimi, S. L., and K. Nakajima, "On Adaptive System Diagnosis," *IEEE Transactions on Computers*, vol. C-33 (March 1984), pp. 234–240.

[Hakimi84b] Hakimi, S. L., and E. F. Schmeichel, "An Adaptive Algorithm for System Level Diagnosis," *Journal of Algorithms*, vol. 5 (December 1984), pp. 526–530.

[Hopcroft73] Hopcroft, J., and R. Karp, "An $O(n^{2.5})$ Algorithm for Maximum Matching in Bipartite Graphs," *SIAM Journal on Computing*, vol. 2 (December 1973), pp. 225–231.

[Hosseini84] Hosseini, S. H., J. G. Kuhl and S. M. Reddy, "A Diagnosis Algorithm for Distributed Computing Systems with Dynamic Failure and Repair," *IEEE Transactions on Computers*, vol. C-33 (March 1984), pp. 223–233.

[Huang92] Huang, K., V. K. Agarwal, L. LaForge, and K. Thulasiraman, "Wafer Testing with Pairwise Comparisons," *Digest of the 22nd International Symposium on Fault-Tolerant Computing*, Boston, MA (July 8–10, 1992), pp. 374–383.

[Kavianpour78] Kavianpour, A., and A. Friedman, "Efficient Design of Easily Diagnosable Systems," *Proceedings of the Third USA-Japan Computer Conference*, San Fransico, CA 1978, pp. 251–257.

[Kavianpour92] Kavianpour, A., and K. Kim, "A Comparative Evaluation of Four Basic System-Level Diagnosis Strategies for Hypercubes," *IEEE Transactions on Reliability*, vol. 41 (March 1992), pp. 26–37.

[Kime86] Kime, C., "System Diagnosis," *In Fault-Tolerant Computing: Theory and Techniques*, D. Pradhan, ed., Vol. II, Englewood Cliffs, NJ, Prentice Hall, pp. 577–626, 1986.

[Kuhl80] Kuhl, J. G., and S. M. Reddy, "Distributed Fault Tolerance for Large Multiprocessor Systems," *Proceedings of the International Symposium on Computer Architecture*, La Baule, France (May 1980), pp. 23–30.

[LaForge94] LaForge, L., K. Huang, and V. K. Agarwal, "Almost Sure Diagnosis of Almost Every Good Element, " *IEEE Transactions on Computers*, vol. 42 (March 1994), pp. 295–305.

[Lee90] Lee, S., and K. Shin, "Optimal Multiple Syndrome Probabilistic Diagnosis," *Digest of the 20th International Symposium on Fault-Tolerant Computing*, Newcastle Upon Tyne UK (June 26–28, 1990), pp. 324–331.

[Lee93] Lee, S., and K. Shin, "Optimal and Efficient Probabilistic Distributed Diagnosis Schemes," *IEEE Transactions on Computers*, vol. 42 (July 1993), pp. 882–886.

[Lee94] Lee, S., and K. Shin, "Probabilistic Diagnosis of Multiprocessor Systems," *ACM Computing Surveys*, vol. 26 (March 1994), pp. 121–139.

[Maeng81] Maeng, J., and M. Malek, "A Comparison Connection Assignment for Self-Diagnosis of Multiprocessor Systems," *Digest of the 11th International Symposium on Fault-Tolerant Computing*, Portland, ME (June 24–26, 1981), pp. 173–175.

[Maheshwari76] Maheshwari, S., and S. L. Hakimi, "On Models for Diagnosable Systems and Probabilistic Fault Diagnosis," *IEEE Transactions on Computers*, vol. C-25 (March 1976), pp. 228–236.

[Malek80] Malek, M., "A Comparison Connection Assignment for Diagnosis of Multiprocessor Systems," *Proceedings 7th International Symposium on Computer Architecture*, LaBaule, France (May 1980), pp. 31–36.

[Mallela78] Mallela, S., and G. M. Masson, "Diagnosable Systems for Intermittent Faults," *IEEE Transactions on Computers*, vol. C-27 (June 1978), pp. 560–566.

[Mallela79] Mallela, S., and G. M. Masson, "Diagnosis without Repair for Hybrid Fault Situations," *IEEE Transactions on Computers*, vol. C-29 (June 1979), pp. 461–470.

[Manber80] Manber, U., "System Diagnosis with Repair," *IEEE Transactions on Computers*, vol. C-29 (October 1980), pp. 934–937.

[Meyer78] Meyer, G. G. L., and G. Masson, "A Efficient Fault Diagnosis Algorithm for Symmetric Multiple Processor Architectures," *IEEE Transactions on Computers*, vol. C-27 (November 1978), pp. 1059–1063.

[Meyer80] Meyer, G. G. L., "A Fault Diagnosis Algorithm for Asymmetric Modular Architectures," *IEEE Transactions on Computers*, vol. C-30 (January 1980), pp. 81–83.

[Meyer84] Meyer, G. G. L., "A Diagnosis Algorithm for the BGM System Level Fault Model," *IEEE Transactions on Computers*, vol. C-33 (August 1984), pp. 756–758.

[Meyer89] Meyer, F. J., and D. K. Pradhan, "Dynamic Testing Stategy for Distributed Systems," *IEEE Transactions on Computers*, vol. 38, no. 3 (March 1989), pp. 356–365.

[Narasimhan86] Narasimhan, J., and K. Nakajima, "An Algorithm for Determining the Fault Diagnosability of a System," *IEEE Transactions on Computers*, vol. C-35 (November 1986), pp. 1004–1008.

[Pelc91] Pelc, A., "Undirected Graph Models for System-Level Fault Diagnosis," *IEEE Transactions on Computers*, vol. 40 (November 1991), pp. 1271–1276.

[Pelc92a] Pelc, A., "Almost Certain Byzantine Agreement in the Presence of Random Faults," Universite du Quebec, Hull Technical Report RR 90/04-5, 1992.

[Pelc92b] Pelc, A., "Reliable Communication in Networks with Byzantine Link Failures," *Networks* vol. 22 (August 1992), pp. 441–459.

[Preparata67] Preparata, F., G. Metze, and R. Chien, "On the Connection Assignment Problem of Diagnosable Systems," *IEEE Transactions on Computers*, vol. C-16 (December 1967), pp. 848–854.

[Preparata91] Preparata, F., private communication to G. Masson, (November 1991).

[Raghavan91a] Raghavan, V., and A. R. Tripathi, "Improved Diagnosability Algorithms," *IEEE Transactions on Computers*, vol. 40 (February 1991), pp. 143–153.

[Raghavan91b] Raghavan, V., and A. R. Tripathi, "Sequential Diagnosability is Co-NP-Complete," *IEEE Transactions on Computers*, vol. 40 (May 1991), pp. 584–595.

[Rangarajan90] Rangarajan, S., D. Fussell, and M. Malek, "Built-In Testing of Integrated Circuit Wafers," *IEEE Transactions on Computers*, vol. 39 (February 1990), pp. 195–205.

[Rangarajan92] Rangarajan, S., and D. Fussell, "Diagnosing Arbitrarily Connected Parallel Computers with High Probability," *IEEE Transactions on Computers*, vol. 41 (May 1992), pp. 606–615.

[Russell75a] Russell, J., and C. Kime, "System Fault Diagnosis: Closure and Diagnosability with Repair," *IEEE Transactions on Computers*, vol. C-24 (November 1975), pp. 1078–1089.

[Russell75b] Russell, J., and C. Kime, "System Fault Diagnosis: Masking, Exposure, and Diagnosability without Repair," *IEEE Transactions on Computers*, vol. C-24 (December 1975), pp. 1155–1161.

[Scheinrman87] Scheinerman, E., "Almost Sure Fault Tolerance in Random Graphs," *SIAM Journal on Computing*, vol. 16 (December 1987), pp. 1124–1134.

[Schmeichel90] Schmeichel, E., S. L. Hakimi, M. Otsuka, and G. Sullivan, "A Parallel Fault Identification Algorithm," *Journal of Algorithms*, vol. 11 (June 1990), pp. 231–241.

[Sengupta92] Sengupta, A., and A. T. Dahbura, "On Self-Diagnosable Multiprocessor Systems: Diagnosis by the Comparison Approach," *IEEE Transactions on Computers*, vol. 41 (November 1992), pp. 1386–1396.

[Somani87] Somani, A., V. Agarwal, and D. Avis, "A Generalized Theory for System-Level Diagnosis," *IEEE Transactions on Computers*, vol. C-36 (May 1987), pp. 538–546.

[Sullivan84] Sullivan, G., "A Polynomial Time Algorithm for Fault Diagnosability," *Digest of the 25th Annual IEEE Symposium on Foundations of Computer Science*, Singer Island, FL (October 1984), pp. 148–156.

[Sullivan86] Sullivan, G., "The Complexity of System Level Diagnosis and Diagnosability," Ph.D. diss., Department of Computer Science, Yale University, 1986.

[Sullivan87] Sullivan, G., "System-Level Fault Diagnosability in Probabilistic and Weighted Models," *Digest of the 17th International Symposium on Fault-Tolerant Computing*, Pittsburgh, PA (July 6–8, 1987), pp. 190–195.

[Sullivan88] Sullivan, G., "An $O(t^3 + |E|)$ Fault Identification Algorithm for Diagnosable Systems," *IEEE Transactions on Computers*, vol. C-37 (April 1988), pp. 388–397.

[Vaidya94] Vaidya, N. H., and D. K. Pradhan, "Safe System Level Diagnosis," *IEEE Transactions on Computers* vol. 43 (March 1994), pp. 367–370.

[Wang94] Wang, H., D. Blough, and L. Alkalaj, "Analysis and Experimental Evaluation of Comparison-Based System-Level Diagnosis for Multiprocessor Systems," *Digest of the 24th International Symposium on Fault-Tolerant Computing*, Austin, TX (June 13–17, 1994), pp. 55–64.

[Yang86a] Yang, C.-L., and G. Masson, "A Fault Identification Algorithm for t_i-diagnosable Systems," *IEEE Transactions on Computers*, vol. C-35 (June 1986), pp. 503–510.

[Yang86b] Yang, C.-L., G. Masson, and R. Leonetti, "On Fault Isolation and Identification in t_1/t_1-Diagnosable Systems," *IEEE Transactions on Computers*, vol. C-35 (July 1986), pp. 639–643.

PROBLEMS

8.1 The original characterization for t-diagnosability given by Hakimi and Amin (1974) is different from the one that was presented in Theorem 8.1. The Hakimi and Amin version is as follows:

Theorem 8.9   A system of n processors is t-diagnosable if and only if (1) $n > 2t + 1$; (2) for all $u_i \in U$, $|\Gamma^{-1}(u_i)| \geq t$; and (3) for all integers p, where $0 \leq p < t$, and any $Z \subseteq U$ such that $|Z| = n - 2t + p$, $|\Gamma(Z)| > p$.

Show that the Hakimi and Amin characterization and the characterization given in Theorem 8.1 are equivalent.

8.2 Conside the system represented by the digraph given in Figure 8.1.

(a) Show that it is two-diagnosable by constructing the network flow graphs discussed in the chapter and exhibiting the maximum flows and minimum cuts in the networks.

(b) The first part of this problem also shows that the system is not three-diagnosable. Show this concretely by exhibiting a syndrome and two distinct sets of faulty processors that could have produced the syndrome. Each set must contain at most three processors.

(c) Consider the system depicted in Figure 8.7. Use the methods given in the first two parts of this problem to show that the system is three-diagnosable but it is not four-diagnosable.

8.3 Prove that the following problem is NP-complete: Given a system digraph and a syndrome, does there exist a set of k or fewer processors that could have generated the syndrome? Note, the system digraph is arbitrary, for example, it is not constrained to be k-diagnosable. (*Hint:* There is a reduction using the vertex cover problem.)

8.4 Consider the following theorem proven by Chwa and Hakimi: A system $G = (U, E)$ is t/t-diagnosable iff $|U| \leq t$ or (for all $Z \subseteq U$ with $|Z| \geq 2$, $|\Gamma^{-1}(Z)| + |Z|/2 > t$).

(a) Using the theorem above show how to use network flow problems to determine in polynomial time whether a system is t/t-diagnosable. (*Hint:* Solve $|U|^2$ network flow problems.)

(b) Prove the theorem. See Chwa and Hakimi (1981a) or Sullivan (1986) for solutions.

8.5 This problem concerns the weighted model introduced by Maheshwari and Hakimi. Consider the following characterization theorem: A system $G = (U, E)$ with weight function w is t-diagnosable if for all $Z \subseteq U$ with $Z \neq \emptyset$, $w(\Gamma^{-1}(Z)) + split(Z) > t$. By convention $w(Z) = \Sigma_{u \in Z} w(u)$. Also, by definition $split(Z) = $ minimum for all $Z_1 \subseteq Z$ of the maximum of $(w(Z_1), w(Z - Z_1))$, that is, split is the weight obtained when the nodes are split into two sets as evenly as possible.

(a) Prove that the following problem is co-NP-complete: Given a weighted system and a value t, is the system t-diagnosable? You may use the characterization theorem. (*Hint:* There is a reduction using the partition problem.)

(b) Using the characterization theorem above, show how to use network flow problems to approximately determine in polynomial time the largest t such that a given system is t-diagnosable. How accurate is your approximation?

(c) Prove the characterization. See Maheshwari and Hakimi (1976) or Sullivan (1986) for solutions.

8.6 For a completely connected digraph corresponding to a testing assignment, find the maximum values of t and t_i for t-diagnosability, t_i-diagnosability, and t/t_i-diagnosability.

8.7 Consider a ring of n processors, denoted $P_0, P_1, \ldots, P_{n-1}$, where each processor P_i tests processors P_{i-1} and P_{i+1}. Determine the maximum values of t and t_i for t-diagnosability and t_i-diagnosability.

8.8 Is it possible that for some system of processors the maximum values of t and t_i for, respectively, t-diagnosability, t_i-diagnosability are equal? If so, show the digraph of one such system.

8.9 Demonstrate that the special case of Theorem 8.4 for the characterization of t/t_i-

diagnosability where $t = t_i$ is equivalent to characterization given in Theorem 8.1 for t-diagnosability.

8.10 Demonstrate that the special case of Theorem 8.4 for the characterization of t/t_i-diagnosability where $t_i = 0$ is equivalent to characterization given in Theorem 8.3 for t_i-diagnosability.

8.11 What is the a priori probability of $F = \{u_2, u_4\}$ in Figure 8.9 under the MH model?

8.12 In the system of Figure 8.10, assume that the test by u_3 on u_2 is failed and all other test outcomes are unchanged. What is the most likely fault set given this new syndrome?

8.13 Given the syndrome of Figure 8.11, call it S, and $F = \{u_3, u_5\}$, what is the smallest collection of syndromes that includes S and for which the conditional probability given F is defined? Assuming $q = 0.7$, what is the conditional probability of this collection of syndromes?

8.14 Assume that a faulty processor and a nonfaulty processor agree with probability 0.1 and that there are 10,000 possible incorrect results. What is the conditional probability of the syndrome shown in Figure 8.17, given $F = \{u_1, u_4\}$, under
(a) the DSK model?
(b) Pelc's model?
(c) the FR model?

8.15 Prove the following statement or provide a counterexample. "Optimal diagnosis in Pelc's model is achieved by choosing the fault set with highest a priori probability among all fault sets that are consistent with the given syndrome."

8.16 Difficult—see Schneinerman (1987) for a solution. Prove the following: Under the MH homogeneous model, $D_{1,c \log_2 n}$ systems, with $c < (1/\log_2(1/p))$ are almost certainly not diagnosable by any algorithm.

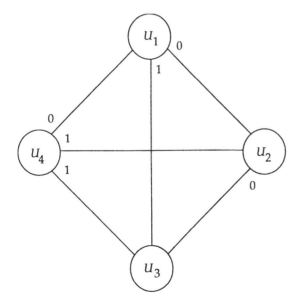

Figure 8.17: Figure for Problem 8.14.

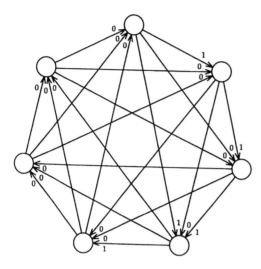

Figure 8.18: Figure for Problem 8.18.

8.17 Prove Theorem 8.6. (*Hint:* Show that, under the theorem's conditions, every processor is almost certainly tested by a majority of nonfaulty processors.)

8.18 Consider the system and syndrome shown in Figure 8.18.

    (a) Determine the output of Algorithm SimpleThresh when applied to this situation, assuming $f = 1/3$.

    (b) What problem exists with this fault set relative to the syndrome in Figure 8.18?

    (c) Modify Algorithm SimpleThresh to eliminate this problem. Compare your algorithm to Algorithm Thresh in Blough, Sullivan, and Masson (1992c).

8.19 Prove that the optimal probabilistic diagnosis problem, that is, to find the conditionally most probable fault set given any system and a syndrome from the system, is NP-hard under Pelc's model.

Index